ALGEBRA 2

ALGEBRA 2

Second Edition

Kathy D. Pilger, Ed.D.
Ron Tagliapietra, Ed.D.

bju press®

Greenville, South Carolina

The fact that materials produced by other publishers may be referred to in this volume does not constitute an endorsement of the content or theological position of materials produced by such publishers. Any references and ancillary materials are listed as an aid to the student or the teacher and in an attempt to maintain the accepted academic standards of the publishing industry.

ALGEBRA 2
Second Edition

Kathy D. Pilger, Ed.D
Ron Tagliapietra, Ed.D.

Contributing Authors
Larry L. Hall, M.S.
Kathy Kohler
Phil Larson, M.Ed
Larry Lemon, M.S.

Consultants
Garry Conn, MAT
Steve McKisic, M.Ed

Produced in cooperation with the Bob Jones University Department of Mathematics of the College of Arts and Science, the School of Education, Bob Jones Academy, and BJ LINC.

The data on Egyptian newborns (Chapter 5) is reprinted from "Principal Components Analysis of Growth of Nahya Infants: Size, Velocity and Two Physique Factors," Human Biology, Volume 57, No. 4 (December 1985), pp. 659-69, by Zeinab E. M. Afifi, by permission of the Wayne State University Press. © Wayne State University Press, 1985.

© 2000, 2009 BJU Press
Greenville, South Carolina 29614
First Edition © 1986 BJU Press

Printed in the United States of America

ISBN 978-1-59166-985-2

15 14 13 12 11 10 9 8 7 6 5 4 3 2

Contents

Introduction

Many students have wondered, "Why do I have to learn math? When am I ever going to use it?" Three reasons for studying math are given below.

People are stewards of all of earth's resources including Mantle Rock, Kentucky, the longest natural arch east of the Rockies, which spans 154 feet.

Creation Mandate

Before the Fall in Eden, God commanded man to "have dominion" and "subdue" the earth (Gen. 1:26–28). You must see this as a responsibility given to you by God. When you perform tasks such as mowing the lawn or feeding the chickens, you are helping to fulfill this mandate. By way of contrast, when you throw a paper cup in the ditch you are marring God's creation. To fulfill God's mandate you must train for a life's work and perform it in such a way that it brings glory to God. In *Education for the Real World*, creationist Henry Morris writes the following:

> Mankind is responsible for exercising dominion over the earth, and this commandment has not in any way been withdrawn. The enterprises of science and technology . . . are man's stewardship under God, to bring honor to Him.[1]

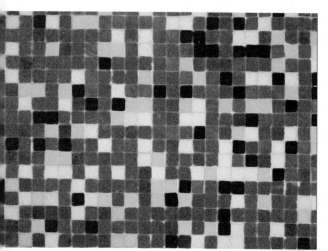

Coordinate systems are an abstract tool useful for describing these colored tiles. Designs can even be planned and plotted on graph paper.

Thinking and Reasoning

Algebra, or any other math course, develops your thinking skills and your ability to reason from known conditions to logical conclusions. This is the basis of decision making in life. This reasoning skill is very helpful, whether or not your life's work involves the direct use of math. Dealing with the abstractions found in algebra will prepare you for the difficult decisions you must make in the business world. To help you to develop these skills in a practical way, this book contains *Dominion*

Modeling exercises, word problems, and more difficult C problems. In addition, the *Algebra Around the World* feature shows thinkers who have achieved much in their field.

Christian Worldview

This text presents illustrations and *Algebra and Scripture* features to help you see that Scripture is the basis of all math and that math is for fulfilling the Creation Mandate. Also, proficiency in math adds to your understanding of Scripture. "Bringing into captivity every thought to the obedience of Christ" (2 Cor. 10:5) includes mathematical thoughts. Algebra is more than arithmetic and symbols. It is part of your stewardship, and is useful for mental and spiritual growth.

Man takes the lessons of nature seen in Mantle Rock and combines them with abstract reasoning to build bridges. The Tacoma Narrows Bridge displays human creativity in the image of God and God-given dominion over the earth.

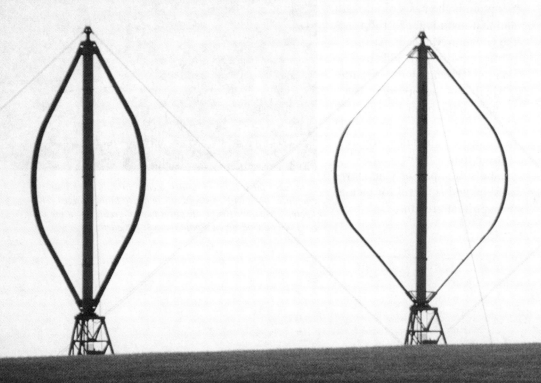

Electricity for computers, gasoline for visiting family, natural gas for warmth—we seem to use energy for everything, and each year we use more than the previous year.

From 1970 to 1998, our total energy usage in North America increased from 76 to 113 quadrillion BTUs each year. With 3412 BTUs equal to one thousand watts of energy for an hour (or kWh), the huge numbers reflect the immensity of our energy consumption.

Of course, energy costs money, and utilities must pass their expenses along to their customers. For instance, most electric companies charge residential customers a flat fee to be connected to the system; after this, customers pay various amounts per kilowatt-hour.

Here are sample rates for several electrical power companies in North America. You will use this data to answer questions throughout the chapter.

Location	Flat fee	per kWh
British Columbia	$3.46	$0.0577
California (southern)	$3.60	$0.0784
Connecticut	$8.12	$0.0856
Michigan	$6.00	$0.0882
Minnesota	$4.50	$0.0635
Pennsylvania	$5.10	$0.0457
Utah	$0.00	$0.0629
Wisconsin	$5.56	$0.0512

After this chapter you should be able to

1. identify the kinds of numbers in the real number system.
2. demonstrate the properties of real numbers.
3. apply the order of operations.
4. classify polynomials by terms and degree.
5. perform the four basic operations with polynomials.
6. state and use the laws of exponents.
7. factor polynomials completely.

1.1 Real Numbers

$\mathbf{A}$lgebra is a generalization of arithmetic using variables (letters) to represent numbers. Mathematicians have classified numbers to facilitate discussion and to investigate their properties. The first diagram below shows the definitions of the various types of numbers, the relationships among them, and the letters used to name the sets. The Venn diagram also shows the names and relationships. Make sure you understand each type of number.

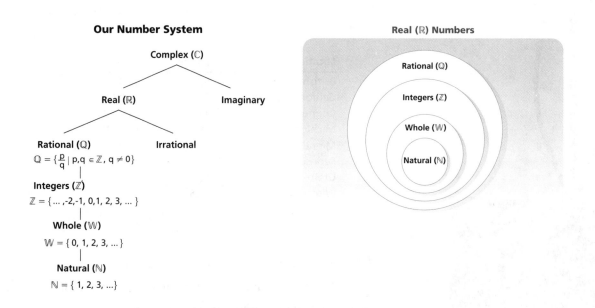

Our Number System

Complex ($\mathbb{C}$)

Real ($\mathbb{R}$)   Imaginary

Rational ($\mathbb{Q}$)   Irrational
$\mathbb{Q} = \{\frac{p}{q} \mid p,q \in \mathbb{Z}, q \neq 0\}$

Integers ($\mathbb{Z}$)
$\mathbb{Z} = \{\dots, -2, -1, 0, 1, 2, 3, \dots\}$

Whole ($\mathbb{W}$)
$\mathbb{W} = \{0, 1, 2, 3, \dots\}$

Natural ($\mathbb{N}$)
$\mathbb{N} = \{1, 2, 3, \dots\}$

Real ($\mathbb{R}$) Numbers

Rational ($\mathbb{Q}$)

Integers ($\mathbb{Z}$)

Whole ($\mathbb{W}$)

Natural ($\mathbb{N}$)

Remember that rational numbers expressed as decimals will be terminating $\left(\frac{3}{4} = 0.75\right)$ or repeating $\left(\frac{1}{12} = 0.08333\dots\right)$. Irrational numbers such as $\sqrt{2}$ have decimals that neither terminate nor repeat.

Numbers and their operations are the basis of algebra. The four basic operations are well known to you: addition, subtraction, multiplication, and division. Subtraction and division can be defined in terms of the two main operations, addition and multiplication.

Subtraction $x - y = x + (-y)$, where $x, y \in \mathbb{R}$.

Division $\frac{x}{y} = x \cdot \frac{1}{y}$, where $x, y \in \mathbb{R}$ and $y \neq 0$.

The main operations on real numbers are characterized by some basic principles. These principles are summarized in the next table.

Property	Of Addition	Of Multiplication
Commutative	$a + b = b + a$	$a \cdot b = b \cdot a$
Associative	$a + (b + c) = (a + b) + c$	$a \cdot (b \cdot c) = (a \cdot b) \cdot c$
Identity	$a + 0 = a = 0 + a$	$a \cdot 1 = a = 1 \cdot a$
Inverse	$a + (-a) = 0$	$a \cdot \frac{1}{a} = 1, a \neq 0$
Closure	If $a + b = c$, then $c \in \mathbb{R}$	If $a \cdot b = c$, then $c \in \mathbb{R}$
Distributive of multiplication over addition		$a(b + c) = ab + ac$

Can you think of some useful measurements in a swamp that involve real numbers?

You should be familiar with most of these properties. However, the closure property is new to our study of algebra. It states that when an operation is performed on any two numbers of a set and the answer is also in the set, the set is closed with respect to that operation. The set of odd integers is closed with respect to multiplication since the product of two odd numbers is odd. It is not closed under addition since the sum of two odd numbers is even. As indicated in the table, the set of real numbers is closed under both operations.

These basic properties of real numbers form the mathematical basis of algebra. A thorough understanding of the properties in this section will provide the necessary mathematical foundation for your study of Algebra 2. Remember that the foundation is the most important part of any structure, whether it is physical or abstract. A Christian's life must be structured by biblical principles and have Jesus Christ as the chief Cornerstone. Ephesians 2:20 states that Christians' lives "are built upon the foundation of the apostles and prophets, Jesus Christ himself being the chief corner stone." Likewise, the Word of God provides the foundation for the properties of numbers upon which algebra is based.

In geometry, you learned about definitions and postulates that form the basis for deriving theorems. In algebra, the properties can serve as postulates, and the term *exponent* is one of several basic definitions.

Definition

Exponent   a superscript written to the right of a term (the base), indicating the number of times the base is to be used as a factor.

From this definition a^3 means $a \cdot a \cdot a$, where a is the base and 3 is the exponent.

The order of operations is another valuable tool in algebra. It is a rule used to determine the correct answer to a numerical expression.

For example, attempting to evaluate the expression

$$8^2 + 2 \cdot 6 - 14 \div 2$$

may produce a variety of answers such as 191, 63, 69, −264, and 31, of which all but one are incorrect. The correct order of operations is needed to obtain the correct answer. Which of the answers above is correct according to the convention below?

Order of Operations

1. Evaluate all exponential expressions.
2. Perform all multiplication or division from left to right.
3. Perform all addition or subtraction from left to right.

The value of $8^2 + 2 \cdot 6 - 14 \div 2$ is **69**. Is that the answer you got?

Review the many properties and principles in this section until you can apply them readily.

▶ A. Exercises

Place each number in the most restrictive set possible, using the definitions given in the section.

1. $\frac{1}{5}$
2. -7
3. 0
4. -182
5. 97
6. $0.232332333\ldots$
7. $\frac{22}{7}$
8. $\sqrt{5}$
9. $\frac{-1}{4}$
10. $0.7\overline{9}$

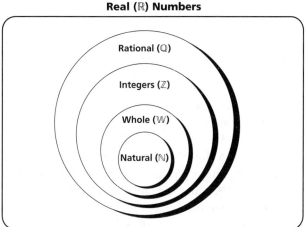

Real (ℝ) Numbers

Rational (ℚ)

Integers (ℤ)

Whole (W)

Natural (ℕ)

Use integers to illustrate the properties listed.

11. Commutative property of addition
12. Associative property of multiplication
13. Identity property of addition
14. Closure property of multiplication, 5 and 6 are integers
15. Inverse property of addition
16. Distributive property of multiplication over addition
17. Commutative property of multiplication
18. Identity property of multiplication

▶ B. Exercises

19. Is the set of whole numbers closed under subtraction? Why?

20. Is the set of rational numbers closed under division? Why?

Evaluate each numerical expression.

21. $7 + 6 \cdot 2 - 10 \div 5$

22. $2^3 - 16 + 4 \cdot 8 - 12$

23. $6 - 7 + 4 \cdot 2 + 8 \div 4$

24. $4^2 + 6 \div 3 \cdot 2^4 - 18$

25. $3^3 - 5 \cdot 9 + 6 - 29$

▶ C. Exercises

Evaluate.

26. $\frac{1}{3} + \frac{5}{6} \cdot \frac{1}{2} - 8 \div 3$

27. $0.42 + (2.7)(0.19) - 0.85 \div 1.7$

▶ Dominion Modeling

28. For the electric utility data given at the opening of the chapter, what are the variables? Which variable would be a suitable input variable? Which would be a suitable output variable?

29. In Minnesota, a power company charges \$4.50 to be connected to their system. Then they charge \$0.0635 for each kWh. Thus an appropriate function rule for this situation, with cost C and energy used e, is $C_{MN}(e) = 0.0635e + 4.50$. What function rules could be used to model the pricing plans for the other electric companies?

30. What would it cost for the following kilowatt-hour usages in the British Columbia plan? 1000 kWh, 1500 kWh, 2000 kWh, 2500 kWh

31. Note that each pricing plan has two parts, a flat fee and a rate. Which of the two parts applies no matter how much electricity is used?

ANCIENT NUMERATION

Egypt, Babylon, and China, three of the world's oldest cultures, each developed a numeration system. These numeration systems permitted each culture to develop algebra skills.

Egyptian

Egyptian numeration symbols are hieroglyphics, or picture symbols, expressed in multiples of ten but without place values. The best preserved Egyptian papyrus is the Rhind Papyrus (dated around 1700 B.C.), which contains about eighty-five mathematical problems and their solutions.

1	10	100	1000	10,000	100,000	1,000,000

The seated Colossi of Pharoah Ramses II at Abu Simbel in Egypt date from about 1257 B.C.

Joseph needed knowledge of Egyptian math to keep track of all the grain, to direct the construction of storage facilities, and to distribute it fairly and efficiently. If Joseph were looking at the following quantities of grain stored in the south Memphis granary, what would he get for a total?

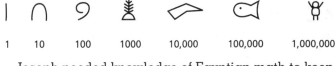

The historical records show that the Egyptians knew enough algebra to use fractions, solve simple quadratics, and calculate areas and volumes. In finding the area of a circle their formula was $A = \left(\frac{8d}{9}\right)^2$ where d is the diameter. This gave a value of 3.1605 for π, which was a very good approximation. Their fractions, however, were always unit fractions (having 1 as the numerator). They used the symbol ro, , for this numerator. Can you identify these Egyptian fractions?

Babylonian

Old Babylonian tablets from 1800-1600 B.C. tell us about the mathematics of the ancient Babylonians. The numeration system used base 60 and place notation. Here are the first twelve numerals written in their cuneiform notation with ⌐ as 1 and ⟨ as ten.

Larger numerals, such as 20, 30, 40, 50, appear as groups of the ten symbol.

With this system, the Babylonians developed multiplication tables, reciprocals, fractions, decimals, squares, square roots, cubes, and cube roots. They could find solutions to equations, and they knew the Pythagorean theorem a millenium before Pythagoras lived.

Daniel and his three friends would have learned a great deal of mathematics from such tablets. Daniel as prime minister needed a thorough knowledge of Babylonian mathematics and its applications.

The ruins of the Palace of Nebuchadnezzar at Babylon, now in Iraq

Chinese

The most significant ancient Chinese mathematical treatise is *Chiu-Chang Suan-Shu*, or *Arithmetic in Nine Sections*. This book included area formulas for triangles and trapezoids and the introduction of negative numbers. For instance, if T indicated 6, then $\mathbf{\bar{T}}$ represented -6.

The diagram illustrates ancient Chinese numeration in a magic square, called lo-shu. A magic square is an arrangement of numbers such that the sum of the rows, columns, or diagonals is always constant. To the right of the lo-shu is the magic square as we would write it today. Can you figure out the rest of the magic square from the lo-shu? What is the constant sum?

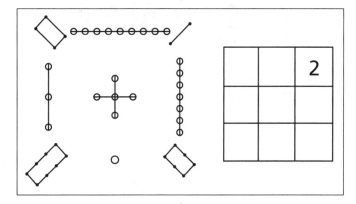

In the thirteenth century the Chinese invented a way to solve equations numerically. Two works by Chu Shih-chieh, *Introduction of Mathematical Studies* and *The Precious Mirror of the Four Elements*, set forth Chinese algebra. By A.D. 906 they had also used matrices to find solutions to systems of equations, a method still used today by computers.

These numeration systems permitted each culture to develop algebra skills.

Sculpted lions guard the entrance to China's Forbidden City.

1.2 Sums of Polynomials

Polynomials are simple algebraic expressions formed by adding even more basic expressions called terms. *Terms* of an algebraic expression are addends of the expression made up of a variable, a number, or a product of numbers and variables. The number in a term is called the *coefficient* and is written before any variables. If no number appears, then the coefficient is 1. Polynomials can be classified according to the number of terms.

Definitions

Polynomial an algebraic expression of one or more terms. Each term must have nonnegative integer exponents.

Monomial a polynomial with only one term.

Binomial a polynomial with exactly two terms.

Trinomial a polynomial with exactly three terms.

The other method of classifying polynomials is by degree. The *degree of a polynomial* is the degree of the highest-degree term in the polynomial. You can determine the *degree of a term* by adding the exponents of the variables in the term. A constant has a degree of 0 since $5x^0 = 5 \cdot 1 = 5$. Zero has no degree.

EXAMPLE 1   Determine the degree of each term.

Answer

Term	Sum of exponents	Degree	
$2xy$	$1 + 1$	2	Add the exponents on
$5x^2 y$	$2 + 1$	3	each variable.
$-4a^3bc^2$	$3 + 1 + 2$	6	
$7x^4$	4	4	

EXAMPLE 2   Find the degree of $4x^3yz + 7x^2y - 15x^4y^3z^2 + 2xyz$.

Answer

Expression	Degree	
$4x^3yz$	5	1. Determine the
$7x^2y$	3	degree of each term.
$15x^4y^3z^2$	9	
$2xyz$	3	
$4x^3yz + 7x^2y - 15x^4y^3z^2 + 2xyz$	9	2. Select the degree of the highest-degree term.

You should already be proficient at performing operations with polynomials from Algebra 1. When you add or subtract polynomials, you must combine only like terms by using the distributive property.

Definition

Like terms   terms that have the same variable(s) with the same exponents.

EXAMPLE 3   Combine $(3x^2 + 2x - 8) + (5x^2 - 3x + 9)$.

Answer

$(3x^2 + 2x - 8) + (5x^2 - 3x + 9)$

$(3x^2 + 5x^2) + (2x - 3x) + (-8 + 9)$

$(3 + 5)x^2 + (2 - 3)x + (-8 + 9)$ 1. Apply the distributive property.

$8x^2 - x + 1$ 2. Combine the coefficients for each term.

EXAMPLE 4   Combine $(4a^3b + 2a^2b - 8ab^3) - (5a^3b + 3ab^2 - 4ab^3)$.

Answer

$(4a^3b + 2a^2b - 8ab^3) - (5a^3b + 3ab^2 - 4ab^3)$

$4a^3b + 2a^2b - 8ab^3 - 5a^3b - 3ab^2 + 4ab^3$ 1. Remove parentheses by distributing -1 times the second polynomial.

$4a^3b + 2a^2b - 8ab^3 - 5a^3b - 3ab^2 + 4ab^3$ 2. Determine like terms.

$-a^3b + 2a^2b - 3ab^2 - 4ab^3$ 3. Combine like terms.

▶ A. Exercises

Classify each polynomial by the two methods described in this section.
1. $4xy$
2. $3x^2y + 4xy - 5xy^3$
3. $5a^3b^2c - 7abc + 3a^4b$
4. $5c^2d + 25cd^2$
5. $4a^2bc + 3x^2y - 5d + 6c^2d^4$
6. $16abc$
7. 9
8. $4x^2 + y$
9. $6a^2b + 3ab^3 - 4$
10. $5x^2 + 12x - 7$

▶ B. Exercises

Perform the indicated operation and simplify.
11. $(2x^2 + 3x - 8) + (5x^2 - 9x + 2)$
12. $(5a^3 - b) - (4a^3 + 2b)$
13. $(12c^2 + 3cd - 5d^2) + (6cd + 2d^2)$
14. $(7a^2 - 9b^2) + (3a^2 + 4ab + 7b^2)$
15. $(5x^4y + 3x^2y^2 - 2xy^5) - (3x^4y + 3xy^2 - 3x^2y^2)$
16. $(4a^2 + 9b^2) - (3a^2 + 2a - b^2) + (6a^2 + 4b^2)$
17. $(13c^2 + 4c - d^2) + (6c^2 - 5c + 6d^2) - (8c^2 - 3d^2)$
18. $(6x^2y + 9xy - 12xy^2) - (4x^2y - 8xy + 7xy^2 + 3y^3)$
19. $(3a + 4b - 9c) + (7a - 3b + c) - (4a - 6b + 2c)$
20. $(5c^2d + 3cd^2 - 8cd) - (2c^2d + 6cd^2)$

▶ C. Exercises

21. $\left(\frac{2}{3}x^2 - \frac{5}{7}x + \frac{1}{2}\right) - \left(\frac{1}{4}x^2 + \frac{2}{5}x - \frac{4}{5}\right)$
22. $(4.75x^2 - 32.6x + 87.5) - (12.8x^2 - 1.79x + 1.74)$

▶ Dominion Modeling

23. Suppose Basilean Enterprises wished to purchase a chalet in British Columbia and another in Wisconsin. What function rule could one use to predict the total cost of electric power if both were expected to use the same amount of electrical energy? What rule would apply if they planned to buy chalets in Michigan and Connecticut?
24. Suppose Basilean Enterprises decided to purchase a chalet in every state and province listed. What function rule would describe the cost of electric power if they all used the same amount of electrical energy?

25. Immediately before agreeing to buy all of the chalets, Basilean Enterprises decided to cancel only the purchase of the Minnesota chalet. From the previous function rule, what would be an easy way to get an updated function rule for the cost of electric power?

Cumulative Review

Identify the property used in each step of the simplification.

Simplify $(5x - 3) + (7x + 4y)$.

26. $(7x + 4y) + (5x - 3)$
27. $(4y + 7x) + (5x - 3)$
28. $4y + (7x + 5x) - 3$
29. $4y + (7 + 5)x - 3$
30. $12x + 4y - 3$

1.3 Products of Polynomials

The laws of exponents are the basis for a thorough understanding of the multiplication of polynomials. A strong foundation is important to every area of life. In your spiritual life you need a strong foundation, which is the Lord Jesus Christ. You can build upon this sturdy foundation with the Word of God, the Bible. Read I Corinthians 3:9-11.

Properties of Exponents Related to Multiplication	
Product property	$x^a \cdot x^b = x^{a+b}$
Power property	$(x^a)^b = x^{ab}$
Power of a product	$(xy)^a = x^a y^a$
Zero Power	$x^0 = 1$

EXAMPLE 1	Multiply $(5a^3b)(2ab)$.	
Answer	$(5a^3b)(2ab)$	1. Because multiplication is commutative and associative, you can rearrange the factors.
	$5 \cdot 2 \cdot a^3 \cdot a \cdot b \cdot b$	
	$10a^{3+1}b^{1+1}$	2. Use the product property of exponents.
	$10a^4b^2$	

EXAMPLE 2	Simplify $(3x^2y)^3$.	
Answer	$(3x^2y)^3$	
	$3^3(x^2)^3y^3$	1. Use the power of a product property to cube the coefficient and each variable factor.
	$27x^6y^3$	2. Use the power property.

The following examples illustrate the use of the exponent properties when multiplying polynomials.

EXAMPLE 3	Multiply $2x(5x^2 + 3x - 7)$.	
Answer	$2x(5x^2 + 3x - 7)$	
	$2x(5x^2) + 2x(3x) - 2x(7)$	1. Distribute the monomial over the polynomial.
	$10x^3 + 6x^2 - 14x$	2. Apply the product property of exponents.

To multiply two binomials, use the FOIL method. This method is actually an application of the distributive property. FOIL is the acronym to help you remember how to multiply binomials.

F → first terms

O → outside terms

I → inside terms

L → last terms

$(3x + 2)(x - 5)$

$(3x + 2)(x - 5)$ 1. Use **FOIL** and the exponent properties.

$3x^2 - 15x + 2x - 10$

F	O	I	L
$3x^2$	$-15x$	$2x$	-10

$3x^2 - 13x - 10$ 2. Combine like terms.

The FOIL method is simply repeated use of the distributive property. The product can be found by applying the distributive property as shown here.

$(3x + 2)(x - 5)$

$3x(x - 5) + 2(x - 5)$

$3x^2 - 15x + 2x - 10$

$3x^2 - 13x - 10$

Sometimes you will be required to multiply polynomials that have more than two terms. You may find it more convenient to write the like term products so they can be added vertically. Example 4 shows the vertical method of multiplying polynomials.

EXAMPLE 4   Multiply $(6a - 2)(9a^2 + 4a - 7)$.

Answer

$$9a^2 + 4a - 7$$
$$6a - 2$$

1. Write the problem in vertical form.

$$-18a^2 - 8a + 14$$
$$54a^3 + 24a^2 - 42a$$

$$54a^3 + 6a^2 - 50a + 14$$

2. Multiply each term of the trinomial by each term of the binomial. This is an application of the distributive property. Place the products in columns containing like terms and add the like terms.

▶ A. Exercises

Perform the indicated operation and simplify.

1. $5x^2 \cdot 3x^3$
2. $6a^2b \cdot 9ab^2$
3. $cd^3 \cdot 4c$
4. f^0
5. $(x^2)^4$
6. $(2a^3b)^2$
7. $(7x^4)^0$
8. $(9c^5d^3)^3$
9. $(8a^2b)(4ab^3)$
10. $(2x^2y^5)^2 + 6x^4y^{10}$
11. $3a^2(2a + 4x - 9)$
12. $5xy^2(x^2y^3 - 14xy)$

13. $a^2cd^3(a^5 - 3acd + 7a)$

14. $(x + y)(x - 2y)$

15. $(a + 6)(a - 4)$

16. $(x + 3)(x + 3)$

17. $(b - 2)(b + 7)$

18. $(y + 8)(y - 8)$

19. $(x - 9)^2$

▶ B. Exercises

Perform the indicated operation and simplify.

20. $(x + 4y)(2x - 3y)$

21. $3(a + b)(a - 2b)$

22. $xy(3x - 2)(x - 5)$

23. $(a + b)^0$

24. $a^3b^2(a - 4b)(a + 3b)$

25. $(x + y)^2$

26. $4ac^2(3a - 2)(a + 6)$

27. $(x + 1)(5x^2 + 2x - 6)$

28. $(x + y)(x^2 - 3xy + y^2)$

29. $(4a - 5)(a^2 + 6a - 2)$

30. $(x^2 + 3x - 2)(2x^2 + 5x + 9)$

▶ C. Exercises

Perform the indicated operation and simplify.

31. $(x^2 - 5x + 2)(3x^2 + 7x - 4)$

32. $(3x^2 - 2x + 1)(2x^3 - x^2 + 5x - 2)$

▶ Dominion Modeling

33. Suppose you owned a home served by the southern California utility company. What would be a reasonable new cost function if the cost of living rose by 3%?

▍Cumulative Review

Give the property that justifies each step in the simplification.

Simplify $(x^4 \cdot 5y^0)(x^2)^3$.

34. $(x^4 \cdot 5y^0)x^6$

35. $(x^4 \cdot 5 \cdot 1)x^6$

36. $(x^4 \cdot 5)x^6$

37. $(5x^4)x^6$

38. $5(x^4 \cdot x^6)$

39. $5x^{10}$

Matrices and Terminology

The Super M grocery-store chain stocks three brands of soft drink: *X, Y,* and *Z.* In each of these brands four flavors are available: cola, grape, orange, and root beer. The table below summarizes the inventory that Store 182 has in stock on April 18 by flavor and brand. To the right of the table is a symbolic representation of their inventory called a matrix (plural: matrices).

Super M Grocery Store 182				
Brand	Cola	Grape	Orange	Root Beer
X	9	7	5	6
Y	10	3	8	4
Z	7	6	3	5

$$A = \begin{bmatrix} 9 & 7 & 5 & 6 \\ 10 & 3 & 8 & 4 \\ 7 & 6 & 3 & 5 \end{bmatrix}$$

Each number in a matrix is called an *entry* (or *element*) of the matrix. The matrix is made up of *rows* and *columns* of entries. Each matrix is described by its *dimensions,* that is, the number of rows by the number of columns. The soft-drink matrix is a 3×4 matrix. The entries are described by the same lowercase letter with subscripts corresponding to their row and column location.

$$A = \begin{bmatrix} a_{11} & a_{12} & a_{13} & a_{14} \\ a_{21} & a_{22} & a_{23} & a_{24} \\ a_{31} & a_{32} & a_{33} & a_{34} \end{bmatrix}$$

In matrix A the entry in the second row and third column is 8. This is symbolized by $a_{23} = 8$. Likewise $a_{13} = 5$ and $a_{33} = 3$.

A matrix that has only one row is called a *row matrix;* likewise, a matrix that consists of only one column is called a *column matrix.* A *zero matrix* is one in which all entries are zero. A matrix with the same number of rows as columns is called a *square matrix.* Examples of each are shown.

Row Matrix

$$B = \begin{bmatrix} 4 & 7 & -2 \end{bmatrix}$$

Column Matrix

$$C = \begin{bmatrix} 5 \\ 9 \\ 8 \end{bmatrix}$$

Zero Matrix

$$D = \begin{bmatrix} 0 & 0 & 0 \\ 0 & 0 & 0 \end{bmatrix}$$

Square Matrix

$$E = \begin{bmatrix} 1 & 2 \\ 3 & 4 \end{bmatrix}$$

Two matrices are *equal* if and only if
1. they have the same dimensions, and
2. the corresponding entries of the matrices are equal.

$$\begin{bmatrix} 2 & 7 \\ 5 & 5 \end{bmatrix} \neq \begin{bmatrix} 7 & 2 \\ 9 & 5 \end{bmatrix} \qquad \begin{bmatrix} 3 & -1 \\ 0 & 2 \end{bmatrix} = \begin{bmatrix} 3 & -1 \\ 0 & 2 \end{bmatrix}$$

▶ Exercises

$$L = [2 \quad 1 \quad 3] \qquad M = \begin{bmatrix} 7 & 4 & -8 \\ 2 & 1 & 3 \end{bmatrix} \qquad N = \begin{bmatrix} 4 & 2 \\ 7 & 1 \\ -8 & 3 \end{bmatrix} \qquad P = \begin{bmatrix} 7 & 4 & -8 \\ 2 & 1 & 3 \end{bmatrix}$$

Give the dimensions of each matrix.
1. M
2. N

Give the entry represented.
3. l_{12}
4. p_{13}
5. Which matrices are equal?

1.4 Quotients of Polynomials

Three other properties of exponents used in division of polynomials are given here.

Quotient Property of Exponents	$\dfrac{x^a}{x^b} = x^{a-b}$, where $x \neq 0$
Negative Exponent Property	$x^{-a} = \dfrac{1}{x^a}$, where $x \neq 0$
Power of Quotient Property	$\left(\dfrac{x}{y}\right)^a = \dfrac{x^a}{y^a}$

The second principle is developed below to help you better understand it.

$$x^4 = x \cdot x \cdot x \cdot x$$
$$x^3 = x \cdot x \cdot x$$
$$x^2 = x \cdot x$$
$$x^1 = x$$

Notice that each time 1 is subtracted from the exponent of the term on the left, the term on the right is divided by x.

The general rule in the sequence is "as the exponent decreases by 1, the expression on the right is divided by x." To develop the second exponent principle we need to extend this sequence.

$$x^2 = x \cdot x$$
$$x^1 = \frac{x \cdot x}{x} = x$$
$$x^0 = \frac{x}{x} = 1$$
$$x^{-1} = \frac{1}{x}$$
$$x^{-2} = \frac{\frac{1}{x}}{x} = \frac{1}{x} \div x = \frac{1}{x} \cdot \frac{1}{x} = \frac{1}{x^2}$$
$$x^{-3} = \frac{\frac{1}{x^2}}{x} = \frac{1}{x^2} \div x = \frac{1}{x^2} \cdot \frac{1}{x} = \frac{1}{x^3}$$

In general, then, the pattern is clear: $x^{-a} = \dfrac{1}{x^a}$. Also, $\dfrac{1}{x^{-a}} = \dfrac{1}{\frac{1}{x^a}} = x^a$.

Note: Since the exponent on a term applies to the symbol immediately to the left of it,

$$2x^{-2} = \frac{2}{x^2} \text{ and } (2x)^{-2} = \frac{1}{(2x)^2} = \frac{1}{4x^2}$$

These exponent laws are essential to your understanding of division of polynomials.

EXAMPLE 1 Apply the properties of exponents to simplify the following.

Answer

a) $x^{-3} = \dfrac{1}{x^3}$

b) $\dfrac{1}{x^{-7}} = \dfrac{1}{\frac{1}{x^7}} = x^7$

c) $\dfrac{x^3}{x^5} = x^{-2} = \dfrac{1}{x^2}$

EXAMPLE 2 Divide $25a^3bc^2 \div 5ab^3c$.

Answer

$\dfrac{25a^3bc^2}{5ab^3c}$	1. Write the division problem in fractional form.
$\dfrac{5a^{3-1}b^{1-3}c^{2-1}}{5a^2b^{-2}c}$	2. Divide the coefficients and use the quotient property of exponents.
$\dfrac{5a^2c}{b^2}$	3. Apply the negative exponent property.

EXAMPLE 3 Divide $(3x^2y^3 + 9x^5yz^2 - x^4yz^5) \div (3xyz)$.

Answer

$\dfrac{3x^2y^3 + 9x^5yz^2 - x^4yz^5}{3xyz}$	1. Write the problem as a fraction.
$\dfrac{3x^2y^3}{3xyz} + \dfrac{9x^5yz^2}{3xyz} - \dfrac{x^4yz^5}{3xyz}$	2. Separate the fraction into three terms.
$\dfrac{xy^2}{z} + 3x^4z - \dfrac{x^3z^4}{3}$	3. Divide the coefficients and mentally use the quotient property of exponents.

The next examples show the division of one polynomial by another polynomial. By following an example carefully, you can see how to solve problems you will face. The same idea is true in many areas of life. Our most reliable examples for life are given to us in the Bible. Read I Corinthians 10:11 and John 13:15. These show us the importance of examples in our lives.

EXAMPLE 4   Divide $(2x^2 + 4x - 9) \div (x + 3)$.

Answer

$x + 3 \overline{)2x^2 + 4x - 9}$

1. Write the problem in long division form. Make sure both polynomials are arranged in descending powers of the variable.

$$\begin{array}{r} 2x \\ x + 3 \overline{)2x^2 + 4x - 9} \\ 2x^2 + 6x \end{array}$$

2. Divide x into $2x^2$. Then multiply $2x$ by $x + 3$ and write it below the appropriate columns.

$$\begin{array}{r} 2x \\ x + 3 \overline{)2x^2 + 4x - 9} \\ 2x^2 + 6x \\ \hline - 2x - 9 \end{array}$$

3. Subtract this product from the dividend and bring the next term down.

$$\begin{array}{r} 2x \ - \ 2 \\ x + 3 \overline{)2x^2 + 4x - 9} \\ 2x^2 + 6x \\ \hline - 2x - 9 \\ - 2x - 6 \\ \hline - 3 \end{array}$$

4. Divide x into the first term found after the subtraction. Multiply -2 by $x + 3$ and write the product under the proper columns. Subtract.

5. You must stop the division now because x will not divide into -3 since the degree of the divisor is less than that of the dividend.

6. The quotient is $2x - 2$ with a remainder of -3.

Then $2x^2 + 4x - 9 = (x + 3)(2x - 2) - 3$.

Another example follows. Study the process and compare it to Example 4.

EXAMPLE 5   Divide $(x^4 + 3x^2 - 12) \div (x + 2)$.

Answer

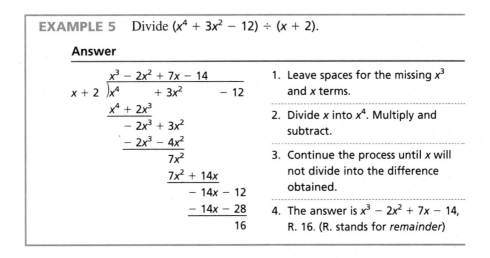

$$\begin{array}{r} x^3 - 2x^2 + 7x - 14 \\ x + 2 \overline{)x^4 + 3x^2 - 12} \\ x^4 + 2x^3 \\ \hline - 2x^3 + 3x^2 \\ - 2x^3 - 4x^2 \\ \hline 7x^2 \\ 7x^2 + 14x \\ \hline - 14x - 12 \\ - 14x - 28 \\ \hline 16 \end{array}$$

1. Leave spaces for the missing x^3 and x terms.

2. Divide x into x^4. Multiply and subtract.

3. Continue the process until x will not divide into the difference obtained.

4. The answer is $x^3 - 2x^2 + 7x - 14$, R. 16. (R. stands for *remainder*)

The remainder from the division can also be expressed as a fraction. For example, the answer in Example 5 could be expressed as follows.

$$x^3 - 2x^2 + 7x - 14 + \frac{16}{x + 2}$$

Notice that the divisor $x + 2$ becomes the denominator for the remainder just as two-thirds is obtained when a division by three leaves a remainder of 2.

EXAMPLE 6   Divide $(a^3 - b^3) \div (a - b)$.

Answer

$$
\require{enclose}
\begin{array}{r}
a^2 + ab + b^2 \\
a - b \enclose{longdiv}{a^3 - b^3} \\
\underline{a^3 - a^2b } \\
a^2b \\
\underline{a^2b - ab^2 } \\
ab^2 - b^3 \\
\underline{ab^2 - b^3} \\
0
\end{array}
$$

Since there is no remainder, we can conclude that
$a^3 - b^3 = (a - b)(a^2 + ab + b^2)$.

▶ A. Exercises

Divide. Write all answers with positive integer exponents.

1. $a^3bc^4 \div ab^3c$

2. $f^2g \div fg$

3. $8x^2y^5 \div 2x^3y^3$

4. $81a^4b^2c \div 3abc$

5. $112x^8y^2 \div 2x^4y^3$

6. $(7a^3b + 2a^2b^2 - 6ab^3) \div (2ab)$

7. $(15c^4dk^3 - 5c^2dk + 40c^8dk^3) \div (5cdk)$

8. $(2x^4y + 8x^3y^2 - x^2y^4 + 3xy^8) \div (xy^3)$

9. $(26a^4 - 13a^3 + 39a^2 + 78a) \div (13a)$

10. $(9x^3yz^4 + 27xyz) \div (3xyz)$

11. $16a^2b^5c \div 2ab^3$

▶ B. Exercises

Divide.

12. $(x^2 - 6x - 16) \div (x + 2)$
13. $(a^2 - 4a - 45) \div (a - 9)$
14. $(y^2 - 9y + 18) \div (y - 6)$
15. $(x^2y - 7xy - 30y) \div (x + 3)$
16. $(x^2 - y^2) \div (x + y)$
17. $(3a^3 - 4a^2 + a - 8) \div (a + 1)$
18. $(7y^4 - 3y^2 - 14) \div (y^2 - 2)$
19. $(9x^4 + 3x^2 - 12) \div (x - 4)$
20. $(5a^3 + 4a^2 - 7a + 9) \div (a + 2)$
21. $(x^2 + 10x + 21) \div (x + 3)$
22. $(x^2 - 4x - 21) \div (x + 3)$
23. $(12y^2 + 26y - 10) \div (2y + 5)$
24. $(x^2 - 11x + 2) \div (x - 6)$
25. $(3a^2 + a - 12) \div (a - 1)$

▶ C. Exercises

Divide. Write remainders as fractions.

26. $(3x^3 - 5x^2 + 7x - 9) \div (x^2 - 2)$
27. $(4x^4 - 2x + 7) \div (2x + 3)$

▶ Dominion Modeling

28. In the power utility data, the Pennsylvania utility covers the city of Philadelphia. For all residential properties within the city, estimate a *revenue function* for this power company. (Use your function rule for the Pennsylvania utility. Revenue refers to all the income before expenses are subtracted.)

▮ Cumulative Review

Perform the indicated operations.

29. $(7x^2y)(3xy^2)$
30. $(3x + 2)(2x - 4)$
31. $(x^2 - x + 4) + (x^2 + 2x - 5)$
32. $(x + 3)^2$
33. $(y + 2)(y^2 + 3y - 5)$

1.5 Factoring Binomials

Factoring is a method of expressing a polynomial as a product. It is an application of the distributive property and the opposite of multiplying.

You can always check your factored answer by multiplying the factors together to produce the original polynomial. Some form of checking answers is a good habit to develop. Checking answers mentally can save you time. God desires that we check everything in life against the Scripture. "Prove [check or test] all things; hold fast that which is good" (I Thess. 5:21). Always check your answer to be sure it is completely factored.

Factoring Binomials

1. Factor out all common monomial factors (if any).

2. Use any special formula (such as the difference of two squares) that applies.

3. Make sure each factor is broken down as far as possible (repeat step two if necessary).

Study the next definition and example to review the important first step in factoring.

Definition

Common monomial factor   a factor of a polynomial common to all terms in the polynomial.

EXAMPLE 1   Factor $5x^2y + 15xy^2$.

Answer

$5x^2y + 15xy^2$	1. Analyze each term of the polynomial, finding any common numerical and variable factors. Each term has in common only the first power of 5, x, and y (GCF = $5xy$).
$5xy(x + 3y)$	2. To find the other factor, divide each term by $5xy$.

To check, multiply the monomial by the polynomial to obtain the original polynomial.

Some special formulas apply to factoring polynomials. The difference of squares is of the form $x^2 - y^2$. Notice that the first and last terms of this special binomial are perfect squares. Notice also that the two terms are subtracted—thus the name, difference of squares. Look at the following multiplication.

$$(x - y)(x + y) = x^2 + xy - xy - y^2 = x^2 - y^2$$

EXAMPLE 2   Factor $a^2 - 9$.

Answer

$a^2 - 9$ $\sqrt{a^2} = a$ $\sqrt{9} = 3$	1. Recognize that this is the difference of squares.
$(a + 3)(a - 3)$	2. Factor into the sum and difference of the square roots of the first and last terms.

In general, to factor the difference of squares, factor the polynomial into two binomials of which the first and last terms are square roots of the first and last terms of the polynomial. Make one binomial the sum of these square roots and the other factor the difference of the square roots.

EXAMPLE 3   Factor $8a^4b^2 - 32a^2b^2$.

Answer

$8a^4b^2 - 32a^2b^2$	
$GCF = 8a^2b^2$	1. Find the GCF of the terms.
$8a^2b^2(a^2 - 4)$	2. Factor the GCF from the polynomial.
$8a^2b^2(a - 2)(a + 2)$	3. Factor the remaining difference of squares.

There are two other special formulas similar to the difference of squares. An explanation for the first formula can be found in Example 6 in Section 1.4. Perform the multiplication below to check the second formula.

Difference of cubes:

$$a^3 - b^3 = (a - b)(a^2 + ab + b^2)$$

Sum of cubes:

$$a^3 + b^3 = (a + b)(a^2 - ab + b^2)$$

Notice that the binomial in each of the factorizations is identical to the polynomial except that the terms are the cube roots of the terms of the polynomial. Also notice that the sign on ab is the opposite of that between a^3 and b^3 and b^2 is always positive.

EXAMPLE 4   Factor $27x^3 + 8y^3$.

Answer

$27x^3 + 8y^3$

$(3x)^3 + (2y)^3$	1. Since $27x^3$ and $8y^3$ are both perfect cubes, write each as the cube of a monomial.
$(3x + 2y)(9x^2 - 6xy + 4y^2)$	2. Write the factors using the formula as a pattern.

▶ A. Exercises

Factor completely.

1. $3x^2 - 15x$
2. $2a^3b^2 - 3a^2b^3$
3. $24xy + 56ab$
4. $10c^3d^3 + 15c^2d^4$
5. $x^2 - 81$
6. $x^2 - 4$
7. $a^2 - b^2$
8. $4x^2 - 9$
9. $25x^2 - 4y^2$
10. $3x^2 - 108$
11. $2x^3 - 8x$

▶ B. Exercises

Factor completely.

12. $x^3 - 8$
13. $y^3 + 64$
14. $ax^3 + 27a$
15. $8xy^3 - 125x$
16. $7x^3y^2z - 63xy^2z$
17. $6x^2 - 294$
18. $a^3 + 125$

19. $x^5 - 64x^2$
20. $4x^3y - 4xy^3$
21. $150y^4 - 6y^2$
22. $c^2 - 9d^2$
23. $288a^5 - 200a^3$
24. $x^4 - 1$

▶ C. Exercises

Factor completely.
25. $x^6 - y^6$
26. $2x^6 - 128y^6$
27. $x^{12} - 1$

▶ Dominion Modeling

28. For an entire town in Wisconsin, the expected revenue function is $R(e) = 6.144e + 667.2$. Estimate the population of this village from this function rule.

▪ Cumulative Review

Name the property that justifies each step in the proof of the difference of squares formula.

$(x - y)(x + y)$

29. $xx + xy - yx - yy$
30. $x^2 + xy - yx - y^2$
31. $x^2 + xy - xy - y^2$
32. $x^2 + 0 - y^2$
33. $x^2 - y^2$

1.6 Factoring Trinomials

Every trinomial of degree 2 or higher can be factored by using complex numbers. However, at this stage you will be asked to factor only over the set of integers. Trial and error will work for any trinomial that factors using integers, but you can save some time if you recognize perfect square trinomials.

Algebra helped engineer this highway interchange at Dallas, Texas.

A perfect square trinomial has first and last terms which are perfect squares. The middle term is twice the product of the square roots of the first and last terms. Check these two perfect square trinomial formulas:

$$a^2 + 2ab + b^2 = (a + b)(a + b) = (a + b)^2$$
$$a^2 - 2ab + b^2 = (a - b)(a - b) = (a - b)^2$$

EXAMPLE 1   Factor $x^2 + 10x + 25$.

Answer

$x^2 + 10x + 25$	1. Recognize the form $a^2 + 2ab + b^2$. x^2 is a perfect square, 25 is a perfect square, and $10x = 2\left(\sqrt{x^2}\right)\left(\sqrt{25}\right)$.
$(x + 5)^2$	2. Factor the perfect square trinomial as $(a + b)^2$ where $a = x$ and $b = 5$.

EXAMPLE 2 Factor $4x^2 - 28x + 49$.

Answer

$4x^2 - 28x + 49$	1. Recognize the form $a^2 - 2ab + b^2$. $4x^2 = (2x)^2$, $49 = 7^2$, and $28x = 2(2x)(7)$.
$(2x - 7)^2$	2. Factor this perfect square trinomial as $(a - b)^2$ where $a = 2x$ and $b = 7$.

As with binomials, there are several steps involved in factoring a trinomial. The main difference is at step three.

Factoring Trinomials

1. Factor out any common monomial factors.
2. Check for special cases.
3. Factor by the trial and error method.
4. Continue factoring until each factor is prime.

To factor by trial and error, factor the first and last terms and select the factorization whose outer and inner products add up to the middle term of the trinomial.

EXAMPLE 3 Factor $x^2 - 4x - 21$.

Answer

$x^2 - 4x - 21$	1. Look for any common monomial factors. This trinomial has none.
$x^2 = x \cdot x$ $(x \quad)(x \quad)$	2. Find the factors of the first term. Place the factors as the first elements in the binomial factors.
$-21 = -3(7)$ $\quad -21 = 3(-7)$ $-21 = -1(21)$ $\quad -21 = 1(-21)$	3. Find the factors of the last term. These are the possible factorizations. Place them as the last elements in the binomial factors.
$(x - 3)(x + 7)$ or $(x + 3)(x - 7)$ $-3x$ $\qquad$ $3x$ $+7x$ $\qquad$ $-7x$ $4x$ $\qquad$ $-4x$	4. Find the factorization that makes the sum of the outer and inner products equal to the middle term, $-4x$.
$(x + 3)(x - 7)$	5. The second choice produces the correct combination. Check the solution mentally.

EXAMPLE 4   Factor $12x^2 - 5x - 2$.

Answer

$12x^2 - 5x - 2$	1. Check for a common monomial. None exists.

$12x^2 = 12x \cdot x$	2. Factor the first term.
$12x^2 = 6x \cdot 2x$	There are several
$12x^2 = 4x \cdot 3x$	choices. Choose one
$(12x\quad)(x\quad)$	and try it in the binomial factors.

$(12x + 1)(x - 2) = 12x^2 - 23x - 2$ Incorrect	3. Factor the last term.
$(12x - 1)(x + 2) = 12x^2 + 23x - 2$ Incorrect	-2 equals $1(-2)$ or $(-1)2$. Try these factorizations in the binomial to see if any of the combinations work.

$(6x\quad)(2x\quad)$		4. Try another pair of
$(6x + 1)(2x - 2)$	$-10x$ Incorrect	factors of the first
$(6x - 1)(2x + 2)$	$+10x$ Incorrect	term of the poly-
$(6x - 2)(2x + 1)$	$+2x$ Incorrect	nomial. Since the
$(6x + 2)(2x - 1)$	$-2x$ Incorrect	polynomial had no common factors, factors having common factors can be instantly eliminated.

$(4x\quad)(3x\quad)$	5. Try the final factor-
$(4x + 1)(3x - 2) = 12x^2 - 5x - 2$ Correct	ization of $12x^2$.
Therefore the factorization is $(4x + 1)(3x - 2)$.	

EXAMPLE 5   Factor $30x^2 - 305x + 310$.

Answer

$30x^2 - 305x + 310$	1. Factor out the common monomial
$5(6x^2 - 61x + 62)$	factor.

$6x^2 = 6x \cdot x$	2. Factor the resulting trinomial by trial
$6x^2 = 3x \cdot 2x$	and error.
$5(6x\quad)(x\quad)$	
$62 = 2(31)\qquad 62 = -2(-31)$	
$62 = 1(62)\qquad 62 = -1(-62)$	

Continued ▶

	O & I term
$5(6x + 2)(x + 31)$	$188x$
$5(6x + 31)(x + 2)$	$43x$
$5(6x - 2)(x - 31)$	$-188x$
$5(6x - 31)(x - 2)$	$-43x$

3. When all combinations have been tried, it will be clear that $6x^2 - 61x + 62$ is a prime polynomial. Note: Attempts to use $1(62)$ or $-1(-62)$ will also result in failure. The same is true if we switch to 2 and 3 as coefficients of x.

Therefore $30x^2 - 305x + 310 = 5(6x^2 - 61x + 62)$.

▶ A. Exercises

Factor completely.

1. $x^2 - 2x - 63$
2. $a^2 + 2ab - 3b^2$
3. $3c^2 - 13c - 10$
4. $7x^2 - 67x - 30$
5. $10e^2f^3g + 6ef^2g^2 - 8ef^5g$
6. $a^2 + 6a + 9$
7. $2x^2 - 11x - 13$
8. $7a^2 - 21ab - 28b^2$
9. $a^2 - 19a + 18$
10. $a^5b^2 + 2a^4b^3 + a^3b^4$
11. $35x^2 - 32x - 12$
12. $5a^2 - 37a - 72$
13. $b^2 - 10bc + 25c^2$

▶ B. Exercises

Factor completely.

14. $4c^4d - 52c^3d + 168c^2d$
15. $12x^3y + 104x^2y - 36xy$
16. $19x^2 - 114x + 171$
17. $30a^3 - 235a^2 + 385a$
18. $4x^2 - 68x + 289$
19. $294y^4 - 24y^2$
20. $8x^2 - 30x - 27$
21. $x^4 + 2x^2 - 15$
22. $12a^5 - 9a^4 + 18a^3$
23. $x^4 - 13x^2 + 36$

Factor completely.

24. $8x^5 - 130x^3 + 32x$
25. $48x^4y - 216x^2y + 243y$

▶ Dominion Modeling

26. Compare the pricing plan for the Utah and Pennsylvania utility companies. If cost were the only concern, when would the Utah plan be best? When is the Pennsylvania plan best? (*Hint*: plot both plans.)
27. Of the two electric pricing plans, which is the least expensive over all? Write a short paragraph to explain your thoughts. (*Hint*: how many kWh is typical?)

Cumulative Review

Simplify.

28. $(3x^2 + 5x - 7) + (x^2 + 5x + 3)$
29. $(3x^2 + 5x - 7) - (x^2 + 5x + 3)$
30. $(3x^2 + 5x - 7)(x^2 + 5x + 3)$
31. $(4x^2 - 8x + 11) \div (2x - 3)$
32. $(x^2 + 7)(x - 3)$

Prove: $1.999\ldots = 2$

1.7 Factoring by Grouping

Polynomials with four or more terms may require a special technique called *factoring by grouping*. When applying this method, the distributive property is used to factor out common binomials.

Remember that factoring means writing the original expression as a product. This means that $x(x - 7) + 5(x - 7)$ is not in factored form because the expression is a sum of $x(x - 7)$ and $5(x - 7)$. This expression could be multiplied out and then factored by trial and error, but it is quicker to recognize the binomial $x - 7$ as a common factor of both terms.

EXAMPLE 1   Factor $x(x - 7) + 5(x - 7)$.

Answer

$x(x - 7) + 5(x - 7)$	1. Observe that the binomial factor $(x - 7)$ is common to both terms.
$(x - 7)(x + 5)$	2. Factor out the common binomial factor.

Factoring by grouping uses the associative property to group the terms of a polynomial to obtain a common binomial factor. In the examples below, factoring by grouping is the primary method used.

EXAMPLE 2   Factor $ax + 3a + bx + 3b$.

Answer

$ax + 3a + bx + 3b$	1. Factor out any common monomial factors. There are none in this polynomial.
$(ax + 3a) + (bx + 3b)$ $a(x + 3) + b(x + 3)$	2. Using the associative property, group terms in binomials and factor any common monomials from them.
$(x + 3)(a + b)$	3. Notice that the factorizations have the factor $x + 3$ in common. Factor it out of both terms just as if it were a monomial.

EXAMPLE 3   Factor $x^3 - 3x + 5x^2 - 15$.

Answer

$x^3 - 3x + 5x^2 - 15$	
$(x^3 - 3x) + (5x^2 - 15)$	1. Group the terms together into binomials.
$x(x^2 - 3) + 5(x^2 - 3)$	2. Factor each binomial.
$(x^2 - 3)(x + 5)$	3. Since the factor $x^2 - 3$ is common to each term, factor it out. $x^2 - 3$ is prime.

EXAMPLE 4   Factor $x^2 + 2xy + y^2 - 4$.

Answer

$x^2 + 2xy + y^2 - 4$	
$(x^2 + 2xy + y^2) - 4$	1. Notice that the first three terms form a perfect square trinomial. Group them together.
$(x + y)^2 - 4$	2. Factor the perfect square trinomial.
$(x + y + 2)(x + y - 2)$	3. Factor as the difference of squares.

Notice that grouping the polynomial in pairs to obtain $(x^2 + 2xy) + (y^2 - 4)$ is useless in Example 4, since there is no common binomial when you factor the polynomial into $x(x + 2y) + (y + 2)(y - 2)$.

EXAMPLE 5   Factor $3y^3 + 6y^2 - 27y - 54$.

Answer

$3y^3 + 6y^2 - 27y - 54$	
$3(y^3 + 2y^2 - 9y - 18)$	1. Factor out the common monomial.
$3[(y^3 + 2y^2) - (9y + 18)]$	2. Group the terms. Notice that $-9 \div (-1) = 9$ and $-18 \div (-1) = 18$
$3[y^2(y + 2) - 9(y + 2)]$	3. Factor each group.
$3[(y + 2)(y^2 - 9)]$	4. Factor out the common binomial $y + 2$.
$3(y + 2)(y + 3)(y - 3)$	5. Notice the difference of squares to finish factoring.

Be alert when you do the exercises. Some problems do not require grouping. You can use the following summary of factoring methods.

Factoring

1. Factor out all common monomial factors.
2. Count the number of terms and use the correct method.
   a. Binomial. Choose a formula: difference of squares; difference of cubes; sum of cubes.
   b. Trinomial. Use trial-and-error or perfect square trinomial formula.
   c. Other polynomial. Factor by grouping.
3. Repeat step 2 until it is completely factored.

▶ A. Exercises

Factor completely.

1. $x(x + 3) - y(x + 3)$
2. $x(x - 1) - 2(x - 1)$
3. $(x^3 - x^2y) + (xy - y^2)$
4. $(a^3 - 2a^2) + (3a - 6)$
5. $x(y + z) + 9(y + z)$
6. $(ab - 7b) + (2a - 14)$
7. $(x + 3)^2 + y(x + 3)$
8. $a^2(b - 5) - 4(b - 5)$
9. $(a - 5)^2 - y^2$
10. $(x + y)^2 - 16$

▶ B. Exercises

Factor completely.

11. $p(q^3 + 8) + 5(q^3 + 8)$
12. $x^2 + xy - 7x - 7y$
13. $x^3 + 6x^2 + 2x + 12$
14. $xy + 3y - 6x - 18$
15. $a^3 + 4a^2b - 4a - 16b$
16. $a^3 + 4a^2 + 3a + 12$
17. $(x - 5)^3 - 1$
18. $a^2 + 2ab + b^2 - 9$
19. $x^2 + 4y^2 - 4xy - 4$
20. $c^2 + 6cd + 9d^2 - 16f^2$
21. $2a^3x + 3ax - 3bx - 2a^2bx$
22. $5ay^2 + 5ax^2 - 10axy - 5az^2$

▶ C. Exercises

Factor completely.

23. $x^{11} + 5x^9 + 9x^7 + 2x^6 + 10x^4 + 18x^2$
24. $x^5 + 3x^4 + 2x^3 - 8x^2 - 24x - 16$
25. $x^7 - x^5 + 2x^4 + 5x^3 - 2x^2 + 10$

▪ Cumulative Review

26. Write a prime polynomial of degree two.
27. What do the letters of FOIL stand for?
28. If $x^ay^b + 3x^ay^4$ is of the sixth degree, what can be said about the size of a and b?
29. Given $A = \{1, 2, 4, 8, 16 \ldots\}$ Is the set closed under addition? under multiplication? Explain.
30. What number on a clock serves as an additive identity? On the clock, what is the inverse of 5? of 6?

Algebra *and* Scripture

Numbers and Operations

The real numbers and their operations form the foundation for algebra. A knowledge of numbers and operations is essential for understanding Scripture. Identify the operation in each of the verses below.

Identify each operation and write it in symbols.

1. Genesis 18:28
2. I Kings 7:3-5
3. Leviticus 25:8
4. Genesis 5:25-27

Match each verse below with the type of number that can be illustrated from it. Use each answer once; identify the number also.

5. Exodus 37:1   A. Natural
6. Ecclesiastes 7:19   B. Whole
7. Luke 16:5-6*a*   C. Integer
8. I Kings 7:23-26   D. Rational
9. Romans 3:10   E. Real

Factoring requires knowledge of even, odd, prime, and composite numbers. For each type of number choose the verse containing such numbers and identify the number(s).

10. Odd and prime
11. Odd and composite
12. Odd and neither prime nor composite
13. Even and prime
14. Even and composite
15. Even and neither prime nor composite

A. Deuteronomy 34:7
B. I Kings 14:21
C. Lamentations 1:4
D. John 18:14
E. Matthew 8:28
F. Joshua 14:10

16. Which property of numbers is illustrated in Luke 12:52?

GREATER AMPLITUDE.

Which verse in questions 1-16 illustrates the closure property of multiplication? Explain.

Absolute Values

FOR FROM HENCEFORTH there shall be five in one house divided, three against two, and two against three.

LUKE 12:52

Chapter 1 Review

State the properties illustrated below.

1. $3 + 2 = 2 + 3$
2. $a(b + c) = ab + ac$
3. $8 \cdot 1 = 8$
4. $x^7 \div x^4 = x^3$
5. Give an example of a monomial.
6. Give an example of a trinomial of degree 2.

Perform the indicated operations and simplify.

7. $(5x^2 + 9) + (2x^2 - 8x + 3)$
8. $(3a + 4b - c) - (7a + 6b - 5c)$
9. $(4x^2 + x - 12) - (3x^2 + 6x + 2)$
10. $3a^3b \cdot 7ab^5$
11. $(12x^2y)^2$
12. $(3a^4b + c^2)^0 + 3$
13. $4z^5(2x + 3z)$
14. $(x + 3)(x - 7)$
15. $(a^3 + b)(a^2 + b)$
16. $(x + 3y)^2$
17. $5a(a + 2)(a - 6)$
18. $(c + 3)(c^2 - 4c + 2)$
19. $x^3yz^4 \div x^2zy$
20. $(8a^2b - 4ab + 16b) \div (2b)$
21. $(x^2 - 4x - 5) \div (x + 1)$
22. $(x^3 - 7x - 6) \div (x - 3)$
23. $(3x^3 - 5x^2 + 2x - 8) \div (x + 5)$

Factor completely.

24. $15a^4b - 6a^2b^2$
25. $x^2 - 36$
26. $a^3 - 49a$
27. $y^2 + 10y + 25$
28. $3x^2 + 16x - 12$
29. $10x^2 - x - 3$
30. $3a^2 + 5ab - 2b^2$
31. $x^3 - 64$
32. $ax + bx - a - b$
33. $x^3 + 2x^2 - 4x - 8$
34. $c^3 + c^2d^2 - cd - d^3$
35. Evaluate the combined cost function when Basilean Enterprises planned to purchase a chalet in each of the areas. That function rule assumed that each chalet would use the same amount of energy. Is it reasonable to assume this? Write a short paragraph to explain your thoughts.
36. Give the mathematical significance of Luke 12:52.

2 Linear Equations

On your mark, get set, go! Imagine the explosion from the starting blocks, extreme exertion for most of a minute, and the final push across the finish line.

Since Pierre de Coubertin's revival of the Olympics in 1896, sprinters have tried to improve their times in the 400 m dash. (How many yards are in 400 m?) From under a minute to well under 44 seconds, sprinters' times have decreased over the years. One wonders how speedy the Olympians might be someday.

Below are the winning times for the 400 m dash at the Olympic Summer Games from 1896 to 1996. Your knowledge of linear equations will enable you to analyze this data.

Year	Time	Year	Time	Year	Time
1896	54.20	1928	47.80	1968	43.80
1900	49.40	1932	46.20	1972	44.66
1904	49.20	1936	46.50	1976	44.26
1906	53.20	1948	46.20	1980	44.60
1908	50.00	1952	45.90	1984	44.27
1912	48.20	1956	46.70	1988	43.87
1920	49.60	1960	44.90	1992	43.50
1924	47.60	1964	45.10	1996	43.49

After this chapter you should be able to

1. identify the properties of equality.
2. solve linear equations and inequalities.
3. solve absolute value equations and inequalities.
4. solve various types of word problems.

2.1 Solving Linear Equations

Solving equations is central to algebra because it is a necessary step in the solution of most word problems. Since many job situations require complicated word problems and the analytical thinking skills used in solving them, solving equations is an important and practical skill to master.

Lines were essential to the construction of this bridge at San Francisco. Not only are the trusses linear, but the problem of supporting a span's weight at the ends must be analyzed using lines of force.

This lesson reviews the methods of solving linear equations. Remember that solving an equation simply means finding the value of the variable that makes the sentence true. The properties of equality in the table below will help you do this.

PROPERTIES OF EQUALITY ($a, b, c \in \mathbb{R}$)	
Reflexive	$a = a$.
Symmetric	If $a = b$, then $b = a$.
Transitive	If $a = b$ and $b = c$, then $a = c$.
Addition	If $a = b$, then $a + c = b + c$.
Multiplication	If $a = b$, then $ac = bc$.

When you perform an operation to one side of an equation, you must do the same operation to the other side of the equation to maintain the equality.

EXAMPLE 1   Solve $x + 8 = 26$.

Answer

$$x + 8 = 26$$
$$x + 8 - 8 = 26 - 8$$

1. Subtract 8 from both sides (addition property of equality).

$$x = 18$$

2. Check mentally by substituting 18 for x in the original equation.

Since subtracting 8 from both sides of the equation above means the same as adding −8 to both sides, this step applies the addition property of equality. Similarly, division is the same as multiplying by the reciprocal. Therefore, dividing both sides by 5 in the next example involves an application of the multiplication property of equality. These relationships explain why there are no subtraction or division properties of equality.

EXAMPLE 2 Solve $5x + 12 = -18$.

Answer

$5x + 12 = -18$	1. Look at the variable x. It is multiplied by 5, and then 12 is added to it.
$5x + 12 - 12 = -18 - 12$ $5x = -30$	2. To solve this equation, do the opposite operations in reverse order. Subtract 12 first.
$\frac{5x}{5} = \frac{-30}{5}$ $x = -6$	3. Divide by 5.

The key to solving equations is to consider the order in which operations affect the variable. To solve the equation you must do *the inverse operations in reverse order to both sides of the equation.* This is shown in the next example. When a linear equation contains parentheses, use the distributive property to remove the parentheses first.

EXAMPLE 3 Solve $6(x + 4) + 3x = 105$.

Answer

$6(x + 4) + 3x = 105$	
$6x + 24 + 3x = 105$	1. Remove parentheses.
$9x + 24 = 105$	2. Combine like terms.
$9x = 81$	3. Solve.
$x = 9$	4. Check mentally or on paper. $6(9 + 4) + 3(9) = 105$ $6(13) + 3(9) = 105$ $78 + 27 = 105$ $105 = 105$

Now that you remember the basics of solving simple linear equations, you will study linear equations that are slightly more difficult. You should never be satisfied with what you know but should want to continually build on your knowledge. This applies to your spiritual life as well. You should not be satisfied with the milk of the Word but should strive to understand and apply the meat of the Word to your life as you grow in Christ (I Cor. 3:1-4).

To expand your knowledge of solving equations, you must learn to solve equations that have variables on both sides of the equal sign. The key is to move all terms containing the variable to the same side of the equation and all constants to the other side.

EXAMPLE 4   Solve $-3(x + 2) = 4x + 71$.

Answer

$-3(x + 2) = 4x + 71$

$-3x - 6 = 4x + 71$	1. Remove the parentheses.
$-6 = 7x + 71$ $-77 = 7x$	2. Using the addition property of equality, move terms containing the variable to one side and constant terms to the other side of the equation.
$-11 = x$	3. Divide by 7.
$x = -11$	4. Apply the symmetric property of equality. Check mentally that $-3(-11 + 2) = 27 = 4(-11) + 71$.

EXAMPLE 5   Solve $3(x + 2) + 5(2x - 7) = 4x - (2x + 3)$.

Answer

$3(x + 2) + 5(2x - 7) = 4x - (2x + 3)$

$3x + 6 + 10x - 35 = 4x - 2x - 3$	1. Remove parentheses by applying the distributive property.
$13x - 29 = 2x - 3$	2. Combine like terms on each side of the equation.
$11x = 26$ $x = \frac{26}{11}$	3. Solve.

▶ A. Exercises

State the property or properties of equality demonstrated by each statement or group of statements below.

1. $3 = 3$
   $3 + 2 = 3 + 2$

2. $x = x$
   $2x = 2x$

3. $x = 9$
   $9 = x$

4. $5 = 5$

5. $x = y$
   $y = 7$
   $x = 7$

6. $x + 2 = 9$
   $x = 7$

7. $\frac{x}{5} = 3$
   $x = 15$

8. $x - 6 = 8$
   $x = 14$

9. $7x = 21$
   $x = 3$

10. $5x - 2 = 8$
    $5x = 10$
    $x = 2$

Solve.

11. $x + 132 = 216$
12. $x - 63 = 63$
13. $3x + 9 = 3$
14. $-3t + 7 = 31$
15. $-17x - 13 = -166$
16. $6z + 8 - 4z = 10$
17. $-12y + 15 - 37y + 8y = -67$
18. $5z - 8 + 3(z + 4) = -36$
19. $2(n + 4) - 5(3n - 7) = -113$
20. $6(2x - 3) + 4(x + 9) = -110$

▶ B. Exercises

Solve.

21. $0.6(4x + 12) - 0.8(x - 4) = 26.4$
22. $\frac{1}{2}(6x + 3) - 8x - (3x - 9) = \frac{13}{2}$
23. $5(2x - 7) + 3(4x - 7) - (x + 2) = -142$
24. $3y + 2(6 - 4y) = -9$
25. $5.2(3x - 7) - (x + 9) = -38.1$
26. $6y + 3(5y - 19) - (y + 2) = -29$
27. $3y + 4 = -140 - 9y$
28. $5x - 30 + 3x = 2x - 8x + 12$
29. $6a + 9 - 3a = a + 3 - 4a$
30. $132x + 12 = 9x - 7$
31. $5a + 3a - 2 = 6a - 9$

32. $4z - 19 + (3z + 2) = 6z - 12$
33. $-8(2x - 5) + 3x = 4(x + 7) - 107$
34. $73 - (b + 8) - 2(3b + 4) = 6b - 2(b - 5) + 69$
35. $5m + 2(8m - 9) = 3(m + 4) - 5(2m + 7)$
36. $0.5(x + 2) - (3x + 8) = 1.6(x - 2) + 9$
37. $4a + 6(2a - 3) - (a + 6) = 5(a + 7) - 19$
38. $7x + 12(x - 9) + 4(3x + 6) = 5(3x - 2) + 8(x - 3)$

▶ C. Exercises

Solve.
39. $(x - 4)(x^2 + 4x + 16) = x(x^2 - 2)$
40. $y(y - x) - 3xy = 4x(3 - y) + y^2 - 3$
    What values can x and y take on?

▶ Dominion Modeling

41. For the Olympic data, what are the variables? Which variable would be a suitable input variable? Which would be a suitable output variable?
42. Graph the Olympic data. Such a graph is called a scatterplot. What general trends do you notice in the data?
43. Would the trends you noticed be clearer without the data in 1896 and 1906?
44. Assume that a linear trend is useful. Generate a linear model from the Olympic data.

Cumulative Review

Give the property that justifies each step.

Solve $5 - (-x + 9) = 7$.

45. $5 + (x - 9) = 7$
46. $5 + (-9 + x) = 7$
47. $[5 + (-9)] + x = 7$
48. $4 + (-4) + x = 4 + 7$
49. $0 + x = 11$
50. $x = 11$

2.2 Linear Inequalities

Inequalities are all around us. For example, some people are richer, stronger, faster, or smarter than others. God has bestowed the gifts necessary to serve Him, and each person receives such gifts in unequal measures. Likewise, Christians differ in the amount of authority and responsibility under God. Parents, pastors, coaches, and employers each have varying numbers of people under their authority, and God intends for us to obey each of the authorities he has put in our lives (Eph. 6:1-5). Mathematical inequalities enable you to quantify and study inequalities in life.

· Definition

Inequality $a < b$ if there exists a positive real number c such that $a + c = b$. $a < b$ implies $b > a$.

The basic inequality properties are summarized in the following table. The properties are expressed with $<$, but similar properties apply to $>$.

INEQUALITY PROPERTIES (a, b, $c \in \mathbb{R}$)	
Addition	If $a < b$, then $a + c < b + c$.
Multiplication	If $a < b$ and $c > 0$, then $ac < bc$.
	If $a < b$ and $c < 0$, then $ac > bc$.

Solving linear inequalities is identical to solving linear equations except when multiplying or dividing by a negative number. If you multiply or divide both sides of the inequality by a negative number, you must reverse the inequality sign.

Look at the inequality statement $2 < 5$. Multiply both sides by -2.

$$2 < 5$$
$$(-2)2 \; ? \; 5(-2)$$
$$-4 \; ? \; -10$$

Which is smaller, -4 or -10? Since -10 is smaller, you must reverse the inequality sign to maintain a true statement.

$$-4 > -10$$

EXAMPLE 1	Solve $4x - 12 < 8$.
Answer	$4x - 12 < 8$

$4x - 12 + 12 < 8 + 12$ $4x < 20$	1. Add 12 to both sides as you would for an equation.
$x < 5$	2. Since you are dividing by a positive number, you do not change the inequality sign.

Notice that the solution set of an inequality is an infinite set called an interval of real numbers. You will sometimes be asked to graph the solution to an inequality. For example, if the solution to an inequality is $x < 5$, it can be graphed as follows.

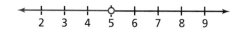

EXAMPLE 2	Solve and graph $2(x + 9) - 6(x + 2) \geq x - 3$.
Answer	$2(x + 9) - 6(x + 2) \geq x - 3$

$2x + 18 - 6x - 12 \geq x - 3$ $-4x + 6 \geq x - 3$ $-5x \geq -9$	1. Solve this inequality just as you would an equation.
$x \leq \dfrac{9}{5}$	2. Reverse the inequality since you are dividing by a negative number.
	3. Graph the solution.

▶ A. Exercises

Graph.

1. $x < 9$

2. $x \leq -2$

3. $x \neq 2$

Solve and graph.

4. $x - 7 < 8$

5. $x + 9 \geq 2$

6. $x + 7 < -2 + 3x$

7. $2x + 3 > 4x - 7$

8. $5x - 9 \neq -2x - 16$

Solve.

9. $2x - 1 \leq 7x + 3$

10. $2x - 6 > 8x + 7$

▶ B. Exercises

Solve.

11. $4x + 1 \geq x - \frac{1}{2}$

12. $3x - 0.06 < 7x - 32.4$

13. $-7x + 3(2x - 4) < 5x - 36$

14. $3(y + 4) + 2(y - 2) \geq 4y - 5$

15. $2z + 6 - 9z < -6z + 9$

16. $8x - 3(x + 9) \neq 4x + 12$

17. $-3x - (x + 9) + 2(x + 3) < 4x + 2(x - 7)$

18. $5y + 3(y - 1) + 19 \geq 12y$

19. $3x - 12(x - 9) - 28 < 2(x + 3) + 7$

20. $2x - 4(3x + 1) > 5(3x - 1) + 2$

▶ C. Exercises

Solve.

21. $\frac{2}{3}x - 7 \leq \frac{3}{4} - 2\left(\frac{5}{6}x + 7\right)$

22. $3.2x + 0.92 \leq 0.759 - 1.4(0.5x + 3.42)$

▶ Dominion Modeling

23. Compare the actual Olympic data with values predicted by your linear model.

24. Evaluate your model. Use the value of r^2 (probably provided when you obtained your model), which represents the percentage of data variation explained by the model. Thus, r^2 is a measure of how well the linear model fits the data.)

▮ Cumulative Review

Simplify.

25. $3x^{-2}$

26. $2x^3x^{-2}x^7$

27. $(3x^{-3})^{-4}$

28. $2 + 2^0 + 2^{-1}$

29. $\dfrac{x^3y^7}{x^{-2}y^4}$

2.3 Absolute Value Equations

God's laws and principles set an absolute standard for man. The term *absolute* describes the principles of Scripture as sure and unchanging, meaning that they set a standard that is not relative (Neh. 9:13 and Ps. 119:160). The principles of nature are also sure and absolute. The astronomical progression of the seasons, the law of gravity, and the properties of numbers each describe God's dependable and unchanging order in creation.

In mathematics, *absolute value* is the magnitude of a quantity. The informal definition of the absolute value of a number is its distance from 0 on the number line. Remember that distance is always positive. The formal definition of absolute value follows.

Definition

Absolute value $\quad |x| = \begin{cases} x, \text{ if } x \geq 0 \\ -x, \text{ if } x < 0 \end{cases}$

This definition has two parts. To determine which part to use, look at the quantity inside the absolute value symbol. If it is greater than or equal to 0, use the first rule, $|x| = x$. If the quantity inside the absolute value sign is less than 0, use the second rule of the definition, or $|x| = -x$ (the opposite of x). To find the absolute value of 5 (symbolized $|5|$), you use the first rule of the definition.

$$|x| = x$$
$$|5| = 5$$

To find $|-5|$, you must use the second rule of the definition.

$$|x| = -x$$
$$|-5| = -(-5) = 5$$

According to the definition of absolute value, there are two possible answers for an equation such as $|x| = 6$.

$$\text{If } x \geq 0, |x| = x = 6.$$
$$\text{If } x < 0, |x| = -x; \text{ so } -x = 6 \text{ or } x = -6.$$
$$\text{Thus } x = 6 \text{ or } x = -6.$$

Notice that both answers are also consistent with the informal definition. Both 6 and −6 are six units from zero on the number line.

EXAMPLE 1 Solve $|x + 5| = 9$.

Answer

$|x + 5| = 9$	1. The absolute value is isolated on the left.
$x + 5 = 9$ or $x + 5 = -9$	2. Use the definition of absolute value to write two equations (for $x + 5 \geq 0$ and $x + 5 < 0$).
$x = 4$ $x = -14$	3. Solve each equation.
	4. Check solutions in the original equation mentally.

The informal definition of absolute value can also help you understand why the original absolute value statement results in two equations. Remember that absolute value represents the distance between the number and zero on the number line. Therefore, in $|x + 5| = 9$, the number $x + 5$ must be 9 units from 0. The numbers 9 units from 0 are 9 and -9, so $x + 5 = 9$ or $x + 5 = -9$.

Before rewriting an absolute value equation as two equations, the absolute value quantity must be on one side of the equal sign and everything else on the other side.

EXAMPLE 2 Solve $|3x - 12| - 8 = 24$.

Answer

$|3x - 12| - 8 = 24$	
$|3x - 12| = 32$	1. Isolate the absolute value on one side of the equation.
$3x - 12 = 32$ or $3x - 12 = -32$	2. Write two equations based on whether $3x - 12 \geq 0$ or $3x - 12 < 0$.
$3x = 44$ $3x = -20$	3. Solve.
$x = \frac{44}{3}$ $x = \frac{-20}{3}$	4. Check mentally.

Solving Absolute Value Equations

1. Isolate the absolute value on one side of the equation.
2. Apply the definition of absolute value to write two equations.
3. Solve each equation.
4. Check the solutions in the original equation. (Any that do not check are called *extraneous*.)

EXAMPLE 3   Solve $\left|2x + 9\right| = 8x - 3$.

Answer

$\left|2x + 9\right| = 8x - 3$	1. The absolute value is isolated on the left.
$2x + 9 = 8x - 3$ or $2x + 9 = -(8x - 3)$	2. Write two equations based on whether $2x + 9 \geq 0$ or $2x + 9 < 0$.
$\begin{aligned} -6x &= -12 \\ x &= 2 \end{aligned}$ $\qquad$ $\begin{aligned} 2x + 9 &= -8x + 3 \\ 10x &= -6 \\ x &= \tfrac{-3}{5} \end{aligned}$	3. Solve each equation.
$\left|2 \cdot 2 + 9\right| = 8 \cdot 2 - 3$ or $\left|2\left(\tfrac{-3}{5}\right) + 9\right| = 8\left(\tfrac{-3}{5}\right) - 3$ $\left|13\right| = 13 \qquad \left|\tfrac{-6}{5} + \tfrac{45}{5}\right| = \tfrac{-24}{5} - \tfrac{15}{5}$ $\left|\tfrac{39}{5}\right| = \tfrac{-39}{5}$	4. Check.

The first check results in a true statement, but the second in a false statement. This means that the value 2 checks but $\tfrac{-3}{5}$ does not. The value $\tfrac{-3}{5}$ is an extraneous solution. The only solution to this equation is $x = 2$.

The following alternate method can be used to check Example 3.
Since the absolute value of any quantity is always positive or zero, $8x - 3$ must be greater than or equal to 0. Solve the inequality to determine possible values for x.

$$8x - 3 \geq 0$$
$$8x \geq 3$$
$$x \geq \tfrac{3}{8}$$

Since the solution $\tfrac{-3}{5}$ is less than $\tfrac{3}{8}$, it is extraneous. The only solution is $x = 2$.

▶ A. Exercises

1. Write what the equation $\left|x\right| = 7$ represents in words; then graph it.
2. Give an absolute value equation that has the following graph.

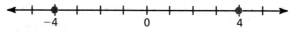

3. Write an absolute value equation (do not solve) for: "The distance between a number and zero is 15 units."

Solve.
4. $|x| = 8$
5. $|y| = 4$
6. $|x - 3| = 7$
7. $|5x - 2| = 12$
8. $|x - 22| = 5$
9. $|3x + 9| = 18$
10. $|5x + 4 - 2x| = 7$

▶ B. Exercises

Solve.
11. $|13y - 23 + y| = 4$
12. $|10x - 16 - 4x| = 8$
13. $|4x + 2| - 9 = 3$
14. $|a - 7 + 6a| - 6 = 22$
15. $|3y - 9| = 2y + 7$
16. $|2x + 5| - 3x = 27$
17. $|5x + 9 - 2x| + 9 = 6x$
18. $|8x + 12 - 7x| + 3x - 2 = 0$

Write an absolute value equation for each sentence. Do not solve.
19. The distance between zero and six less than a number is 2 units.
20. Six less than the distance between zero and a number is 2 units.

▶ C. Exercises

Solve.
21. $|3x - 5 - (2x - 3)| - 2|(4x - 7) - (3x - 5)| = -8$
22. $|4x - 7| = |5x - 9|$

▮ Cumulative Review

Factor.
23. $7x - 14y + 7$
24. $100x^2 - 1$
25. $x^2 - 5x - 24$
26. $x^3 + 8$
27. $x^3 - 3x^2 + x - 3$

2.4 Distances on Number Lines

How would you solve $|2x + 3| = -7$? Using the methods you learned earlier, you could apply the definition to obtain two equations: $2x + 3 = -7$ or $2x + 3 = 7$. Solving these you find that $x = -5$ or $x = 2$. Now check the answers. In both cases you get a false statement. This means that both answers are extraneous and there are no solutions to the original equation.

Using the distance concept of absolute value, the equation above could be solved at a glance.

EXAMPLE 1   Solve $|2x + 3| = -7$.

Answer $|2x + 3| = -7$ Distance cannot be negative, so the distance between $(2x + 3)$ and zero cannot be -7.

no solutions

Before doing other distance calculations, you should know how to find the midpoint of two numbers on a number line. The midpoint is the average of the two coordinates.

> **Midpoint Formula for Number Lines**
>
> If M is the midpoint of the segment joining A and B, then $m = \dfrac{a + b}{2}$.

EXAMPLE 2   Find the midpoint of the segment joining -3 and 11.

Answer $m = \dfrac{a + b}{2} = \dfrac{-3 + 11}{2} = \dfrac{8}{2} = 4$

You can check on a number line that 4 is exactly halfway between -3 and 11.

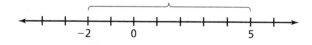

What is the distance between -2 and 5? You could count on a number line to find that it is seven units. Another method involves subtraction of the coordinates: $5 - (-2) = 7$. However, if you subtract in the other order you will get a negative distance: $-2 - 5 = -7$. Because distances are positive, you must reject an answer of -7. You might ask, "Why not just subtract the smaller from the larger?" If one point is unknown and therefore represented by a variable, you will not know which coordinate is larger. Since $|7| = |-7| = 7$, taking the absolute value of the difference will allow you to subtract in either order.

Distance Formula for Number Lines

If d is the distance between points with coordinates a and b, then
$d = |a - b| = |b - a|$.

EXAMPLE 3   Find the distance between points with coordinates -3 and 11.

Answer $d = |a - b| = |-3 - 11| = |-14| = 14$ or
$d = |b - a| = |11 - (-3)| = |14| = 14$

EXAMPLE 4   Write an absolute value equation for the graph.

Answer

$m = \dfrac{-1 + 3}{2} = \dfrac{2}{2} = 1$	1. Find the midpoint.
$d = |3 - 1| = |2| = 2$	2. Find the distance from either point to the midpoint. The endpoint 3 is used here.
$|x - 1| = 2$	3. The distance from the original point x to the midpoint 1 is 2 units.

EXAMPLE 5   If the point represented by x is 5 units away from the point with a coordinate of 3, find all possible values of x.

Answer

The distance from x to 3 is 5.	1. Paraphrase.
$|x - 3| = 5$	2. Translate.
$x - 3 = 5$ or $x - 3 = -5$	3. Solve.
$x = 8$ $x = -2$	4. The possible coordinates of x are 8 and -2. Both answers check.

▶ A. Exercises

Find the distance between each pair of points and find the coordinate of the midpoint of the segment joining them.

1. 8 and −12
2. 11 and 37
3. −5 and 6

4. −3 and −20
5. $\frac{2}{3}$ and $\frac{5}{3}$
6. $\frac{-2}{3}$ and $\frac{5}{8}$

Solve.

7. $|x - 8| = 5$
8. $|3x - 11| = -5$

9. $|8x + 3| + 7 = 3$
10. $|x + 4| = \frac{1}{2}$

▶ B. Exercises

Translate into equations. Do not solve.

11. The distance between the number x and 6 is 5.
12. The distance between 3 and a number is 2.
13. 4 is 7 units from a number.
14. A certain number is 4 units from 9.

Write an absolute value equation and solve.

15. A number's distance from zero is 5. Find the number.
16. If 5 is four units from a certain number, what is the number?
17. If x and −4 are 12 units apart, find x.
18. The distance from x to 5 is 9.

Write a sentence about distances for each.

19. $|x - 7| = 4$
20. $|x + 4| = 1$
21. $|x| = 3$

▶ C. Exercises

Write an absolute value equation representing each graph.

22.

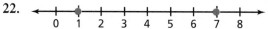

```
0  1  2  3  4  5  6  7  8
```

23.
```
-5 -4 -3 -2 -1  0  1  2
```

24.
```
-6 -5 -4 -3 -2 -1  0  1
```

25.
```
-1  0  1  2  3  4  5
```

Solve.

26. $5(x - 1) = 4(3x + 2)$
27. $4 - (x + 3) = 4 - 2x$

Name the property illustrated.

28. If $2x = 5$, then $5 = 2x$
29. $7(5 \cdot 3) = (7 \cdot 5)3$
30. $\pi = \pi$

2.5 Problem Solving

Life includes frustrating situations that require thought and application of previously learned knowledge. These situations require the thought process called problem solving. Good problem solving skills will enable you to solve the problems of everyday life more easily.

Perhaps the biggest problem that faces Christian young people today is how to live a consistent life for Christ and to develop Christlike traits. Romans 8:29 states that Christians are "to be conformed to the image of his Son." To solve any problem, you must have a plan of attack. Christians have the plan for solving the problems of life written out in God's Holy Word, the Bible. That is why it is important for you to know and apply the principles of the Word of God.

To solve word problems successfully in mathematics, you also need a plan of attack. A helpful plan used throughout this book follows.

Problem Solving

1. *Read.* Carefully read the problem, noting important words, key phrases, and the type of problem. Assign a variable to the main unknown.
2. *Plan.* Describe any other unknowns in terms of the variable you have chosen. Organize the information into tables or diagrams if possible.
3. *Solve.* Find a relationship between two quantities in the problem and write an equation. Solve the equation.
4. *Check.* Relate the solution to the problem and answer all questions. Evaluate your answer by asking "Is it reasonable?"

An SR-71 "Blackbird" flew at 2193 mph to set the record as the world's fastest aircraft. How long would a 7677-mile reconnaissance mission to Tehran require at this speed?

There are several types of word problems that you need to know how to solve. Although you can solve each type of problem by using the general strategy described here, more specific strategies apply to some common types of problems. Recognizing the type of problem is therefore important for determining the specific strategy needed to solve it. In this section, you will solve some general word problems and then investigate a more specific strategy for motion problems.

EXAMPLE 1 Each boy in Mr. Pierson's drama class is to be paired with a girl in the class to perform a comedy reading. After each boy is assigned to a particular girl, there are four girls left. If there are twenty-six students in the class, how many girls are there?

Answer

Let x = the number of girls in the class.	1. **Read.** Identify the unknown and represent it with a variable.
$x - 4$ = the number of boys in the class.	2. **Plan.** Think about what the problem states. How many boys are there in terms of the number of girls?
$x + (x - 4) = 26$ $2x - 4 = 26$ $2x = 30$ $x = 15$	3. **Solve.** The key relationship in the problem is the fact that there are a total of twenty-six students in the class. Write an equation and solve.
There are fifteen girls in the class.	4. **Check.** Relate the answer to the problem. Make sure you have answered all the questions. Verify that the answer is reasonable.

For motion problems, making a table is a specific strategy that helps you organize the information as you plan your solution. Construct the table using the basic formula "rate times time equals distance."

$$rt = d$$

EXAMPLE 2 Ted and Jeff plan to meet at a campground at noon. Ted leaves at 9:00 A.M., and Jeff leaves at 9:30 A.M. If Jeff drives an average of 8 mph faster than Ted, find the speed of each if they both arrive on time.

Continued ▶

Answer

Let x = Ted's driving speed.	1. **Read.** Carefully read the problem. Notice that the problem is a motion problem. Assign the variable to equal Ted's speed.

Then $x + 8$ = Jeff's speed.

	r	t	d
Ted	x	3	
Jeff	$x + 8$	2.5	

2. **Plan.** Express Jeff's speed in terms of Ted's speed. Make a table. Complete two columns using your variables and the information in the problem.

	r	t	d
Ted	x	3	$3x$
Jeff	$x + 8$	2.5	$2.5(x + 8)$

Fill in the third column by using the formula $rt = d$.

$$3x = 2.5(x + 8)$$
$$3x = 2.5x + 20$$
$$0.5x = 20$$
$$x = 40$$

3. **Solve.** Find information relating the distances. Since the boys are going to the same place from the same place, set the distances equal. Solve the equation.

Ted travels 40 mph, and Jeff travels 48 mph.

4. **Check.** Answer all the questions. The answers are reasonable.

EXAMPLE 3 A marble rests on a ruler three inches from the 8-inch mark. Where does it rest?

Answer

Let x = position of marble.	1. **Read.** Read carefully and assign a variable.
Distance from the marble to 8 is 3.	2. **Plan.** Paraphrase to identify the distance relationship.

$$|x - 8| = 3$$
$$x - 8 = 3 \quad \text{or} \quad x - 8 = -3$$
$$x = 11 \qquad\qquad x = 5$$

3. **Solve.** Use absolute value to translate the distance phrase into an equation; then solve.

The marble rests at the 11-inch or 5-inch mark on the ruler.

4. **Check.** Relate your answers to the problem. Verify that the answers are reasonable.

▶ A. Exercises

1. The mayors of Clarkston and Blair drive 50 mph and 55 mph respectively. How far apart are the cities if they must drive 3 hours to meet?

2. Joey has a sack of 56 marbles. There are three colors of marbles in the sack: red, yellow, and blue. If he has half as many red as blue marbles and 8 more yellow than red marbles, how many of each color does he have in the sack?

3. If the same number is added to the numerator of $\frac{12}{13}$ and subtracted from the denominator, the new fraction is equal to $\frac{3}{2}$. What is the number? (*Hint:* Let x = number. Represent the new fraction using x.)

4. John uses 114 feet of fencing to enclose a field whose length is 21 feet longer than its width. What are the dimensions of the field?

5. The sum of two numbers is −23, and the difference of the larger and the smaller is 81. What are the two numbers?

6. Two angles are supplementary. The measure of one is one-fourth the measure of the other. What is the measure of each angle?

7. The sum of three consecutive odd integers is 63. What are the integers?

8. Two airplanes leave at the same time from airports that are 880 miles apart and travel toward each other. If one plane travels 126 mph faster than the other and they pass each other in 2 hours, how fast is each plane traveling?

9. Brandon goes on a Cub Scout hike and hikes to a waterfall in 3 hours and hikes back along the same route to the campground in 2 hours. If the hiking rate is 1 mph faster returning than going, how fast are the boys hiking each way?

10. A jet travels from Chicago to Kansas City at a speed of 440 knots. If it takes a plane 3 hours longer to fly from Kansas City to Chicago when flying at a speed of 110 knots, what is the air distance between the two cities?

▶ B. Exercises

11. Susan bought a combination of peanut candy bars and chocolate bars. If the peanut bars and chocolate bars cost 69¢ and 59¢ respectively and the total amount Susan paid for the 17 candy bars was $10.83, how many of each type of bar did she buy?

12. Karen saves her change and has dimes, nickels, and pennies totaling $4.52. If there is 1 more dime than three times the number of nickels and 10 more pennies than nickels, how many of each type of coin are there?

13. Mr. Fisher travels from Boise, Idaho, toward Casper, Wyoming, at a rate of 56 mph while Mr. Collins leaves Casper for Boise at the same time, traveling at a rate of 64 mph. If the cities are 658 miles apart, how long will it be before the two men meet?

14. John and Jim are going on a bike ride. On the trip to Mill Park, they ride at an average of **8** mph on a route that is **4** miles less than the route on the return trip. They travel **7** mph on the return trip. If it takes them **1** hour longer to return than to go, how much total time do they spend riding their bicycles?

15. Paige and Mary are planning a trip to the mountains. For the first part of their trip, they travel at an average rate of **52** mph, and on the second part of the trip, which takes half as much time as the first part, they travel at an average rate of **35** mph. If the odometer shows that they traveled a distance of **104.25** miles to the mountains, how long did they travel at each rate?

16. A train leaves Perryville at **6:00** A.M. and travels east at a rate of **64** mph. As it reaches its destination, Granite City, a westbound train departs from Granite City for Perryville, traveling at a rate of **48** mph. How far is it from Perryville to Granite City by train if the westbound train gets to Perryville at **9:30** A.M.?

▶ C. Exercises

Write absolute value equations and solve.

17. On Interstate 80 in Nebraska, Joe's car stalled. The only milepost he noticed was milepost **154** which was **7** miles back. Where is he?

18. Mary lives in a 30-story high rise. Six less than twice her distance above the ground (in stories) is twelve. On what floor does she live?

19. Kevin is hiking the Appalachian Trail this summer. He begins at Springer Mountain, Georgia, which is the start of the trail. Today he saw a sign for Newfound Gap **17** miles ahead. If Newfound Gap is the **230**-mile mark of the trail, where is he?

▶ Dominion Modeling

20. From the model for the **400** m dash, what was predicted for the **2000** Olympics? Compare the prediction with the actual value.

21. According to your Olympic model, what would be the time for the **400** m in the **2012** Olympics? Is this a reasonable value?

Cumulative Review

Simplify

22. $(3x + 2) - (5x - 7)$

23. $(2x - 1)(x + 1) - 2(x^2 + 1)$

Solve.

24. $(3x + 2) - (5x - 7) = 1$
25. $(2x - 1)(x + 1) - 2(x^2 + 1) = 3x + 2$
26. $\left| 2x + 3 \right| = 1$

HYPATIA

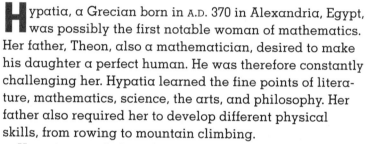

Hypatia, a Grecian born in A.D. 370 in Alexandria, Egypt, was possibly the first notable woman of mathematics. Her father, Theon, also a mathematician, desired to make his daughter a perfect human. He was therefore constantly challenging her. Hypatia learned the fine points of literature, mathematics, science, the arts, and philosophy. Her father also required her to develop different physical skills, from rowing to mountain climbing.

Hypatia attended a school in Athens, where she began to gain recognition for her ability in mathematics. When she returned from Athens, she was offered a position teaching philosophy and mathematics at the Alexandrian university.

Hypatia was known for her excellent lectures on the *Arithmetica* of Diophantus, which is a study of first-degree and quadratic equations similar to those studied in algebra. Her home library was a center for students whom she encouraged to use books from her personal collection. Her enthusiasm for the subject of mathematics was the key factor in her success as a teacher. Students enjoyed listening to her because she taught the subject that brought delight to her own clever and curious mind.

Since Hypatia was a great teacher of mathematics and was concerned that her students understand it, she wrote several books that were used as textbooks for her students. She coauthored with her father a work on Euclid. She also wrote her own works, including commentaries on the *Arithmetica* of Diophantus of Alexandria and the *Conics* of Apollonius of Perga.

Hypatia used her mathematical abilities to study science. In fact, she invented an astrolabe and a planisphere to aid in the study of the stars. Two of her books were on astronomy—*On the Astronomical Canon of Diophantus* and a commentary on the astronomical works of Ptolemy. She also invented a device called a hydroscope, which was the forerunner of the present-day hydrometer, which measures the specific density of liquids.

In A.D. 415, an angry mob dragged her from her chariot and tortured her to death because of her pagan religious views. Instead of focusing on her tragic death, we should remember her explanatory books and enthusiastic teaching which encouraged many young math students.

Her enthusiasm for the subject of mathematics was the key factor in her success as a teacher.

2.6 Interest and Mixture Problems

At the Tokyo Stock Exchange all trading is now done by computer.

Two types of word problems that have very practical applications in everyday life are interest and mixture problems. There are specific strategies that will help you solve each of these types of problems. When solving interest problems, you must keep in mind the formula for simple interest.

$$I = Prt$$

The variable P represents the principal, or the amount of money invested or borrowed; r represents the annual interest rate in decimal form; t represents the period of time of the investment or loan in years; and I represents the amount of interest paid on the investment or due on the loan.

EXAMPLE 1   Mr. Jamison invested $9500 in two accounts. He makes $904.50 annual interest. How much did he invest in each account if one account pays **9%** annual interest and the other pays **10.5%** annual interest?

Answer

x = the amount invested at 9% interest.

1. **Read.** Read carefully and assign a variable to the unknown quantity.

$9500 - x$ = amount invested at 10.5% interest.

2. **Plan.** Express the other unknown in terms of the variable. Use the fact that the total amount invested is $9500.

You should recognize it as an interest problem and organize the given information in a table. Make sure you change the rate to decimal form

	P	r	t	I
9% investment	x	0.09	1	
10.5% investment	$9500 - x$	0.105	1	

Continued ▶

	P	r	t	I
9% investment	x	0.09	1	0.09x
10.5% investment	9500 − x	0.105	1	0.105(9500 − x)

and fill in the rate column. Since the problem asks for annual interest, place a 1 in the time column.

Complete the final column using the formula $I = Prt$.

$$0.09x + 0.105(9500 - x) = 904.50$$
$$1000[0.09x + 0.105(9500 - x)] = 1000(904.50)$$
$$90x + 105(9500 - x) = 904,500$$
$$90x + 997,500 - 105x = 904,500$$
$$997,500 - 15x = 904,500$$
$$-15x = -93,000$$
$$x = 6200$$

3. **Solve.** Since the last column completed was I, look for information about the interest. The total interest for the year is $904.50. Set the sum of the entries in the interest column equal to 904.50 and solve.

Thus $6200 was invested at 9%, and $9500 − x, or $3300, was invested at 10.5% to yield an annual interest of $904.50.

4. **Check.** Remember to find both principals and evaluate whether your answers are reasonable.

The next interest problem illustrates the amount of work you should show.

EXAMPLE 2   Teresa wants to borrow $8200 to purchase a used car. She found it necessary to get smaller loans figured at simple interest and borrowed $3600 from one institution and $4600 from the other. If the total annual interest paid is $974, what is the annual interest rate she must pay to each lending institution if the rate of the smaller loan is 2% more than that of the larger loan?

Answer

Let x = rate on the $4600 loan.

1. **Read.** Identify a variable.

$x + 0.02$ = rate on the $3600 loan.

2. **Plan.** Define other unknowns and make a table.

	P	r	t	I
1st loan	4600	x	1	4600x
2nd loan	3600	x + 0.02	1	3600(x + 0.02)

Continued ▶

$$4600x + 3600(x + 0.02) = 974$$
$$4600x + 3600x + 72 = 974$$
$$8200x = 902$$
$$x = \frac{902}{8200}$$
$$x = 0.11$$

3. **Solve.** Write the equation expressing total interest and solve.

The $4600 loan charges 11% interest, and the $3600 loan charges interest at a rate of $x + 0.02$, or 13%.

4. **Check.** Relate the answer to the context.

As with motion and interest problems, the specific strategy of making a table is useful in mixture problems. The headings for the table will depend on whether the purpose of the mixture involves the ratio of the substances mixed or the prices of the substances mixed. The next two examples illustrate these two types of mixture problems.

EXAMPLE 3 Two types of soft drinks are mixed together to make a fruit punch. Orange drink sells for $0.89 for a two-liter bottle, and lemon-lime drink sells for $1.19 for a two-liter bottle. How many two-liter bottles of each must be mixed to produce 30 liters of fruit punch that sells for $1.09 for a two-liter bottle?

Answer

Let x = number of two-liter bottles of orange drink.

1. **Read.** Let the variable represent the unknown. Recognize that the mixture problem focuses on prices.

	Number of bottles	Price/bottle	Total Price
Orange	x	89	$89x$
Lemon-Lime	$15 - x$	119	$119(15 - x)$
Mix	15	109	1635

2. **Plan.** Organize the data in a table. Since 30 liters are desired from two-liter bottles, 15 must be purchased. If x of these are orange drink, then $15 - x$ are lemon-lime. Also, be sure to use cents (or dollars) consistently in the price column.

$$89x + 119(15 - x) = 1635$$
$$89x + 1785 - 119x = 1635$$
$$-30x = -150$$
$$x = 5$$

3. **Solve.** Write an equation using the total price column and solve it.

Mix 5 two-liter bottles of orange drink and $15 - x$, or 10, two-liter bottles of lemon-lime drink.

4. **Check.** This mix yields 30 liters of drink valued at $1.09 per bottle.

EXAMPLE 4 A chemist has a solution that is **3%** alcohol (in water) and another solution that is **8%** alcohol. How many kilograms of each should he mix to make **12** kilograms of a **5%** alcohol solution?

Answer

	1. *Read.* Assign the variable.
Let x = number of kilograms of the 3% alcohol solution.	

2. *Plan.* Make a table.

	Kilograms of Solution	% of Alcohol	Kilograms of Alcohol
3% Alcohol Solution	x	0.03	$0.03x$
8% Alcohol Solution	$12 - x$	0.08	$0.08(12 - x)$
New Mix	12	0.05	0.6

$$0.03x + 0.08(12 - x) = 0.6$$
$$3x + 8(12 - x) = 60$$
$$3x + 96 - 8x = 60$$
$$-5x = -36$$
$$x = 7.2$$

3. *Solve.* Write an equation obtained from column 3 and solve.

Mix 7.2 kilograms of 3% alcohol solution with $12 - x$, or 4.8, kilograms of 8% alcohol solution.

4. *Check.* Is it reasonable?

▶ A. Exercises

1. Find the annual interest from a savings account containing $148 and bearing **6%** simple interest.
2. How much salt is there in **50** gallons of a **3%** salt solution?
3. What is the strength of a salt solution that contains **12** gallons of salt and **18** gallons of pure water?
4. How much simple interest is earned in one year from two accounts bearing **4%** and **6%** respectively? The first contains **$3000** and the second **$2500**.
5. How much salt is in a mixture containing **10** gallons of an **11%** salt solution and **6** gallons of a **7%** salt solution?
6. Give the percentage of pure water contained in the mixture in exercise 5.
7. Paul invests **$15,250** in two different accounts. One account pays an interest rate of **8.5%** while the other account pays **10%**. If he gains a total of **$1411.75** annually, how much money did he invest in each account?

8. Mary Auburn makes three investments. The investment that pays 12% is twice the amount of the account that pays 9%. The amount invested at 10% is $500 more than the amount invested at 9%. If the annual interest income is $1555, how much money is invested at each rate?

9. Karen is working in the chemistry lab and needs a solution that is 8% hydrochloric acid. She has two solutions that she can mix together to make the solution of the required strength. The first solution is 2% hydrochloric acid, and the other is 11% hydrochloric acid. How many kilograms of each solution should she mix to produce 3 kilograms of the solution of the required strength?

10. John receives a total of $1282 a year from two investments. He has invested $4000 in one account and $8200 in another account that pays 1.5% more than the first account. What is the interest rate for each account?

11. Peanuts sell for $1.90 per pound, and cashews sell for $2.50 per pound. Mr. Bruckner wants to make a mix of these two types of nuts. How many pounds of each type should he mix together to make 12 pounds of deluxe mix that sells for $2.05 per pound?

▶ B. Exercises

12. Grace needs to get a loan for a house that she is going to purchase. She discovers that she must get two loans instead of one large loan. She borrows $30,000 from one institution and $48,000 from another institution whose lending rate is 2% more than the other. If her total monthly interest charge on the loans is $600, what interest rate does she pay on each loan?

13. The business manager for the L & L Manufacturing Company makes two investments totaling $152,000. One investment pays 15% and the other investment pays 21%. If the total six-month interest income is $13,350, how much is invested at each rate?

14. Rebecca invests money in two accounts. One bank pays 8.5% on her investment of $1200 while the other pays 9% on her investment of $2000. How long is the term of investment if the total interest is $70.50?

15. Susie is making a mixture of acetic acid and water, which forms vinegar. If she has a mixture of 100 ml of 2% acetic acid, how many ml of pure acetic acid should she add to produce the required 8% acetic acid vinegar? (Round to the nearest tenth.)

16. A certain contact lens solution is preserved with 0.1% sorbic acid. If a company has made a mistake and produced a solution containing 3% sorbic acid, how much pure water must be added to 300 liters of the solution to make the correct percentage in the solution?

17. Mr. Mitchell wants to mix corn and oats to make feed for his farm animals. The price of corn is $3.72 per bushel, and the price of a bushel of oats is $2.12. How many bushels of each should he mix to have 180 bushels of feed worth $3.10 a bushel?

18. Common household bleach is made of 5.25% sodium hypochlorite. If a company mixes 50 liters of a solution that has 3% less sodium hypochlorite than another solution to make 180 liters of the required bleach, what is the percentage of sodium hypochlorite in each solution? (Round to the nearest tenth of a percent.)

19. A mixture of sugar and cinnamon is made to sell as a cooking product. Sugar is worth 52¢ per kilogram, and cinnamon is worth 10¢ per kilogram. How many kilograms of each should be mixed to form 25 kilograms of mix worth 50¢ per kilogram? (Round to the nearest tenth.)

► C. Exercises

20. Given 50 liters of a 15% acid solution, write the equations required to produce
    a. a 20% solution by adding more acid.
    b. a 10% solution by adding water.

21. Mr. Briggs owns a small store and is planning a back-to-school special on selected school supplies. He wants to make a package of pens and pencils. If pens sell for 39¢ each and pencils sell for 3 for 50¢, how many pens and pencils are in a set that contains 16 writing instruments and sells for $3.56 per package?

► Dominion Modeling

22. According to the model for the Olympic data, when would someone run the 400 m dash in no time at all? Briefly explain your results.

23. According to Bishop Ussher, the world was created on Sunday, October 23, 4004 B.C. Assuming Ussher's chronology and using your model, how fast would Adam have run the 400 m dash? Briefly explain your results.

24. Define "extrapolate." What does this word mean for the Olympic data?

Cumulative Review

Simplify.

25. $5 - 3 \cdot 8 \div 6 + 2(7 - 1) + 4$
26. $(5xy^2 - 3x^2y) - (4x^2y - 2xy + 7xy^2)$
27. $(3x + 5y)^2$
28. $(18x^2 - 27xy + 3x) \div (3x)$
29. $(x^2 + 4x - 1) + (3x^2 - 7x + 1)$

Matrix Addition

In the last chapter you saw data on the soft drink inventory for a Super M grocery store. The data is given again, together with corresponding data from a second store.

Brand	Super M Grocery Store 182			
	Cola	Grape	Orange	Root Beer
X	9	7	5	6
Y	10	3	8	4
Z	7	6	3	5

Brand	Super M Grocery Store 97			
	Cola	Grape	Orange	Root Beer
X	8	3	9	7
Y	12	1	5	3
Z	15	6	12	10

As you saw earlier, matrices can summarize this data.

$$A = \begin{bmatrix} 9 & 7 & 5 & 6 \\ 10 & 3 & 8 & 4 \\ 7 & 6 & 3 & 5 \end{bmatrix} \qquad B = \begin{bmatrix} 8 & 3 & 9 & 7 \\ 12 & 1 & 5 & 3 \\ 15 & 6 & 12 & 10 \end{bmatrix}$$

Notice that matrices A and B have the same dimension (3×4) but are not equal since their entries differ.

At the company headquarters of Super M Groceries, the vice president in charge of inventory wants to know the combined number of cases of each flavor and brand of soft drink in stores 182 and 97. You should understand how this procedure is accomplished.

To find the total number of cases of soft drink for each brand and flavor, you must add each brand and flavor in the two stores together. You can do this with matrix addition. To find the sum of two matrices, you add the corresponding entries of the matrices. Notice that you cannot add two matrices together unless they have the same dimensions. The definition of *matrix addition* follows.

Definition

Matrix addition   The sum of two $m \times n$ matrices A and B is an $m \times n$ matrix C found by adding the corresponding entries of A and B.

The vice president in charge of inventory for the Super M grocery chain will receive the matrix $A + B$.

$$A + B = \begin{bmatrix} 9 & 7 & 5 & 6 \\ 10 & 3 & 8 & 4 \\ 7 & 6 & 3 & 5 \end{bmatrix} + \begin{bmatrix} 8 & 3 & 9 & 7 \\ 12 & 1 & 5 & 3 \\ 15 & 6 & 12 & 10 \end{bmatrix} = \begin{bmatrix} 17 & 10 & 14 & 13 \\ 22 & 4 & 13 & 7 \\ 22 & 12 & 15 & 15 \end{bmatrix}$$

▶ Exercises

Find the sum or write "impossible" using the matrices shown.

$$A = \begin{bmatrix} 5 & 1 & -7 \\ 2 & 0 & -6 \end{bmatrix} \quad B = \begin{bmatrix} -4 & 1 \\ 0 & 2 \end{bmatrix} \quad C = \begin{bmatrix} 1 \\ 2 \\ 7 \end{bmatrix} \quad D = \begin{bmatrix} 0 \\ 0 \\ 0 \end{bmatrix}$$

$$E = \begin{bmatrix} 7 & 4 & 9 \\ -4 & 2 & -8 \end{bmatrix} \quad F = \begin{bmatrix} 2 & 7 \\ -8 & 2 \end{bmatrix}$$

1. $A + E$

2. $B + F$

3. $D + C$

4. $A + C$
5. Is matrix addition commutative? Explain.

2.7 Compound Linear Inequalities

Sometimes two inequalities are expressed in one statement. Such a statement is called a *compound inequality*. There are two types of compound inequalities, *conjunctions* and *disjunctions*. A conjunction involves the intersection of two inequalities, while a disjunction deals with the union of two inequalities. Remember that the word *and* signals a conjunction (intersection), while the word *or* signals a disjunction (union). Graphing both inequalities that compose the compound statement will help you find the answer to the compound statement.

EXAMPLE 1   Solve $5x + 9 \le 24$ and $-3x - 7 > 14$.

Answer

$5x + 9 \le 24$ and $-3x - 7 > 14$ Solve each inequality separately, graph
$5x \le 15$ $-3x > 21$ each, and find the intersection of the
$x \le 3$ and $x < -7$ graphs for the final solution.

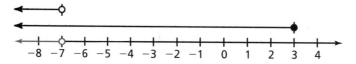

The answer is the intersection of the two graphs, or $x < -7$.

If an algebraic sentence contains two inequality symbols, it defines a conjunction (intersection). The inequality $3 < x - 2 < 5$ means that $x - 2$ lies between 3 and 5 and is exactly the same as the conjunction $x - 2 > 3$ and $x - 2 < 5$. Disjunctions cannot be written this way.

EXAMPLE 2   Solve $8 < 5x - 7 \le 18$.

Answer

$8 < 5x - 7 \le 18$ 1. Rewrite the two inequalities to
$8 < 5x - 7$ and $5x - 7 \le 18$ identify the conjunction.

Continued ▶

$$15 < 5x \qquad\qquad 5x \le 25 \qquad \text{2. Solve both inequalities.}$$
$$3 < x$$
$$x > 3 \qquad\qquad\qquad x \le 5$$

3. Graph both inequalities to identify the solution.

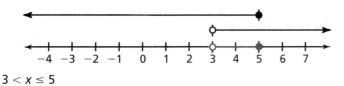

$$3 < x \le 5$$

In the alternate solution following, notice that the operations are performed on all three parts of the compound inequality simultaneously. This is equivalent to breaking it into two separate inequalities, solving each, and putting them back together as shown in the first solution. This method saves writing and does not require graphing to interpret your result.

$$8 < 5x - 7 \le 18$$
$$15 < 5x \quad\quad \le 25 \qquad\qquad \text{1. Add seven to all "sides."}$$
$$3 < x \quad\quad \le 5 \qquad\qquad \text{2. Divide all "sides" by 5.}$$

The solution set then includes all values between 3 and 5 including 5, but not including 3.

Now consider a disjunction.

EXAMPLE 3   Solve $9x + 6 > 60$ or $-2(x + 7) - 3x \ge 11$.

Answer

$9x + 6 > 60$ or $-2(x + 7) - 3x \ge 11$ 1. Solve each inequality.

$$9x > 54 \qquad -2x - 14 - 3x \ge 11$$
$$-5x \ge 25$$
$$x > 6 \quad \text{or} \qquad\qquad x \le -5$$

2. Graph each inequality and find the union of the two solutions for the final answer.

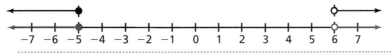

$x \le -5 \qquad \text{or} \qquad x > 6$ 3. Write the solution. Remember that you cannot write a disjunction as a single statement.

► A. Exercises

Graph and solve the following compound inequalities.

1. $x < -2$ or $x \geq 4$
2. $x > -2$ or $x \geq 4$
3. $x > -2$ and $x \geq 4$
4. $x > -2$ and $x \leq 4$
5. $-2 < x < 4$
6. $x < -2$ and $x \geq 4$
7. $x > -2$ or $x \leq 4$

Solve each compound inequality.

8. $3 < x + 2 \leq 9$
9. $5x + 9 \leq 2$ and $x + 6 > 12$
10. $3x - 8 \leq 7$ or $2x + 5 > 7$

► B. Exercises

Solve each compound inequality.

11. $4x - 9 \leq 7$ and $-3x + 4 \leq 16$
12. $3y + 9 < 4y + 7$ or $7y - 2(y - 4) > -2y + 43$
13. $9 \leq 2(x + 7) + 3x - 9 < 35$
14. $9(z - 2) + 3(z + 1) \leq 4z$ or $5z - 7 > 2$
15. $-3x + 9 \geq 15$ or $5x + 7 - 3x \geq 52 - 5x + 2x$
16. $6x + 9 < -3(x + 4)$ and $3x + 12 \geq 4(x - 7) + 3x$
17. $4z - 9 + 2(z - 6) \geq 5z - 7$ and $3z + 4(2z - 8) - 6z > 16$

► C. Exercises

18. Solve the compound inequality for x. Assume $a > 0$.
    $ax + b < c$ and $-ax + b \geq c$
19. Give the solution for all possible relationships of b and c in exercise 18.

► Dominion Modeling

20. From the Olympic data, when might someone run the 400 m dash in 40 seconds?

▉ Cumulative Review

Divide.

21. $(2x^2 - 5x + 7) \div (x + 3)$
22. $\dfrac{x^3 - 8}{x^2 + 2x + 4}$
23. $(2xy^2 - 9x^2y + 15x^3y^2) \div 3x^2y^2$

Factor.

24. $6x^3 + 48$
25. $5x^2 - 3x - 14$
26. $3x^3 - 6x^2 - 27x + 54$

2.8 Absolute Value Inequalities

$$|x| = \begin{cases} x, \text{ if } x \geq 0 \\ -x, \text{ if } x < 0 \end{cases}$$

This is the definition of absolute value that was given earlier. It can be used to solve absolute value inequalities.

EXAMPLE 1 Solve $|x| > 2$.

Answer

$|x| > 2$

If $x \geq 0$, then $|x| > 2$ means $x > 2$
If $x < 0$, then $|x| > 2$ means $-x > 2$

1. Use the definition of absolute value to find all possible solutions.

$x > 2$ or $-x > 2$
$x > 2$ $x < -2$

2. Solve each of these possibilities separately to find the solution. Graph on a number line.

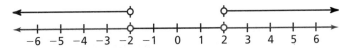

The final answer to this problem is $x < -2$ or $x > 2$. Notice that the answer is a disjunction.

Do you think it is hard to know whether to use a conjunction or disjunction? Think again about Example 1 using your knowledge of absolute values as distances.

Interpret $|x| > 2$ as the distance of a number from zero is more than 2 units. From this you can see that the number must be more than 2 or less than -2. This is a disjunction since the number cannot be both places at once. Similarly, for $|x - 3| \leq 2$ the number $x - 3$ is at most 2 units from zero, so it must be between -2 and 2 indicating a conjunction. The following theorem summarizes this.

Theorem

Compound Inequality Theorem. If N is a positive real number, then $|x| < N$ represents the conjunction $x > -N$ and $x < N$ ($-N < x < N$). $|x| > N$ represents the disjunction $x < -N$ or $x > N$.

The proof of the Compound Inequality Theorem will follow as an exercise, and its use is illustrated in the following examples.

EXAMPLE 2   Solve $|2x - 7| > 4$.

Answer

$|2x - 7| > 4$	
$2x - 7 < -4$ or $2x - 7 > 4$	1. Use a disjunction according to the Compound Inequality Theorem.
$\begin{array}{ccc} 2x < 3 & & 2x > 11 \\ x < \frac{3}{2} & \text{or} & x > \frac{11}{2} \end{array}$	2. Solve each inequality separately.
The solution is $x < \frac{3}{2}$ or $x > \frac{11}{2}$.	

EXAMPLE 3   Solve $|x| < -3$.

Answer

$|x| < -3$	
$x < -3$ and $x > 3$	1. Apply the Compound Inequality Theorem.
No solutions	2. There is no intersection, so the solution set is $\varnothing$.

Look again at Example 3. Since absolute values cannot be negative, $|x| < -3$ could not have any solutions. Did you guess the answer before you saw the solution? Be careful, though. Every real number is a solution to $|x| > -3$, because all numbers have absolute values which are greater than -3. You can check that this solution set is $\mathbb{R}$ using the Compound Inequality Theorem.

You can use the compound theorem with any absolute value expression, but be sure that the absolute value is isolated on the left side of the inequality.

EXAMPLE 4   Solve $\left|-4x + 9\right| - 11 < 4$.

Answer

$\left|-4x + 9\right| - 11 < 4$	
$\left|-4x + 9\right| < 15$	1. Isolate the absolute value.
$-15 < -4x + 9 < 15$	2. Use the Compound Inequality Theorem.
$-24 < -4x < 6$	3. Solve for x using the addition principle of inequality.
$6 > x > \frac{-3}{2}$	4. Apply the multiplication principle of inequality (reverse inequalities when multiplying by $\frac{-1}{4}$.)
$\frac{-3}{2} < x < 6$	5. Rewrite using less than symbols.

EXAMPLE 5   Write an absolute value inequality for the graph.

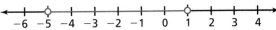

Answer

$\frac{-5 + 1}{2} = -2$	1. Find the midpoint.
$\left|-5 - (-2)\right| = 3$	2. Find the distance between one endpoint and the midpoint.
$\left|x - (-2)\right| < 3$ $\left|x + 2\right| < 3$	3. Let x represent any number between -5 and 1. The x values are less than 3 units from -2.

▶ A. Exercises

Solve.

1. $\left|x\right| < 9$

2. $\left|x\right| \geq 2$

3. $\left|3x + 4\right| \leq 7$

4. $\left|5x - 12\right| < 3$

5. $\left|4y - 8 + 2y\right| > 8$

6. $\left|3z + 4\right| > 1$

7. $\left|8x - 9 + 3x\right| \geq 13$

8. $|27z + 18 - 9z| < 6$

9. $\left|\frac{5x}{2} - 5\right| < 1$

10. $|6x + 4| + 9 \geq 17$

▶ B. Exercises

Solve.

11. $|0.5x + 3 - 0.8x| \leq 5$

12. $|0.09z - 6| \geq 0.3$

13. $|7x - 12 - 10x| - 2 > 0$

14. $\left|\frac{x}{3} + \frac{1}{6}\right| + 3 \leq 9$

15. $|2x + 1| \geq -3$

16. $|5 - 3x| \leq -2$

17. $|5x + 1| > 0$

18. $|x - 1| < 0$

19. $|4x - 3| \geq 0$

20. $|2x - 1| \leq 0$

Give an absolute value inequality.

21.

22.

Proof of Compound Inequality Theorem (1st part)

Given $|y| < a$ and $a > 0$. Supply reasons for the proof.

23. $y < a$ and $-y < a$

24. $y < a$ and $y > -a$

25. $-a < y < a$

26. Could this set be empty? Why?

▶ C. Exercises

Solve.

27. $\left|3x - 8\right| > 12 - x$

28. $\left|0.6z - 7 + 0.3z\right| < 0.4z + 9$

Cumulative Review

Solve.

29. $\left|x - 2\right| = 3$
30. $\left|3x + 11\right| = 0$
31. $5(3x - 2) = 4(2x + 1)$
32. $7 - x < 4$
33. $2x + 6 \geq 3$

 Solve the general linear absolute value equation $\left|ax + b\right| = c$.

Algebra *and* Scripture

Monetary Units

As a Christian you must have a good testimony to other people and a clear conscience before God. This includes having your finances above reproach. We must neither squander God's money nor selfishly hoard it.

1. What verse demonstrated this principle in an earlier lesson?

You have already learned to solve some interest problems. Finances provide major practical applications of algebra that will frequently arise in this course. Let's begin a study of finances in Scripture. The first thing you must know to study finances is the denominations of currency. In the New Testament, the basic unit of currency is the penny (or denarius).

2. How much does a day's work earn in Matthew 20:2?

3. How much will a day's work buy in the tribulation according to Revelation 6:6 (a "measure" is roughly a quart)?

4. How many day's wages would have been needed to pay for food for the 5000 according to Mark 6:37?

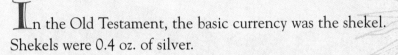

In the Old Testament, the basic currency was the shekel. Shekels were 0.4 oz. of silver.

5. How much did the priest earn annually according to Judges 17:10?

Because shekels were the basic Old Testament coin (silver), the "30 pieces of silver" in the prophecy predicting the Lord would be betrayed is probably 30 shekels.

> **GREATER AMPLITUDE.**
> Find the Old Testament prediction of this betrayal. Then find the New Testament fulfillment.

A talent is 3000 shekels.

6. According to II Kings 5:23, what is the equivalent number of shekels that Naaman gave Gehazi.

> ## Absolute Values
>
> He answered and said unto them, Give ye them to eat. And they say unto him, Shall we go and buy two hundred pennyworth of bread, and give them to eat? ❧
>
> MARK 6:37

Chapter 2 Review

State the properties illustrated.
1. If $x = 3$ and $3 = y$, then $x = y$.
2. If $-3x < 15$, then $x > -5$.
3. $5 + x = 9$
   $x = 4$
4. $x = x$
5. $3x = 12$
   $x = 4$

Solve.
6. $5x + 2 = 47$
7. $4y + 3(y - 6) = -4$
8. $8a + 2(a + 3) + 12 = 4a + 66$
9. $-5z + 9 - 4(z + 2) = 3(z - 2) + 43$
10. $6y + 3(y + 5) - 7(y + 3) = 6y - 9 + 2(y + 5)$
11. $\left| 3x + 9 \right| = 15$
12. $\left| 5y + 12 \right| - 5 = 22$
13. The sum of three numbers is 54. The largest number is twice the smallest, and the third number is six less than the largest. Find the numbers.
14. A train heads south out of Bloomington an hour after a northbound train leaves Bloomington. The northbound train travels 63 mph, while the southbound train travels at a rate of 57 mph. How long will each train have traveled when the trains are 243 miles apart?
15. Dave has $3000 more in a passbook account than in a money market. The passbook account pays 8%, and the money market account pays 10%. How much is invested in each account if the annual interest that he gets on the 8% investment is $80 more than the interest on the 10% investment?
16. A common antiseptic in the United States is a 2% iodine solution. A nurse has two solutions that she wants to mix to make the required 2% solution. One of her solutions is 0.5% iodine, and the other is 4% iodine. How many kilograms of the 4% solution should she mix with 1 kilogram of the 0.5% solution to produce the required mix?
17. $3x + 4 \leq 9$
18. $4(x + 2) - (6x + 9) > 19$
19. $2x - 7 > 3$ or $x + 4 \leq 6$
20. $-4x + 9 > 12$ and $2x + 7 \geq 1$
21. $\left| 3x + 7 \right| < 6$
22. $7 - 3x > 16$

23. $4x + 5 \geq 4$ or $3x + 1 < 2$

Write an absolute value equation or inequality for each graph.

24.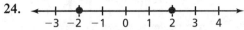

25.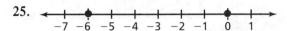

26.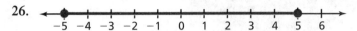

27.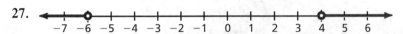

28. Recall your model for the Olympic data; reconsider the scatterplot and the value of r^2. Also remember the extrapolations from the model. From these, write a paragraph evaluation of your model.

29. Give the mathematical significance of Mark 6:37.

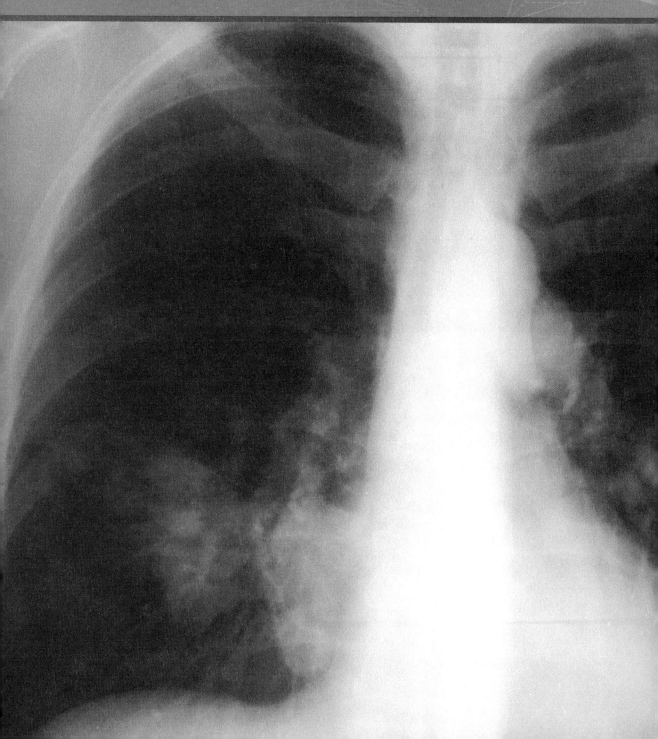

Imagine the shock of being diagnosed with cancer. When people hear such bad news, some respond with despair, some with anger, but some with increased faith (Proverbs 18:10).

Today, most sources agree that smoking cigarettes increases the likelihood of contracting lung cancer. You may be surprised to know that this was not always the case. In the 1560s, Jean Nicot de Villemain claimed that tobacco leaves could heal diseases. So why have we changed our minds? Linear relations will help us answer this question.

Below is data from twenty states and the District of Columbia. For each, the number of cigarettes sold per capita is listed with the rate of lung cancer patients per 100,000.

State	Cigarettes	Lung	State	Cigarettes	Lung
Arkansas	1824	15.98	Ohio	2638	21.89
California	2860	22.07	Pennsylvania	2378	22.11
District of Columbia	4046	27.27	South Carolina	1806	17.45
Florida	2827	23.57	South Dakota	2094	14.11
Illinois	2791	22.80	Tennessee	2008	17.60
Indiana	2618	20.30	Texas	2257	20.74
Massachusetts	2692	22.04	Utah	1400	12.01
Michigan	2496	22.72	Washington	2117	20.34
Nevada	4240	23.03	West Virginia	2125	20.55
New Jersey	2864	25.95	Wisconsin	2286	15.53
New York	2914	25.02			

After this chapter you should be able to

1. define and recognize functions and relations.
2. find the domain and range of a relation.
3. use function notation.
4. determine the slope of a line.
5. graph lines and linear inequalities.
6. find equations of lines.
7. recognize several special functions.
8. perform operations with functions.

3.1 Relations

As the old saying goes, "A picture is worth a thousand words." Pictures are also worthwhile in mathematics and can be used to represent equations. A point on a number line represents the answers to the linear equations that you studied in Chapter 2. Often the graph or picture of an algebraic concept will help you understand the concept and predict results about it.

The control screen in this F-15 cockpit employs a graph.

You should be familiar with the *Cartesian plane.* It is composed of two basic reference lines, the *x*-axis and the *y*-axis. The plane extends indefinitely and is divided into four quadrants by the two axes. The important components of the Cartesian plane are labeled here.

Points in the plane are named by ordered pairs. The first number in an ordered pair is the *x*-coordinate, and the second number is the *y*-coordinate. To locate a point on the graph, move horizontally *x* units from the origin and then *y* units vertically (remember that positive is right for *x* and up for *y*).

EXAMPLE 1 Graph A (2, 4), B (3, −2), C (−1, 0), D (−3, −4).

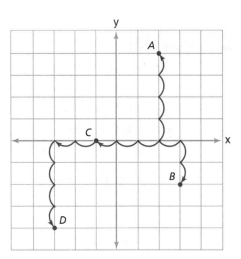

Answer 1. Draw a Cartesian plane and label it.

2. To plot A, start at the origin and move two units right and four units up. Label the point.

3. Locate and label the other points.

Graphs provide a picture of a relation. To graph the relation {(2, 4), (3, −2), (−1, 0), (−3, −4)} plot the points as in Example 1. You should also be able to write down the relation pictured in a graph.

EXAMPLE 2 Give the relations shown by the graphs.

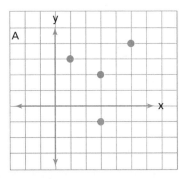

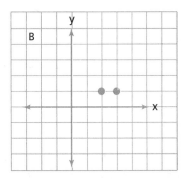

Answer $A = \{(1, 3), (3, −1), (3, 2), (5, 4)\}$

$B = \{(2, 1), (3, 1)\}$

What does the word *relation* mean to you? Your relatives are connected to you by a common bloodline. Christians are related to one another and to Christ by His blood, which makes them heirs of God and brothers and sisters in Christ (Gal. 4:7). Common root words indicate when languages are related. In general, then, a relation shows a connection between objects. This is also true in math since each set of ordered pairs relates x- and y-coordinates.

Relation   Any set of ordered pairs.

This is a broad definition. All of the following sets are relations because they comply with the definition.

   {(1, 3), (2, 1), (7, 6), (8, 9)}

   {(dog, puppy), (cat, kitten)}

   {(Ohio, Columbus), (California, Sacramento), (Georgia, Atlanta)}

A mapping diagram also illustrates a relation. Mapping diagrams show two circles, one containing all the first coordinates and the other containing all the second coordinates. Arrows show which coordinates are related.

EXAMPLE 3   Draw circle mappings for the relations in Example 2.

Answer

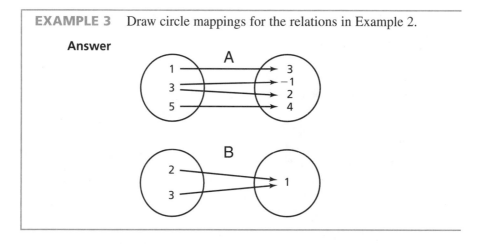

You should be able to think of any relation in all three forms: the set, the graph, and the circle mapping. The circle mapping illustrates the next two definitions.

Definitions

Domain   The set of first coordinates of a relation.

Range   The set of second coordinates of a relation.

EXAMPLE 4   Give the domain and range for each relation shown.

Answer   Give domains by listing
x-coordinates:

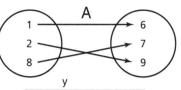

$D_A = \{1, 2, 8\}$

$D_B = \{0, 1, 2, 3\}$

$D_C = \{1, 3, 5\}$

Give ranges by listing
y-coordinates:

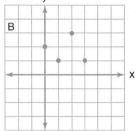

$R_A = \{6, 7, 9\}$

$R_B = \{1, 2, 3\}$

$R_C = \{2, 4, 6\}$

$C = \{(1, 2), (3, 4), (5, 6)\}$

▶ A. Exercises

Plot each point and label. Exercises 1-5 can be done on one graph.
1. $A(2, 3)$
2. $B(-1, -4)$
3. $C(8, -2)$
4. $D(3, -4)$
5. $E(5, 0)$

Give the coordinates of each point.
6. L
7. M
8. N
9. O
10. P

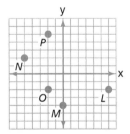

▶ B. Exercises

Graph each relation.
11. $\{(2, 3), (1, -2), (5, 4)\}$
12. $\{(-1, 4), (0, 2), (2, -1), (2, -3)\}$
13.   14.

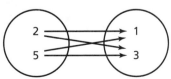

Give the set notation for each relation.

15.

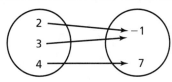

17.

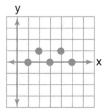

16.

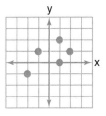

18.

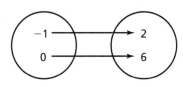

Give the circle mapping for each relation.

19. {(0, 4), (3, 1)}

20. {(−1, 1) (−1, 2), (−2, 2)}

21.

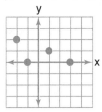

22.

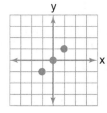

Give the domain and range of each relation.

23. {(5, 4), (2, 7), (−3, 4), (0, 0)}

24.

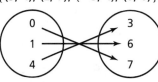

25.

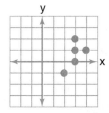

▶ C. Exercises

26. Graph $\{(x, y) \mid y = 4, 0 < x < 5\} \cup \{(x, y) \mid y = -x + 4, x < 0\}$. Is it a relation?

27. Write a relation that would give a rectangle 4 units wide horizontally and 6 units vertically with center at the origin.

▶ Dominion Modeling

28. For the cancer data, what are the variables? What variable would be a suitable independent variable (input)? Which would be a suitable dependent variable (output)?

29. Make a scatterplot for the cancer data. What is notable about the data? Are there any general trends in the data?

30. What should one expect for states in which more cigarettes are sold?

31. What appears to be the case for states in which fewer cigarettes are sold?

Cumulative Review

32. Simplify $(5x - 8) + x$.
33. Divide $(5x - 8) \div x$.
34. Solve $5x - 8 = x$.
35. Multiply $(5x - 8)x$.
36. Solve $|5x - 8| = x$.

3.2 Functions

Look at the two relations below. What is the *y*-coordinate of each when *x* is 2?

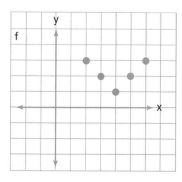
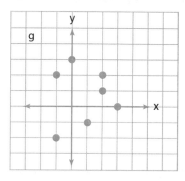

In the first graph $y = 3$ when $x = 2$ since the point (2, 3) is plotted for relation *f*. In the second graph there are two possible answers. When *x* is 2, $y = 1$, or $y = 2$. Both graphs represent relations, but the first graph is a special kind of relation called a *function*, in which there is only one *y*-value for any *x*-value.

In chess, the row and column coordinates are called the rank and file. Thus, black's move P QN-4 means that a black pawn is to move to the fourth rank in the file of the Queen's Knight. Do you see a better move?

Definition

Function   A relation in which every domain element (first coordinate) is paired with one and only one range element (second coordinate).

In the graphs above, *f* is a function but *g* is not. Points that have the same domain element lie on a vertical line. We can use this idea to determine if a graph represents a function. Notice that relation *g* above is not a function and the vertical line *x* = 2 contains two points of the relation.

Definition

Vertical Line Test   If two or more points of a graph lie on a single vertical line, then the relation is not a function.

EXAMPLE 1   Which relations are functions?
$f = \{(1, 5), (3, -1), (3, 2), (5, 4)\}$
$g = \{(-1, 5), (2, -1), (3, 5)\}$

Answer   (3, −1) and (3, 2) have the same domain element.

Since *x* = 3 is paired with more than one range element, relation *f* is not a function.

Relation *g* is a function.

You can also answer the above question by graphing each relation and applying the vertical line test.

Sometimes functions are described by rules. In this case, range elements depend on the value of the domain element. Therefore, a variable that represents a domain element is an *independent variable* and a variable that represents a range element is a *dependent variable*. Rules for functions are written using function notation as in

$f(x) = 2x + 3$ which is equivalent to $y = 2x + 3$.

In this notation, *x* represents the independent variable and *f(x)* represents the dependent variable. *f(x)* is read "function of *x*" or "*f* of *x*." The 2*x* + 3 of the function notation states the rule for finding the value of the dependent variable given the value of the independent variable. The notation *f*(6) means "the value of the function when *x* is 6" or "find *y* when *x* is 6." Function notation is used in all higher mathematics and will be used throughout this book.

EXAMPLE 2   Evaluate $f(x) = 2x + 3$, if $x = -5, 1, 4$.

Answer

$f(x) = 2x + 3$
$f(-5) = 2(-5) + 3$
$\quad = -7$

1. Substitute the value of x into the function and evaluate. For $x = -5$, replace x by -5, and evaluate.

$f(x) = 2x + 3$
$f(1) = 2(1) + 3$
$\quad = 5$

2. Evaluate the function for each of the other values.

$f(x) = 2x + 3$
$f(4) = 2(4) + 3$
$\quad = 11$

Describe the function in set builder notation by pairing each value of the independent variable with the corresponding value of the dependent variable.

$$f = \{(x, f(x)) \mid f(x) = 2x + 3 \text{ if } x = -5, 1, 4\}$$

$$f = \{(-5, -7), (1, 5), (4, 11)\}$$

In Example 2 the domain $\{-5, 1, 4\}$ was specifically stated. If no domain is given, the domain is the set of all real numbers. This means the function contains an infinite number of ordered pairs. One such function is a linear function.

Definition

Linear function   A function whose graph is a line.

To graph a linear function obtain several ordered pairs by substituting arbitrary values for x, plotting the ordered pairs, and drawing a line through them. The *standard form* of a line is $ax + by = c$, where $a, b, c \in \mathbb{R}$.

EXAMPLE 3   Graph $\{(x, y) \mid x + y = 5\}$.

Answer

$x + y = 5$
$y = -x + 5$
$f(x) = -x + 5$

$f(0) = 0 + 5$
$f(2) = -2 + 5$
$f(5) = -5 + 5$

1. Select x values.

Continued ▶

$f(0) = 5$	2. Find $f(x)$	
$f(2) = 3$	for each	
$f(5) = 0$	x chosen.	
(0, 5)	3. Find each	
(2, 3)	ordered	
(5, 0)	pair.	
	4. Graph.	

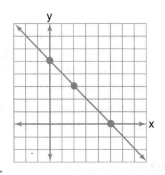

The condition $x + y = 5$ means the same as $y = -x + 5$ and $f(x) = -x + 5$. In each case x is the independent variable and y or $f(x)$ the dependent. Since all three describe the same linear function, they will have the same graph.

► A. Exercises

Decide which sets are functions. If one is not a function, explain why.

1. $\{(3, 4), (2, 9), (8, -4)\}$
2. $\{(-1, 6), (3, 2), (4, -2), (-1, 3)\}$
3. $\{3, 2, 4, 7\}$
4. $\{(0, 1), (4, 2), (-5, 1), (3, 7)\}$
5. $\{(4, 1), (5, -6), (3, 2), (6, 0)\}$

Which relations are functions? Explain.

6.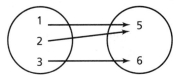

9.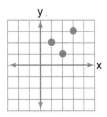

7.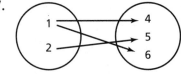

10.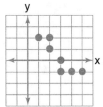

8.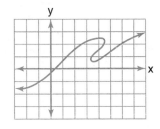

Evaluate the given functions for the given values. Use function notation to express your answers.

11. $f(x) = x + 7$ if $x = 0, -3, 8$.
12. $g(x) = 4x - 2$ if $x = -9, 2, 6$.
13. $h(x) = \frac{x}{2} + 5$ if $x = 2, 6, -4$.
14. $g(x) = x^2 + 3x - 9$ if $x = 4, -1, -3$.
15. $f(x) = -5x + 2$ if $x = -2, 5, 0$.

▶ B. Exercises

Graph each linear function.

16. $\{(x, f(x)) \mid f(x) = x - 2 \text{ if } x = 0, 2, 4, 6\}$
17. $\{(x, y) \mid y = -2x + 6\}$
18. $f(x) = 5x + 6$
19. $f(x) = -x + 4$
20. $\{(x, y) \mid 4x + 3y = 9\}$

Use $h(r) = 5r$.

21. Give the independent variable.
22. Give the dependent variable.
23. If the domain is $\{-1, 0, 1, 2\}$, find the range.
24. If the range is $\{100, 200\}$, find the domain.
25. Find $h(-3)$ and $h(2x)$.

▶ C. Exercises

26. Show that $x = y^2$ is not a function. Do not give numerical ordered pairs.
27. Is the relation shown graphically a function? Why or why not?

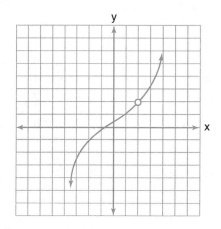

▶ Dominion Modeling

28. According to the lung cancer data, which state had the fewest cigarettes sold? How does this compare with this state's lung cancer rate? Explain.

29. Are there any states that do not fit the trend in the data?

▪ Cumulative Review

Factor.

30. $x^2 - 9$

31. $4x^2 + 12x + 9$

32. $2x + 2y + x^2 - y^2$

33. $24x^4 - 81x$

34. $x^2 + 6xy + 9y^2 - z^2$

Gauss had a mathematical genius superior to that of any other man in history.

GERMAN MATH

During the eighteenth and nineteenth centuries, one school in Europe stood above the others in importance—the University of Göttingen. The university served as a center of mathematics taught by David Hilbert, Emmy Noether, Richard Dedekind, and Felix Klein. Famous physicists such as Max Born, Werner Heisenberg, and Wolfgang Pauli also taught there. Most importantly though, Karl Gauss and Georg Riemann each took a turn presiding over the chair of mathematics at Göttingen.

Gauss had a mathematical genius superior to that of any other man in history. This self-assured, confident genius, was recognized early, and his position as professor of astronomy at Göttingen provided a comfortable living.

Gauss's fertile mind pursued about every avenue of mathematical thought. He proved the Fundamental Theorem of Arithmetic as his doctoral dissertation, and he used complex numbers to solve all kinds of problems in algebra and number theory. When Italian scientists lost track of the large asteroid *Ceres*, he calculated its orbit by the method of least squares. Naturally, *Ceres* was exactly where he told them to look. Gauss had even developed the theory of elliptic functions long before Abel and Jacobi were born—despite the fact that these two are credited for its discovery.

The Aula, completed in 1837 by William IV, is still the main building at the University of Göttingen, Germany.

Riemann, in contrast, was a godly Christian who was shy and modest and had little awareness of his own extraordinary abilities. After he obtained his doctor's degree in 1851, he endured eight years of abject poverty before becoming an unpaid lecturer. In 1854 he submitted his probationary essay, known today as the Riemann Integral, in much the same form as it is seen today in calculus textbooks. This essay became the basis for a new branch of mathematics called the theory of functions of a real variable. Two months later he delivered a required lecture that still stands as a great classical masterpiece of mathematical history on the foundations of Euclidean and non-Euclidean geometries.

In 1859 Riemann published a ten-page paper on number theory that influenced research for the next century. Riemann showed the deepest meaning of the distribution of primes by using a function called the Riemann zeta function, which has the complex numbers for its domain. He proved some properties of this function and stated many other results that have kept mathematicians busy ever since. The only statement about this function that remains unproved involves its zeros. It is the most important unsolved problem in mathematics and has been called the most difficult mathematical problem ever conceived.

However, Göttingen was not the only center of mathematics in German history. Not far to the north at Hanover, Gottfried von Leibnitz discovered the following series expression for π during the century before Gauss.

Gauss lived and worked in this observatory at Göttingen from 1807 until his death in 1855.

$$\frac{\pi}{4} = 1 - \frac{1}{3} + \frac{1}{5} - \frac{1}{7} + \frac{1}{9} - \dots$$

Leibnitz also recognized two central ideas of calculus. The first was that the tangent to a curve was a limiting value as two points on the curve came closer together. The second was that the area under a curve is the sum of infinitely thin rectangles making up the area. Leibnitz also coined several important terms still in use today: *constant, variable, parameter, abscissa, ordinate, coordinates,* and *function.*

Built in the 17th century near Berlin, Charlottenburg Castle would have been a familiar sight to the mathematicians of Germany. The castle was the palace of Queen Charlotte, wife of Frederick I, king of Prussia.

Besides Hanover and Göttingen, the cities of Halle, Bonn, and Berlin also served as key centers for the study of mathematics in Germany. Georg Cantor taught at Halle, and Felix Hausdorf at Bonn. The University of Berlin boasted teachers such as Carl Jacobi, Karl Weierstrass, and Leopold Kronecker. Peter Dirichlet also taught at Berlin and provided the correct understanding and definition of *function* as we use it today.

3.3 Graphing Lines

The equation $2x - 3y = 6$ represents a line and is in the *standard form* $ax + by = c$ where $a, b, c \in \mathbb{R}$.

Every linear equation can be written in function notation by solving for y and replacing y with $f(x)$.

EXAMPLE 1   Write $2x - 3y = 6$ in function notation.

Answer $2x - 3y = 6$

$\qquad\qquad -3y = -2x + 6$ 1. Solve for y.

$\qquad\qquad\quad y = \frac{2}{3}x - 2$

- -

$\qquad\qquad f(x) = \frac{2}{3}x - 2$ 2. Replace y by $f(x)$.

The point where the graph of a line crosses the y-axis is called the y-intercept. Since all points on the y-axis have an x-coordinate of zero, you can find the y-intercept of a linear function by finding $f(0)$.

EXAMPLE 2   Find the y-intercept of $f(x) = \frac{2}{3}x - 2$.

Answer $f(0) = \frac{2}{3}(0) - 2 = -2$

The y-intercept is $(0, -2)$.

By following the process in Example 1, any linear equation in standard form can be written in function notation: $f(x) = mx + b$. What is the y-intercept of the graph? Since $f(0) = b$, it is $(0, b)$. The b in the formula gives the y-intercept, and in the next examples you will see that m represents the slope of the line. Thus, *slope-intercept form* of a linear function is $f(x) = mx + b$ where $m, b \in \mathbb{R}$.

A level confirms that a slope is zero.

Slope measures the deviation of a line from the horizontal. A horizontal line has a slope of 0, or no deviation from the horizontal.

Slope of a line The ratio of the change in *y* values of two points on a line to the change in *x* values of the two points.

A lowercase *m* is used to symbolize the slope of a line. Look at the graph of the line given here which passes through the points (1, 5) and (−3, 2).

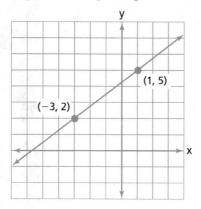

To find the slope of this line, start at one of the points (we will choose (−3, 2)) and move vertically until you are even with the second point. In this case we would need to move **3** units upward (positive direction, downward being negative).

We then move **4** units horizontally to the right (positive direction, left being negative) to reach the point **(1, 5)**.

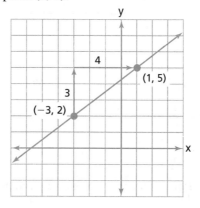

The slope of this line is $m = \dfrac{\text{change in } y}{\text{change in } x} = \dfrac{3}{4}$.

The following formula is used to find the slope of a line when two points on the line are given.

Some mathematicians think that the letter m
is used for slope from the French la montée,
meaning "the climb."

$m = \frac{y_2 - y_1}{x_2 - x_1}$, where (x_1, y_1) and (x_2, y_2)
are two points on the line.

This formula will verify the slope of the line
graphed above. The line passes through $(-3, 2)$
and $(1, 5)$.

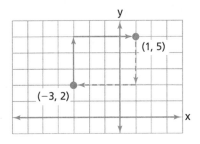

$m = \frac{5 - 2}{1 - (-3)} = \frac{3}{4}$ or $m = \frac{2 - 5}{-3 - 1} = \frac{-3}{-4} = \frac{3}{4}$

EXAMPLE 3   Find the slope of the line that passes through the points
$(4, -8)$ and $(1, 6)$.

Answer

Let $(x_1, y_1) = (4, -8)$	1. Choose either of the points to be (x_1, y_1) and the other will be (x_2, y_2).
$m = \frac{y_2 - y_1}{x_2 - x_1}$ $m = \frac{6 - (-8)}{1 - 4}$ $= \frac{14}{-3}$ $= -\frac{14}{3}$	2. Use the slope formula to find the slope of the line.

The slope of the line that passes through $(4, -8)$ and $(1, 6)$
is $-\frac{14}{3}$.

Slopes can also be read from any linear equation that is in slope-intercept
form.

EXAMPLE 4   Find the slope of the line $2x - 3y = 6$.

Answer

$2x - 3y = 6$	1. Find slope-intercept form as in
$y = \frac{2}{3}x - 2$	Example 1.
$m = \frac{2}{3}$	2. Identify m in $y = mx + b$.

In Example 1 the equation $2x - 3y = 6$ was written in function notation, and in Example 2 the y-intercept of the line was identified as $(0, -2)$, that is, $b = -2$. In Example 4, the slope of the same line is identified as $m = \frac{2}{3}$. This information is a valuable aid to graphing. First, plot the y-intercept $(0, b)$ or in this case $(0, -2)$. Next, recall that slope is vertical change over horizontal change. Since $m = \frac{2}{3}$, for a vertical change of 2 the horizontal change is 3. Starting at the y-intercept $(0, -2)$, move vertically $+2$ (up two) and then horizontally $+3$ (right 3). Finally, draw a line through the two points.

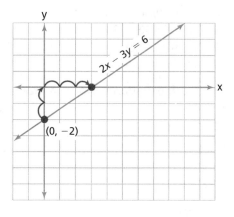

EXAMPLE 5   Graph $3x + y = 4$.

Answer

$3x + y = 4$	
$y = -3x + 4$	1. Obtain slope-intercept form.
$m = \frac{-3}{1}$ $b = 4$	2. Read the slope and y-intercept from $y = mx + b$.
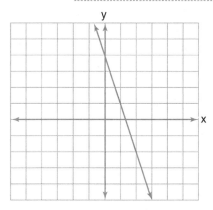	3. Count the slope from the y-intercept to find a second point and draw the line.

▶ A. Exercises

Write each line using function notation and identify the slope and *y*-intercept.

1. $8x + y = 5$
2. $x - 2y = 6$

Find the slope of the line that passes through each pair of points.

3. $(-4, -9), (3, -6)$
4. $(8, -2), (10, -8)$
5. $(12, 9), (3, -14)$
6. $(11, 4), (7, -3)$
7. $(0, 2), (5, 18)$
8. $(-6, -4), (0, 0)$
9. $(10, 6), (-12, 19)$
10. $(-6, -1), (-9, -13)$

Write each equation in slope-intercept form and graph.

11. $x = y$
12. $4x - y = 8$
13. $2x + 4y = 7$
14. $x - y = -2$
15. $3x + y = -1$
16. $2x + y = 9$

▶ B. Exercises

Write each equation in slope-intercept form and graph.

17. $5x + 3y = -15$
18. $7x + 3y = 12$
19. $8x - 5y = 10$
20. $x + 6y = -8$

21. Graph the points $(3, 2)$ and $(5, 2)$. Connect these points with a line. What kind of line is it? Find the slope of this line.
22. Is the relation in exercise 21 a function?
23. Two points (p, r) and (q, r) have the same *y*-coordinate. What kind of line is the graph? What is the slope? Is it a function? Give the slope-intercept and standard forms of its equation.
24. Graph the points $(2, 8)$ and $(2, -3)$ and draw a line through them. What kind of line is it? Find the slope of this line.
25. Is the relation in exercise 24 a function? Give its equation. Place it in slope-intercept form and standard form.
26. Make a generalization from exercise 25 regarding two points (p, q) and (p, r) with equal *x*-coordinates. What kind of line is determined? What is the slope? Is it a function? Give the forms of its equation.

▶ C. Exercises

27. Graph $\{(x, y) \mid y = x^2, x \geq 1\} \cup \{(x, y) \mid -1 < x < 1\} \cup \{(x, y) \mid y = -x^2, x < -1\}$. Is it a function?
28. Consider a graph in three dimensions whose equation is $z = f(x, y)$. What do you think this means? Write an example using $f(x, y)$. Why does the graph represent a surface rather than a solid figure?

► Dominion Modeling

29. Recall the lung cancer data. Generate a linear model to describe the data.

■ Cumulative Review

Use $f = \{(x, y) \mid y = 3x - 1$ if $x = -1, 1, 3\}$

30. Give the domain and range.
31. Graph.
32. Make a circle mapping.
33. Express one of the ordered pairs using function notation.

3.4 Finding Equations of Lines

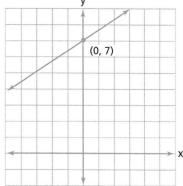

You have learned to graph equations on a Cartesian plane. Now you will learn to write the equation of a line from the graph or other given information. You have seen the slope-intercept form of an equation in the previous section.

The Red Arrows of the British Royal Air Force can draw lines too.

Slope-intercept form of an equation is

$$y = mx + b$$

where m is the slope and b is the y value of the y-intercept of the graph. If you know the slope and the y-intercept of a line, you can immediately write the equation of the line in slope-intercept form.

EXAMPLE 1   Write the equation of the line with slope $\frac{2}{3}$ and y-intercept (0, 7).

Continued ►

Answer $m = \frac{2}{3}$ $b = 7$	1. Determine m and b from the given information.
$y = mx + b$ $y = \frac{2}{3}x + 7$	2. Substitute these values in slope-intercept form to write the equation.
$3y = 2x + 21$ $-2x + 3y = 21$	3. For standard form, eliminate the fractions and rearrange the terms.
$2x - 3y = -21$	4. Multiply both sides of the equation by -1 to obtain the standard form with $a \geq 0$.

The equation of the line with slope $\frac{2}{3}$ and y-intercept (0, 7) in slope-intercept form is $y = \frac{2}{3}x + 7$. In standard form the equation is $2x - 3y = -21$.

You can also write the equation of a line if you know the slope and a point on the line, two points on the line, or the graph of the line. The remaining examples in this section show methods of writing equations from such given information.

The main form of a linear equation that will help you write equations is the *point-slope form*. Study the development of this formula.

Using P to represent any general point and P_1 to represent a given point with known coordinates, the slope of the line shown is found to be $m = \frac{y - y_1}{x - x_1}$.

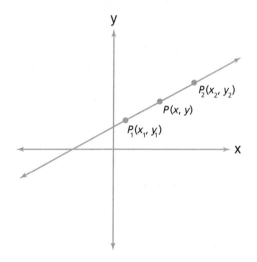

By multiplying both sides of this equation by $x - x_1$, you can obtain the point-slope form of a linear equation.

$$y - y_1 = m(x - x_1)$$

By substituting the slope and the known particular point (x_1, y_1), the equation of a line can be found.

EXAMPLE 2   Write the equation of the line that has slope $\frac{-4}{5}$ and passes through the point (1, 4). Express your answer in slope-intercept form.

Continued ▶

Answer

$$y - y_1 = m(x - x_1)$$

$y - 4 = \frac{-4}{5}(x - 1)$	1. Substitute the slope and the coordinates of the point in the point-slope form of the equation.
$y - \frac{20}{5} = \frac{-4}{5}x + \frac{4}{5}$ $y = \frac{-4}{5}x + \frac{24}{5}$	2. Multiply to eliminate the parentheses in the equation, solve for y, and write in slope-intercept form.

EXAMPLE 3   Write the equation of the line that passes through the points $(-4, 3)$ and $(2, 6)$. Express your answer in standard form.

Answer

$m = \frac{y_2 - y_1}{x_2 - x_1}$ $m = \frac{6 - 3}{2 - (-4)}$ $m = \frac{3}{6}$ $m = \frac{1}{2}$	1. To use the point-slope form of the equation, you must determine the slope. Use the slope formula.
$y - y_1 = m(x - x_1)$ $y - 6 = \frac{1}{2}(x - 2)$	2. Now use the slope, $\frac{1}{2}$, and one of the given points to write the equation in point-slope form.
$2y - 12 = x - 2$ $-x + 2y = 10$ $x - 2y = -10$	3. Convert the equation to standard form. Make the coefficient of x positive.

EXAMPLE 4   Write the equation of the line graphed here. Express your answer in both forms.

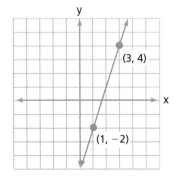

Continued ▶

Answer

$m = \frac{y_2 - y_1}{x_2 - x_1}$

$m = \frac{-2 - 4}{1 - 3}$

$m = \frac{-6}{-2}$

$m = 3$

1. Find two points through which the line passes. (3, 4) and (1, −2) are marked. Determine the slope.

$y - y_1 = m(x - x_1)$

$y - 4 = 3(x - 3)$

$y - 4 = 3x - 9$

2. Use the slope and one of these points to write the equation of the line. Use the methods shown in Example 3.

$y = 3x - 5$ (Slope-intercept form)

$3x - y = 5$ (Standard form)

▶ A. Exercises

Change each equation to standard form.

1. $y = 2x + 7$

2. $y = \frac{1}{3}x + 6$

3. $y = 4x - 2$

4. $y = \frac{2}{3}x - \frac{4}{3}$

5. $f(x) = \frac{1}{2}x + \frac{2}{3}$

6. $f(x) = 5x - \frac{1}{2}$

Write the equation of each line described here. Express your answers in slope-intercept form.

7. slope is 2 and y-intercept is (0, −4)

8. slope is $\frac{-5}{2}$ and y-intercept is $\left(0, \frac{3}{4}\right)$

9. slope is −3 and y-intercept is (0, 1)

10. slope is −4 and passes through (2, 7)

11. slope is $\frac{1}{2}$ and passes through (−1, 3)

12. passes through (5, −3) and (1, 4)

13. passes through (1, 6) and (2, −3)

14. passes through (0, 8) and (3, −4)

Write the equation of each line that is graphed. Express your answer in standard form.

15.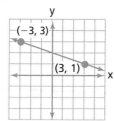

16.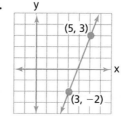

17.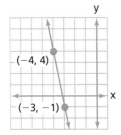

19.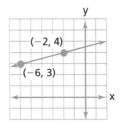

18.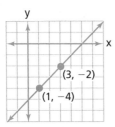

20.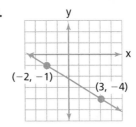

▶ B. Exercises

21. Connect (1, 3) and (3, −2) with a line and then connect (−2, 1) and (0, −4). What appears to be true about these two lines? Find the slopes of each line. What is true about the slopes?

22. Connect (−4, 6) and (−1, 9) with a line, and then connect (−1, 2) and (0, 3). What appears to be true about these two lines? Find the slope of each line. What is true about the slopes?

23. Make a general statement that can be deduced from exercises 21 and 22.

Find the equation of the line passing through

24. (0, 5) and parallel to $y = 3x + 2$.

25. (1, 8) and parallel to $x + y = 4$.

26. Connect (3, 7) and (1, 2) with a line and then connect (1, 2) with (6, 0). What appears to be true about these two lines? Find the slope of each line. What is true about the slopes?

27. Connect (−4, 2) and (0, 0) with a line and then connect (−4, 2) with (−3, 4). What appears to be true about these two lines? Find the slope of each line. What is true about the slopes?

28. Make a general statement that can be deduced from exercises 26 and 27.

Find the equation of the line passing through

29. (0, 4) and perpendicular to $y = -3x + 1$.

30. (−1, 3) and perpendicular to $x + 2y = 7$.

▶ C. Exercises

31. Find any point on the line $2x − 3y = 7$ and write the equation of the line perpendicular to it at that point.

32. The circle shown has equation $x^2 + y^2 = 9$. Find the coordinate of any point P on the circle, then prove $\overline{PA} \perp \overline{PB}$.

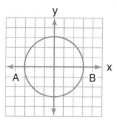

▶ Dominion Modeling

33. Review the lung cancer data. Compare the actual data with values predicted by the model.
34. After considering the scatterplot and r^2, how would you initially evaluate the model?

■ Cumulative Review

35. Graph the relation $\{(x, y)\,|\,y = -3x + 2$ if $x = -1, 0, 3\}$.
36. Is the relation in exercise 35 a function? Give the domain, range, and dependent variable.

Write the equation in slope-intercept form; then graph.

37. $3x - 6y = 6$
38. $4x + 5y = 10$

39. Given $x - 7 \div y + 3z - w^2 \div 5$, which of the following is an equivalent expression?

   a. $\dfrac{x-7}{y} + \dfrac{3z - w^2}{5}$

   b. $x - \dfrac{7}{y} + \dfrac{3z - w^2}{5}$

   c. $x - \dfrac{7}{y + 3z - w^2} \div 5$

   d. $x - \dfrac{7}{y} + 3z - \dfrac{w^2}{5}$

MIND OVER MATH

Lindsey measures the circumference of a golf ball that has a 1-inch diameter. Next, she considers an outer shell 1 inch from the ball and finds the circumference of this outer sphere. How do the two circumferences compare? She wonders how this experiment would work if the inner sphere being considered were the earth, whose diameter is about 8000 miles. If a shell were placed at a height of 1 mile around the earth, how would its circumference compare to that of the earth?

3.5 Special Functions

This chapter has been devoted to the study of functions, especially linear functions. Before considering other types of functions, review the definition.

Definition

Function   A relation in which every domain element is paired with one and only one range element.

Do you remember how this definition applies to graphs? The domain elements are the *x*-coordinates and the range elements are the *y*-coordinates. Since every *x*-coordinate must have a unique *y*-coordinate, there cannot be two ordered pairs with the same *x*-coordinate. The vertical line test summarizes this requirement by saying that no function has two points which lie on the same vertical line.

Look at the graph of the line $x = 3$, which is a vertical line. The domain is {3} since 3 is the only value of *x*. Since every real number is the *y*-coordinate of some point on the line, the range of the relation is $\mathbb{R}$. The vertical line has more than one point on it, so it is not a function. The slope of a vertical line is undefined as you discovered in exercises 24-26 of Section 3.3.

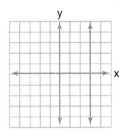

Now consider the horizontal line $y = 4$. What is the slope of the line? In exercises 21-23 of Section 3.3 you learned that the slope of a horizontal line is zero (no change from the horizontal). For any relation you should be able to find the domain and range. Can you identify them from the graph? You should also be able to tell if a relation is a function by applying the vertical line test.

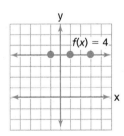

Notice this relation passes the vertical line test and therefore is a function. It is called a *constant function* because the *y*-coordinates of the points remain constant regardless of the value of *x*. Since it is a function, it is best represented using function notation.

$$f(x) = c \text{ where } x, c \in \mathbb{R}$$

Each Christian needs to remain constant in his stand for the Lord. No matter what adversity comes his way, he must not waver but must stand true to the Lord as Stephen did in Acts 7:54-60. Are you as constant and unchanging in your beliefs as Stephen?

The next graph shows the *absolute value function* described by $f(x) = |x|$ where $x \in \mathbb{R}$. Notice $y \geq 0$ for all *x*, since absolute value is always positive or zero. Also verify that $|-x| = |x|$ for all *x*.

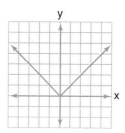

Another special function is the *greatest integer function*. The domain of the function is the set of real numbers. The range is the set of integers. For each value of *x*, find the greatest integer less than or equal to *x*. The notation for the greatest integer function is

$$f(x) = [x] \text{ where } x \in \mathbb{R}.$$

EXAMPLE If $f(x) = [x]$, evaluate the function when $x = 2, -5, \frac{3}{2}, \frac{-2}{3}$.

Answer

$f(2) = [2]$ $\quad = 2$	1. The greatest integer ≤ 2 is 2.
$f(-5) = [-5]$ $\quad = -5$	2. The greatest integer ≤ -5 is -5.
$f\left(\frac{3}{2}\right) = \left[\frac{3}{2}\right]$ $\quad = 1$	3. The greatest integer $\leq \frac{3}{2}$ is 1.
$f\left(\frac{-2}{3}\right) = \left[\frac{-2}{3}\right]$ $\quad = -1$	4. The greatest integer $\leq \frac{-2}{3}$ is -1.

The graph of the greatest integer function is shown here.

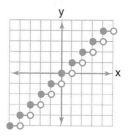

The last special function that you will study here is the *exponential function*. It is called an exponential function because the variable is in the exponent. For example, $f(x) = 3^x$ is an exponential function. In general the exponential function is defined by

$$f(x) = a^x \text{ where } a, x \in \mathbb{R}, a \neq 1, \text{ and } a > 0.$$

The graph of $f(x) = 3^x$ is shown here.

x	f(x)
0	1
1	3
2	9
3	27
−1	$\frac{1}{3}$
−2	$\frac{1}{9}$

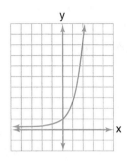

In the graph shown, *y* increases as *x* increases. You should realize that when $0 < a < 1$, the function will decrease as *x* increases. If $a = \frac{1}{2}$, then $\left(\frac{1}{2}\right)^2 = \frac{1}{4}$, $\left(\frac{1}{2}\right)^3 = \frac{1}{8}$. As *x* increases from two to three, $f(x)$ decreases from $\frac{1}{4}$ to $\frac{1}{8}$.

▶ A. Exercises

Determine which relations are functions.

1.
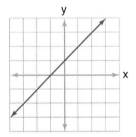

2.
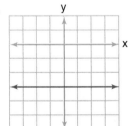

3.
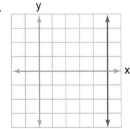

4.
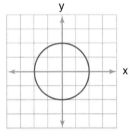

5.
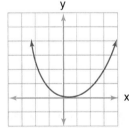

Give the name of each type of function.

6. $f(x) = |x|$

7. $f(x) = \left(\frac{1}{3}\right)^x$

8. $f(x) = 3$

9. $f(x) = [x]$

10. $f(x) = x$

For each function, find the indicated values.

11. $f(x) = 4^x$. Find $f(3)$, $f(-1)$.

12. $f(x) = |x|$. Find $f(-8)$, $f\left(\frac{1}{3}\right)$.

13. $f(x) = [x]$. Find $f(-3)$, $f\left(\frac{11}{4}\right)$.

14. $f(x) = 3|x + 2|$. Find $f(-2)$, $f(-5)$.

Express the following functions as sets of ordered pairs.

15. $f = \{(x, y) \mid y = 5 \text{ for } x = \frac{1}{2}, -100\}$

16. $f = \{(x, y) \mid y = 3x + 2, x = -6, 2\}$

17. $\{(x, f(x)) \mid f(x) = \left(\frac{2}{3}\right)^x \text{ if } x = -1, 3\}$

18. $\{(x, f(x)) \mid f(x) = 7^0 \text{ if } x = -8, 4\}$

19. Given $f = \{(4, 1), (-3, 2), (5, 1), (-2, 8)\}$. Find $f(4)$, $f(-2)$.

20. Given $f = \{(1, 7), (5, 6), (2, -1)\}$. Find $f(2)$, $f(6)$.

▶ B. Exercises

Graph each function and state the domain and range.

21. $f(x) = 2|x|$

22. $f = \{(x, y) \mid y = 2^x \text{ if } x = -1, 0, 1, 2\}$

23. $f(x) = 2$

24. $f(x) = [x] + 2$

25. $f(x) = \left(\frac{1}{2}\right)^x$

26. Graph the relation $x = 4$ and state the domain and range.

▶ C. Exercises

27. Graph the relation $\{(x, y) \mid x^2 = 4 \text{ and } |y| = 3\}$ and state the domain and range.

Use the general linear equation $ax + by = c$ (standard form of a line).

28. What condition guarantees that the line is vertical?

29. What condition guarantees that the line is horizontal?

30. Does every line in standard form represent a function? Explain your answer.

▶ Dominion Modeling

31. Consider your model for the lung cancer data. According to your model, how many cases of lung cancer would there be in a state that sold 2500 cigarettes per capita? Is this a reasonable value?

32. According to this model, how many cases of lung cancer would be expected if cigarettes were banned? Briefly explain your results.

■ Cumulative Review

Find the slope of the line

33. passing through $(-2, 7)$ and $(3, 1)$.

34. passing through $(5, 4)$ and $(1, 7)$.

35. passing through $(-3, -2)$ and $(-6, 9)$.

36. parallel to $5x - 7y = 3$.

37. perpendicular to $y = 3x + 2$.

3.6 Algebra of Functions

If $h(x) = 3^x + 3x$, find the ordered pairs that make up the function when $x \in \{-1, 0, 1, 2\}$.

x	$h(x) = 3^x + 3x$
-1	$\frac{1}{3} - 3 = \frac{-8}{3}$
0	$1 + 0 = 1$
1	$3 + 3 = 6$
2	$9 + 6 = 15$

$h = \left\{ \left(-1, \frac{-8}{3}\right), (0, 1), (1, 6), (2, 15) \right\}$

Think about the function above. Notice that to find each value of $h(x)$ you calculate 3^x and $3x$ and then add. Let $f(x) = 3^x$ and $g(x) = 3x$. When $x = 2$, $f(2) = 3^2 = 9$ and $g(2) = 3 \cdot 2 = 6$. Next you find $h(2)$ by adding 9 and 6 to get 15. Therefore $h(2) = f(2) + g(2) = 9 + 6 = 15$.

This tells us how to add the functions $f(x) = 3^x$ and $g(x) = 3x$. Since domain values must be substituted into both functions, they must have the same domain (in this case $\mathbb{R}$). When two functions have the same domain, corresponding range values must be added to find the range value of the function representing their sum.

EXAMPLE 1 If $f = \{(-2, 4), (2, 5), (4, 9)\}$ and $g = \{(-2, 1), (2, 4), (4, -5)\}$, find $f + g$.

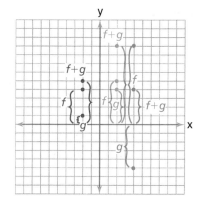

Answer f and g have the same domain $\{-2, 2, 4\}$, so the sum is obtained by adding corresponding range values. Compare the ordered pairs in set $f + g$ with the figure shown. The function $f + g = \{(-2, 5), (2, 9), (4, 4)\}$ is shown point by point on the graph.

The sum of functions is defined to be $(f + g)(x) = f(x) + g(x)$. Using this definition you can determine the function rule for a function representing the sum of two given functions. The other three operations on functions are defined in a similar manner.

In summary:

$$(f + g)(x) = f(x) + g(x)$$

$$(f - g)(x) = f(x) - g(x)$$

$$fg(x) = f(x) \cdot g(x)$$

$$\frac{f}{g}(x) = \frac{f(x)}{g(x)} \text{ where } g(x) \neq 0$$

EXAMPLE 2 If $f(x) = 3x - 9$ and $g(x) = 5x$, find $(f + g)(x)$, $(f - g)(x)$, $fg(x)$ and $\frac{f}{g}(x)$.

Answer
$(f + g)(x) = f(x) + g(x)$
$\qquad\quad = 3x - 9 + 5x$
$\qquad\quad = 8x - 9$

$(f - g)(x) = f(x) - g(x)$
$\qquad\quad = 3x - 9 - 5x$
$\qquad\quad = -2x - 9$

$fg(x) = f(x)\,g(x)$
$\qquad = (3x - 9)(5x)$
$\qquad = 15x^2 - 45x$

$\frac{f}{g}(x) = \frac{f(x)}{g(x)}$
$\qquad = \frac{3x - 9}{5x}; x \neq 0$

There is one more operation involving functions, which is called composition.

Definition

The **composition** of two functions f and g denoted by $f \circ g$ is $f \circ g = f(g(x))$.

EXAMPLE 3   If $f(x) = x^2$ and $g(x) = 2x + 1$, find $f \circ g$, $g \circ f$, and $(g \circ f)(-3)$.

Answer

$$f \circ g = f(g(x)) = f(2x + 1) = (2x + 1)^2 = 4x^2 + 4x + 1$$
$$g \circ f = g(f(x)) = g(x^2) = 2x^2 + 1$$
$$(g \circ f)(-3) = 2(-3)^2 + 1 = 2(9) + 1 = 19$$

▶ A. Exercises

Find the function rule for the indicated operations.

$f(x) = 3x - 12$ $\qquad\qquad$ $g(x) = x^2$ $\qquad\qquad$ $h(x) = \frac{x}{9}$

1. $(g + f)(x)$
2. $hg(x)$
3. $(g - h)(x)$
4. $(f + h)(x)$
5. $\frac{g}{h}(x)$
6. $(f - g)(x)$
7. $fh(x)$
8. $(f \circ g)(x)$
9. $(h \circ g)(x)$
10. $(f \circ h)(x)$

For $f = \{(-2, 9), (3, -8), (4, 0)\}$ and $g = \{(-2, 3), (3, 2), (4, 7)\}$ find
11. $(f + g)(x)$.
12. $\left(\frac{f}{g}\right)(x)$.

▶ B. Exercises

Find $(f + g)\left(\frac{-1}{2}\right)$ and $(f - g)(1)$.
13. $f(x) = [x]$, $g(x) = 9^x$
14. $f(x) = 6x$, $g(x) = |x|$

Find $fg\left(\frac{1}{2}\right)$ and $\frac{f}{g}(3)$.

15. $f(x) = [x]$, $g(x) = 3^0$
16. $f(x) = 4^x$, $g(x) = 6x - 10$

Find $(f \circ g)(-2)$ and $(f \circ g)(3)$.

17. $f(x) = |x|$, $g(x) = 3x$
18. $f(x) = 2x - 1$, $g(x) = 2^x$

Find $(f \circ g)(2)$ and $(g \circ f)(2)$.

19. $f(x) = \frac{1}{2}x + 1$, $g(x) = 2x - 2$
20. $f(x) = 3^x$, $g(x) = 2x$

Give $(f \circ g)(x)$ and $(g \circ f)(x)$.

21. $f(x) = 5x + 1$, $g(x) = 2x - 3$
22. $f(x) = 2^x$, $g(x) = 5x$
23. $f(x) = |x|$, $g(x) = 3x + 2$
24. $f(x) = 3x - 1$, $g(x) = 4$
25. Is composition of functions commutative?

▶ C. Exercises

26. Suppose $f(x) = \dfrac{1}{x^2 - 4}$, $g(x) = 2x + 1$. What would the domain of $(f + g)(x)$ be? Why?

27. Using $x = -2, 0, 2$ make a table of values for functions $f(x) = 2x + 1$ and $g(x) = \frac{-1}{2}x - 3$. Add the y-values from the tables, making a new table, and then add the functions themselves. Check the values from the new functions against the new table.

■ Cumulative Review

Find the equation of each line.

28. y-intercept is $(0, 5)$ and slope is -5
29. slope is $\frac{-1}{3}$ and passes through $(-3, 1)$
30. passes through $(2, 7)$ and $(4, -3)$
31. passes through $(1, 2)$ and is parallel to $2x + y = 7$
32. passes through $(3, 0)$ and is perpendicular to $y = \frac{1}{4}x - 1$

Matrix Operations

The soft-drink inventory from Super M Grocery Store is reproduced once again.

Super M Grocery Store 182

Brand	Cola	Grape	Orange	Root Beer
X	9	7	5	6
Y	10	3	8	4
Z	7	6	3	5

The manager wants to have three times as much soft drink in his store as currently in stock. To determine the amount of soft drink he will have he could describe the desired inventory with a matrix in which every entry is three times the corresponding entry in *M*. This is called *scalar multiplication* because 3 is a scalar (or constant) rather than a matrix.

$$M = \begin{bmatrix} 9 & 7 & 5 & 6 \\ 10 & 3 & 8 & 4 \\ 7 & 6 & 3 & 5 \end{bmatrix}$$

$$3M = \begin{bmatrix} 3 \cdot 9 & 3 \cdot 7 & 3 \cdot 5 & 3 \cdot 6 \\ 3 \cdot 10 & 3 \cdot 3 & 3 \cdot 8 & 3 \cdot 4 \\ 3 \cdot 7 & 3 \cdot 6 & 3 \cdot 3 & 3 \cdot 5 \end{bmatrix} = \begin{bmatrix} 27 & 21 & 15 & 18 \\ 30 & 9 & 24 & 12 \\ 21 & 18 & 9 & 15 \end{bmatrix}$$

Definition

Scalar multiplication   If *A* is a matrix and *k* is any number, the scalar product *kA* is the matrix that is formed by multiplying every entry a_{ij} of *A* by *k*.

EXAMPLE   Find $2A - 3B$ if $A = \begin{bmatrix} 1 & -8 \\ 3 & 4 \end{bmatrix}$ and $B = \begin{bmatrix} 5 & 4 \\ -2 & 1 \end{bmatrix}$

Answer $2A - 3B = 2\begin{bmatrix} 1 & -8 \\ 3 & 4 \end{bmatrix} - 3\begin{bmatrix} 5 & 4 \\ -2 & 1 \end{bmatrix}$

Continued ▶

$$= \begin{bmatrix} 2 & -16 \\ 6 & 8 \end{bmatrix} + \begin{bmatrix} -15 & -12 \\ 6 & -3 \end{bmatrix}$$

$$= \begin{bmatrix} -13 & -28 \\ 12 & 5 \end{bmatrix}$$

Notice that in the example, a negative scalar multiplier was used, along with addition of matrices. This resulted in the subtraction of two matrices.

Definition

Matrix subtraction   The difference $A - B$ of two $m \times n$ matrices is an $m \times n$ matrix C found by $A + (-1)B$.

▶ **Exercises**

Find the following matrices using

$$A = \begin{bmatrix} 1 & 5 & -7 & 4 & 2 \\ 2 & 3 & 6 & -1 & 9 \end{bmatrix} \qquad B = \begin{bmatrix} 8 & 5 & 4 & 6 & 3 \\ 1 & -2 & 0 & -7 & -1 \end{bmatrix} \qquad C = \begin{bmatrix} 2 \\ 0 \\ 3 \end{bmatrix}$$

$$D = \begin{bmatrix} 1 & 0 & 4 \end{bmatrix} \qquad E = \begin{bmatrix} 5 \\ -1 \\ -3 \end{bmatrix}$$

1. $3A$

3. $5D - E$

2. $-B$

4. $5C + 2E$

5. Using matrix M in the text and matrix S as the sales for the week at store 182, give the inventory at the end of the week. $S = \begin{bmatrix} 3 & 0 & 4 & 2 \\ 5 & 3 & 4 & 0 \\ 2 & 4 & 1 & 5 \end{bmatrix}$

3.7 Linear Inequalities

Linear equations and their graphs have been the main topic of this chapter. In this section you will see a modification of the linear equation called linear inequality. Linear inequalites are easy to graph if you understand the methods of graphing linear equations. Linear inequalities are not functions but are relations.

To graph a linear inequality, treat it as an equation, decide which portion of the plane represents the solution, and shade it.

EXAMPLE 1   Graph $2x + y \geq 5$.

Answer

$2x + y \geq 5$	1. Consider this linear inequality as if it were a linear equation and graph it. Place it in slope-intercept form.
$y \geq -2x + 5$	2. Determine which side of this equation should be shaded to satisfy the inequality. The slope-intercept form of the inequality says "y is greater than or equal to . . .". Since the line represents equality and y increases as we move upward, shade all points above the line.

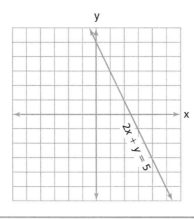
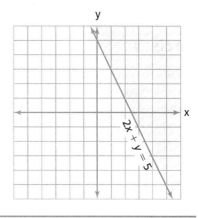

EXAMPLE 2   Graph $R = \{(x, y) \mid 4x - 3y > 6\}$.

Answer

$4x - 3y > 6$

$\quad -3y > -4x + 6$

$\qquad y < \dfrac{-4}{-3}x + \dfrac{6}{-3}$

$\qquad y < \dfrac{4}{3}x - 2$

1. Place the inequality in slope-intercept form.

Remember to reverse the direction of the inequality symbol when you divide or multiply by a negative number.

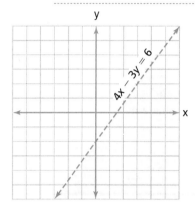

2. Graph this inequality as a linear equation, using a dotted line to indicate a strict inequality ($<$, not $\leq$). Since the inequality is "less than" in slope-intercept form, and y decreases as we go downward, all solutions are below the line.

▶ A. Exercises

Graph.

1. $y \geq x$
2. $y \leq -x + 3$
3. $y > -2x + 1$
4. $y < 3x + 5$
5. $x + y \leq 6$
6. $2x - y \geq 4$
7. $y > 4$
8. $x \leq 3$
9. $x > -4$
10. $y \leq 2$

▶ B. Exercises

Graph.

11. $3x - 5y \leq -15$
12. $x + 3y < 9$
13. $4x - 3y > 12$
14. $3x - 2y \leq 8$
15. $y < |x|$
16. $y \geq |x| + 2$
17. $y \leq 2^x$
18. $y > 3^x$

Which are relations? Which are functions? Which are both? Which are neither?

19. $y = |x|$
20. $\{5, 3, 2, 4, 7, 1\}$
21. $y > 3x - 1$
22. $x = 4$
23. $\{(1, 6), (3, 6), (5, 6)\}$

▶ C. Exercises

Graph.

24. $y \geq \left(\frac{1}{4}\right)^x$

25. $y < \left(\frac{3}{2}\right)^x$

▶ Dominion Modeling

26. Think about the model for the lung cancer data. In states with more than 23 lung cancer patients per 100,000, how many cigarettes per capita would be expected?

Cumulative Review

Evaluate the following functions for the values $x = -5, \frac{1}{2}, 3, 0$

27. $f(x) = 2^x$
28. $f(x) = |x|$
29. $f(x) = x + 8$
30. $f(x) = 9$
31. $f(x) = [x]$

3.8 Distances and Midpoints

In the last chapter you learned that if A and B are points on a number line, the absolute value of their difference is the distance between them, and their average is the coordinate of the midpoint of the segment joining them. Now you will learn how to compute distances and midpoints in the plane, where points are represented by ordered pairs. Suppose you are trying to find the distance from A to B; call this distance d.

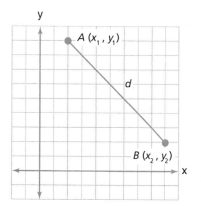
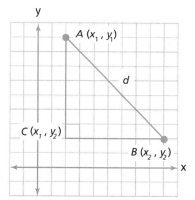
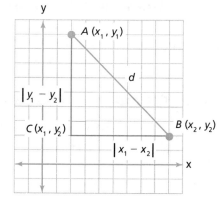

To find d, form a right triangle as shown in the next graph.

Since C is on the same vertical line as A, it has the same x-coordinate as A. Since C is on the same horizontal line as B, it has the same y-coordinate as B. Now you can determine the horizontal distance CB and the vertical distance CA.

Using the Pythagorean theorem, relate the lengths of the sides of this right triangle.

$d^2 = \lvert x_1 - x_2 \rvert^2 + \lvert y_1 - y_2 \rvert^2$	1. Pythagorean theorem
$d^2 = (x_1 - x_2)^2 + (y_1 - y_2)^2$	2. Squares of numbers are always positive, so the absolute values are not needed.
$d = \sqrt{(x_1 - x_2)^2 + (y_1 - y_2)^2}$	3. Solve for d. Since distance is positive take only the positive root.

This formula finds the distance between any two points in the plane.

EXAMPLE 1 Find the distance between $(-3, 4)$ and $(1, 7)$.

Answer

$(x_1, y_1) = (-3, 4)$

$(x_2, y_2) = (1, 7)$

1. Label the points.

$d = \sqrt{(x_1 - x_2)^2 + (y_1 - y_2)^2}$

$d = \sqrt{(-3 - 1)^2 + (4 - 7)^2}$

$d = \sqrt{(-4)^2 + (-3)^2}$

$d = \sqrt{16 + 9}$

$d = \sqrt{25}$

$d = 5$

2. Use the distance formula to find the distance between them.

The distance between $(-3, 4)$ and $(1, 7)$ is 5 units.

Another formula that you will use is the *midpoint formula.* You use this formula to find the coordinates of the midpoint of a segment joining two given points. In the figure shown, draw a line through the midpoint M of AB, parallel to the x-axis. Drop perpendiculars to the line from A and B, meeting the line in P and Q respectively. The two triangles formed are congruent by HA, therefore $PM = QM$ and M is the midpoint of $\overline{PQ}$. Since $PQ = x_2 - x_1$, it follows that $PM = \frac{x_2 - x_1}{2}$. Then the first coordinate of M is $x_1 + \frac{x_2 - x_1}{2} = \frac{x_1 + x_2}{2}$.

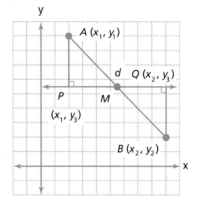

By drawing a vertical line through M, a similar argument gives $\frac{y_1 + y_2}{2}$ for the second coordinate. Thus the coordinates of the midpoint are $\left(\frac{x_1 + x_2}{2}, \frac{y_1 + y_2}{2}\right)$, where (x_1, y_1) and (x_2, y_2) are the given endpoints.

EXAMPLE 2 Find the midpoint of a line segment with endpoints $(5, 2)$ and $(-4, 0)$.

Answer

$(x_1, y_1) = (5, 2)$

$(x_2, y_2) = (-4, 0)$

1. Label the points.

$\left(\frac{x_1 + x_2}{2}, \frac{y_1 + y_2}{2}\right)$

$\left(\frac{5 + (-4)}{2}, \frac{2 + 0}{2}\right)$

$\left(\frac{1}{2}, 1\right)$

2. Substitute the appropriate values in the midpoint formula and simplify to find the coordinates.

Do you see how a solid foundation in the many different concepts of mathematics is necessary for understanding at each successive level? This also applies to your spiritual growth and understanding of biblical principles. Isaiah 28:10 says, "For precept must be upon precept, precept upon precept; line upon line, line upon line; here a little, and there a little."

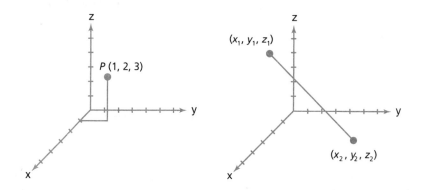

Just as we designate a point in a plane using ordered pairs, we can designate a point in space by an ordered triple. To better understand this, pick a corner of your room where two walls meet the floor. Let this corner represent the origin. The vertical line where the two walls intersect will represent the z-axis. The left-hand wall intersects the floor along the x-axis, and the other wall intersects the floor along the y-axis.

Now suppose the point $P(1, 2, 3)$ is to be plotted. Begin at the origin and move out the x-axis one unit; then proceed 2 units to the right (positive direction) parallel to the y-axis. From this point, proceed up 3 units (positive direction) parallel to the z-axis. Label the point P.

The distance formula for two points (x_1, y_1, z_1) and (x_2, y_2, z_2) in space follows. The formula extends the formula for distance in the plane to three dimensions. The formula for the midpoint in three dimensions is also an extension of the formula in the plane. You will prove these formulas as exercises.

$$d = \sqrt{(x_1 - x_2)^2 + (y_1 - y_2)^2 + (z_1 - z_2)^2} \text{ and the midpoint is}$$
$$\left(\frac{x_1 + x_2}{2}, \frac{y_1 + y_2}{2}, \frac{z_1 + z_2}{2} \right)$$

The Vehicle Assembly Building at Cape Kennedy, Florida, is 525 ft. high, 715 ft. long, and 518 ft. wide. Use the distance formula to find the length of the diagonal.

EXAMPLE 3   Find the length and midpoint of the segment with endpoints $(2, -1, 3)$ and $(3, 5, -1)$.

Answer $(x_1, y_1, z_1) = (2, -1, 3)$ $(x_2, y_2, z_2) = (3, 5, -1)$

$d = \sqrt{(x_1 - x_2)^2 + (y_1 - y_2)^2 + (z_1 - z_2)^2}$ Midpoint $= \left(\frac{x_1 + x_2}{2}, \frac{y_1 + y_2}{2}, \frac{z_1 + z_2}{2}\right)$

$d = \sqrt{(2 - 3)^2 + (-1 - 5)^2 + [3 - (-1)]^2}$ $= \left(\frac{2 + 3}{2}, \frac{-1 + 5}{2}, \frac{3 + (-1)}{2}\right)$

$d = \sqrt{(-1)^2 + (-6)^2 + 4^2}$ $= \left(\frac{5}{2}, 2, 1\right)$

$d = \sqrt{1 + 36 + 16}$

$d = \sqrt{53}$

▶ A. Exercises

Find the distance between the two given points and then find the midpoint of the segment that joins them.

1. $(3, 7), (-1, 5)$

2. $(1, 6), (-3, -4)$

3. $(4, 6), (8, 3)$

4. $(-4, -7), (-3, 0)$

5. $(1, 4), (-8, -7)$

6. $(3, -5), (-2, -1)$

7. $(8, 4), (-6, -3)$

8. $(-2, -1), (-6, -9)$

9. $(3, 12), (6, 4)$

10. $(1, 9), (-7, 2)$

▶ B. Exercises

Find the distances between each pair of points.

11. (5, 1) (2, −3)

12. 4, −7

13. (5, 0, 6), (1, 1, −2)

14. −8, −7

15. (2, 1, 4), (−1, −3, −1)

Find the midpoints indicated.

16. (2, 6), (−1, 2)

17. 3, −6

18. −2, −8

19. (2, 5, 1), (6, 7, −3)

20. (4, 1, 0), (−3, 6, 2)

Plot the following points on separate sets of axes.

21. (3, 2, 5)

22. (2, 4, 1)

▶ C. Exercises

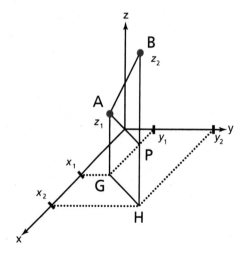

Follow the steps to prove the distance formula in space between $A(x_1, y_1, z_1)$ and $B(x_2, y_2, z_2)$.

23. Give the coordinates of point P in the diagram.

24. Distance AP is the same as the distance from $G(x_1, y_1)$ to $H(x_2, y_2)$ in the xy plane. Give this distance.

25. Find distance *BP* on the vertical number line.
26. Apply the Pythagorean theorem to right triangle *ABP*.
27. Substitute and solve for *d*.

Cumulative Review

Graph in the plane.

28. $y > |x|$
29. $x \geq 5$

Solve.

30. $3x - 7 = 5(x - 2)$
31. $|x - 1| = 5$
32. $|3x + 2| > 8$

Algebra *and* Scripture

Units of Time

You use functions all the time in daily life—even though you do not normally write them in function notation. For example, you use functions in converting units of time. Such conversions are especially important for understanding Scripture. Write functions to express each conversion below.

1. The number of days in *x* months of 30 days each.
2. The number of days in *x* prophetic years of 360 days each.
3. The number of years in *x* prophetic "weeks" of 7 years each.
4. The number of months in *x* years.

Read the prophecy in Daniel 9:24 and remember that the weeks and years refer to prophetic weeks and years. Use your functions above to calculate each.

5. The number of years referred to by Daniel in verse 24.
6. The number of years in verse 27. This period is called the Tribulation.
7. The number of days in half of the Tribulation period.
8. The number of days in Revelation 11:2.

The calculations you did are important for interpretation of these prophecies. Notice that Revelation 11:2-3 refers to exactly half of the Tribulation length. This period then is $3\frac{1}{2}$ years. This throws light on references to the $3\frac{1}{2}$-year time periods in Daniel 7:25, 12:7, and Revelation 12:14. These parallel passages take work to understand; it would be impossible without knowledge of math to recognize the various expressions for half of the Tribulation period. These expressions may be in days, months, years (time, times, and the dividing of time = $3\frac{1}{2}$), or sevens of years, so God certainly expects enough mathematics to convert units!

Other functions are specifically described in the Bible, such as in the building of the temple. Read about the sea in I Kings 7:23-24.

9. What was the circumference of the brim of the sea?

10. Consult Bible reference materials to determine what the knops are under the brim of the sea (v. 24).

11. How many knops per cubit?

12. Translate v. 24 into a mathematical function. (The number of knops depends on the number of cubits; name the number of cubits).

13. Use the function to determine the total number of knops around the sea.

GREATER AMPLITUDE

Find a function in the Bible that assigns numbers to the tribes of Israel. The numbers may represent populations or troops.

Now let's look at a constant function. In Exodus 38:26 there is a function that maps the set of all Israelites to their tax.

14. What was the amount of the tax (in shekels)?

In Psalm 90:10 the average life span since the days of Moses appears as a constant.

15. How old can a person normally expect to live?

Absolute Values

THE DAYS OF OUR YEARS are threescore years and ten; and if by reason of strength they be fourscore years, yet is their strength labour and sorrow; for it is soon cut off, and we fly away.

PSALM 90:10

Chapter 3 Review

Which are functions?

1. $\{(1, 3), (2, 3)\}$
2.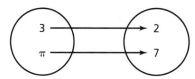
3.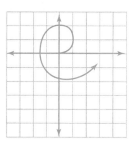
4.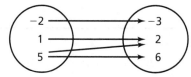
5.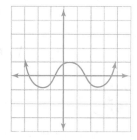
6. $\{(2, 5), (3, -1), (1, 5)\}$
7. $x = 6$
8. $y = |x|$

Evaluate the given functions if $x = -2, 0, 3, 5$.

9. $f(x) = 2x - 10$
10. $g(x) = \frac{3}{2}x + 3$
11. $h(x) = x^2 + 4$

Give the domain and range of each function.

12. $f(x) = 3x + 5$
13. $f(x) = 2|x|$
14. $f = \{(-4, 6), (0, 1), (2, 1), (3, 5)\}$

For each pair of points find the distance between them, their midpoint, and the slope of the line passing through them.

15. $(2, -1)$ and $(-2, 7)$
16. $(1, -7)$ and $(4, 0)$
17. Are the pair of lines described by $3x - y = 7$ and $x + 3y = 2$ parallel, perpendicular, or neither? Why?

Write each equation in slope-intercept form and graph it.

18. $f = \{(x, y) \mid x - 5y = 15\}$
19. $f(x) = x - 2$
20. $3x + y = 7$
21. $4x - 5y = 25$
22. Write the equation of the line with slope $\frac{-1}{2}$ and y-intercept $(0, 5)$.
23. Write the equation of the line that passes through $(2, 4)$ with slope 3.
24. Write the equation of the line that passes through $(1, 3)$ and $(-7, 4)$.

Do the indicated operations and simplify.

$$f(x) = 3x; \; g(x) = x - 5; \; h(x) = \frac{x}{2}$$

25. $(f + g)(x)$
26. $(f - h)(x)$
27. $gh(x)$
28. $\frac{g}{f}(x)$
29. $(h \circ g)(x)$

Graph.

30. $f(x) = [x]$
31. $5x - y \le 4$
32. $x + 2y < -6$
33. $(4, 1, 3)$
34. Recall the cancer data. Does the data support the claim that smoking cigarettes causes lung cancer? What additional information would strengthen the claim that smoking cigarettes causes lung cancer? (While you may know other evidence on this issue, limit your discussion to the cancer data in this chapter.)
35. Give the mathematical significance of Psalm 90:10.

4 Quadratic Equations

$$y = \frac{a}{b}$$

If a 300-pound man and a 100-pound girl jumped from a bungee-cord tower at the same time, would they drop at the same rate? You probably remember from science class that they would drop together, if you neglect air—or bungee—resistance.

Tradition alleges that Galileo made a similar experiment, dropping two balls (one heavy and one light) from the Tower of Pisa. While we are not certain that Galileo did this, his other experiments support the same conclusion. To develop a model for his experiment, you will need quadratic equations.

The data below is from Galileo. Records suggest that he conducted his 1604 experiment by rolling balls down a grooved ramp. The units for distance were in "points." He did not have precise timepieces then, and he probably kept time by humming an Italian tune!

Your experiences with quadratic equations in this chapter will give you important tools to analyze this data.

Time	Distance	Time	Distance
1	33	5	824
2	130	6	1192
3	298	7	1620
4	526	8	2104

After this chapter you should be able to

1. solve quadratic equations by factoring.

2. state and use the zero product property.

3. solve quadratic equations by completing the square.

4. state, prove, and apply the quadratic formula.

5. find the discriminant and use it to classify solutions to a quadratic equation.

6. solve problems involving quadratic equations.

7. solve quadratic inequalities.

135

4.1 Solving Quadratic Equations by Factoring

A *quadratic equation* is an equation of the form

$$ax^2 + bx + c = 0 \text{ where } a, b, c \in \mathbb{R} \text{ and } a \neq 0.$$

The word *quadratic* is derived from Latin and means "square," and any equation whose highest-degree term is a squared term is called a quadratic equation. Solutions of equations must be based on a good foundation of mathematical principles, and those principles are the basis of the methods that you learned in the first few chapters of this book. Likewise, a Christian's spiritual life needs to be built on biblical principles. Being first grounded in the fundamentals of the Bible, he should use this foundation to build a strong life for Jesus Christ. This strong life will develop only through daily study of the Word of God. Acts 17:11 admonishes the Christian to search the Scripture daily.

One method of solving a quadratic equation is by factoring. This method depends on the *zero product property*.

Zero Product Property

If the product of two or more factors equals 0, at least one of the factors is 0. This means that if $ab = 0$, then one of the following three statements is true:

$$a = 0, \text{ or } b = 0, \text{ or both } (a = 0 \text{ and } b = 0)$$

To apply this property to solve a quadratic equation by the factoring method, place the equation in standard form as $ax^2 + bx + c = 0$. Factor the polynomial on the left, set each factor equal to zero, and solve the resulting equations.

EXAMPLE 1   Solve $x^2 + 2x - 24 = 0$.

Answer

$x^2 + 2x - 24 = 0$	
$(x + 6)(x - 4) = 0$	1. Factor the left side.
$x + 6 = 0$ or $x - 4 = 0$	2. Apply the zero product property by setting each factor equal to 0.

Continued ▶

$x = -6$	$x = 4$	3. Solve the linear equations.

Check.

$(-6)^2 + 2(-6) - 24 = 0$ 4. Check each solution in the
$(4)^2 + 2(4) - 24 = 0$ equation.

Can you see that -6 will make the first factor 0 and the product 0? Likewise, the 4 will make the second factor 0 and the product 0. The zero product property is essential to this method of solving a quadratic equation.

EXAMPLE 2 Solve $3x^2 + 11x + 6 = 0$.

Answer

$3x^2 + 11x + 6 = 0$
$(3x + 2)(x + 3) = 0$ 1. Factor the left side.

$3x + 2 = 0$ or $x + 3 = 0$ 2. Set each factor equal to 0.

$3x = -2$ $x = -3$ 3. Solve.
$x = \frac{-2}{3}$

The solutions are $\frac{-2}{3}$ and -3.

EXAMPLE 3 Solve $3x^2 - 4x = 0$.

Answer

$3x^2 - 4x = 0$
$x(3x - 4) = 0$ 1. Factor the left side.

$x = 0$ or $3x - 4 = 0$ 2. Set each factor equal to 0 and
$3x = 4$ solve.
$x = \frac{4}{3}$

The solutions are 0 and $\frac{4}{3}$.

▶ A. Exercises

Solve.

1. $x^2 + 6x + 8 = 0$
2. $x^2 - x - 42 = 0$
3. $2x^2 - 9x - 5 = 0$
4. $9x^2 - 34x - 8 = 0$
5. $x^2 - 4x - 45 = 0$
6. $6x^2 + 37x + 56 = 0$
7. $x^2 + x - 2 = 0$

8. $5x^2 + 4x = 0$

9. $4x^2 - 15x + 9 = 0$

10. $5x^2 - 32x - 21 = 0$

11. $2x^2 + 7x = 0$

12. $x^3 - 9x^2 + 18x = 0$

13. $8x^2 + 23x - 3 = 0$

14. $10x^2 + x - 3 = 0$

15. $3x^2 - 20x - 32 = 0$

16. $x^2 - 4x + 4 = 0$

17. $x^2 - 49 = 0$

18. $x^3 - 4x = 0$

▶ B. Exercises

Solve. Remember to place in standard form first.

19. $7x = 8 - x^2$

20. $3x^2 + 7x + 11 = x^2 - 8x - 7$

21. $x^2 + 27 = 12x$

22. $5 = 6x^2 + 7x$

23. $7x + 30 = 2x^2$

24. $x^3 + 81x = -18x^2$

▶ C. Exercises

Solve.

25. $x^4 + 15 = 8x^2$

26. $5x^3 - 39x^2 + 27x + 7 = 0$ (Hint: use polynomial division.)

▶ Dominion Modeling

27. What are the variables for Galileo's data? What variable would be a suitable independent variable (input)? Which would be a suitable dependent variable (output)?

28. Fit a linear model to the data.

Cumulative Review

Solve.

29. $|x - 3| = 4$

30. $2x + 7 = 3x - 5$

31. $4x - 1 < 3x + 2$

32. $|2 - x| > 4$

33. $2 - x^2 = 2$

4.2 Completing the Square

In addition to factoring, there are other methods used to solve quadratic equations. If all of the variable terms are on one side of the equation and form a perfect square, the solution can be found by taking the square root of each side. Examples 1 and 2 illustrate this method.

EXAMPLE 1   Solve $x^2 = 16$.

Answer

$x^2 = 16$	
$\sqrt{x^2} = \sqrt{16}$	1. Take the square root of each side.
$\lvert x \rvert = 4$	2. Apply the definition of square root.
$x = \pm 4$	3. Apply the definition of absolute value.

To obtain all of the solutions, you must use both the positive and negative root. You can solve a more difficult quadratic with this method also.

EXAMPLE 2   Solve $(x + 3)^2 = 5$.

Answer

$$(x + 3)^2 = 5$$
$$\sqrt{(x + 3)^2} = \sqrt{5}$$
$$\lvert x + 3 \rvert = \sqrt{5}$$
$$x + 3 = \pm\sqrt{5}$$
$$x = -3 \pm \sqrt{5}$$

In this problem there are two solutions for x: $x = -3 + \sqrt{5}$ and $x = -3 - \sqrt{5}$. Notice that the original problem could have also been written as $x^2 + 6x + 9 = 5$. The polynomial on the left is a perfect square trinomial. You must always have a perfect square trinomial in order to use this method of solution. If there is not one in an equation, you can obtain one using a process called *completing the square*.

To complete the square in a quadratic equation with leading coefficient $a = 1$, change the standard form $x^2 + bx + c = 0$ into $x^2 + bx = -c$ thus isolating the constant term. Take one-half of b, the numerical coefficient of x, square it, and add it to both sides of the equation. This will result in a perfect square, permitting the equation to be solved as in Example 2.

EXAMPLE 3   Solve $x^2 + 8x - 9 = 0$ by completing the square.

Answer

$x^2 + 8x - 9 = 0$

$x^2 + 8x = 9$ 1. Move the constant term to the other side of the equation.

$x^2 + 8x + 16 = 9 + 16$
$x^2 + 8x + 16 = 25$ 2. Complete the square on the left by dividing 8, the numerical coefficient of x, by 2 and adding its square to both sides of the equation.

$$\frac{8}{2} = 4, \ 4^2 = 16$$

$(x + 4)^2 = 25$ 3. Factor the perfect square trinomial on the left side.

$\sqrt{(x + 4)^2} = \pm\sqrt{25}$ 4. Find the square root of both sides (use $\pm$).

$x + 4 = \pm 5$ 5. Solve.
$x = -4 \pm 5$
$x = 1$ or $x = -9$

Notice that the absolute value step was omitted in Example 3. It is acceptable for you to skip this step as long as you remember that there are two solutions. The best way to remember this is to introduce the $\pm$ whenever you take the square root of both sides (as in step 4 of the example).

If the leading coefficient of the polynomial is not 1, factor the leading coefficient from the polynomial before completing the square.

EXAMPLE 4   Solve $3x^2 + 6x + 2 = 0$.

Answer

$3x^2 + 6x + 2 = 0$

$3x^2 + 6x = -2$ 1. Move the constant term to the right.

Continued ▶

$3(x^2 + 2x) = -2$	2. Factor the 3 from the left, leaving a coefficient of 1 on the x^2 term.
$3(x^2 + 2x + 1) = -2 + 3$	3. Complete the square inside the parentheses. $\left(\frac{2}{2} = 1, 1^2 = 1\right)$
$3(x^2 + 2x + 1) = 1$	Add $3(1) = 3$ to the right side to balance the left when 3 is distributed.
$(x^2 + 2x + 1) = \frac{1}{3}$	4. Divide both sides by 3 and then factor the polynomial.
$(x + 1)^2 = \frac{1}{3}$	
$\sqrt{(x + 1)^2} = \pm\sqrt{\frac{1}{3}}$	5. Find the square root of both sides and solve.
$x + 1 = \pm\frac{\sqrt{3}}{3}$	6. Rationalize the radical denominator.
$x = -1 \pm \frac{\sqrt{3}}{3}$	
$x = \frac{-3 \pm \sqrt{3}}{3}$	

EXAMPLE 5 Solve $3x^2 - 13x = 10$.

Answer

$3x^2 - 13x = 10$ $3\left(x^2 - \frac{13}{3}x\right) = 10$	1. Factor 3 from the left side. Notice that $13 \div 3 = \frac{13}{3}$.
$3\left(x^2 - \frac{13}{3}x + \frac{169}{36}\right) = \frac{120}{12} + \frac{169}{12}$ $3\left(x - \frac{13}{6}\right)^2 = \frac{289}{12}$ $\left(x - \frac{13}{6}\right)^2 = \frac{289}{12} \cdot \frac{1}{3}$ $\left(x - \frac{13}{6}\right)^2 = \frac{289}{36}$	2. Add $\left[\frac{1}{2}\left(\frac{13}{3}\right)\right]^2 = \left(\frac{13}{6}\right)^2 = \frac{169}{36}$ to form a perfect square trinomial, and $3\left(\frac{169}{36}\right) = \frac{169}{12}$ to the other side.
$\sqrt{\left(x - \frac{13}{6}\right)^2} = \pm\sqrt{\frac{289}{36}}$ $x - \frac{13}{6} = \pm\frac{17}{6}$ $x = \frac{13}{6} \pm \frac{17}{6}$ $x = \frac{13 \pm 17}{6}$ $x = \frac{30}{6}$ or $x = \frac{-4}{6}$ $x = 5$ or $x = \frac{-2}{3}$	3. Take the square root of both sides and solve.

Just as the squares on these polynomials must be completed before this method can be used, so a life must be completed in Christ before it can be used of God. Jesus Christ has completed our salvation in His shed blood and work on the cross of Calvary. Colossians 2:10 says, "Ye are complete in him, which is the head of all principality and power."

▶ A. Exercises

Solve each quadratic equation by completing the square.

1. $x^2 - 4x = 45$
2. $x^2 - 3 = 2x$
3. $x^2 = -8x - 7$
4. $x^2 - 4x = 60$
5. $x^2 - 8x = -12$
6. $x^2 - 2x = 35$
7. $x^2 - x - 12 = 0$
8. $x^2 - 3x - 10 = 0$
9. $x^2 - 19x + 84 = 0$
10. $x^2 + 5x - 8 = 0$

▶ B. Exercises

Solve each quadratic equation by completing the square.

11. $3x^2 + 6x - 7 = 0$
12. $5x^2 + 20x + 3 = 0$
13. $2x^2 + 1 = 8x$
14. $2x^2 + 12x - 7 = 0$
15. $3x^2 + 4x - 2 = 0$
16. $2x^2 + 7x - 4 = 0$
17. $3x^2 - 14x = 5$
18. $4x^2 + 12x + 5 = 0$
19. $4x^2 + 23x - 6 = 0$
20. $5x^2 - 2x - 3 = 0$

▶ C. Exercises

Solve each quadratic equation by completing the square.

21. $4x^2 - \sqrt{2}x - 1 = 0$

22. $\pi x^2 + \sqrt{3}x - 5 = 0$

▶ Dominion Modeling

23. What does your linear model for Galileo's data give for $t = 8$? How different is this from the actual value?
24. Does a linear model make sense? Why?

Cumulative Review

Find the domain (*D*) and range (*R*) of each relation.

25. $f = \{(1, 3), (2, -1), \left(5, \frac{1}{2}\right), (6.7, -1)\}$

26. $f = \{(-1, 5), \left(0, \frac{1}{3}\right), \left(-\frac{3}{4}, 2\right)\}$

27. $f(x) = |x|$

28. $f(x) = [x]$

29.

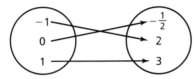

30.

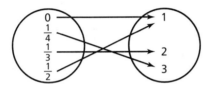

31.

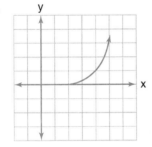

32.

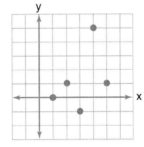

4.3 The Quadratic Formula

Sometimes quadratic equations can be difficult to solve by completing the square because of large fractions. The *quadratic formula* makes solving such quadratic equations simpler. The proof of the formula, however, involves completing the square on the general form of a quadratic equation, which is

$$ax^2 + bx + c = 0 \text{ where } a, b, c \in \mathbb{R} \text{ and } a \neq 0.$$

$ax^2 + bx + c = 0$ $ax^2 + bx = -c$	1. First move the constant term c to the right side.
$a\left(x^2 + \frac{b}{a}x\right) = -c$	2. Factor the a from the variable terms.
$a\left(x^2 + \frac{bx}{a} + \frac{b^2}{4a^2}\right) = -c + \frac{b^2}{4a}$	3. Complete the square. Think $\frac{1}{2} \cdot \frac{b}{a} = \frac{b}{2a}$ and $\left(\frac{b}{2a}\right)^2 = \frac{b^2}{4a^2}$ Note: $a\left(\frac{b^2}{4a^2}\right) = \frac{b^2}{4a}$ is added to the right side.
$a\left(x + \frac{b}{2a}\right)^2 = \frac{-4ac + b^2}{4a}$	4. Factor the perfect square on the left. Combine terms on the right, using the common denominator $4a$.
$a\left(x + \frac{b}{2a}\right)^2 = \frac{b^2 - 4ac}{4a}$	5. Rearrange the terms in the numerator so that the positive term appears first.
$\frac{1}{a} \cdot a\left(x + \frac{b}{2a}\right)^2 = \frac{1}{a} \cdot \frac{b^2 - 4ac}{4a}$ $\left(x + \frac{b}{2a}\right)^2 = \frac{b^2 - 4ac}{4a^2}$	6. Multiply both sides by $\frac{1}{a}$ to eliminate the factor of a on the left.
$\sqrt{\left(x + \frac{b}{2a}\right)^2} = \sqrt{\frac{b^2 - 4ac}{4a^2}}$ $\left\|x + \frac{b}{2a}\right\| = \frac{\sqrt{b^2 - 4ac}}{2a}$	7. Find the square root of both sides. Absolute values are included for a precise proof.

Continued ▶

$$x + \frac{b}{2a} = \pm \frac{\sqrt{b^2 - 4ac}}{2a}$$

8. Use the definition of absolute value.

$$x = -\frac{b}{2a} \pm \frac{\sqrt{b^2 - 4ac}}{2a}$$

To solve for x, subtract $\frac{b}{2a}$ from both sides.

$$x = \frac{-b \pm \sqrt{b^2 - 4ac}}{2a}$$

9. Since the fractions have a common denominator, combine them.

This concludes the proof of the quadratic formula. You should understand the proof and be able to derive it yourself.

Quadratic Formula

If $ax^2 + bx + c = 0$ where $a, b, c \in \mathbb{R}$ and $a \neq 0$, then

$$x = \frac{-b \pm \sqrt{b^2 - 4ac}}{2a}$$

EXAMPLE 1   Solve $4x^2 + 3x - 9 = 0$.

Answer

$4x^2 + 3x - 9 = 0$
$a = 4, b = 3, c = -9$

1. Determine the values of a, b, and c in this quadratic equation.

$$x = \frac{-b \pm \sqrt{b^2 - 4ac}}{2a}$$

2. Substitute these values into the quadratic formula.

$$x = \frac{-3 \pm \sqrt{3^2 - 4(4)(-9)}}{2(4)}$$

$$= \frac{-3 \pm \sqrt{9 + 144}}{8}$$

3. Simplify.

$$= \frac{-3 \pm \sqrt{153}}{8}$$

$$= \frac{-3 \pm 3\sqrt{17}}{8}$$

The solutions are $\frac{-3 + 3\sqrt{17}}{8}$ and $\frac{-3 - 3\sqrt{17}}{8}$.

EXAMPLE 2 Solve $x^2 - 3x - 28 = 0$.

Answer

$x^2 - 3x - 28 = 0$ 1. Determine the values of a, b, and c.

$$a = 1, b = -3, c = -28$$

$x = \dfrac{-b \pm \sqrt{b^2 - 4ac}}{2a}$ 2. Substitute these values into the quadratic formula and solve.

$$x = \frac{-(-3) \pm \sqrt{(-3)^2 - 4(1)(-28)}}{2(1)}$$

$$= \frac{3 \pm \sqrt{9 + 112}}{2}$$

$$= \frac{3 \pm \sqrt{121}}{2}$$

$$= \frac{3 \pm 11}{2}$$

$x = \dfrac{3 + 11}{2}$ or $x = \dfrac{3 - 11}{2}$

$x = 7$ or $x = -4$

Remember that before you use the quadratic formula, you must make sure your equation is in the form $ax^2 + bx + c = 0$. The quadratic formula will work for any quadratic equation, but it must be in this form. You may find the factoring method easier in some cases, but many quadratics do not factor.

▶ A. Exercises

Use the quadratic formula to solve each quadratic equation.

1. $x^2 + x - 2 = 0$
2. $6x^2 + 13x + 5 = 0$
3. $2x^2 - 5x - 7 = 0$
4. $x^2 - 2x - 48 = 0$
5. $x^2 - 2x - 63 = 0$
6. $3x^2 - 2x - 16 = 0$
7. $2x^2 + 5x - 7 = 0$

8. $5x^2 + x - 2 = 0$
9. $4x^2 - 3x - 7 = 0$
10. $x^2 - 3x + 1 = 0$
11. $3x - 4 + 2x^2 = 0$
12. $x + 7x^2 - 1 = 0$
13. $2x^2 - 18 = 9x$

▶ B. Exercises

Use the quadratic formula to solve each quadratic equation.

14. $4x^2 = 3 - 2x$
15. $55 - 7x = 6x^2$
16. $x^2 + 2x = 3$
17. $2x^2 + 5x + 4 = 1$

18. $2x^2 + x - 4 = x$
19. $2x^2 + 3x = x^2 - 5x + 1$
20. $2x^2 + 8x - 2 = 2x - x^2$

21. Which step in the proof of the quadratic formula was the first time when $a \neq 0$ was important?

▶ C. Exercises

22. Solve $3\pi^2 - 5\pi + 2 = 0$.
23. If the solutions to a quadratic equation are $3 - \sqrt{2}$ and $2 - \sqrt{2}$, find the original equation. Express coefficients as 3-place decimals. *Hint:* Apply the factoring process in reverse.

▶ Dominion Modeling

24. Fit a quadratic model to Galileo's data. What model do you get?
25. What does your quadratic model give for $t = 8$? How different is this from the actual value?

Cumulative Review

Assume $P(x)$ and $Q(x)$ are functions described by polynomials. If $P(x)$ has degree 2 and $Q(x)$ has degree 1, identify the maximum number of solutions possible to each equation below.

26. $P(x) = 0$
27. $Q(x) = 5$
28. $P(x)\, Q(x) = 0$
29. $P(x) = Q(x)$
30. $\left| Q(x) \right| = 3$

Solve for x.

$$x^4 = \frac{5^{3a + 2} \cdot 9^{2b^2 + 3b} \cdot 27}{3^{(2b - 1)(2b + 1)} \cdot 729^b \cdot 5^{2a^2 + 3a - 1}} \div \frac{18^0}{5^{2a^2 + 1}}$$

ARABIC MATH

The ceramic tiles and golden domes of Kadhamain Mosque display the wealth of Islam in Baghdad, Iraq. In the ninth century, Baghdad was the second most important city in Islam.

The Arabic astronomer and mathematician Mohammed al-Khwarizmi, born about 825 A.D., described one of his formulas as "completing the square." We use this same process to prove the quadratic formula.

Here is his question. "A square and ten of its roots are equal to nine and thirty dirkems, that is, you add ten roots to one square, and the sum is equal to nine and thirty." We would write: $x^2 + 10x = 39$.

Here is his answer. "Take half the number of roots, in this case five, then multiply this by itself and the result is five and twenty. Add this to nine and thirty, which gives four and sixty. Take the square root, which is eight, and subtract from it half the number of roots, namely five, and there remains three. This is the root."

$$x^2 + 10x + 25 = 39 + 25$$
$$(x + 5)^2 = 64$$
$$x + 5 = 8$$
$$x = 8 - 5 = 3$$

Notice how the problem and the solution were written in verbal rather than symbolic form. If it seems awkward, you can be glad for the symbolic form.

Al-Khwarizmi also wrote a book called *Al-jabr wal muqabala*, roughly translated "restoring". Mathematically, this refers to the balance that must be maintained when solving an equation. Our modern term *algebra* comes from the word *Al-jabr* in the Arabic title.

Our numbers are called Hindu-Arabic numerals. Notice the similarities between these third century B.C. Hindu

> The connection between cubic equations and conic sections was probably the greatest Arabic contribution to algebra.

numerals and ours today. However, if it had not been for the Arabs, this practical place-value system would not have come to Europe. Although the Arabic numerals are not as similar to ours, it was the Arabs who adopted the Hindu system and brought it to Europe.

Hindu

| _ | = | ≡ | ϒ | Ь | | 6 | ? | ५ | ? |

Arabic

| ١ | ٢ | ٣ | ٤ | ٥ | | ٧ | ٧ | ٨ | ٩ | ٠ |

15th Century
Western

| 1 | 2 | 3 | 2 | 5 | | 6 | ٨ | 8 | 9 | 0 |

Constantinople, now Istanbul in Turkey, was one of the most important commercial and cultural centers in the world.

Since Arabic was the trade language of the Muslim world from Persia to Spain, Arab scholars translated mathematical works of both the Hindus and the Greeks into Arabic. The numerals came to Europe through international commerce, and the original sources in Arabic came to the attention of Europe during the Reformation. Such sources included Greek works by Euclid, Ptolemy, Appolonius, and Archimedes. Hindu sources included Brahmagupta (ca. A.D. 628), the first mathematician to work extensively with negative numbers (introduced for debts in the marketplace). The Hindus developed the algebraic rules governing operations on negative numbers and even studied irrational numbers like $\sqrt{3}$ and π. Earlier cultures, like the Greeks, had tried to deny the existence of these numbers, but by the fourth century B.C., the Hindus had approximated the value of $\sqrt{2}$.

Another Arabic mathematician, Omar Khayyám (1100 A.D.), believed he could justify the solution to any cubic equation by using the geometric idea of conic sections. The connection between cubic equations and conic sections was probably the greatest Arabic contribution to algebra because it showed that geometry and algebra are intrinsically related. This idea eventually grew into the field of mathematics called analytic geometry.

Omar Khayyám

4.4 Solving Quadratic Equations

In some instances there are several ways to solve a problem while in other instances there is only one way. How many solutions are there to the all-important problem of where you will spend eternity? There is only one way to be saved. Salvation comes through faith in the shed blood of Jesus Christ as a cleansing from our sins. Each person must accept this by faith to claim heaven as his eternal home. As Acts 4:12 states, "Neither is there salvation in any other: for there is none other name under heaven given among men, whereby we must be saved."

Even a country road may require the engineering of an uphill curve.

When the polynomial is already a perfect square, all you have to do is take the square root of both sides.

EXAMPLE 1 Solve $3x^2 = 54$.

Answer

$3x^2 = 54$ $x^2 = 18$	1. Since $b = 0$, the square root method is easiest. Isolate the square.
$\sqrt{x^2} = \pm\sqrt{18}$	2. Take the square root of both sides to find x.
$x = \pm 3\sqrt{2}$	3. Simplify the radical.

The square root method is simple if $b = 0$ and the factoring method should be used if the polynomial factors easily. In all other cases you should use the quadratic formula. Completing the square has two values. First, the proof of the quadratic formula depended on it, and second, it will be useful in the study of parabolas and conic sections later. However, it is not a practical method for solving quadratic equations because it is such a long process. Complete the square only when directed.

Look for easy methods first. Use the square root method if $b = 0$. Use the factoring method if the quadratic in standard form factors easily or if there is no constant. Use the quadratic formula otherwise.

EXAMPLE 2   Solve $4x^2 - 12x = 0$.

Answer $4x^2 - 12x = 0$

$4x(x - 3) = 0$ Use the factoring method.

$4x = 0$ or $x - 3 = 0$

$x = 0$ $x = 3$

The two solutions of this quadratic equation are 0 and 3.

EXAMPLE 3   Solve $3x^2 - 4x - 1 = 0$.

Answer

$3x^2 - 4x - 1 = 0$	1. Since $b \neq 0$ and it doesn't factor, use the quadratic formula.
$a = 3, b = -4, c = -1$	2. Identify a, b, and c.
$x = \dfrac{-b \pm \sqrt{b^2 - 4ac}}{2a}$ $x = \dfrac{-(-4) \pm \sqrt{(-4)^2 - 4(3)(-1)}}{2(3)}$	3. Substitute into the quadratic formula.
$x = \dfrac{4 \pm \sqrt{16 + 12}}{6}$	4. Simplify.
$x = \dfrac{4 \pm \sqrt{28}}{6}$	
$x = \dfrac{4 \pm 2\sqrt{7}}{6}$	
$x = \dfrac{2(2 \pm \sqrt{7})}{6}$	
$x = \dfrac{2 \pm \sqrt{7}}{3}$	

EXAMPLE 4   Solve $4x^2 + 49 = 28x$.

Answer

$4x^2 + 49 = 28x$ $4x^2 - 28x + 49 = 0$	1. Put into $ax^2 + bx + c = 0$ form.
$(2x - 7)(2x - 7) = 0$	2. Factor.
$2x - 7 = 0$ $2x = 7$ $x = \dfrac{7}{2}$	3. Solve the equation. This equation has only one solution.

The word *discriminant* derives from the word *discriminate,* which means to distinguish or differentiate. A Christian should strive to distinguish between those things that are God-honoring and things that are not. Ezekiel 44:23 shows that Christians are to know "the difference between the holy and profane, . . . to discern between the unclean and the clean." As a Christian, can you distinguish between what is right in the eyes of God and what is not? The key to knowing the difference is daily studying God's Word and responding to the Holy Spirit, who dwells within you. In algebra, the discriminant helps you distinguish types of solutions.

Definition

The **discriminant**, $d = b^2 - 4ac$, is the radicand of the quadratic formula.

By examining only the value of the discriminant, you can classify the roots of a quadratic equation as real or complex, and the real roots as rational or irrational.

Notice that the answers to Example 3 are both real numbers—in fact, they are both irrational numbers. Also notice that the discriminant is $b^2 - 4ac = 28$, which is not a perfect square. When the discriminant is a perfect square, the square root in the formula simplifies to an integer. The answers to such a quadratic equation are rational.

When the discriminant is negative, you obtain the root of a negative number. Such numbers are called imaginary numbers, and the solution to the quadratic is called a complex number. You will study such numbers in Chapter 8. For Example 5 classify the solutions as indicated in the following table.

Nature of Solutions of a Quadratic Equation			
$ax^2 + bx + c = 0$, $a, b, c \in \mathbb{R}$ and $a \neq 0$			
Value of the Discriminant (d)	Number of Solutions	General Nature	Specific Nature
$b^2 - 4ac > 0$	2	Real	Rational if d is a perfect square
			Irrational if d is not a perfect square
$b^2 - 4ac = 0$	1	Real	Rational
$b^2 - 4ac < 0$	2	Complex	Conjugates

Notice the word *conjugate* in the table. The term refers to the sum and difference of the same two quantities and is applied to the sum and difference of a real and imaginary number, such as $3 + \sqrt{-1}$ and $3 - \sqrt{-1}$.

EXAMPLE 5   Classify the solutions to $3x^2 + 5x + 8 = 0$.

Answer

$a = 3$ $b = 5$ $c = 8$	1. Identify the coefficients.
$b^2 - 4ac = 5^2 - 4(3)(8)$	2. Calculate the discriminant.
$= 25 - 96$	
$= -71$	
There are two complex solutions, and they are conjugates.	3. Interpret the answer.

▶ A. Exercises

Identify the simplest method for solving each equation. Do not solve.

1. $5x^2 - x - 2 = 0$
2. $x^2 + 1 = 7$
3. $3x^2 + 19x - 14 = 0$
4. $3x^2 + 5x + 7 = x + 7$

Determine the number and nature of the solutions for each quadratic equation. Do not solve the equation.

5. $x^2 + 4x - 32 = 0$
6. $4x^2 - 5x - 2 = 0$
7. $x^2 + 16x + 64 = 0$
8. $5x^2 + 2x + 8 = 0$
9. $6x^2 - 5x + 3 = 0$
10. $x^2 - 14x + 49 = 0$

▶ B. Exercises

Describe the number and nature of the solutions for each equation and then find each solution.

11. $x^2 + 6x + 9 = 0$
12. $5x^2 + 2x = 10$
13. $4y^2 + 5y - 3 = 0$
14. $y^2 + 10y + 25 = 0$
15. $2t^2 - 10t = 48$
16. $7z^2 + 2z = 8$
17. $2m^2 - 11m = 6$
18. $t^2 - 9 = 0$
19. $6a^2 = -11a + 10$
20. $c^2 = 6c + 16$

21. $3b^2 + 8b + 1 = 0$

22. $8s^2 - 10s - 3 = 0$

23. $49c^2 + 4 = -28c$

24. $(4a - 7)^2 = 9$

25. $5z^2 + 2z - 4 = 0$

26. $3b^2 + 4b = 2b^2 + 3b + 1$

▶ C. Exercises

27. In an equation of the form $ax^4 + bx^2 + c = 0$, y is substituted for x^2. If $b = -2$ and the discriminant for y is $d = 28$, give the nature of the solutions for y and then for x.

▶ Dominion Modeling

28. Does a quadratic model for Galileo's data make sense? Why?

Cumulative Review

Find the equation of the line that passes through the point (2, 5) and

29. has slope 6.

30. passes through (1, 3).

31. has y-intercept 4.

32. is parallel to $3x + 2y = 5$.

33. is perpendicular to $y = \frac{1}{4}x + 1$.

Determinants

The determinant of a matrix is a number associated with the matrix. Only square matrices have determinants. In Chapter 6 you will learn how to apply determinants to solve systems of equations.

The notations used for determinants and matrices are very similar. Matrices are enclosed by square brackets, but vertical lines similar to those used for absolute value enclose determinants. The abbreviation *det* can also be used for determinants. Do not confuse matrices with their determinants.

Matrix	Determinant of a matrix
$A = \begin{bmatrix} 3 & 5 \\ 2 & 4 \end{bmatrix}$	$\|A\| = \det A = \begin{vmatrix} 3 & 5 \\ 2 & 4 \end{vmatrix} = 3(4) - 5(2) = 2$

To evaluate this two-by-two determinant, take the difference of the products of the diagonals, upper left times lower right minus upper right times lower left. Evaluation of a three-by-three determinant is similar if you copy the first two columns to the right of the determinant as shown.

$$\text{Given matrix } B = \begin{bmatrix} 1 & 7 & 2 \\ 3 & -8 & 4 \\ 1 & -2 & 9 \end{bmatrix}$$

$$|B| = \begin{vmatrix} 1 & 7 & 2 \\ 3 & -8 & 4 \\ 1 & -2 & 9 \end{vmatrix} = \begin{array}{ccc} 1 & 7 & 2 & 1 & 7 \\ 3 & -8 & 4 & 3 & -8 \\ 1 & -2 & 9 & 1 & -2 \end{array}$$

$$= (1)(-8)(9) + (7)(4)(1) + (2)(3)(-2) - (2)(-8)(1) - (1)(4)(-2) - (7)(3)(9)$$

$$= -72 + 28 - 12 + 16 + 8 - 189 = -221$$

In summary,

$$\begin{vmatrix} a & b \\ c & d \end{vmatrix} = ad - bc \text{ and } \begin{vmatrix} a & b & c \\ d & e & f \\ g & h & i \end{vmatrix} = aei + bfg + cdh - ceg - afh - bdi$$

▶ Exercises

Evaluate each determinant.

1. $\begin{vmatrix} 5 & -8 \\ 12 & 2 \end{vmatrix}$
2. $\begin{vmatrix} 7 & 4 \\ 6 & -3 \end{vmatrix}$
3. $\begin{vmatrix} 1 & 0 \\ 2 & 6 \end{vmatrix}$
4. $\begin{vmatrix} a & 4 \\ c & 2 \end{vmatrix}$
5. $\begin{vmatrix} 5 & 9 & 8 \\ 2 & -4 & 6 \\ 3 & 5 & -1 \end{vmatrix}$

4.5 Problem Solving

How wide a frame was needed for this 24.5 in. by 16.75 in. painting if the area covered by painting and frame is 508.25 square inches?

The work that you have been doing in this chapter has not been just for mental exercise. You have been working to learn skills to apply to problem situations. In this section you will be required to think through a problem and apply your skills to solve it. This important concept should be applied to a Christian's spiritual life as well. James 1:22 says, "But be ye doers of the word, and not hearers only, deceiving your own selves." You must not only listen to and read the Word of God but also apply it to all areas of your life. Just as it is important to apply the Word of God to your life, it is also important to apply the algebraic skills that you have learned to solve problems.

EXAMPLE 1   Find two consecutive integers whose product is 812.

Answer

Let x = first integer	1. **Read.** Identify the main variable.
$x + 1$ = second integer	2. **Plan.** Express the next consecutive integer, which is one more than the first.
$x(x + 1) = 812$ $x^2 + x - 812 = 0$ $(x - 28)(x + 29) = 0$	3. **Solve.** Write an equation, obtain the proper form, and solve.
$x - 28 = 0$ or $x + 29 = 0$ $x = 28$ or $x = -29$ $x + 1 = 29$ $x + 1 = -28$	4. **Check.** 28 and 29 is one solution, -29 and -28 is another.

You will now see how quadratic equations can be used to solve practical problems.

EXAMPLE 2   A grocery store has a parking lot that is 20 feet longer than it is wide. The owner wants to make a 3-foot-wide sidewalk along the outside of the parking lot. If the total surface area of the sidewalk and parking lot together is 50,976 square feet, find the dimensions of the parking lot.

Answer

Let x = the width of the parking lot
$x + 20$ = the length of the parking lot

1. **Read.** Determine what you are looking for.

2. **Plan.** Draw a picture of the situation in the problem.

$$(x + 6)(x + 26) = 50,976$$
$$x^2 + 32x + 156 = 50,976$$
$$x^2 + 32x - 50,820 = 0$$

$$x = \frac{-b \pm \sqrt{b^2 - 4ac}}{2a}$$

$$x = \frac{-32 \pm \sqrt{(32)^2 - 4(1)(-50,820)}}{2(1)}$$

$$x = \frac{-32 \pm \sqrt{1024 + 203,280}}{2}$$

$$x = \frac{-32 \pm \sqrt{204,304}}{2}$$

$$x = \frac{-32 \pm 452}{2}$$

$$x = \frac{420}{2} \quad \text{or} \quad \frac{-484}{2}$$

$$x = 210 \quad \text{or} \quad -242$$

3. **Solve.** Write an equation describing the situation. Solve the equation by the method of your choice.

The width is 210. The length is $x + 20 = 230$ feet.

4. **Check.** Since x represents a distance (width of the parking lot), the value cannot be negative.

Remember the steps for solving word problems.

1. **Read.** Read the problem carefully and identify what you are looking for.
2. **Plan.** Express any other quantities in terms of the variable. If possible, draw a picture or make a table.
3. **Solve.** Translate the problem into an equation and solve.
4. **Check.** Determine whether the answer is reasonable in the context.

▶ A. Exercises

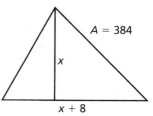

1. Find two consecutive integers whose product is 342.
2. The area of a triangle is 384 square feet. If its base is 8 feet longer than its altitude, find the length of the base and the altitude.
3. Find two consecutive odd integers whose product is 1935.
4. Find two consecutive even integers whose product is 1224.
5. One number is 18 more than the other. Find the two numbers if their product is 1215.
6. One number is 9 less than the other. Find the two numbers if their product is 736.
7. Five times the square of a number is 980. Find the number.

▶ B. Exercises

8. Joe wants to make a path around the outside perimeter of his vegetable garden, which is 50' × 70'. If the path is of uniform width and the entire garden and path are to cover a surface area of 4524 square feet, how wide should the path be?
9. The original plan for Mr. Harris's house is a rectangle that measures 40' × 50'. Because of an increase in cost, the square footage of the house must be decreased to 1739 square feet. To do this, the length and width will be decreased by the same amount. By how much should the dimensions be decreased?
10. A guy wire from the top of a 20-foot pole is anchored to the ground 12 feet from the base of the pole. How long is the wire?
11. A box is to be made by cutting out the corners of a square piece of cardboard and folding the edges up. If 3-inch squares are to be cut out of the corners and the box contains 243 cubic inches, what is the length of a side of the original cardboard square?
12. A rectangular piece of metal is 13" × 18". Four equal squares will be cut from the corners and the metal folded up to make a box whose bottom has an area of 176 square inches. What is the length of each square that is cut from the corners?

13. The base of a 20-foot ladder rests 5 feet from a wall. How high does it reach on the building?

14. A rectangular picture frame contains a 12" × 14" picture. What is the width of the frame if the total area of picture and frame is 288 square inches?

15. An isosceles right triangle has a hypotenuse of 8 inches. How long are the legs?

▶ C. Exercises

16. A metric print (picture) is square with sides of 15 cm. If it is to be enlarged so as to double its area, how much will the length of a side be increased?

17. A rectangle is 10 units longer than it is wide. When the length is decreased by 2-units and the width is increased by 3, the area is 141 square units. Find the original dimensions.

▶ Dominion Modeling

18. According to the quadratic model for Galileo's data, where is the ball when $t = 0$? Explain what this means.

19. According to the quadratic model, where is the ball when $t = -8$? Explain what this means.

■ Cumulative Review

Solve.

20. $3x - 6 = 0$
21. $3x^2 - 6 = 0$
22. $\left| 3x - 6 \right| = 0$
23. $3x - 6 \leq 0$
24. $\left| 3x - 6 \right| > 0$

4.6 Solving Quadratic Inequalities

The methods you have learned in this chapter for solving quadratic equations can be extended to solve quadratic inequalities. The method shown here will require the three following steps.

1) Complete the square.
2) Take the square root of each side.
3) Use the compound inequality theorem (Section 2.8).

Be sure to use the absolute values. The short cut that you learned for quadratic equations does not apply to inequalities.

EXAMPLE 1 Solve $x^2 + 2x - 5 > 0$.

Answer

$x^2 + 2x - 5 > 0$ $x^2 + 2x > 5$	1. Transfer the constant to the right side.
$x^2 + 2x + 1 > 5 + 1$ $(x + 1)^2 > 6$	2. Complete the square.
$\sqrt{(x + 1)^2} > \sqrt{6}$	3. Take the square root.
$\lvert x + 1 \rvert > \sqrt{6}$	4. Apply the compound inequality theorem and solve.

$$x + 1 < -\sqrt{6} \quad \text{or} \quad x + 1 > \sqrt{6}$$
$$x < -1 - \sqrt{6} \quad \text{or} \quad x > -1 + \sqrt{6}$$

A 20-room bed and breakfast is full at $80 per night. It has one unoccupied room for each $10 price increase. If x is the number of price increases, $(20 - x)$ is the number of rooms and $(80 + 10x)$ is the price. How many increases would guarantee an income exceeding $1800?

EXAMPLE 2   Solve $4x^2 - 32x - 3 \le 0$.

Answer

$4x^2 - 32x - 3 \le 0$ $4x^2 - 32x \le 3$	1. Transfer the constant to the right side.
$x^2 - 8x \le \frac{3}{4}$	2. Divide by 4 to get a leading coefficient of 1.
$x^2 - 8x + 16 \le \frac{3}{4} + \frac{64}{4}$ $(x - 4)^2 \le \frac{67}{4}$	3. Complete the square.
$\sqrt{(x - 4)^2} \le \sqrt{\frac{67}{4}}$	4. Take the square root.
$\|x - 4\| \le \frac{\sqrt{67}}{2}$	5. Solve.
$-\frac{\sqrt{67}}{2} \le x - 4 \le \frac{\sqrt{67}}{2}$	
$4 - \frac{\sqrt{67}}{2} \le x \le 4 + \frac{\sqrt{67}}{2}$	
$\frac{8 - \sqrt{67}}{2} \le x \le \frac{8 + \sqrt{67}}{2}$	

▶ A. Exercises

Solve each quadratic inequality.

1. $x^2 - 4x - 45 < 0$
2. $x^2 + 4x - 5 > 0$
3. $x^2 + 16x + 28 \ge 0$
4. $x^2 - 7x - 30 \le 0$
5. $x^2 + 3x - 4 > 0$
6. $x^2 + 5x - 6 > 0$
7. $x^2 - 7x + 12 \le 0$
8. $3x^2 - x - 10 < 0$
9. $2x^2 - 11x + 5 < 0$
10. $x^2 + 2x + 1 > 0$

▶ B. Exercises

Express the solutions to the exercises 11-15 as absolute value inequalities.

11. Exercise 1
12. Exercise 2
13. Exercise 3
14. Exercise 4
15. Exercise 5

Solve.

16. $x^2 + 11x > -18$
17. $6 - x^2 \le x$
18. $0 < x^2 - 2x - 15$
19. $16x^2 - 9 \le 0$
20. $8x^2 - 7 < -10x$
21. $3x^2 \le -26x - 16$
22. $22x^2 + 16x + 64 < 0$
23. $x^2 + 16x + 64 \le 0$

If $a > 0$, do you represent the solution to each equation below with a conjunction or disjunction?

24. $ax^2 + bx + c > 0$
25. $ax^2 + bx + c < 0$

▶ C. Exercises

Graph each quadratic system. Shade the solution. Label the values of all zeros and the points of the intersection of the curves.

26. $y \le \frac{1}{4}x^2 - 1$
    $y \ge (x - 1)^2 - 3$
27. $x^2 + y \le 4$
    $y \ge (x + 1)^2 - 1$

▶ Dominion Modeling

28. Would you trust the quadratic model of Galileo's data for $t = 20$? Explain.
29. The quadratic model for Galileo's data curves up more and more as time continues. What does this say about the rolling ball?

Cumulative Review

If $f(x) = 3x - 2$ and $g(x) = 4x + 1$, find

30. $f(-3)$

31. $(f - g)(x)$

32. $(f \circ g)(x)$

Graph.

33. $\{(x, y) \mid y = 3^x\}$

34. $y < 5x + 2$

$\mathfrak{A}$lgebra *and* $\mathfrak{S}$cripture

Finances and Debt

Now you know how to solve a greater variety of word problems. On page 158, problem 8; Joe will need to know the width before he can determine the amount of bricks and sand paving base to purchase. His costs will depend on this amount. Likewise, in problem 9, Mr. Harris had to reduce his plans because of cost considerations.

In both instances, careless math could put Joe or Mr. Harris into debt. What does God say about finances and debts?

Read II Kings 4:1-7.

1. What evidence is given to show that this widow did not want to be in debt?
2. How could the creditor obtain his money back?

> **GREATER AMPLITUDE.**
> The power of the creditor illustrates why the Scripture says that "the borrower is servant to the lender." Find the reference to that proverb.

Now read Matthew 18:21-35.

3. How much did one servant owe the other servant?
4. What power did the servant have over his debtor?
5. How much did the servant owe the king?
6. What power did the king exercise over this servant?
7. What principle in the Lord's prayer is the moral of this parable?

You have seen two principles in finances so far: a debt principle and a forgiveness principle.

8. How are these principles expressed in Psalm 37:21?

Read the Book of Philemon and see how these principles are illustrated.

9. Who was the formerly wicked debtor?

10. Who was the creditor?

11. Who sought mercy for the debtor and offered to pay the debt?

Imagine that you attempted to be good enough to deserve to go to heaven.

12. What debt does a man have who wants to be good enough to go to heaven according to Galatians 5:3?

13. According to Romans 4:4, who would be in debt to whom?

14. What phrase in Ephesians 2:8-9 tells us that we cannot earn heaven?

15. Both Romans 4:4-5 and Ephesians 2:8-9 explain how God gives men salvation. What terms describe God's act? Which term is used in both passages?

Jesus paid your debt of sin through his death on the cross (I Pet. 2:21-25, II Cor. 5:21). If you have never accepted this gift of grace you can do so now. If you have accepted Jesus' death in your place, then Romans 1:14-15 discusses your debt to people in this life.

16. To whom are you debtor?

17. What do you owe?

Romans 13:8 tells us our financial responsibility and our responsibility to others. They are opposites. Do not be in debt financially but fulfill your debt to love others. A good way to do this is by sharing the gospel.

> ## Absolute Values
>
> OWE NO MAN ANY THING, but to love one another: for he that loveth another hath fulfilled the law.
>
> ROMANS 13:8

Chapter 4 Review

Solve by factoring.
1. $x^2 - 4x - 32 = 0$
2. $x^2 + 10x + 9 = 0$
3. $6x^2 + 22x - 8 = 0$
4. $y^2 + 3y = 18$

Solve by completing the square.
5. $10x^2 + x = 3$
6. $x^2 + 12x = -32$
7. $z^2 + 6z = 12$
8. $3x^2 + 24x - 7 = 0$

Solve by using the quadratic formula.
9. $x^2 + 3x - 108 = 0$
10. $x^2 - 9x + 14 = 0$
11. $5a^2 + 8a - 6 = 0$
12. $3c^2 - 2c - 1 = 0$

Determine the number and nature of the solutions and whether the solutions are real. Then find the solutions if they are real numbers.
13. $2x^2 - 5x - 1 = 0$
14. $x^2 + 14x + 49 = 0$
15. $3x^2 - 11x - 42 = 0$
16. $x^2 + x + 1 = 0$
17. Find two consecutive even integers whose product is 728.

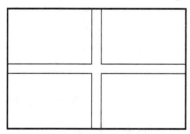

18. A path of uniform width is to be placed in a large flower garden as shown in the diagram. If the rectangular garden is 120' × 180' and the gardener wants to keep 19,836 square feet for flowers, what is the width of the path?
19. The sides of a right triangle are 3 consecutive even integers. Find them.
20. Prove the quadratic formula.

Solve.

21. $x^2 - 6x - 27 > 0$

22. $2x^2 + 9x - 18 \leq 0$

23. Express the solution to exercise 21 as an absolute value.

24. Solve $x^2 - 21 < 4x$ and give the answer as an absolute value inequality.

Solve using the best method.

25. $3t^2 - t - 1 = 0$

26. $4x^2 = 12x$

27. $4x^2 = 12$

28. $3x + 7 \leq 2x + 1$

29. $7x - 3 > x^2 + x + 2$

30. Evaluate the model for Galileo's data. How is the model different from a linear model? Is a quadratic model better? Explain.

31. Give the mathematical significance of Romans 13:8.

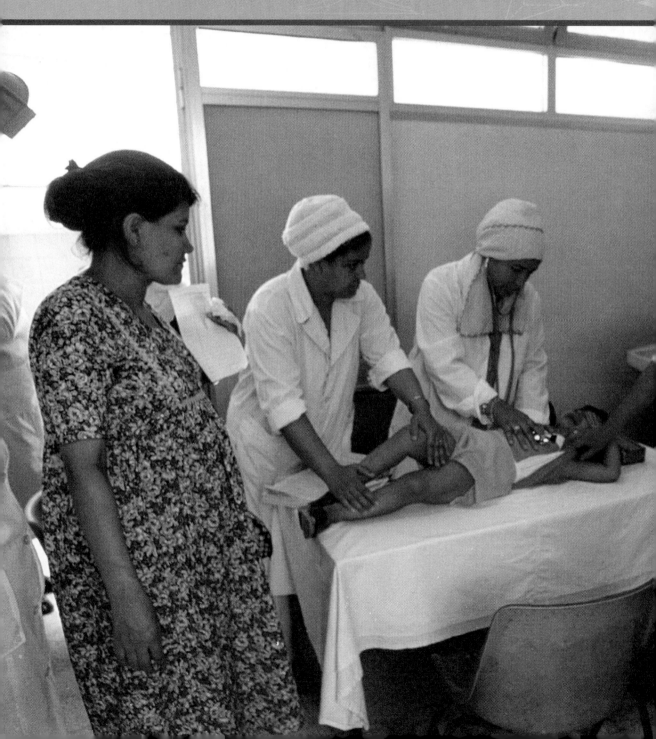

Do you know how much you weighed when you were born? Newborn infants in the United States typically weigh about 7 pounds (3.2 kg); babies below about $5\frac{1}{2}$ pounds (2.5 kg) are considered "low weight." Do babies grow the same amount each month? If so, what is the usual growth rate; if not, what is the normal growth pattern?

A study conducted in the Egyptian village of Nahya (west of Cairo) attempted to describe how infants grow. Among other measurements that the researcher calculated, the mean weights of 170 infants were measured for each month of the first year. In this chapter you will see how polynomial functions can help you analyze this data.

Age (mo.)	Weight (kg)	Age (mo.)	Weight (kg)
0	3.3	7	7.2
1	4.3	8	7.2
2	5.1	9	7.2
3	5.7	10	7.2
4	6.3	11	7.5
5	6.8	12	7.8
6	7.1		

After this chapter you should be able to

1. distinguish between equations and functions, both linear and quadratic.

2. find the vertex and the axis of symmetry of a quadratic function.

3. graph and translate quadratic functions.

4. solve maximum and minimum problems using quadratic functions.

5. graph quadratic inequalities.

6. find the zeros of functions.

7. apply the factor and remainder theorems.

8. graph polynomial functions.

169

5.1 Quadratic Functions

In Chapter 3 you studied linear functions, building upon your knowledge of linear equations from the previous chapter. Now you are going to study quadratic functions by building upon your knowledge of quadratic equations. An example of each is shown here.

	Linear	Quadratic
equation:	$2x + 3 = 7$	$3x^2 - 5x + 8 = 0$
function:	$y = 2x + 1$	$y = x^2 - 3x + 1$

Section 3.1 defined a relation as a set of ordered pairs. Section 3.2 defined a function as a relation with a particular property. Review these definitions.

Recall that a linear equation has a single solution, but a linear function consists of an infinite set of ordered pairs that form a line.

A quadratic equation has two solutions, but a quadratic function consists of an infinite set of ordered pairs. The points will form a curve rather than a line.

Consider the quadratic function $y = x^2 + 2x - 15$. The x and y in the rule describe a set of ordered pairs, some of which are in the following table. Plot the ordered pairs on a coordinate plane to see the pattern.

$$y = x^2 + 2x - 15$$

x	y
-7	20
-6	9
-5	0
-4	-7
-3	-12
-2	-15
-1	-16
0	-15
1	-12
2	-7
3	0
4	9
5	20

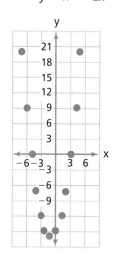

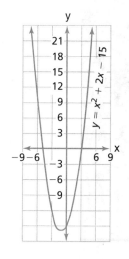

If it were possible to find ordered pairs for every value of x in the real number system, the graph of $y = x^2 + 2x - 15$ would look like the curve shown. The curve representing a quadratic function is called a *parabola,* and the general equation for a quadratic function is

$$y = ax^2 + bx + c \text{ where } a, b, c \in \mathbb{R} \text{ and } a \neq 0.$$

In function notation the quadratic function looks like this:

$$f(x) = ax^2 + bx + c \text{ where } a, b, c \in \mathbb{R} \text{ and } a \neq 0.$$

Remember that y and $f(x)$ mean the same thing.

There are some distinguishing features about a parabola. Look at those graphed here.

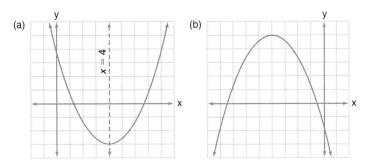

Notice that each parabola has either a lowest point or a highest point. This point is called the *vertex* of the parabola and represents the smallest value of y or the largest value of y. Therefore, these points are called *minimum* or *maximum* points.

Also notice that the parabolas are symmetrical. This means they look the same on both sides of a certain line. In figure *a* the parabola is mirrored in the line $x = 4$. The line that represents the mirror is called the *line of symmetry* or *axis of symmetry*. The axis of symmetry in the first graph of this section is $x = -1$. What is the line of symmetry in figure *b*? If you can graph one half of the curve, the other half can be determined by symmetry (See table for first graph shown, noting $f(-7) = f(5)$, $f(-6) = f(4)$, etc.).

The domain of a quadratic function is $\mathbb{R}$. The range depends on the vertex. If the vertex (h, k) is a minimum point, then the range is $\{y \mid y \geq k\}$. What is the range if the vertex is a maximum? It is helpful visually to give the coordinates of the y-intercept. As in the case of linear functions, it has coordinates $(0, f(0))$.

In this chapter you will study quadratic functions and their graphs in detail and extend this knowledge to polynomial functions of higher degree.

► A. Exercises

Determine which equations have a finite number of solutions (tell how many) and which must be graphed on a coordinate plane. Also state which ones are linear equations, linear functions, quadratic equations, or quadratic functions.

1. $3x + 8 = 12$
2. $4x^2 + 3x - 5 = y$
3. $2x + y = 5$
4. $4x - 7 = 9$
5. $6x^2 - 4x + 7 = 0$
6. $x = 3$

Use the graph to match.

7. $(-1, 1)$
8. $x = -1$
9. $x^2 + 2x + 2 = y$
10. $(0, 2)$
11. $\{y \mid y \geq 1\}$

A. axis of symmetry
B. domain
C. maximum
D. quadratic function
E. range
F. vertex
G. y-intercept

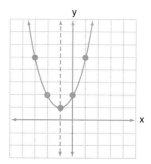

Look at each parabola and give the minimum or maximum point, the equation of the line of symmetry, and the domain and range.

12.

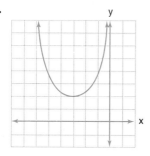

14.

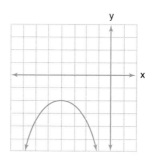

13.

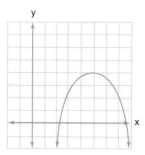

15.

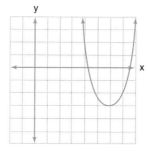

▶ B. Exercises

Find at least six ordered pairs for each quadratic function; graph the function.

16. $f(x) = x^2 + x - 4$
17. $f(x) = 2x^2 + x + 6$
18. $f(x) = -x^2 + 3x - 5$
19. $f(x) = 3x^2 + x + 4$
20. $f(x) = -2x^2 + 3x - 2$

▶ C. Exercises

Recall that any quadratic function can be written in general form $f(x) = ax^2 + bx + c$. Use this form to answer the questions.

21. Give the y-intercept.
22. Find $f\left(-\frac{c}{b}\right)$
23. If the x-coordinate of the vertex is h, find the y-coordinate.
24. If the x-coordinate of the vertex is h, give the vertex as an ordered pair.
25. Graph $f(x) = -x^2 + 4x - 2$. Label the axis of symmetry, y-intercept, and the vertex.

▶ Dominion Modeling

26. For the Egyptian infant data, what are the variables? Which variable would be a suitable independent variable (input)? Which would be a suitable dependent variable (output)?
27. If the babies grew the same amount each month, what kind of model would be appropriate?
28. What do the seventh through tenth months show? How could you explain this?

▪ Cumulative Review

Find the distance between the points.

29. -2 and 5
30. $(2, -3)$ and $(5, 1)$
31. $(2, -2, -1)$ and $(4, 1, 5)$
32. $(4, -1, 6)$ and $(3, 2, 3)$
33. $(3, 2)$ and $(6, -1)$

5.2 Graphing Quadratic Functions

The general form of a quadratic function is

$$\{(x, y) \mid y = ax^2 + bx + c\} \text{ where } a, b, c \in \mathbb{R} \text{ and } a \neq 0.$$

You can graph quadratic functions by choosing values for x, finding their corresponding $f(x)$ or y values, plotting these ordered pairs, and connecting them with a parabolic curve. All quadratic functions defined by $y = ax^2 + bx + c$ are parabolic curves when graphed. In the next few sections you will learn some short cuts for graphing.

The simplest quadratic functions have the form $y = ax^2$ where $a \in \mathbb{R}$ and $a \neq 0$. Notice that this is the general form of a quadratic function where $b = c = 0$. Consider the graph of such a quadratic function in which $a = 1$.

$y = x^2$

x	y
-3	9
-2	4
-1	1
0	0
1	1
2	4
3	9

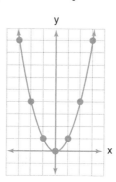

This parabola opens upward, has a minimum point at $(0, 0)$, and has $x = 0$ as its line of symmetry.

EXAMPLE 1 Graph $y = -2x^2$. In this equation $a = -2$.

Answer

x	y
-3	-18
-2	-8
-1	-2
0	0
1	-2
2	-8
3	-18

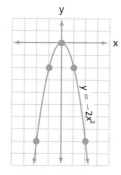

Here the parabola opens downward and has a maximum point at (0, 0). The axis of symmetry is $x = 0$. These examples suggest some principles for graphing a quadratic function of the form $y = ax^2$.

$y = ax^2$	$a > 0$	$a < 0$
Maximum or minimum	Minimum point (0, 0)	Maximum point (0, 0)
Opens upward or downward	Opens upward	Opens downward
Line of symmetry	$x = 0$	$x = 0$

Look at the parabolas in the next graph. Compare the graphs with their respective equations to see if you can determine a general principle.

The general principle is that as the $|a|$ increases, the graph of $y = ax^2$ narrows.

In the following sections, you will graph more complicated quadratic functions. It will help you to know about zeros of functions.

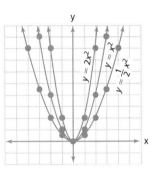

A *zero of a function* is a value of x for which $f(x) = 0$. Since these are points on the x-axis, they will aid you in graphing. You should realize that a quadratic function may have 0, 1, or 2 zeros. All functions graphed in this lesson so far have had only one and it was at the origin.

EXAMPLE 2 Find the zeros of the function from the graph.

Answer Determine the points where the graph intersects the x-axis. The x-intercepts are $(-6, 0)$, $(-2, 0)$, and $(3, 0)$. Therefore the zeros of this function are -6, -2, and 3.

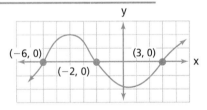

EXAMPLE 3 Find the zeros of $f(x) = 3x^2 + 16x - 12$ algebraically.

Answer

$f(x) = 3x^2 + 16x - 12$
$3x^2 + 16x - 12 = 0$
$(3x - 2)(x + 6) = 0$

$3x - 2 = 0$	or	$x + 6 = 0$
$x = \frac{2}{3}$	or	$x = -6$

The zeros are -6 and $\frac{2}{3}$.

▶ A. Exercises

Without graphing, give the equation for the line of symmetry, state whether the parabola opens upward or downward, tell whether the vertex is a maximum or minimum point, and give the ordered pair of the vertex.

1. $y = -4x^2$

2. $y = \frac{1}{2}x^2$

3. $y = \frac{-2}{3}x^2$

4. $y = \frac{-1}{8}x^2$

5. $y = 5x^2$

6. $y = 2x^2$

Give the zeros of each function.

7.

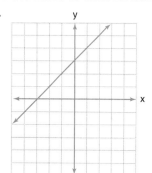

9.

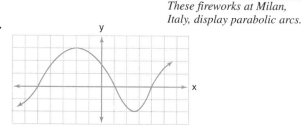

These fireworks at Milan, Italy, display parabolic arcs.

8.

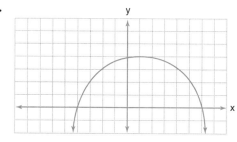

10.

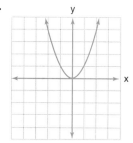

▶ B. Exercises

11. Which of the parabolas described by the equations in exercises 1-6 would be the narrowest? the widest?

Graph each function. Give the equation of the axis of symmetry, the vertex, the domain, and the range; state whether the vertex is a maximum or minimum.

12. $f(x) = \frac{-3}{2}x^2$

13. $f(x) = -6x^2$

14. $f(x) = \frac{1}{3}x^2$

15. $f(x) = -3x^2$

Place the graphs of the following pairs of quadratic functions on the same coordinate plane. How do the values of a compare in each pair?

16. $y = 3x^2,\ y = -3x^2$

17. $y = -3x^2,\ y = \frac{1}{3}x^2$

18. To find the exact zeros of a function,
   a. substitute zero for x.   c. either a or b.
   b. set the quadratic equal to zero.   d. neither a nor b.

19. The function in exercise 8 has a _____ (maximum or minimum) value of _____ when $x =$ _____.

20. If a parabola has (b, c) as its vertex, what would the equation of its axis of symmetry be?

► C. Exercises

21. Suppose $f(x) = ax^2$ and $a > 0$. Under what circumstances would you have a maximum value for the function? Give an example.

22. Suppose a parabola opens sideways instead of up or down. What conclusion can be drawn?

► Dominion Modeling

23. What linear model fits the data on the Egyptian infants?

24. Is a linear model a good one?

Cumulative Review

Use the given functions to find $(f + g)(x)$, $fg(x)$, $(f \circ g)(x)$, and $(g \circ f)(x)$.

25. $f(x) = x^2 - 3;\ g(x) = x^2$

26. $f(x) = x^2 - 3x + 5;\ g(x) = |x|$

27. $f(x) = 5;\ g(x) = x^2 + x$

28. $f(x) = x^2 - 7;\ g(x) = 2^x$

29. $f(x) = x^2 + 3x - 2;\ g(x) = 3x^2 - 5$

5.3 Translation of Quadratic Functions

In the last section you saw how the graph of a simple quadratic function of the form $f(x) = ax^2$ varied, depending on the value of a. The other numerical values of the general quadratic function also affect the parabola that the equation defines. In fact, the parabola is translated vertically by an amount that corresponds to the constant value in the quadratic function. You will soon see how a parabola is translated horizontally.

First, look at the following function and its graph.

$$f(x) = x^2 + 3$$

x	$f(x)$
0	3
±1	4
±2	7
±3	12

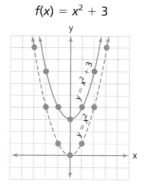

Parabolic arcs form in the spray of a fountain, such as the Royal Palace Fountain in Aranjuez, Spain.

Compare the functions $f(x) = x^2$ and $f(x) = x^2 + 3$. Notice that each y-coordinate of the second function is three more than that of the first function for any value of x chosen. Therefore the graph of $f(x) = x^2 + 3$ has the same shape and size as the dotted parabola $f(x) = x^2$. Anytime you see an equation in the form $f(x) = ax^2 + k$, it is graphed exactly like the equation $f(x) = ax^2$ but translated vertically k units. The function $f(x) = x^2$ can be viewed as being translated up three units to produce $f(x) = x^2 + 3$.

EXAMPLE 1   Graph $y = -2x^2 - 4$.

Answer

1. Analyze the equation. It is in the form $y = ax^2 + k$, where $a = -2$ and $k = -4$. The graph of this equation will be the graph of $y = -2x^2$ translated down 4 units, since k is negative.

Continued ▶

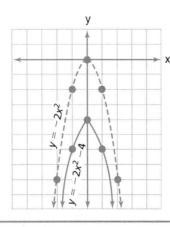

2. Since $a < 0$, the graph of the parabola opens downward and has a maximum point. The entire parabola is translated down 4 units, so the maximum point is $(0, -4)$. The line of symmetry is still $x = 0$.

Let us now consider a horizontal translation. Consider the function $f(x) = (x - 2)^2$.

EXAMPLE 2   Graph $f(x) = (x - 2)^2$.

Answer

x	y
0	4
1	1
2	0
3	1
4	4

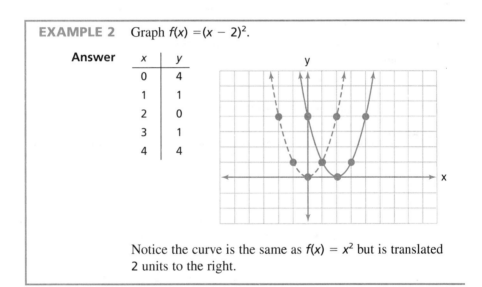

Notice the curve is the same as $f(x) = x^2$ but is translated 2 units to the right.

An investigation of the graph of $f(x) = -(x + 2)^2$ would reveal that it is the same curve as $f(x) = x^2$ also, but translated left 2 units and opening downward.

Now consider this example of a function translated both horizontally and vertically. The function $f(x) = (x - 2)^2 + 3$, when changed to the general form, is $f(x) = x^2 - 4x + 7$; but it is much easier to graph when it is in the first form. Several ordered pairs have been found and graphed. Notice the location of the parabola and particularly its vertex.

x	$f(x)$
0	7
1	4
2	3
3	4
4	7

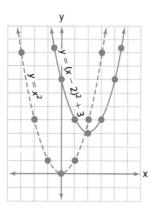

The parabola is translated horizontally 2 units and vertically 3 units. Notice the 2 and 3 in the equation $f(x) = (x - 2)^2 + 3$. The parabola has a minimum point at (2, 3).

Although we refer to $y = ax^2 + bx + c$ as the general form of a quadratic, the form $y = a(x - h)^2 + k$ is much more useful both for graphing and for applications. You need only put a quadratic function in this form to read the vertex (h, k) when graphing, and any maximum or minimum applications can also be answered from these coordinates.

EXAMPLE 3   Graph $y = \frac{1}{2}(x + 4)^2 + 1$.

Answer

$a = \frac{1}{2}$

$h = -4$ since $-(-4) = 4$

$k = 1$

1. Analyze the equation to determine its general location, maximum or minimum point, and line of symmetry.

Since $a > 0$, $(-4, 1)$ is a minimum point. The axis of symmetry is $x = -4$. The parabola is translated 4 units left and 1 unit up from the graph of $y = \frac{1}{2}x^2$.

x	y
-3	1.5
-2	3

2. Find two ordered pairs to the right of the vertex and use symmetry to locate additional points on the left to confirm the general shape and location of the parabola.

Continued ▶

By symmetry $f(-5) = 1.5$
and $f(-6) = 3$.

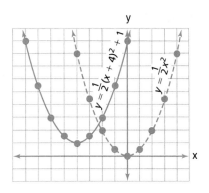

EXAMPLE 4   Find the zeros of $g(x) = (x - 2)^2 - 25$ and graph the function.

Answer $g(x) = (x - 2)^2 - 25$ 1. The vertex is $(2, -25)$.

$$(x - 2)^2 - 25 = 0$$ 2. Set $g(x) = 0$ and solve.

$$x^2 - 4x + 4 - 25 = 0$$

$$x^2 - 4x - 21 = 0$$

$$(x - 7)(x + 3) = 0$$

$$x = -3 \text{ or } x = 7$$

The graph crosses the x-axis at $(-3, 0)$ and $(7, 0)$.

3. Graph. Notice how the
zeros and the vertex
help in the graphing
process.

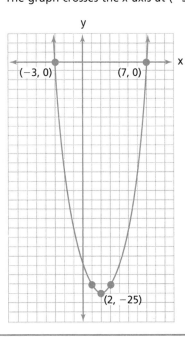

▶ A. Exercises

Give the maximum or minimum point, the equation of the line of symmetry, and the distance and direction of the translation of the parabola from the origin; then state whether the parabola opens upward or downward. Do not graph the equations.

1. $y = x^2 + 3$
2. $y = -3x^2 - 4$
3. $y = (x - 6)^2 + 1$
4. $y = (x + 2)^2 + 6$
5. $y = -3(x - 4)^2 + 7$
6. $f(x) = \frac{1}{2}x^2 - 6$
7. $f(x) = -x^2 - 2$
8. $y = -\frac{1}{2}(x + 3)^2 - 1$
9. $y = (x - 4)^2 + \frac{5}{4}$
10. $f(x) = 8(x + 1)^2 - 9$

▶ B. Exercises

Use the information you learned in this lesson to graph each equation. You need not find the zeros.

11. $y = x^2 - 1$
12. $y = -5x^2 + 2$
13. $y = (x - 4)^2 + 3$
14. $y = -(x + 3)^2 - 5$
15. $y = 4(x - 1)^2 - 2$
16. $y = \frac{1}{2}(x + 2)^2 - 6$
17. $f(x) = 4(x - 5)^2 + 3$
18. $f(x) = -3(x + 1)^2 - 2$

Find the zeros of each function.

19. $f(x) = (x + 1)^2 - 16$
20. $g(x) = 2(x - 1)^2 - 5$
21. $h(x) = x^2 + x - 20$
22. $k(x) = 2x^2 - 5x - 12$

Use the zeros to graph the functions in

23. exercise 19.
24. exercise 22.

▶ C. Exercises

Give the vertex, domain, range, axis of symmetry, y-intercept, and zeros for each function.

25. $f(x) = ax^2 + k$ if $a < 0$
26. $g(x) = a(x - h)^2 + k$ if $a > 0$

Solve.

27. $3x + 1 = x + 5$

28. $3x^2 + 1 = x + 5$

29. $3x^2 + 1 = x^2 + 5$

30. $3x^2 + x = x^2 + 5$

31. $3x^2 + x = 3x^2 + 5$

32. $3x^2 + 1 = 3x^2 + 5$

5.4 Graphing General Quadratic Functions

$\mathbf{Y}$ou should have a solid understanding of how to graph quadratic functions of the form $f(x) = a(x - h)^2 + k$. Often a quadratic function does not appear in this form, but you can change it to this form by the algebraic method of *completing the square.*

EXAMPLE 1   Complete the square for $f(x) = x^2 + 4x + 1$

Answer

$f(x) = x^2 + 4x + 1$	
$f(x) = (x^2 + 4x) + 1$	1. Group the variable terms in parentheses.
$\frac{4}{2} = 2;\ 2^2 = 4$	2. Divide the coefficient of x by 2; square the quotient. Add the result inside the parentheses and subtract the same number outside the parentheses.
$f(x) = (x^2 + 4x + 4) + 1 - 4$	
$f(x) = (x^2 + 4x + 4) - 3$	
$f(x) = (x + 2)^2 - 3$	3. The quantity inside the parentheses should be a perfect square trinomial. Factor it.

The value of the quadratic function has not been changed; only its form has been changed. You can easily graph the function $f(x) = (x + 2)^2 - 3$. Study the following example to make sure you can complete the square when the leading coefficient is not 1.

EXAMPLE 2   Graph $f(x) = 3x^2 - 6x + 7$.

Answer

$f(x) = 3x^2 - 6x + 7$

$f(x) = (3x^2 - 6x) + 7$ 1. Group the variable terms together

$f(x) = 3(x^2 - 2x) + 7$ and factor out 3 from them.

                              2. Divide the coefficient of x by 2, and square the quotient: 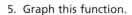 $\frac{-2}{2} = -1; (-1)^2 = 1$.

$f(x) = 3(x^2 - 2x + 1) + 7 - 3$ 3. Add this amount inside the paren-

$f(x) = 3(x^2 - 2x + 1) + 4$ theses. Since the quantity in parentheses is multiplied by 3, you actually added 3 to the equation when you placed the 1 inside the parentheses. Therefore, subtract 3 from the constant term to keep the quadratic function unchanged.

$f(x) = 3(x - 1)^2 + 4$ 4. Factor the perfect square trinomial.

                              5. Graph this function.

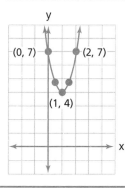

Graphing a General Quadratic Function

1. Complete the square if necessary to obtain the form $f(x) = a(x - h)^2 + k$.
2. Identify the vertex (h, k) from the form obtained in step 1 and graph it.
3. Find another ordered pair for the function and plot it; use symmetry to plot a third point. Repeat to find another pair of points.
4. Draw the parabola through the points.

▶ A. Exercises

Change each quadratic function to the form $f(x) = a(x - h)^2 + k$.
Do not graph.

1. $f(x) = x^2 + 6x + 5$
2. $f(x) = 2x^2 - 12x + 26$
3. $y = -x^2 - 2x + 1$
4. $f(x) = 4x^2 + 56x + 195$
5. $y = \frac{1}{2}x^2 + 8x + 30$
6. $y = 5x^2 - 90x + 409$
7. $f(x) = x^2 + 12x + 18$
8. $f(x) = 2x^2 - 8x + 14$
9. $y = x^2 - 10x + 16$
10. $f(x) = -3x^2 - 6x - 4$
11. $y = x^2 - 4x + 8$
12. $f(x) = x^2 + 8x + 18$
13. $f(x) = x^2 + 10x + 25$
14. $f(x) = x^2 - 3$
15. $y = -x^2 - 6x - 9$

▶ B. Exercises

Change each quadratic function to the form $f(x) = a(x - h)^2 + k$. Graph.

16. $f(x) = 2x^2 + 12x + 13$
17. $y = -2x^2 - 4x - 8$
18. $f(x) = 7x^2 + 28x + 25$
19. $y = x^2 + 6x - 1$
20. $f(x) = 3x^2 + 12x - 6$
21. $g(x) = -2x^2 + 8x - 7$
22. $y = -x^2 + 8x - 1$
23. $y = x^2 + 2x - 4$

▶ C. Exercises

Complete the square on $f(x) = ax^2 + bx + c$ for $a, b, c \in \mathbb{R}$ and $a \neq 0$. Use the result to determine the general form of each of the following.

24. axis of symmetry
25. vertex

26. Find a quadratic model for the Egyptian infant data.
27. Is the quadratic model a good one?

Cumulative Review

28. (2, 5) is the midpoint between $(-1, 3)$ and point P. Find P.
29. Find the zeros and y-intercept of $f(x) = x^2 + 3x + 2$.
30. Find b if $f(x) = x^2 - bx + 9$ has one rational root and $b > 0$.
31. Find the range of values for c if $f(x) = x^2 - 3x + c$ has conjugate complex roots.
32. Write an equation describing the set of points less than 4 units from k on a number line.

5.5 Problem Solving Using Quadratic Functions

Learning methods of problem solving and acquiring skill in their use are important reasons for studying mathematics. The most important skill that you will learn in your math classes is how to think, which will be of great value in solving problems you will face in the future. You should apply logical-thinking skills to every area of your life, and in particular, to your Bible study. The Bible says in I John 4:1 that Christians are to "try the spirits whether they are of God: because many false prophets are gone out into the world." When you listen to a sermon or a Bible lesson, compare each point with Scripture and accept only what is biblical.

The Cross of the Plains at Groom, Texas, is 190 feet high, making it the largest Christian monument in the hemisphere. Engineers used math to design the cross to withstand 140 mph winds.

Quadratic functions provide additional tools for thinking through various practical problems.

The graph of $f(x) = -2(x - 3)^2 + 1$ is shown here.

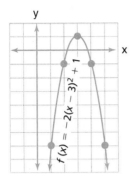

The Cross of Peace, or Bald Knob Cross, near Alto Pass, Illinois, is 111 feet high and was previously the largest Christian monument.

This function has a maximum point at (3, 1). Maximum and minimum points have many applications. Study the following examples.

EXAMPLE 1   A projectile is shot vertically from ground level at a rate of 992 feet per second. Disregarding wind resistance, the motion of the projectile is described by the equation $h(t) = -16t^2 + 992t$, where $h(t)$ represents the height above ground in t seconds. What is the maximum height it will reach, and how long will it take to get to that height?

Answer

$h(t) = -16t^2 + 992t$	1. **Read.** Read carefully and note the formula.
$h(t) = -16(t^2 - 62t)$ $h(t) = -16(t^2 - 62t + 961) + 15{,}376$ $h(t) = -16(t - 31)^2 + 15{,}376$	2. **Plan.** The maximum point of the quadratic function can be determined by placing the equation in $f(x) = a(x - h)^2 + k$ form.
$(t, h(t)) = (31, 15{,}376)$	3. **Solve.** Find the maximum point by giving the vertex $(t, h(t))$.
After 31 seconds the projectile will be at the maximum height of 15,376 feet (ignoring air resistance as instructed).	4. **Check.** Interpret the answer and verify that it makes sense in the context.

EXAMPLE 2   An airline flies between two major cities daily. It normally transports eighty-one people a day at a cost of **$210** per person. The airline estimates that it will lose two passengers for every **$6** that it increases the fare. What should the airline charge to gain the maximum income?

Answer

Let x = number of $6 increases.	1. **Read.** Identify the key quantity and assign a variable to it.
Price per person = $210 + 6x$ Number of passengers = $81 - 2x$ $R(x) = (81 - 2x)(210 + 6x)$	2. **Plan.** Express other unknowns in terms of the number of $6 increases. The total income, $R(x)$, is the number of passengers times the price per passenger.
$R(x) = 17{,}010 + 66x - 12x^2$ $R(x) = -12x^2 + 66x + 17{,}010$ $R(x) = -12(x^2 - 5.5x) + 17{,}010$ $R(x) = -12(x^2 - 5.5x + 7.5625) + 17{,}010 + 90.75$ $R(x) = -12(x - 2.75)^2 + 17{,}100.75$	3. **Solve.** Complete the square to find the vertex of the parabola.
The maximum point is (2.75, 17,100.75). This means $x = 2.75$ and $R \approx 17{,}101$. The airline should make 2.75 six-dollar increases to make a maximum income of $17,101. To answer the question in the problem, evaluate $210 + 6x$ when $x = 2.75$.	4. **Check.** Interpret the answer and be sure to answer all the questions in the problem.

$$210 + 6(2.75) = 226.5$$

Each customer should be charged $226.50 for a maximum income of $17,101.

EXAMPLE 3   Philip wants to construct a dog pen at the back of his garage. He will use the wall of the garage as one side of the pen and will construct the rest of the rectangular pen from **28** yards of fencing. What should the dimensions of the pen be if Philip wants it to have the maximum area.

Continued ▶

Answer

Let x = width of the pen.	1. ***Read.*** Assign a variable to an unknown.
Length = $28 - 2x$	2. ***Plan.*** Draw a picture and express other quantities in terms of the variable.

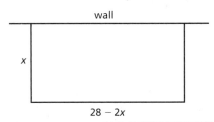

wall

x

$28 - 2x$

$A(x) = x(28 - 2x)$ $A(x) = 28x - 2x^2$ $A(x) = -2x^2 + 28x$ $A(x) = -2(x^2 - 14x)$ $A(x) = -2(x^2 - 14x + 49) + 98$ $A(x) = -2(x - 7)^2 + 98$ The maximum point is (7, 98).	3. ***Solve.*** Write an equation for the area of the rectangle. $A(x)$ = length $\cdot$ width. Complete the square to find the vertex.
The width of the pen is $x = 7$ yards, and the length is $28 - 2x = 14$ yards. The maximum area is $A(x) = 98$ square yards.	4. ***Check.*** Interpret the result and answer all questions.

Notice that no equations were solved in the previous examples. Instead, we used a function to describe the quantity of interest and completing the square to find its extreme point. Many practical problems can be solved using quadratic functions in this way.

▶ A. Exercises

Give the function to be maximized or minimized. Do not solve.

1. Find two numbers whose product is 120 and whose sum is a minimum.
2. Find the maximum area of a rectangle having a perimeter of 100 meters.

Solve.

3. Find two numbers whose difference is 8 and whose product is a minimum. (*Hint:* Let x = the first number and $x + 8$ = the second number.)
4. Find two numbers whose sum is 36 and whose product is a maximum.
5. Find two numbers whose sum is 42 and whose product is a maximum.
6. John wants to enclose a rectangular field with 420 feet of fencing, which will be electrified. What should the dimensions be to provide a maximum amount of area in the field?

7. What are the dimensions of a rectangular piece of carpet that has a perimeter of 56 feet and a maximum area?

▶ B. Exercises

8. Julie has 52 feet of decorative fencing that she wants to place along the border of her new rectangular rose garden. How big should she make the garden if she wants to use a side of the house as one boundary, wants to use all of her fencing, and wants a maximum amount of area for her roses? How many square feet of garden will she have?

9. Mr. Burns wants to make sure his company produces a maximum profit. The profit he makes is a function of the number of items the company produces and sells. The profit function for the company is $P(x) = -3x^2 + 252x + 650$, where x is the number of hundreds of items produced and sold and $P(x)$ is the amount of profit in hundreds of dollars. What is the number of items that should be produced to make a maximum profit, and what is the maximum profit?

10. The Sound Sleeper Pillow Company makes pillows and sells them to motel chains. The plant is trying to minimize costs in the production of pillows. The cost function for the company follows this equation: $C(x) = 2x^2 - 96x + 6837$, where x represents the number of lots of 100 pillows made and $C(x)$ represents the cost of manufacturing the pillows. How many pillows should be produced and sold for the company's cost to be minimized? What is the minimum cost?

11. Doug throws a ball vertically into the air while standing on a platform that is 10 feet off the ground. The motion of the ball is described by $f(t) = -16t^2 + 96t + 10$, where t represents seconds and $f(t)$ represents the height (in feet) of the ball above ground level in t seconds. What is the maximum height above ground the ball will reach, and how many seconds will pass before it reaches this height?

12. Mr. Cassidy owns a farm that has land adjacent to a river where he wants to make a pasture for his cattle. He has 312 yards of wire that he will electrify to enclose the three sides of the pasture, and he will use the riverbank as the fourth side. What should the dimensions of the pasture be if he wants the maximum area? What is the area?

13. A fireworks rocket is shot vertically at a rate of 160 feet per second. The height of the rocket as a function of time is described by $f(t) = -16t^2 + 160t$. How long will it take the rocket to reach the highest point, and what is the highest point?

14. The profit function for the Haggard Apple Orchard's out-of-state sales is $P(x) = -x^2 + 276x - 11,454$, where x is the number of pounds of apples in hundreds and $P(x)$ is the profit in dollars. How many pounds should be sold out of state to produce a maximum profit, and what is that profit?

15. Sounds Good Music sells sixty CD players every day at $80 each. Each $4 increase in price reduces their sales by 2 players. Find the maximum daily income from sales and the price they should charge to get it.

16. The accountants for the C & S Manufacturing Company have found that the profit for the company can be described by the following profit function: $P(x) = -5x^2 + 80x + 15{,}170$, where x represents the number of thousands of items. What is the number of items that should be made to produce a maximum profit? What is the maximum profit?

17. A fast food restaurant sells 200 Megaburger combos daily at $4.59 each. Every 10¢ price increase reduces sales by 3 combo meals. Find the maximum income from Megaburger combo sales and the price for which they should be sold.

18. The Cycle Shop on the average sells 20 mountain bikes per week when they charge $270 a piece. They lose one sale for each $15 increase. What is their maximum income and what price will generate that income?

▶ C. Exercises

19. Assume the perimeter of a rectangle is P and that the area is to be maximized. Let x represent the width of the rectangle. Use the methods of this section to show that the rectangle must be square.

20. Rework Example 3, this time assuming the garage abuts the rear of the property and a neighbor was permitted to attach 6 feet of fencing to it as shown. Use this section of fence as well as the side of the garage as part of the pen.

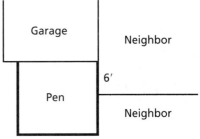

Cumulative Review

Simplify.

21. $(4x^2 + 6x) - 2x$
22. $(4x^2 + 6x) \div 2x$
23. $(4x^2 + 6x)2x$

Find the zeros of each function.

24. $g(x) = x^2 + 13x + 42$
25. $f(x) = 2x^2 - 5x - 3$
26. $h(x) = (x + 2)(x - 8)(x - 6)$
27. $k(x) = 3x - 1$

FRANÇOIS VIÈTE

François Viète was born in Poitou, a French province, in 1540. Viète worked as a lawyer and also served as a member of the French parliament and as a private counselor to King Henry IV. Mathematics was not his work but his hobby, and he spent most of his leisure time exploring it. He soon became known as the greatest French mathematician of the sixteenth century. In 1584 political enemies banished him from the royal court, and he devoted himself completely to mathematics for the next five years. As a rich aristocrat, he published most of his works himself, an unusual event for mathematicians of that time.

Viète used his mathematics at a level beyond the comprehension of his contemporaries. This skill precipitated some interesting circumstances. When France was at war with Spain, the Spanish king, Philip II, used a secret code that was supposedly impossible to decipher. Although the code contained several hundred characters, Viète deciphered it, helping France considerably in the war. Realizing that his plans were known and yet still not believing that the code could be deciphered, King Philip II accused the French of using black magic against his country. On another occasion, a Low Country ruler challenged King Henry IV by saying that France did not have a mathematician able to solve a particular forty-fifth degree equation. Within minutes after reading the problem, Viète found two roots, and with more time, twenty-one additional roots. This greatly impressed King Henry.

Viète is sometimes called the father of modern algebra. Much of the symbolization and many concepts that he introduced are still used in algebra classes today. He introduced the practice of using letters to represent unknowns, as in $2 + a = 5$. While Viète always used vowels to represent unknowns and consonants to represent known quantities, a practice not followed today, his introduction of letter substitutions has gone far toward the development of algebra. Our present-day symbols x, x^2, and x^3 would have been written A, A quadratum, and A cubum. He was the first to use $+$ and $-$ signs, but he did not have a symbol for equals. By abbreviating Latin words, he would have written $7A^2 - 3A + A^3 = C$ as 7 in A quad -3 in $A + A$ cub aequatur C solido.

Viète also invented a method for approximating the solution to an equation. Although tedious, his method applied to equations as high as the sixth degree.

Viète also studied the number π and found a formula that would give its approximate value. The study of π before that time had been in a geometric sense; π had been found by carefully measuring the circumference and diameter of a circle and finding their ratio. Viète was also first to apply the six trigonometric functions to plane and spherical trigonometry.

Viète produced and published many works on algebra, geometry, and trigonometry. His most famous work, *In Artem Analyticam Isogoge (Introduction to the Analytical Art)*, introduced the use of vowels for variables and consonants for constants. He published this work (often referred to as *In Artem* for short) in 1591—twelve years before his death in Paris in 1603.

Viète is sometimes called the father of modern algebra.

5.6 Graphing Quadratic Inequalities

To graph quadratic inequalities, begin as if graphing a quadratic function by solving for y and putting the right side in the form $a(x - h)^2 + k$. Then consider the curve and shading.

Graphing Quadratic Inequalities

1. Graph the quadratic inequality as if it were a quadratic function.
2. Use a dotted curve if it is a strict inequality, $<$ or $>$; use a solid curve if it has an equality in it, $\leq$ or $\geq$.
3. Shade the subset of the plane (either above or below the curve) that makes the inequality true.

Look at the two examples below.

EXAMPLE 1   Graph $y > 2(x - 4)^2 - 3$.

Answer

1. Use a dotted curve to graph
   $y = 2(x - 4)^2 - 3$.

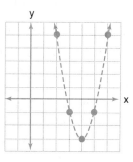

2. Decide which side of the parabola to shade by choosing a point inside or outside the parabola. Substitute the coordinates into the inequality to determine if it results in a true statement. If so, shade the side that contains that point. If not, then shade the other side.

   (4, 0) is inside the parabola. Does it work in the inequality?

   $y > 2(x - 4)^2 - 3$

   $0 > 2(4 - 4)^2 - 3$

   $0 > 2(0)^2 - 3$

   $0 > -3$

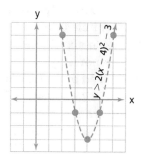

This is a true statement, so shade the area containing (4, 0), which is inside the curve.

EXAMPLE 2 Graph $y \leq -x^2 + 4x - 7$.

Answer

$y \leq -x^2 + 4x - 7$

$y \leq -(x^2 - 4x) - 7$

$y \leq -(x^2 - 4x + 4) - 7 + 4$

$y \leq -(x - 2)^2 - 3$

1. Complete the square to obtain $y = a(x - h)^2 + k$ form.

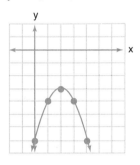

2. Graph, using a solid curve because of the $\leq$ symbol.

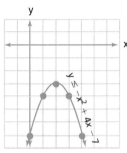

3. Determine which area to shade. Since the $\leq$ symbol occurs when solved for y and y decreases as we proceed downward, shade below the curve.

▶ A. Exercises

Graph.

1. $y > x^2 - 2$
2. $y \leq (x + 1)^2$
3. $y \geq -4x^2$
4. $y > \frac{1}{2}(x - 2)^2 + 3$

5. $y < -3(x + 4)^2 - 1$
6. $y \leq 2(x - 5)^2 + 3$
7. $y \geq -(x - 2)^2 - 1$
8. $y > 2x^2$

Give the domain and range of each relation below.

9. $y \geq -5(x + 3)^2 + 2$
10. $y \leq -4(x - 2)^2 + 5$
11. $y < -3(x + 1)^2 + 4$
12. $y > -2(x + 4)^2 + 3$

▶ B. Exercises

Put into $f(x) = a(x - h)^2 + k$ form and graph.

13. $y > 2x^2 + 12x + 21$
14. $y \geq -x^2 + 8x - 18$
15. $y < -\frac{1}{2}x^2 - x + \frac{3}{2}$
16. $y \leq 3x^2 + 12x + 17$

Give the domain, range, and equation of the axis of symmetry for

17. exercise 13
18. exercise 14.
19. exercise 15.
20. exercise 16.

▶ C. Exercises

Select the correct range for each quadratic inequality below. Assume $a > 0$.

21. $y \geq a(x - h)^2 + k$
22. $y < a(x - h)^2 + k$
23. $y > a(x - h)^2 + k$
24. $y \leq a(x - h)^2 + k$

A. $\mathbb{R}$
B. $\{y \mid y > k\}$
C. $\{y \mid y < k\}$
D. $\{y \mid y \geq k\}$
E. $\{y \mid y \leq k\}$
F. $\varnothing$

Cumulative Review

Match the expression to the correct term.

25. $\sqrt{(x_1 - x_2)^2 + (y_1 - y_2)^2}$
26. $a^3 - b^3$
27. $y = ax^2 + bx + c$
28. $y = mx + b$
29. $b^2 - 4ac$
30. $y = a^x$

A. difference of cubes
B. discriminant
C. distance
D. exponential function
E. linear function
F. quadratic function

5.7 Remainder and Factor Theorems

Recall from an earlier chapter the method of dividing a polynomial, $P(x)$, by a binomial.

$$(3x^3 - 4x^2 + 2x - 8) \div (x - 2)$$

$$
\begin{array}{r}
3x^2 + 2x + 6 \\
x - 2 \,\overline{)\,3x^3 - 4x^2 + 2x - 8} \\
\underline{3x^3 - 6x^2} \\
2x^2 + 2x \\
\underline{2x^2 - 4x} \\
6x - 8 \\
\underline{6x - 12} \\
4
\end{array}
$$

Now evaluate the polynomial $P(x) = 3x^3 - 4x^2 + 2x - 8$ where $x = 2$.

$$
\begin{aligned}
P(2) &= 3(2)^3 - 4(2)^2 + 2(2) - 8 \\
&= 3(8) - 4(4) + 2(2) - 8 \\
&= 24 - 16 + 4 - 8 \\
&= 4
\end{aligned}
$$

Notice that the remainder of the division problem and the evaluation of the polynomial function are the same. This example illustrates the remainder theorem.

Remainder Theorem
If a polynomial $P(x)$ is divided by a binomial $(x - a)$, the remainder obtained in the division is equal to the value of $P(a)$.

EXAMPLE 1   Find the remainder when $(2x^4 - 6x^3 - x^2 + 2x + 7) \div (x - 1)$.

Answer

$P(x) = 2x^4 - 6x^3 - x^2 + 2x + 7$	1. Let $P(x) = 2x^4 - 6x^3 - x^2 + 2x + 7$.

$P(1) = 2(1)^4 - 6(1)^3 - 1^2 + 2(1) + 7$ 2. Evaluate $P(1)$.
$\quad\;\; = 2 - 6 - 1 + 2 + 7$
$\quad\;\; = 4$

The remainder of the division is 4.

EXAMPLE 2   Find the remainder when $(x^5 + 3x^2 - 9) \div (x + 2)$.

Answer

$P(x) \quad = x^5 + 3x^2 - 9$	1. Let $P(x) = x^5 + 3x^2 - 9$.
$P(-2) = (-2)^5 + 3(-2)^2 - 9$	2. Evaluate $P(-2)$. Notice that you use
$\quad\quad = -32 + 12 - 9$	-2 because the remainder theorem says
	the divisor is of the form $x - a$.
$\quad\quad = -29$	$x + 2 = x - (-2)$, so $a = -2$.

The remainder of the division is -29.

The remainder theorem shows that long division is unnecessary for determining a remainder. You may wonder why you would even care what the remainder of a division problem is. The remainder theorem is often used in conjunction with the factor theorem.

Factor Theorem
The binomial $(x - a)$ is a factor of a polynomial, $P(x)$, if and only if the remainder of the division $P(x) \div (x - a)$ is 0.

By using these theorems, you can easily factor polynomials of the form

$$P(x) = a_n x^n + a_{n-1}x^{n-1} + a_{n-2}x^{n-2} + a_{n-3}x^{n-3} + \ldots + a_1 x + a_0$$

To factor polynomials we introduce one more theorem.

Integral Root Theorem
If $P(x)$ is a polynomial function with integer coefficients, then any integral root is a factor of a_0.

You can determine possible factors of a polynomial by letting a in $x - a$ be any factor of the constant term in the polynomial.

EXAMPLE 3   Solve $x^3 - 4x^2 + x + 6 = 0$ by factoring.

Answer

Factors of 6 are $\pm 6, \pm 3, \pm 2, \pm 1$.

1. To find possible $(x - a)$ binomial factors, you must determine the factors of the constant 6.

The possible factors of the polynomial are

$(x - 6)$ $(x - 2)$
$(x + 6)$ $(x + 2)$
$(x - 3)$ $(x - 1)$
$(x + 3)$ $(x + 1)$

Let $P(x) = x^3 - 4x^2 + x + 6$

$P(6) = 6^3 - 4(6)^2 + 6 + 6$
$ = 216 - 4(36) + 6 + 6$
$ = 216 - 144 + 6 + 6$
$ = 84$

2. Use the remainder theorem to determine the remainder when the polynomial is divided by $x - 6$. Since $P(6) \neq 0$, $(x - 6)$ is not a factor of the polynomial according to the factor theorem.

$P(3) = 3^3 - 4(3)^2 + 3 + 6$
$ = 27 - 4(9) + 3 + 6$
$ = 27 - 36 + 3 + 6$
$ = 0$

3. Continue using the remainder theorem to test the possible integral roots. Because $P(3) = 0$, $(x - 3)$ is a factor of the polynomial.

$P(x) = (x - 3)(x^2 - x - 2)$
$P(x) = (x - 3)(x - 2)(x + 1)$

4. Divide $P(x)$ by $x - 3$ to obtain the other factor. Be sure to factor completely.

$0 = (x - 3)(x - 2)(x + 1)$
$x = 3$ or $x = 2$ or $x = -1$

5. Set the factors of $P(x)$ equal to zero and solve.

Since the remainder theorem does not provide the quotient, long division was necessary at the fourth step. Since integer factors are frequently needed and involve long division, a short cut for such division would be useful. Consider the long division at the beginning of the section.

$$
\begin{array}{r}
3x^2 + 2x\ + 6 \\
x - 2 \overline{)\,3x^3 - 4x^2 + 2x - 8} \\
\underline{3x^3 - 6x^2} \\
2x^2 + 2x \\
\underline{2x^2 - 4x} \\
6x - 8 \\
\underline{6x - 12} \\
4
\end{array}
$$

Notice that every time the next term of the quotient is multiplied by the divisor, the first term of the product is exactly equal to the term from which it is being subtracted. This means that writing the x in the divisor and the underlined terms is not necessary.

$$
\begin{array}{r}
3x^2 + 2x\ + 6 \\
-\ 2\ )\overline{3x^3 - 4x^2 + 2x - 8} \\
\underline{-\ 6x^2} \\
2x^2 + 2x \\
\underline{-\ 4x} \\
6x - 8 \\
\underline{-\ 12} \\
4
\end{array}
$$

Notice also that every term is the same power of the variable as that from which it is subtracted. We need not write the variables either, but rather understand what power they represent. Remember the leading coefficient of the divisor is one.

$$
\begin{array}{r}
3\ 2\ 6 \\
-\ 2\ )\overline{3\ -\ 4\ 2\ -\ 8} \\
\underline{-\ 6} \\
2\ 2 \\
\underline{-\ 4} \\
6\ -\ 8 \\
\underline{-\ 12} \\
4
\end{array}
$$

$$
\begin{aligned}
3 \div 1 &= 3 \\
3(-2) &= -6 \\
-4 - (-6) &= 2* \\
2 \div 1 &= 2 \\
2(-2) &= -4 \\
2 - (-4) &= 6* \\
6 \div 1 &= 6 \\
6(-2) &= -12 \\
-8 - (-12) &= 4*
\end{aligned}
$$

In each step denoted by an asterisk, we subtracted; but addition is easier than subtracting negatives, so we will add the opposite. We do this by changing the sign on the divisor. This means that when we multiply, each sign will be the opposite of what it was previously, allowing us to add.

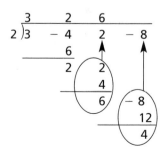

To simplify further, slide the columns circled up. To begin bring the 3 down.

2	3	−4	2	−8		$2(3)$	$=$	6
	↓	6	4	12		$-4 + 6$	$=$	2
	3	2	6	4		$2(2)$	$=$	4
						$2 + 4$	$=$	6
						$2(6)$	$=$	12
						$-8 + 12$	$=$	4

The table above is used to obtain the coefficients of the terms in the quotient. Remember that the last term (4) is the remainder. Thus, the term to the left (6) is the constant and each term further left increases by a power of x. The quotient is $3x^2 + 2x + 6$ R. 4. This time-saving short cut is called *synthetic division*.

EXAMPLE 4 $(4x^5 - 35x^3 + 2x - 7) \div (x + 3)$. Divide synthetically to obtain the quotient.

Answer

−3	4	0	−35	0	2	−7	Insert 0 as a place
		−12	36	−3	9	−33	holder for the coefficients of x^4 and x^2.
	4	−12	1	−3	11	−40	

The quotient is $4x^4 - 12x^3 + x^2 - 3x + 11$ R. −40.

EXAMPLE 5 Solve $x^3 - 3x^2 - 24x - 28 = 0$ by factoring using synthetic division.

Answer

The divisors of −28 are ±1, ±2, ±4, ±7, ±14, and ±28.

1. Obtain possible integral roots.

1	1	−3	−24	−28
		1	−2	−26
	1	−2	−26	−54

2. Divide synthetically to determine actual factors.
   Since R. ≠ 0, $x - 1$ is not a factor.

−2	1	−3	−24	−28
		−2	10	28
	1	−5	−14	0

R. = 0, so $x - (-2) = x + 2$ is a factor.

$x^3 - 3x^2 - 24x - 28$	$=$	0
$(x + 2)(x^2 - 5x - 14)$	$=$	0

3. Write the factors.

$(x + 2)(x + 2)(x - 7)$	$=$	0

4. Factor the remaining trinomial.

$x = -2$ or $x = 7$

5. Solve.

▶ A. Exercises

If $P(x) = 3x^3 + 7x^2 - 2x + 6$, use the remainder theorem to find the remainder when this polynomial is divided by the following binomials.

1. $x - 1$
2. $x - 3$
3. $x + 4$
4. $x + 2$
5. $x - 7$
6. $x + 1$
7. $x + 6$
8. $x - 5$

Use the factor theorem to determine whether the following binomials are factors of $x^4 - 10x^3 + 17x^2 + 52x - 60$.

9. $x - 5$
10. $x + 1$
11. $x - 2$
12. $x - 6$
13. $x + 3$
14. $x - 4$
15. $x + 2$
16. $x - 1$

▶ B. Exercises

Factor the following polynomials completely using synthetic division.

17. $x^3 - 5x^2 + 2x + 8$
18. $x^3 + 9x^2 + 27x + 27$
19. $x^3 - 6x^2 + 11x - 6$
20. $x^4 - 4x^3 - 13x^2 + 28x + 60$

Solve.

21. $x^3 - 4x^2 - 7x + 10 = 0$
22. $x^3 + 4x^2 - x - 4 = 0$
23. $x^3 - 5x = 6 - 2x^2$
24. $x^3 - 3x^2 + 2x + 4 = 4$
25. Find $f(7)$ using the remainder theorem if
$f(x) = x^5 + 3x^4 - 50x^3 - 200x^2 + 500x - 3$

▶ C. Exercises

26. Solve $x^3 + x^2 - 12x + 12 = 0$
27. Given $f(x) = 3x^3 - 2x^2 + 7x - 1$, $f(0) = -1$ and $f(1) = 7$.
    a. Estimate the value of the zero between $x = 0$ and $x = 1$.
    b. Evaluate $f(x)$ for your estimate.
    c. Make a second estimate.

▶ Dominion Modeling

28. Find the zeros of your quadratic model for Egyptian infant growth. Interpret the results.

▮ Cumulative Review

Find the zeros and y-intercepts of each function.

29. $f(x) = x - 9$
30. $g(x) = 5x + 2$
31. $y = x^2 - 4x - 45$
32. $f(x) = x^2 - 10x + 16$
33. $g(x) = 3x^2 + 5x - 2$

IND OVER ATH

For any polynomial $P(x)$, let $Q(x)$ be the quotient and R the remainder when $P(x)$ is divided by $(x - a)$.
1. Prove the Remainder Theorem.
2. Prove the Factor Theorem.

Determinants and Minors

To evaluate a determinant for a higher-order matrix, for example, a 4 × 4 or 5 × 5 matrix, you may use determinants of lower-order matrices that you already know how to evaluate. These determinants are called minors, and every entry has one. A *minor* of an entry of a square matrix is the determinant found by crossing out the row and column of the entry. The minors of the 7 and the 3 in the following matrix are shown.

$$\begin{bmatrix} 5 & 6 & 7 \\ 3 & -4 & 2 \\ 1 & 0 & 5 \end{bmatrix}$$

Minor of 7

$$\begin{bmatrix} \cancel{5} & \cancel{6} & \cancel{7} \\ 3 & -4 & \cancel{2} \\ 1 & 0 & \cancel{5} \end{bmatrix} \qquad \begin{vmatrix} 3 & -4 \\ 1 & 0 \end{vmatrix}$$

Minor of 3

$$\begin{bmatrix} \cancel{5} & 6 & 7 \\ \cancel{3} & \cancel{-4} & \cancel{2} \\ \cancel{1} & 0 & 5 \end{bmatrix} \qquad \begin{vmatrix} 6 & 7 \\ 0 & 5 \end{vmatrix}$$

Choose either a row or column of the matrix, then multiply each entry of that row or column by its minor. Add or subtract the products as shown to find the determinant. This method works on large determinants as well as offering an alternative for 3 × 3 determinants.

$$\begin{vmatrix} a & b & c \\ d & e & f \\ g & h & i \end{vmatrix} = a \begin{vmatrix} e & f \\ h & i \end{vmatrix} - d \begin{vmatrix} b & c \\ h & i \end{vmatrix} + g \begin{vmatrix} b & c \\ e & f \end{vmatrix}$$

The signs of the terms always alternate between positive and negative. Each term is the product of an entry and its minor, and the location of the entry determines the sign. Add the column number and row number of the entry. If the sum is even, the sign for the term is positive. If the sum is odd, the sign is negative.

Choose the easiest row to expand. In the example below, row two is easiest because the zero products make it unnecessary to evaluate three of the four minors. Since the first entry of that row is in row 2, column 1, and their sum is 3, which is odd, the first term is negative. The signs alternate.

a b a
c d c
$-$ $+$ $+$ C^T $X = \dfrac{\det(A_i)}{\det(A)}$ $(m \times n)(n \times p)$ $[A : I]$

Matrix Algebra 5

$$\begin{vmatrix} 5 & 3 & 2 & 8 \\ 0 & 0 & 4 & 0 \\ 2 & 8 & 3 & 1 \\ 0 & 7 & -4 & 2 \end{vmatrix} = -0\begin{vmatrix} 3 & 2 & 8 \\ 8 & 3 & 1 \\ 7 & -4 & 2 \end{vmatrix} + 0\begin{vmatrix} 5 & 2 & 8 \\ 2 & 3 & 1 \\ 0 & -4 & 2 \end{vmatrix} - 4\begin{vmatrix} 5 & 3 & 8 \\ 2 & 8 & 1 \\ 0 & 7 & 2 \end{vmatrix} + 0\begin{vmatrix} 5 & 3 & 2 \\ 2 & 8 & 3 \\ 0 & 7 & -4 \end{vmatrix}$$

$$= -4\left[5\begin{vmatrix} 8 & 1 \\ 7 & 2 \end{vmatrix} - 2\begin{vmatrix} 3 & 8 \\ 7 & 2 \end{vmatrix} + 0\begin{vmatrix} 3 & 8 \\ 8 & 1 \end{vmatrix} \right]$$

$$= -4[5(16 - 7) - 2(6 - 56) + 0]$$

$$= -4[45 + 100]$$

$$= -580$$

▶ Exercises

$$\begin{vmatrix} 1 & -6 & 4 \\ 0 & 2 & 1 \\ 1 & -5 & 7 \end{vmatrix}$$

Expand the determinant using the row or column indicated.

1. last column
2. first row
3. diagonal-product method of Chapter 4
4. Expand the literal formula given to verify that it is always the same as the formula of Chapter 4.
5. Evaluate the following determinant by using minors.

$$\begin{vmatrix} 3 & 6 & -1 & 4 \\ 0 & 2 & 8 & 3 \\ 0 & 4 & -6 & 2 \\ 0 & 5 & 10 & 6 \end{vmatrix}$$

5.8 Graphing Polynomial Functions

In the last two sections you studied zeros of polynomials and how to factor higher order polynomials. These ideas can help you graph a polynomial function. Graphs are very important in mathematics because they provide pictures of equations.

Polynomials can be used to model curves, such as that formed as this fly fisherman casts.

Similarly, the Bible gives a picture in Ephesians 5:21-33. Marriage is a gift from God (Prov. 18:22, 19:14; see also I Cor. 7:1-7). But it is also a picture of the relationship Christ has with His church (II Cor. 11:2; Eph. 5:21-33). In this picture, Christ is the husband, and all true believers are the bride-to-be. The wedding has not happened yet, but Christians are still "betrothed" or promised to our Heavenly Bridegroom. We eagerly look forward to the day when we will be married to the Son of God (Rev. 19:7-9; 22:20). Marriage helps us understand the relationship between Christians and the Savior by providing a picture.

The goal of this section is to help you better picture polynomial functions. A general polynomial function is of the form

$$f = \{(x, y) \mid y = P(x)\}, \text{ where}$$

$$P(x) = a_n x^n + a_{n-1} x^{n-1} + a_{n-2} x^{n-2} + a_{n-3} x^{n-3} + \ldots + a_1 x + a_0$$

The important points on the graph of a polynomial function are the zeros and the points where the curve changes from going up to going down or vice versa.

You have learned how to find the integral zeros of functions. Frequently a polynomial function has zeros that are not integers. In such cases you can approximate the zeros as in the following examples.

EXAMPLE 1 Graph $P(x) = x^3 + 7x^2 + 4x - 12$.

Answer

The factors of 12 are ± 1, ± 2, ± 3, ± 4, ± 6, ± 12. Try 1.	1. Use the integral roots theorem to identify possible roots.

$$\begin{array}{r|rrrr} 1 & 1 & 7 & 4 & -12 \\ & & 1 & 8 & 12 \\ \hline & 1 & 8 & 12 & 0 \end{array}$$

2. Use synthetic division to factor the polynomial if its degree is larger than two.

Since the remainder is zero, $x - 1$ is a factor of the polynomial. The trinomial quotient is $x^2 + 8x + 12$.

Therefore

$$x^3 + 7x^2 + 4x - 12 = 0$$
$$(x - 1)(x^2 + 8x + 12) = 0$$
$$(x - 1)(x + 6)(x + 2) = 0$$

3. Set $P(x) = 0$ and factor the left side from your division. The quadratic also factors.

$$x - 1 = 0 \quad x + 6 = 0 \quad x + 2 = 0$$
$$x = 1 \qquad x = -6 \qquad x = -2$$

4. Solve for the zeros, which tell you that the graph crosses the x-axis in three places.

$$\begin{array}{r|rrrr} -4 & 1 & 7 & 4 & -12 \\ & \downarrow & -4 & -12 & 32 \\ \hline & 1 & 3 & -8 & 20 \end{array}$$

5. To obtain more ordered pairs, either substitute into the function or use synthetic division (shown here for $x = -4$).

The point $(-4, 20)$ lies on the curve.

$$P(x) = x^3 + 7x^2 + 4x - 12$$

x	$P(x)$
-7	-40
-4	20
-1	-10
0	-12
2	32

The three zeros divide the number line into four intervals. Choose at least one value of x in each interval.

Notice that the y-intercept is the constant (all other terms will be zero for $x = 0$).

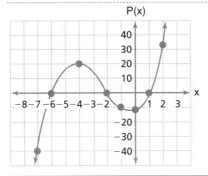

6. Plot these points and the zeros. Connect them with a smooth curve.

EXAMPLE 2   Graph $P(x) = x^5$.

Answer

$x^5 = 0$ 1. Set $P(x) = 0$ and solve for x to
$x = 0$ find the zeros.

x	$P(x)$
-3	-243
-2	-32
-1	-1
1	1
2	32
3	243

2. Find several ordered pairs on
    both sides of the zero.

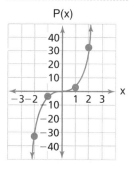

$P(x)$

3. Draw the graph.

EXAMPLE 3   Approximate the zero of $P(x) = 3x^3 - 2x^2 + x - 4$
and graph.

Answer   Synthetic division is used here to find a series of points on the
curve. The intermediate step of writing the product is not
shown, but rather the product is obtained and added mentally.
Each line contains one complete division.

	3	-2	1	-4
-3	3	-11	34	-106
-2	3	-8	17	-38
-1	3	-5	6	-10

The points $(-3, -106)$, $(-2, -38)$, and $(-1, -10)$ are on the
curve. Additional points are given in the table below.

Continued ▶

x	P(x)
−3	−106
−2	−38
−1	−10
0	−4
1	−2
2	14
3	62

1. You cannot find the zero of this function directly by factoring, so you must approximate it by examining the graph.

   Find enough ordered pairs to see the pattern of this function.

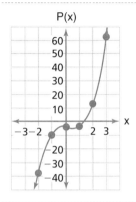

2. Graph the ordered pairs and connect the points with a smooth curve. Notice that the intercept is between $x = 1$ and $x = 2$. You can also see this on the table since the function values change from negative to positive.

x	P(x)
1.5	3.125
1.3	0.511
1.2	−0.496

3. Since $f(1)$ is closer to zero than $f(2)$, the zero is probably closer to 1 than 2. Check ordered pairs as needed to obtain $x \approx 1.25$ (to two decimal places).

▶ A. Exercises

Find the zeros of the following polynomial functions. Express irrational zeros as decimals to the nearest tenth.

1. $P(x) = x^3 + 7x^2 + 10x$
2. $P(x) = x^2 - 7$
3. $P(x) = x^2 + 3x - 5$
4. $P(x) = x^3 + 2x^2 - 9x - 18$
5. $P(x) = x^3 - 5x^2 - x + 5$
6. $P(x) = x^3 - 3x^2 - 10x + 24$
7. $P(x) = x^2 + 4x - 12$
8. $P(x) = 2x^3 + 3x^2 - x + 2$

▶ B. Exercises

Graph.
9. $P(x) = (x + 3)^3$
10. $P(x) = x^3 - 4x^2 - 5$
11. $P(x) = x^3 + 4x + 3$
12. $P(x) = 3x^3 - 2x^2 + x - 2$
13. $P(x) = 4x^3 + 3x^2 - x + 5$
14. $P(x) = x^2 + 2x - 3$
15. $P(x) = x^4 - 2x^3 + x^2 - 2x + 1$
16. $P(x) = 6x^3 - 19x^2 + x + 6$

Graph the following polynomial functions. Find the zeros expressed as decimals to the nearest tenth.
17. $P(x) = x^3 - x + 1$
18. $P(x) = x^4 - x^2 - 2$

▶ C. Exercises

Graph each polynomial inequality.
19. $y < x^3 - 2x^2 - 5x + 6$
20. $y \geq x^3 + x^2 - 4x - 4$

▶ Dominion Modeling

21. Fit a cubic model to the Egyptian infant data. What do you get?
22. What does the cubic model predict for an Egyptian that reaches ten years of age? Evaluate.
23. Since babies begin as a single cell at conception, what would be the average weight of this cell at conception according to the cubic model?

Cumulative Review

Match each theorem to its name.

24. $(a + b)(c + d) = ac + ad + bc + bd$.

25. $ab = 0 \rightarrow a = 0$ or $b = 0$.

26. $ax^2 + bx + c = 0$, $a \neq 0 \rightarrow$
    $x = \dfrac{-b \pm \sqrt{b^2 - 4ac}}{2a}$

27. If $P(x) \div (x - a)$ has remainder 0, then $x - a$ is a factor of $P(x)$.

28. The remainder from $P(x) \div (x - a)$ is the same as $P(a)$.

29. For $a > 0$, $|x| < a \leftrightarrow -a < x < a$.

A. Compound inequality theorem

B. Factor theorem

C. FOIL Method

D. Remainder theorem

E. Quadratic formula

F. Zero product property

Algebra and Scripture

Algebra and You

Thinking skills constitute a very valuable gift from God. The tool of reasoning is one of the qualities that marks man as in the image of God and as different from animals. Algebra provides one means of sharpening this tool.

1. According to Ecclesiastes 10:10, if you do not sharpen your tools before you use them what will happen?

This shows how important it is for you to prepare your tools for God's use. Ball players run to exercise their legs; you must do your algebra daily to exercise your reasoning skills. If you fail to exercise now, you may not be ready to win the contests God has for you.

2. How does Jeremiah 12:5 illustrate that there are greater challenges ahead?
3. Find the passage in which Jesus spoke of ten virgins preparing for the groom's coming. How many were ready? What did they do? Give the reference.

"Whatsoever ye do" certainly includes the work we do in algebra. In light of this, what does each passage below tell you about your algebra exercises?

4. I Corinthians 10:31
5. Colossians 3:17
6. Colossians 3:23
7. What is the whole duty of man (Ecc. 12:13)?

God wants us to diligently develop our tools and talents for Him. This includes our reasoning skills. There are many commands and promises to the diligent in the Book of Proverbs.

8. Find at least one command to be diligent.

9. Find at least two promises for diligence.

GREATER AMPLITUDE

Find the other commands and promises to the diligent in Proverbs.

In what way did the men mentioned in the following passages fail to prepare?

10. Proverbs 12:27

11. Proverbs 24:30-34

We should prepare our thoughts through diligent Bible study together with diligent study of the arts and sciences to understand God's created order.

In fact we can learn diligence from a study of nature. Read Proverbs 6:6.

12. What should we emulate?

Let us seek to study diligently and to bring "into captivity every thought unto the obedience of Christ" (II Cor. 10:5).

Absolute Values

If thou hast run with the footmen, and they have wearied thee, then how canst thou contend with horses? and if in the land of peace, wherein thou trustedst, they wearied thee, then how wilt thou do in the swelling of Jordan?

JEREMIAH 12:5

Chapter 5 Review

Find at least six ordered pairs for each quadratic function and graph.
1. $y = x^2 - 10x + 25$
2. $y = x^2 - 4x + 4$

Graph each quadratic function and give the maximum or minimum point.
3. $y = 4x^2$
4. $y = -\frac{1}{2}x^2$
5. $y = 2x^2 - 3$
6. $y = -5(x - 4)^2 + 1$
7. $f(x) = (x - 2)^2$
8. $g(x) = x^2 + 6x + 11$
9. $y = -x^2 + 2x - 2$
10. $h(x) = x^2 + 6x + 5$
11. The Barnett Construction Company is enclosing a school playground with fencing. The school will act as one side of the rectangular play area. If 252 feet of fencing will be used around the play area, what dimensions would make a maximum play area for the children? What is the maximum area?

Graph.
12. $y > x^2 + 12x + 36$
13. $y \leq -2x^2 + 4x - 5$

Find the zeros of each function.
14. $P(x) = x^2 + 2x - 3$
15. $P(x) = x^3 - x^2 - 2x$

Factor each polynomial.
16. $x^3 - 7x^2 + 36$
17. $x^3 - 6x^2 + 3x + 10$

Graph.
18. $P(x) = x^4$
19. $P(x) = 3x^3 + 2x^2 - x + 1$
20. $P(x) = -2x^3$

$f(x) = 2(x + 3)^2 + 4$
21. Identify the axis of symmetry and y-intercept.
22. Give the domain and range.

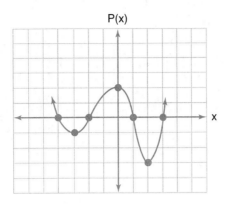

P(x)

23. Give the zeros of $P(x)$.
24. Give the y-intercept of $P(x)$.
25. Give the domain and range of $P(x)$.
26. What is the minimum point of $P(x)$?
27. Graph $y = x^3$.

Use your knowledge of translation to graph
28. $y = x^3 + 2$.
29. $y = (x - 1)^3$.
30. $y = (x + 2)^3 - 3$.
31. Evaluate the cubic model for the Egyptian infant data.
32. Give the mathematical significance of Jeremiah 12:5.

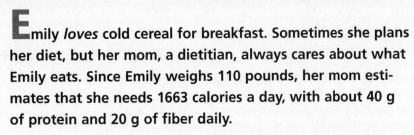

$y = \dfrac{a}{b}$

Emily *loves* cold cereal for breakfast. Sometimes she plans her diet, but her mom, a dietitian, always cares about what Emily eats. Since Emily weighs 110 pounds, her mom estimates that she needs 1663 calories a day, with about 40 g of protein and 20 g of fiber daily.

Emily and her mom made a table from the nutrition panels on the cereal boxes. Emily rated each cereal in the "Taste Index" column. Throughout this chapter you will see how systems of equations and inequalities help to analyze this data.

Name	Calories	Fiber (g)	Protein (g)	Taste Index
100% Natural	280	5	7	6.0
All-Bran	130	16	6	1.7
Cap'n Crunch	100	1	1	9.0
Cheerios	60	1	2	9.0
Corn Flakes	80	1	1	8.7
Golden Grahams	90	0	1	9.7
Life	120	2	3	7.3
Raisin Bran	130	5	3	7.0
Special K	70	1	4	3.0
Toasted Oatmeal Squares	160	3	5	4.3
Total	80	2	2	5.0
Wheaties	90	2	2	5.7

After this chapter you should able to

1. solve a system of linear equations by three methods—graphing, substitution, and addition.
2. determine whether a system is inconsistent or dependent.
3. solve word problems using systems of equations.
4. solve systems of inequalities.
5. solve linear programming problems.
6. solve systems of quadratic equations.
7. solve systems of linear equations in three variables.

6.1 Solving Systems by Graphing

Those who work in the business world sometimes have to work with systems of equations. Equations that affect business may relate several variables. Successful businessmen recognize the factors that influence their business and make decisions that cause the business to operate smoothly and efficiently.

In the body of Christ, the church, Christians must work together effectively for the Lord. The Lord has given each Christian gifts and talents to be used to honor and glorify Him. There must not be contention within this body, but all must work together to edify other believers and proclaim the gospel of Jesus Christ to the unsaved (I Cor. 12:12-31).

This chapter will develop your understanding of systems of equations and will provide a basis for further study of business and other areas. The simplest form of a system of equations is two linear equations in two variables. We will concentrate on this type of system before branching out into more difficult types.

A solution to a system of equations is the set of points that make all the equations in the system true simultaneously. There are several methods of solving a system. The first method is graphing. The solution to a system of linear equations in two variables is the ordered pair that describes the intersection of their respective line graphs.

EXAMPLE 1 Solve the system.
$$x + y = 4$$
$$x - y = 2$$

Answer

$x + y = 4$	$x - y = 2$	1. Place each equation in slope-intercept form and graph on a Cartesian plane.
$y = -x + 4$	$-y = -x + 2$	
	$y = x - 2$	

Continued ▶

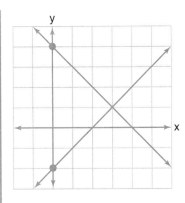

2. The answer to the system is the point where the two equations intersect.

The answer to the system is (3, 1).

In Example 1 the only ordered pair that will work in both equations is (3, 1). A theorem from geometry explains why the solution is unique. The theorem states "If two lines intersect, they intersect in one and only one point." A second example follows.

EXAMPLE 2   Solve the system.

$$2x + y = 0$$
$$3x + 2y = 2$$

Answer

| $2x + y = 0$ $3x + 2y = 2$ | 1. Place each equation in slope-intercept form. |

$2x + y = 0$ $3x + 2y = 2$

       $y = -2x$ $2y = -3x + 2$

                     $y = \frac{-3}{2}x + 1$

1. Place each equation in slope-intercept form.

2. Graph each equation on a Cartesian plane.

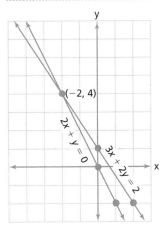

(−2, 4) is the solution to the system.

▶ A. Exercises

Solve each system by graphing.

1. $x + y = 4$
   $x - y = -2$
2. $2x + y = 2$
   $3x - y = -2$
3. $4x + y = 6$
   $2x - y = 0$
4. $2x - y = 10$
   $3x + y = 0$
5. $3x - y = -7$
   $4x + y = -14$
6. $x - 2y = -16$
   $2x + y = -7$
7. $2x - 3y = -30$
   $x + y = 5$
8. $4x - y = -15$
   $3x + 2y = -14$
9. $3x + y = 17$
   $x - 2y = 1$
10. $x + 5y = -14$
    $2x - y = 5$
11. $3x - 4y = 5$
    $2x + 5y = 11$

▶ B. Exercises

Solve each system by graphing.

12. $3x - 2y = -2$
    $x - 4y = -24$
13. $x + 3y = 21$
    $x - 9y = -27$
14. $x + 3y = -7$
    $2x + 4y = -12$

Graph each system and identify the number of points that are solutions. You do not need to write the solution. If the answer is other than one, explain why.

15. $2x + 5y = 3$
    $5x - 7y = 1$
16. $3x + y = 5$
    $6x + 2y = 6$

17. $x - 2y = 4$
    $3x - 6y = -12$
18. $5x + 2y = 6$
    $10x + 4y = 12$
19. $2x + 2y = 6$
    $x + y = 3$
20. $y = 2x - 1$
    $y = \frac{-1}{2}x + 3$

▶ C. Exercises

21. The function $C(x) = 119x + 750$ represents the cost of producing x three-pronged stainless steel widgets. $R(x) = 169x$ represents the revenue from selling x of them. Find the following.
    a. number that must be sold to break even
    b. profit from selling 500
    c. profit or loss from selling 200 at the regular price and 300 at half price

▶ Dominion Modeling

22. For the cereal data, what are the variables? What would be suitable independent variables? Which would be suitable dependent variables?

23. What is Emily's favorite cereal? What cereal would be best to supplement her favorite to obtain more calories, fiber, and protein?

Cumulative Review

Find $f(-3)$ and $f\left(\frac{5}{2}\right)$ if
24. $f(x) = |x|$
25. $f(x) = 4x^2 + 6x - 1$
26. $f(x) = [x] + 1$
27. $f(x) = 7$
28. $f(x) = -2x - 3$

6.2 Solving Systems by Substitution

The solution to most systems of two equations in two variables is the point where the two equations intersect. Some systems involve lines that do not intersect and therefore have no solution. Others may consist of two equations representing the same line and therefore have an infinite number of solutions. If the graph has an intersection point with very large coordinates or the coordinates are fractional, then the correct answer to the system is difficult to find by graphing.

You will use two algebraic methods for solving systems of equations in this chapter. The first one is the substitution method. The basic idea is expressed in the substitution property.

Substitution Property

For all numbers or expressions a and b, if $a = b$, then a can be replaced by b in an equation or inequality.

Substitution is a blessed principle to the Christian. Because of the substitutionary death of Jesus Christ and His shed blood, Christians have a secure home in heaven with God for eternity. "But God commendeth his love toward us, in that, while we were yet sinners, Christ died for us" (Rom. 5:8). Do you know that heaven is your eternal home?

The substitution property can be extremely useful for solving systems of equations. As you gain more experience with solving systems, you will know when to use this method and when to use some other method. Study the following examples.

EXAMPLE 1   Solve the system.
$$3x + y = -20$$
$$y = x - 8$$

Answer

$$3x + y = -20$$
$$y = x - 8$$

Continued ▶

$3x + (x - 8) = -20$ $4x - 8 = -20$ $4x = -12$ $x = -3$	1. Notice that in the second equation, y is expressed in terms of x. You can substitute $x - 8$ for y in the first equation to obtain an equation in one variable. Solve this equation for x.
$y = x - 8$ $y = -3 - 8$ $y = -11$	2. To find the value of y, substitute -3 for x in the equation $y = x - 8$.
$(-3, -11)$	3. Write the solution as an ordered pair.

In real life applications, the solution to a system of equations will usually be an ordered pair having fractional coordinates. In this case the substitution method is much better than graphing.

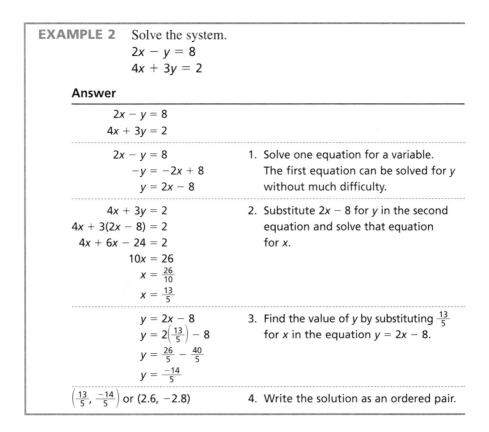

EXAMPLE 2   Solve the system.
$$2x - y = 8$$
$$4x + 3y = 2$$

Answer

$2x - y = 8$ $4x + 3y = 2$	
$2x - y = 8$ $-y = -2x + 8$ $y = 2x - 8$	1. Solve one equation for a variable. The first equation can be solved for y without much difficulty.
$4x + 3y = 2$ $4x + 3(2x - 8) = 2$ $4x + 6x - 24 = 2$ $10x = 26$ $x = \frac{26}{10}$ $x = \frac{13}{5}$	2. Substitute $2x - 8$ for y in the second equation and solve that equation for x.
$y = 2x - 8$ $y = 2\left(\frac{13}{5}\right) - 8$ $y = \frac{26}{5} - \frac{40}{5}$ $y = \frac{-14}{5}$	3. Find the value of y by substituting $\frac{13}{5}$ for x in the equation $y = 2x - 8$.
$\left(\frac{13}{5}, \frac{-14}{5}\right)$ or $(2.6, -2.8)$	4. Write the solution as an ordered pair.

Systems such as those in Examples 1 and 2 having solutions that are ordered pairs are called *consistent*.

When graphing a system of equations, you may find the lines are parallel. This means no solution exists. Such a system is called *inconsistent* and we designate the solution as the empty set ($\varnothing$). If a system is inconsistent and you attempt to solve it by substitution, all the variables will disappear and you will get a false statement of numerical equality. The following example illustrates this.

EXAMPLE 3   Solve the system.
$$8x - 4y = 1$$
$$2x - y = -3$$

Answer

$8x - 4y = 1$
$2x - y = -3$

$2x - y = -3$ $-y = -2x - 3$ $y = 2x + 3$	1. Solve one of the equations for a variable. The easiest equation to work with is the second equation because the y has a coefficient of -1. Solve it for y.
$8x - 4y = 1$ $8x - 4(2x + 3) = 1$ $8x - 8x - 12 = 1$	2. Substitute $2x + 3$ for y in the first equation.
$-12 = 1$	3. The variable vanishes and this statement is false; therefore the system is inconsistent. Since there are no solutions, the solution is $\varnothing$.

▶ **A. Exercises**

Solve each system by the substitution method and state whether the system is consistent or inconsistent.

1. $x + y = -6$
   $2x + 3y = -20$
2. $x + y = 8$
   $x + y = -2$
3. $3x + 4y = -36$
   $y = 2x - 9$
4. $-4x + y = 26$
   $x = 5y + 3$

5. $3x + 5y = 18$
   $x - 6y = -17$
6. $4x - y = -3$
   $y = 4x + 6$
7. $-3x + y = 8$
   $x + 7y = 1$
8. $5x = 9$
   $x - 3y = 6$
9. $6x - 2y = -1$
   $y = 3x + 4$
10. $5x + y = 41$
    $x - 2y = 6$
11. $3x + 8y = 8$
    $x - 3y = \frac{5}{4}$
12. $3x - y = -2$
    $3x + y = 2$
13. $x - 3y = 16$
    $3x + y = -2$
14. $4x - y = -8$
    $2x + 3y = 24$
15. $x + y = -3$
    $2x - 5y = -13$

▶ B. Exercises

Consider: $10x - 17y = -6$;
$10x + 17y = 20.$

16. Graph the system. Which point looks like the solution on the graph? Does it check?
17. Solve the system by substitution. Would you have found the solution graphically?

Solve each system below by substitution and graphing. Identify each as consistent or inconsistent.

18. $x + 2y = -1$
    $3x - y = 4$
19. $3x + y = 5$
    $6x + 2y = 4$
20. $x + y = 1$
    $3x + 3y = 3$

▶ C. Exercises

Solve by substitution using a calculator. Round answers to tenths.

21. $5.3x + 2.7y = 19$
    $y = 0.015x - 8.4$
22. $57.5x + 114y = 6270$
    $21.9x + 92y = 3910$

▶ Dominion Modeling

Using the cereal data for Raisin Bran and Special K, write equations for each. (*Hint:* Let x be the number of Special K servings, and let y be the number of Raisin Bran servings.)

23. The number of servings of each to obtain 25% of Emily's daily requirement of fiber.
24. The number of servings of each to obtain 25% of Emily's daily protein needs.
25. The number of servings of each to obtain a taste index total of 12.

Cumulative Review

Graph.

26. $y = 2[x]$
27. $f = \{(-2, 3), (5, 1), (-1, -3), (0, 4)\}$
28. $y = (x + 3)^2 - 1$
29. $y = |x - 2| + 4$
30. $y < 4$

6.3 Solving Systems by Addition

The second algebraic method of solving systems of equations is the *addition method*. This method is relatively simple, and you should enjoy using it. You will add or subtract two equations for the purpose of eliminating one of the variables. Subtraction is still the addition method because subtraction is, by definition, adding the opposite.

To eliminate a variable by adding, the coefficients of the variable to be eliminated must be additive inverses. If the coefficients are the same you will subtract to eliminate the variable. An alternate approach to subtraction is to use a negative multiplier on one of the equations and then add.

EXAMPLE 1 Solve the system.
$$x + y = -1$$
$$2x - y = 10$$

Answer

$x + y = -1$ $2x - y = 10$	1. Write the equations with the variables aligned and compare coefficients. If the absolute values of the coefficients are the same on either variable, add or subtract the equations to eliminate that variable.
$x + y = -1$ $2x - y = 10$	Here you should add the equations to eliminate y.
$3x = 9$ $x = 3$	2. Solve the resulting equation for x.
$x + y = -1$ $3 + y = -1$ $y = -4$	3. Substitute 3 for x in either of the original equations, and find the value of y.
$(3, -4)$	4. Write the solution as an ordered pair.

The following example is done twice in parallel columns using addition on the left and subtraction on the right. Also, in the addition column, the second variable is found by elimination rather than by substitution.

EXAMPLE 2   Solve the system.
$$3x + 7y = -34$$
$$5x + 2y = 11$$

Answer

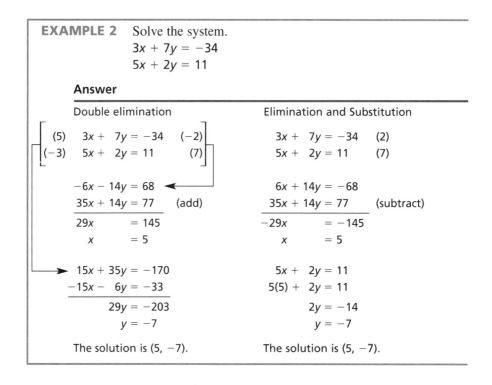

Double elimination	Elimination and Substitution
(5) $3x + 7y = -34$ (-2)	$3x + 7y = -34$ (2)
(-3) $5x + 2y = 11$ (7)	$5x + 2y = 11$ (7)
$-6x - 14y = 68$	$6x + 14y = -68$
$35x + 14y = 77$ (add)	$35x + 14y = 77$ (subtract)
$29x = 145$	$-29x = -145$
$x = 5$	$x = 5$
$15x + 35y = -170$	$5x + 2y = 11$
$-15x - 6y = -33$	$5(5) + 2y = 11$
$29y = -203$	$2y = -14$
$y = -7$	$y = -7$
The solution is $(5, -7)$.	The solution is $(5, -7)$.

Recall that if you solve a system of equations algebraically where the variables disappear and you get a false statement such as $5 = 9$, the system is an inconsistent system (no solution).

If you solve an equation algebraically where the variables disappear and you get a true expression such as $0 = 0$, the system is called a *dependent system*. A system that is not dependent is *independent*.

If you attempt to graph a dependent system, you will discover that both equations represent the same line. A dependent system has an infinite number of solutions. In fact, every point on the line is a solution.

EXAMPLE 3   Solve the system.
$$2x + 3y = 4$$
$$10x + 15y = 20$$

Answer

$2x + 3y = 4$ (5)   1. Multiply the first equation by 5.

$10x + 15y = 20$

Continued ▶

$10x + 15y = 20$ 2. Subtract.
$10x + 15y = 20$
‾‾‾‾‾‾‾‾‾‾‾‾‾‾‾‾‾‾‾‾‾‾‾‾‾‾‾‾‾‾‾‾‾‾‾‾‾‾‾
        $0 = 0$

Taking the simpler equation, every point on the line
$2x + 3y = 4$ is a solution to the system.

▶ A. Exercises

Solve each system by the addition method. Identify any dependent systems.

1. $x + y = 10$
   $3x + y = 14$
2. $4x + 3y = -2$
   $5x - 3y = 38$
3. $x + y = -8$
   $x - 2y = 10$
4. $3x - 9y = 18$
   $x + y = 2$
5. $2x + y = 15$
   $3x - 2y = -2$

6. $4x + 3y = 11$
   $2x - 5y = 25$
7. $x - 3y = -1$
   $3x + 4y = 10$
8. $5x + 3y = -15$
   $2x - 5y = -6$
9. $2x - 3y = 5$
   $x + 7y = 28$
10. $x + 2y = 2$
    $3x + 6y = 6$

▶ B. Exercises

Solve each system by the addition method. Identify any dependent systems.

11. $8x - 6y = -3$
    $4x + 12y = 11$
12. $3x - y = 8$
    $6x + y = -2$
13. $0.4x + 0.1y = 2.9$
    $3x - 6y = -39$
14. $5x + 2y = -17$
    $\frac{2}{3}x - \frac{4}{5}y = 2$
15. $4x + y = 1$
    $6x + 3y = 0$
16. $2x + 3y = 5$
    $3y = 5 - 2x$
17. $4.5x + 1.5y = -15$
    $0.25x - 0.5y = -2$

Use the following system to answer the questions.

$$3x - 5y = 10$$
$$4x + 3y = 15$$

18. Graph the system. Can you find the solution from the graph?
19. Solve by substitution.
20. Solve by the addition method.
21. Compare the methods; which was easiest and why?

▶ C. Exercises

Solve by addition.

22. $ax + by = c$
    $dx + 2by = 4c$

23. $\frac{1}{a} + \frac{2}{b} = 3$
    $\frac{2}{a} - \frac{5}{b} = 6$

▶ Dominion Modeling

Recall your equations for fiber, protein, and taste index from the cereal data.

24. When do the fiber and taste index equations intersect? Explain the practical meaning of this solution. (*Hint:* Consider the methods of substitution or addition to solve these systems.)
25. When do the protein and taste index equations intersect? Explain the practical meaning of this solution. (*Hint:* Consider the methods of substitution or addition to solve these systems.)

▪ Cumulative Review

Solve.

26. $3x^2 + x - 5 = 0$
27. $2 - 3x > 5$
28. $x^2 - 10 = 3x$
29. $|x + 4| = 7$
30. $7x - 1 < 4 - 6x^2$

Solving Systems by Cramer's Rule

Gabriel Cramer, a Swiss physicist of the 1700s, developed a rule to solve systems of equations by using determinants. The rule is stated formally here.

Cramer's Rule

The solution to the system $\begin{array}{l} a_{11}x + a_{12}y = b \\ a_{21}x + a_{22}y = c \end{array}$ is given by

$$x = \frac{\det(A_1)}{\det(A)}, \quad y = \frac{\det(A_2)}{\det(A)}$$

where $A = \begin{bmatrix} a_{11} & a_{12} \\ a_{21} & a_{22} \end{bmatrix}$, $A_1 = \begin{bmatrix} b & a_{12} \\ c & a_{22} \end{bmatrix}$, $A_2 = \begin{bmatrix} a_{11} & b \\ a_{21} & c \end{bmatrix}$ and $\det(A) \neq 0$.

The matrix A is called the *coefficient matrix* for the system. Form the matrices A_1 and A_2 from the coefficient matrix by replacing a column with the constants from the system (b and c). Replace the x column when solving for x and the y column when solving for y. Notice that the fractions in Cramer's rule have the same denominator, the determinant of the coefficient matrix, which must therefore not equal zero. Also, to use Cramer's rule, the equations must be placed in standard form, $ax + by = c$.

EXAMPLE 1   Solve the system by using Cramer's rule.
$$3x - 5y = 11$$
$$2x + y = 16$$

Answer

$|A| = \begin{vmatrix} 3 & -5 \\ 2 & 1 \end{vmatrix} = 3(1) - (-5)(2) = 13$ 1. Find the determinant of the coefficient matrix A.

$|A_1| = \begin{vmatrix} 11 & -5 \\ 16 & 1 \end{vmatrix} = 11(1) - (-5)(16) = 91$ 2. Find the determinants of A_1 and A_2.

$|A_2| = \begin{vmatrix} 3 & 11 \\ 2 & 16 \end{vmatrix} = 3(16) - 11(2) = 26$

Continued ▶

$$x = \frac{\det(A_1)}{\det(A)} = \frac{91}{13} = 7$$

3. Solve for x and y.

$$y = \frac{\det(A_2)}{\det(A)} = \frac{26}{13} = 2$$

The solution is (7, 2).

Cramer's rule can be extended to systems of equations of higher order, which a calculator or computer can be programmed to solve. For a 3×3 system, you can compute determinants A, A_1, A_2, and A_3 by using the constant column in place of the appropriate variable column. Then $x = \frac{\det(A_1)}{\det(A)}$, $y = \frac{\det(A_2)}{\det(A)}$, and $z = \frac{\det(A_3)}{\det(A)}$ as before.

▶ Exercises

Solve each system of equations by using Cramer's rule.

1. $3x - 8y = -37$
   $2x + 7y = 37$
2. $4x + 7y = 4$
   $2x - 4y = -28$
3. $6x + 9y = -69$
   $x - 2y = 13$
4. $3x - y + 4z = -7$
   $2x + y - z = 16$
   $5x - 3y + 2z = -13$
5. Consider the following system.
   $4x - 3y = 5$
   $-8x + 6y = 7$
   a. Solve using the addition method.
   b. Find $\det(A)$. What will happen to the values of x and y when Cramer's rule is used to solve the system?

6.4 Problem Solving Using Systems

You can solve many word problems by using either a single variable as you learned to do in Chapter 1 or by using a system of equations. The thought process is the same. While systems apply to many types of word problems, in this chapter you will focus on motion, interest, and digit problems. The following examples will help you relate systems to the thought process you used earlier.

In a sculling competition, the winning team finished the 2000-meter race 34 seconds ahead of the last place team. If the winners paddled one-half mile per hour faster than the losers, what was the range of times?

EXAMPLE 1 Two buses 412 miles apart head toward each other. One travels 3 mph slower than the other, and they meet in 4 hours. What is the average speed of each bus?

Answer

x = rate of slow bus	1. **Read.** Identify this as a motion problem
y = rate of fast bus	and name the rates with variables.

	r	t	d
slow bus	x	4	$4x$
fast bus	y	4	$4y$

2. **Plan.** Make a table based on the formula $d = rt$. Fill in the time column. Multiply rate times time to fill in the distance column.

$$x = y - 3$$
$$4x + 4y = 412$$
$$4(y - 3) + 4y = 412$$
$$4y - 12 + 4y = 412$$
$$8y = 424$$
$$y = 53$$
$$x = 50$$

3. **Solve.** Write a system of equations to solve for x and y. One rate is 3 mph slower than the other, $x = y - 3$. Identify the distance relation. The total distance is 412 miles, so $4x + 4y = 412$. Use the substitution method to solve the system.

Substitute 53 for y in $x = y - 3$.

One bus is going 50 mph, and the other bus is traveling 53 mph.

4. **Check.** Interpret your answer and make sure you have answered the question.

EXAMPLE 2　Mr. Perry has a total of $10,000 invested in two accounts. The older account pays 8%, while the new one pays 10%. How much does he have invested in each account if his total annual interest income is $850?

Answer

1. **Read.** Classify the problem as an interest problem. Let the variables represent principal, since that is what you are trying to find.

	P	r	t	I
1st account	x	0.08	1	$0.08x$
2nd account	y	0.10	1	$0.10y$

2. **Plan.** Make a table using the formula $I = Prt$, where P is principal, r is annual interest rate in decimal form, t is time in years, and I is interest. Fill in three columns from the given information. Fill in the last column by using the formula $I = Prt$.

$$x + y = 10,000 \ (10)$$
$$0.08x + 0.10y = 850 \ (100)$$

3. **Solve.** Use the columns with variables to get two equations. The total principle is $10,000, and the total interest $850.

$$10x + 10y = 100,000$$
$$8x + 10y = 85,000$$

The addition method is used to solve the system. (Subtract.)

$$2x = 15,000$$
$$x = 7,500$$

$$7500 + y = 10,000$$
$$y = 2,500$$

He has $7500 invested at 8% and $2500 at 10%, producing $850 in annual interest.

4. **Check.** Interpret the answer in the context.

The last kind of problem is a digit problem. This type of problem usually compares the digits of a number, such as the units and tens digits.

EXAMPLE 3　The sum of the digits of a two-digit number is 11. The difference of the number and a number obtained by reversing the digits is 45. What is the original number?

234　CHAPTER 6　SYSTEMS OF EQUATIONS AND INEQUALITIES

Answer

Let t = the tens digit u = the ones digit	1. **Read.** Identify the problem as a digit problem and define the variables as the digits of the original two-digit number.
$10t + u$ = original number $10u + t$ = reversed number	2. **Plan.** Represent the number and the reversed number in terms of t and u.
$t + u = 11$ $(10t + u) - (10u + t) = 45$	3. **Solve.** Translate the first sentence. The sum of the digits is 11. Translate the second sentence. The difference of the number and the number with its digit reversed is 45.
$10t + u - 10u - t = 45$ $9t - 9u = 45$ $(\div\, 9)$ $t - u = 5$	Simplify the second equation by noticing that both sides are divisible by 9.
$\begin{aligned} t - u &= 5 \\ \underline{t + u} &= \underline{11} \\ 2t &= 16 \\ t &= 8 \\ 8 + u &= 11 \\ u &= 3 \end{aligned}$	The addition method is used to solve the system.
The original number is 83.	4. **Check.** Answer the question in the problem. Reverse the digits to check.
$83 - 38 = 45$	

▶ A. Exercises

1. Greg has $5000 invested in two separate accounts. On the passbook account he receives 6% interest, and on the money market account he receives 9% interest. How much does he have invested in each account if his total annual interest earned is $375?

2. Two cars are 100 miles apart. They both start toward each other at the same time and pass in 1 hour. One car is traveling 4 mph faster than the other. How fast is each car traveling?

3. John invests $10,000 in two different stocks. One stock yields 10% interest, and the other yields 5% interest. How much is invested in each of the stocks if the total investment brings in $650 per year?

4. The sum of two digits of a certain two-digit number is 15. If the digits are reversed, the number formed is nine less than the original number. What is the original number?

5. The units digit is eight times the tens digit of a two-digit number. The original number minus the number when the digits are reversed is −63. What is the original number?

6. Two motorboats leave the dock at the same time and travel in opposite directions. One travels 9 mph faster than the other. After 2 hours the boats are 170 miles apart. How fast is each boat traveling?

7. John invested one amount at 10% and $100 less than the first amount at 12%. If the total amount of interest is $605.10 annually, how much money is invested in each account?

8. The tens digit is six less than the units digit of a two-digit number. When the digits are reversed, the sum of the original and reversed numbers is 132. What is the original number?

▶ B. Exercises

9. Two cars leave Rochester at noon, one traveling north and the other traveling south. The northbound car travels at an average rate of 38 mph, and the southbound car travels at an average rate of 43 mph. The southbound car travels 4 hours longer than the northbound car before they reach their destinations. The final destinations of the two cars are 334 miles apart. How long did each car travel?

10. A man has $37,000 in a passbook account and $43,000 in a money market account that pays 10% more. What is the interest rate of each account if his total annual interest income is $8500?

11. The sum of the digits of a two-digit number and the number with the digits reversed is 34. The difference of the number and the number with the digits reversed is 36. Find the original number.

12. A plane leaves Buffalo, New York, and heads for San Diego, California, 2217 nautical miles away. At the same time a plane leaves San Diego for Buffalo. If the plane from Buffalo is traveling 130 knots faster than the other plane and they pass in 4 hours, how fast is each traveling?

13. Millville and Johnsburg are 235 miles apart. Joe leaves Millville and travels toward Johnsburg at the same time Mary leaves Johnsburg and heads towards Millville along the same road. If Joe travels 8 mph faster than Mary and it takes $2\frac{1}{2}$ hours for them to meet, how fast is each of them traveling?

14. The Bunker Manufacturing Company wants to invest in two accounts. An account that gives more cash-flow freedom pays 8.2% annual interest while the other account pays 12.5% annual interest. If they invest $5000 less in the 8.2% account than in the other account and make $4558 total interest income a year, how much is invested at each rate?

15. The sum of the digits of a two-digit number is 12. If the digits are reversed and the original number is subtracted from the new number, the difference is 36. What is the number?

▶ C. Exercises

16. If the first and third digits of a three-digit number are interchanged, the difference between the original number and the new one is 198. If the first and second digits of the original are interchanged, the new one is 90 less than the original. The difference between the first and third digits is equal to the second digit. Find the original number.

17. A two-digit number is 72 less than the number obtained by reversing the digits. Find the number.

▶ Dominion Modeling

18. Refer to Emily's cereal data. How many servings each of Special K and Raisin Bran must she eat to obtain 25% of her daily protein and fiber needs?

▬ Cumulative Review

Give the domain and range for each relation.

19. $y = |x| - 2$
20. $y = 3^x$
21. $y = [x]$
22. $y = 3$
23. $f = \{(0, 1), (1, 2), (2, 3), (3, 4) \ldots\}$

6.5 Quadratic Systems

In this chapter you studied systems of linear equations extensively. You can solve systems of quadratic equations by the same three methods. The first example consists of a parabola and a line. By graphing, you could identify one of the three possible relationships that result in zero, one, or two real solutions.

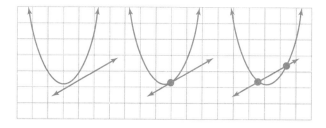

EXAMPLE 1 Solve the system algebraically.
$$y = x^2 + 1$$
$$x - y = -3$$

Answer

$$y = x^2 + 1$$
$$x - y = -3$$

$x - y = -3$	1. Place the linear equation in slope-
$-y = -x - 3$	intercept form.
$y = x + 3$	

$y = x^2 + 1$	2. Substitute for y in the quadratic
$x^2 + 1 = x + 3$	equation and solve for x.
$x^2 - x - 2 = 0$	
$(x - 2)(x + 1) = 0$	
$x = -1$ or $x = 2$	
$y = 2$ $y = 5$	Find the corresponding values of y from $y = x + 3$.

$(-1, 2)$ and $(2, 5)$ are solutions.

Continued ▶

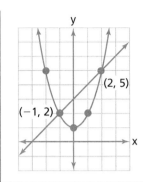

We conclude that the line intersects the parabola in these two points. The graph of the system verifies this conclusion.

Quadratic relations with two variables, in which exactly one of the variables is only to the first power, are always parabolas (although some may open sideways). Quadratic relations containing the second power of both variables may graph as any of the following figures. You will learn to graph them in Chapter 14.

circle   ellipse   hyperbola

The exercises will include equations that graph as any of these three as well as those that graph as parabolas or lines. These systems may have from zero to four solutions. Some examples are shown. While graphing clearly illustrates the number of solutions, it is impractical when the coordinates of the solutions involve fractions. You should solve all quadratic systems of equations algebraically.

4 solutions   3 solutions   2 solutions   1 solution   no solution

EXAMPLE 2 Solve the system.
$$x^2 + y^2 = 9$$
$$x + y^2 = 7$$

Answer

$x^2 + y^2 = 9$ $x + y^2 = 7$ $y^2 = 7 - x$	1. Solve the second equation for y^2 and substitute it for y^2 in the first equation.
$x^2 + y^2 = 9$ $x^2 + (7 - x) = 9$ $x^2 - x - 2 = 0$	2. Solve this quadratic equation for x.

Continued ▶

$$(x - 2)(x + 1) = 0$$
$$x = 2 \quad \text{or} \quad x = -1$$

$y^2 = 7 - x \quad y^2 = 7 - x$ $y^2 = 7 - 2 \quad y^2 = 7 - (-1)$ $y^2 = 5 \quad\quad y^2 = 8$ $y = \pm\sqrt{5} \quad\quad y = \pm\sqrt{8} = \pm 2\sqrt{2}$	3. Substitute these values of x in the equation $y^2 = 7 - x$ to find the corresponding values of y.

$\left(2, \sqrt{5}\right), \left(2, -\sqrt{5}\right),$ $\left(-1, 2\sqrt{2}\right), \left(-1, -2\sqrt{2}\right)$	4. Express the solutions as ordered pairs. The graph of this system is shown to help you see what is happening.

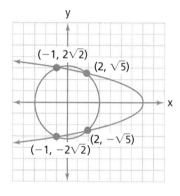

EXAMPLE 3 Solve the system.
$$3x^2 - 5y^2 = 4$$
$$x^2 + y^2 = 4$$

Answer

$3x^2 - 5y^2 = 4$ $x^2 + y^2 = 4 \quad (5)$	1. This equation can be solved easily by addition. Multiply the second equation by 5 and add.

$$3x^2 - 5y^2 = 4$$
$$\underline{5x^2 + 5y^2 = 20}$$
$$8x^2 \quad\quad = 24$$
$$x^2 \quad\quad = 3$$
$$x \quad\quad = \pm\sqrt{3}$$

$x^2 + y^2 = 4$ $(\pm\sqrt{3})^2 + y^2 = 4$ $3 + y^2 = 4$ $y^2 = 1$ $y = \pm\sqrt{1}$ $y = \pm 1$	2. Substitute for x in the second equation and solve for y. Notice that since x is being squared, both $x = \sqrt{3}$ and $x = -\sqrt{3}$ result in the same equation.

The solutions are $\left(\sqrt{3}, 1\right), \left(\sqrt{3}, -1\right), \left(-\sqrt{3}, 1\right), \left(-\sqrt{3}, -1\right)$.

▶ A. Exercises

Solve.

1. $x + y = 4$
   $x^2 = 3y - 8$

2. $xy = 14$
   $x + y = 9$

3. $y^2 = x + 3$
   $x - 2y = 12$

4. $y = 5x$
   $xy = 25$

5. $x^2 + y^2 = 20$
   $x + y = 6$

6. $x^2 + y^2 = 8$
   $2x^2 + y^2 = 12$

7. $x^2 + 3y^2 = 10$
   $x^2 - y^2 = 6$

8. $y = x^2$
   $x^2 + y = 24$

9. $x^2 + y^2 = 16$
   $x + y = 4$

10. $y = x^2$
    $1 + y = 2x$

▶ B. Exercises

Solve.

11. $x - y = 4$
    $y = x^2 - 34$

12. $x^2 + y^2 = 16$
    $x^2 + 2y^2 = 25$

13. $x^2 + y^2 = 9$
    $2x^2 - y^2 = 18$

14. $y = x^2 + 5x - 7$
    $y - x = 5$

15. $y = 3x^2 - x - 1$
    $2x + y = 5$

16. $x + y = -4$
    $y = x^2 - 3$

17. $y = 2x^2 - 3x + 5$
    $3 + y = 5x$

18. $y = x^2$
    $x^2 + y^2 - 4y = 0$

▶ C. Exercises

Solve.

19. $x^2 + y^2 = 5$
    $x^2 + 2y^2 + x = 8$

20. $3x^2 + y^2 = 15$
    $x^2 - y^2 + y = 5$

Cumulative Review

21. Give the slope of a line perpendicular to $3x + 4y = 7$.
22. Find the slope of a line through $(2, 6)$ and $(-5, 1)$.
23. Give the equation of a line with an x-intercept at 4 and a y-intercept at 3.
24. Give the equation of the line through $(2, -1)$ and $(5, 3)$.
25. Give a line parallel to $y = 3x - 1$.

ITALIAN MATH

You know the formula for solving quadratic equations. Did you ever wonder whether there is a formula for solving cubic equations? Nicolo of Brescia, better known as Tartaglia, discovered the general solution for cubic equations. He found the general solution to a cubic equation of the form $x^3 + mx = n$ to be $a - b$, where

$$a = \sqrt[3]{\left(\frac{n}{2}\right) + \sqrt{\left(\frac{n}{2}\right)^2 + \left(\frac{m}{3}\right)^3}} \text{ and } b = \sqrt[3]{-\left(\frac{n}{2}\right) + \sqrt{\left(\frac{n}{2}\right)^2 + \left(\frac{m}{3}\right)^3}}.$$

See if you can use the formula to solve $x^3 + 9x = 6$. The desired solution is $\sqrt[3]{9} - \sqrt[3]{3} \approx 0.6378$.

Later, this solution was stolen from Tartaglia and published by the Italian mathematician Girolamo Cardan in his book *Ars Magna*. In this book Cardan also included some other rules that are commonly used in algebra, such as the rules for multiplying integers. In addition, Cardan worked with imaginary numbers, which he named *fictitious numbers*.

Another Italian mathematician who greatly influenced mathematics is Leonardo of Pisa, commonly called Fibonacci. Fibonacci lived around A.D. 1200 and was the mathematician who introduced the Arabic numeration system to Europe. He eventually converted Europe to this new numeration system.

The need for trained clergy made Rome, Italy, a center of learning during the middle ages before the establishment of modern universities.

The Fibonacci sequence, 1, 1, 2, 3, 5, 8, . . . *x, y, x + y* . . . is the idea for which Fibonacci is best known. He developed this sequence while working on the following problem. How many pairs of rabbits can be produced from a single pair in a year if every month each pair begets a new pair, which from the second month on becomes productive? Draw a picture of this problem and see whether you can discover where he got his sequence.

Do you remember Cavalieri's principle from geometry? In the 1600s, the Italian mathematician Bonaventura Cavalieri discovered this principle for finding volume. Cavalieri's principle, the rules for multiplying integers, the use of the Arabic numeration system, and the general solution for cubic equations were all important contributions made by Italian mathematicians.

The University of Bologna, Italy, was founded in 1088 as a school of law, making it the oldest college in Europe.

Fibonacci introduced the Arabic numeration system to Europe.

St. Mark's Basilica in Venice was a familiar sight to Tartaglia, who taught at the University of Venice (1534-48, 1550-57) and wrote most of his mathematical works there.

6.6 Graphing Systems of Inequalities

In previous chapters you learned how to graph linear and quadratic inequalities. Now you will apply your knowledge to solve systems of them. To solve a system of inequalities, graph them and find the intersection of the graphs. The set of points that satisfies all of the inequalities is the answer to the system.

EXAMPLE 1   Solve.
$$3x + y \leq 4$$
$$x + 3y < -6$$

Answer

$3x + y \leq 4$
$\quad y \leq -3x + 4$

1. Place each inequality in slope-intercept form. Remember to reverse the inequality sign if you multiply or divide both sides by a negative number.

$x + 3y < -6$
$\quad 3y < -x - 6$
$\quad y < \frac{-1}{3}x - 2$

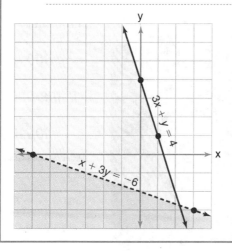

2. Graph both inequalities on the same Cartesian plane. The solution is the intersection of the two graphs (green).

EXAMPLE 2   Solve.

$$3x - y < -3$$
$$y < 3x - 1$$

Answer

$3x - y < -3$	1. Place both inequalities in slope-
$-y < -3x - 3$	intercept form.
$y > 3x + 3$	
$y < 3x - 1$	

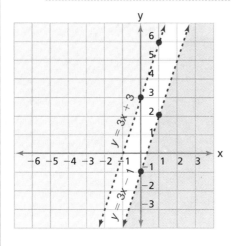

2. Graph each inequality on the same Cartesian plane and find the intersection. Since there is no intersection of the shaded areas, the solution is ∅.

EXAMPLE 3   Solve.

$$y \geq x^2$$
$$y \leq \tfrac{1}{2}x^2 + 1$$

Answer

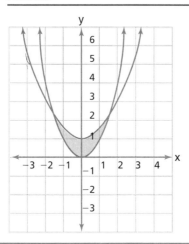

1. Both equations are already in the form $a(x - h)^2 + k$. Find (h, k) for each. $(0, 0)$ is the first vertex and $(0, 1)$ is the second.

2. Graph each equation.

3. Shade above ($\geq$) the first curve and below ($\leq$) the second curve. The solution is the closed region between the two curves.

▶ A. Exercises

Solve each system of inequalities graphically.

1. $3x - y \leq 2$
   $2x + y > 1$
2. $x + 4y > 4$
   $x - 2y \geq -6$
3. $3x - y > -2$
   $x - 5y < 10$
4. $2x - y \geq -3$
   $2x - y \leq 4$
5. $2x - 3y < -12$
   $x + 2y < 10$
6. $x \geq 0$
   $y \leq 0$
7. $y < x^2$
   $y \geq 2x^2 - 3$
8. $y \leq x^2 + 1$
   $y \geq -x^2 - 2$
9. $y \geq x^2$
   $y > (x - 1)^2$
10. $y > x^2 - 3$
    $y \geq x^2$

▶ B. Exercises

Solve each system of inequalities graphically.

11. $5x - 3y > 6$
    $x + 3y > 9$
12. $x - 4y \leq -8$
    $x - 3y < -3$
13. $2x - 5y < -15$
    $x + 3y > -3$
14. $x + 2y \leq 6$
    $x - y > 2$
    $y \geq 0$
15. $3x - y \geq 5$
    $4x + y \leq 8$
    $y \leq 0$
    $x \geq 0$

16. $y \geq (x - 2)^2$
    $y < (x + 2)^2$
17. $y > x^2 - 4x + 4$
    $y < x^2 + 1$
18. $y \leq x^2 - 6x + 9$
    $y \leq 3$
19. $y \geq x^2 - 10x + 25$
    $y > x^2 - 10x + 28$

▶ C. Exercises

Solve each system of inequalities graphically.
20. $x \geq -2$
    $y \geq x$
    $y \leq x^2 + 2x + 1$
21. $y < x + 2$
    $y < x - 1$
    $x \geq 1$
    $y \geq x^2 - 2x - 4$

▶ Dominion Modeling

Using the cereal data for Raisin Bran and Special K, write inequalities for each. (*Hint:* Let x be the number of Special K servings, and let y be the number of Raisin Bran servings.)
22. The number of servings of each to obtain at least 25% of the daily requirement of fiber.
23. The number of servings of each to obtain at least 25% of the daily protein needs.
24. The number of servings of each to obtain a taste index total of at least 12.
25. Graph this system of inequalities on a single set of axes.

■ Cumulative Review

Multiply.
26. $3xy(x - y^2 + 4)$
27. $(8xy^{-3})^2(4x^{-1}y)^{-2}$
28. $(4x - 3y)(5x - 7y)$
29. $(x + 2)(3x^2 + 4x - 5)$
30. $(2x - 5)(4x^2 + 10x + 25)$

6.7 Linear Programming

Many students think only a math teacher or a computer programmer uses mathematics. Although these occupations most certainly require a strong mathematical foundation, so do many others. The world of business is a highly structured and mathematically oriented area of service, and many of you will serve the Lord in it. You can influence many businessmen for Christ if you purpose in your heart to guide others to Jesus Christ and if you maintain a good testimony as a knowledgeable professional. Each Christian's work must focus on Jesus Christ and His salvation that He offers to all. "Wherefore we labour, that, whether present or absent, we may be accepted of him" (II Cor. 5:9).

If you are serving in the business world, you must consider how to maximize profit and minimize costs, as well as track the factors and conditions under which you must work. Linear programming is a practical application of systems of inequalities that seeks to maximize or minimize a particular function subject to various conditions.

Linear programming problems like the following one can be solved by applying some algebraic procedures after graphing. More advanced methods for solving linear programs have been developed from this method.

EXAMPLE 1   The Audio Attic makes compact disc (CD) players and cassette players. The manager wants to maximize the company's profit while staying within the limits of available material and manpower. He has a total of **300** units of metal and **400** units of plastic. Each CD player requires 2 units of plastic and a unit of metal, while each cassette player requires one unit each of plastic and metal. The company makes a profit of **$30** on each CD player and **$25** on each cassette player. How many CD players and how many cassette players should the company make to realize the maximum profit?

Answer   Since profit is to be maximized, a function must be written for the profit. The function to be maximized or minimized is called the *objective function*.

Continued ▶

Let z = the profit
$\quad$ x = number of CD players sold
$\quad$ y = number of cassette players sold.
Then $z = 30x + 25y$.

Even with unlimited storage space and workers, the production of the CD players and cassette players is constrained by limited materials (metal and plastic). Consider the *constraint* on plastic. We will produce x CD players, each requiring two units of plastic, or a total of $2x$ units. We will also produce y cassette players using 1 unit of plastic or a total of y units. Since only 400 units are available,

$\quad$ $2x + y \leq 400$ is the constraint on plastic.

Similarly, production is constrained by **300 units of metal**, and each product requires one unit. Therefore

$\quad$ $x + y \leq 300$ is the constraint on metal.

There are two other unstated but obvious constraints. Since we cannot produce a negative number of items,

$\quad$ $x \geq 0$ and $y \geq 0$.

The problem, then, is to maximize $z = 30x + 25y$ when

$x \geq 0$
$y \geq 0$
$2x + y \leq 400$
$x + y \leq 300$

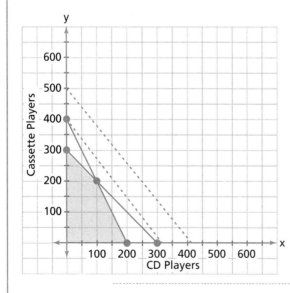

Graph the four constraints, and shade the region representing their intersection. This is called the *feasible region*. All the points in this region satisfy the constraints, but which of these points also maximize the profit function?

Now consider the objective function. Put it into slope-intercept form.

$$z = 30x + 25y$$
$$-25y = 30x - z$$
$$y = \frac{-6}{5}x + \frac{z}{25}$$

Continued ▶

We do not know the value of z or $\frac{z}{25}$ but we know the slope of the line is $\frac{-6}{5}$. The dotted lines on the graph represent the objective function for various y-intercepts. If we "slide" this line toward the feasible region, while maintaining the same slope, its first point of contact with the feasible region will be a *corner point*, where two constraint lines intersect. In this case, the corner point is (100, 200), but if the objective function had a different slope, it might first come in contact with a different corner point such as (200, 0) or (0, 300). This means the maximum value of the objective function will always occur at a corner point, and we need only evaluate each of them to determine the maximum.

The corner points are solutions to systems of equations. You can either use the graph or solve the system to find them. The corner point where the lines $2x + y = 400$ and $x + y = 300$ intersect is obtained below by solving the system using addition.

$2x + y = 400$ Substituting,

$x + y = 300$ (-1) $x + y = 300$

$100 + y = 300$

$2x + y = 400$ $y = 200$

$\underline{-x - y = -300}$

$x = 100$ The point is (100, 200).

Evaluate each corner point in the objective function to find the corresponding profit.

<u>Corner points</u>

(200, 0)	$z = 30(200) + 0$	$= 6000$
(100, 200)	$z = 30(100) + 25(200)$	$= 8000$
(0, 300)	$z = 0 + 25(300)$	$= 7500$
(0, 0)	$z = 0 + 0$	$= 0$

In conclusion, the maximum profit of **$8000** is obtained when we allocate the plastic and metal in such a way as to produce **100 CD players** and **200 cassette players**.

As you can see, the origin can be ignored for typical maximum problems since it is obviously not the maximum.

EXAMPLE 2 Maximize $z = 18x + 10y$
when $x \geq 0$
$y \geq 0$
$8x + 5y \leq 800$
$2x + 4y \leq 500$

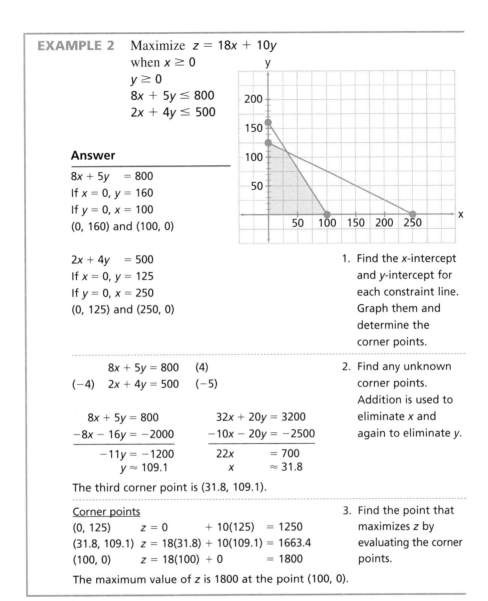

Answer

$8x + 5y = 800$
If $x = 0$, $y = 160$
If $y = 0$, $x = 100$
$(0, 160)$ and $(100, 0)$

$2x + 4y = 500$
If $x = 0$, $y = 125$
If $y = 0$, $x = 250$
$(0, 125)$ and $(250, 0)$

1. Find the x-intercept and y-intercept for each constraint line. Graph them and determine the corner points.

$8x + 5y = 800$ (4)
(-4) $2x + 4y = 500$ (-5)

$8x + 5y = 800$	$32x + 20y = 3200$
$-8x - 16y = -2000$	$-10x - 20y = -2500$
$-11y = -1200$	$22x = 700$
$y \approx 109.1$	$x \approx 31.8$

The third corner point is $(31.8, 109.1)$.

2. Find any unknown corner points. Addition is used to eliminate x and again to eliminate y.

Corner points
$(0, 125)$ $z = 0$ $+ 10(125) = 1250$
$(31.8, 109.1)$ $z = 18(31.8) + 10(109.1) = 1663.4$
$(100, 0)$ $z = 18(100) + 0 = 1800$
The maximum value of z is 1800 at the point $(100, 0)$.

3. Find the point that maximizes z by evaluating the corner points.

In Example 2, if x represented the number of product A to be manufactured and y the number of product B, you would need to truncate the decimal values since you don't produce or sell portions of items. To maximize profit, the company would put all resources into producing 100 of item A.

► A. Exercises

Maximize each objective function subject to the constraints represented by the feasible region shown.

1. $z = 2x + 3y$
2. $z = 5x + 2y$
3. $z = 4x + 3y$

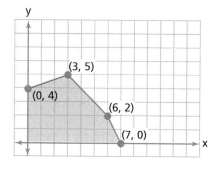

Minimize each objective function subject to the constraints represented by the feasible region shown.

4. $z = x + 3y$
5. $z = 5x + 3y$
6. $z = 3x + y$

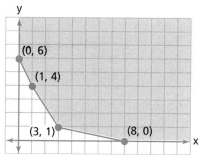

► B. Exercises

If there were no constraints on materials, labor, or storage space, how many items of a manufactured product would you make in each situation? Explain in each case why the answer is impossible.

7. to maximize profit
8. to minimize cost

Graph the constraints and shade the feasible region; find the corner points and maximize or minimize the objective function as directed.

9. Maximize $z = 2x + 5y$ subject to
$$x \geq 0$$
$$y \geq 0$$
$$x + 3y \leq 15$$
$$x + y \leq 7.$$

10. Maximize $z = 3x + 9y$ subject to
$$x \geq 0$$
$$y \geq 0$$
$$x + 2y \leq 4$$
$$5x + 6y \leq 36.$$

11. Maximize $z = 9x + 10y$ subject to
$$x \geq 0$$
$$y \geq 0$$
$$x + 2y \leq 10$$
$$3x + 2y \leq 14.$$

12. Minimize $z = 30x + 50y$ subject to
$$x \geq 0$$
$$y \geq 0$$
$$9x + 2y \geq 900$$
$$8x + 3y \geq 1200.$$

13. Minimize $z = 3x + 2y$ subject to
$$x \geq 0$$
$$y \geq 0$$
$$7x + 3y \geq 30$$
$$3x + 5y \geq 24.$$

▶ C. Exercises

14. A glove-manufacturing company wants to make the maximum profit while considering the manpower and materials available. It makes two types of gloves, ultra-suede and sport gloves. The profit gained on the ultra-suede is $50 per unit box, and that on the sport gloves is $30 per unit box. The company has a total of 1200 square feet of leather and 800 work hours. Each box of ultra-suede gloves requires 5 square feet of leather and 3 hours of work time. A box of sport gloves requires 2 square feet of leather and 2 hours of work time. How many boxes of ultra-suede gloves and how many boxes of sport gloves should be made to produce a maximum profit?

15. Before the solution to problem 14 could be implemented, the company was notified that a previous shipment of gloves containing 200 boxes of sport gloves and 50 boxes of ultra-suede gloves were destroyed in a transportation accident and never reached the buyer. They wish to refill this order as soon as possible. What new constraints are now added to problem 14? Which original constraint is no longer needed? Find the new answer to the problem.

▶ Dominion Modeling

16. Using the cereal model, what objective function describes the total calories Emily would consume from Raisin Bran and Special K?

17. On the graph of Emily's system drawn in Section 6.6, add a representative line for the objective function. (*Hint:* You can't get the y-intercept of the objective function until you know the total calorie count, but you can't get that until you know how much of each cereal Emily will eat. Just for now, assume that the total number of calories is 50.)

18. For Emily's problem, to minimize calories, how many servings should she have of Raisin Bran and Special K? (*Hint:* Watch where the objective function could first intersect the shaded region.)

Cumulative Review

19. What kind of number is -4?

20. Give an absolute value inequality for this graph.

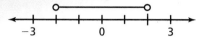

21. Solve by completing the square: $x^2 + 6x = 7$.

22. Find the discriminant and identify the type of solutions: $5x - 6x^2 + 1 = 0$.

23. Graph $y < (x + 1)(x - 2)$.

24. The tens digit is five less than the units digit of a certain two-digit number. Find the number if the sum of twice the units digit and five times the ten digit is 31.

Explain how you could find the corner points of a system of linear constraints without graphing.

6.8 Systems With Three Variables

The systems of equations you have studied so far have contained two equations in two variables. The methods of solving these systems are graphing, substitution, and addition. Since most real situations involve more than two factors, their mathematical models require more than two variables. For this reason, it is useful to extend the methods of solving systems to three equations in three variables.

The Bridge of Sighs at Venice would have been familiar to Cavalieri but not Tartaglia. Why?

When there are more than three variables, graphing is impractical and algebraic methods are used.
In business contexts with multitudes of variables, computers become essential even for an algebraic solution. To solve a system of three equations in three variables algebraically, you will use the addition method.

EXAMPLE 1   Solve the system.

$$x + y - 2z = -9$$
$$3x - y + z = 13$$
$$2x + y + 4z = 17$$

Answer

$x + y - 2z = -9$ $3x - y + z = 13$ $2x + y + 4z = 17$	1. Decide which variable would be the easiest to eliminate in the three equations. Group the equations into two pairs and use the addition method to eliminate the same variable from each pair.

$x + y - 2z = -9$ $3x - y + z = 13$ $\overline{4x \quad\;\; - z = 4}$	$3x - y + \;z\; = 13$ $2x + y + 4z = 17$ $\overline{5x \qquad + 5z = 30}$	2. Adding the first two equations will eliminate y, and adding the last two equations will also eliminate y.

Continued ▶

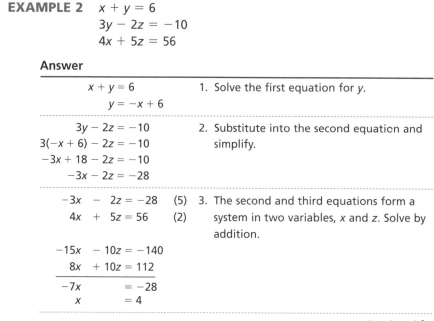

$$x \quad + \ z \ = 6$$

3. Simplify this equation by dividing each term by 5.

$$
\begin{array}{r}
4x \ - \ z \ = 4 \\
\underline{x \ + \ z \ = 6} \\
5x \qquad = 10 \\
x \qquad = 2
\end{array}
$$

4. Pair the two resulting equations together and solve the resulting two-variable system.

$$
\begin{array}{r}
x \ + \ z \ = 6 \\
2 \ + \ z \ = 6 \\
z \ = 4
\end{array}
$$

5. Find the value of z by substituting for x in one of the equations from the two-variable system.

$$
\begin{array}{r}
x + y - 2z \ = -9 \\
2 + y - 2(4) = -9 \\
2 + y - 8 \ = -9 \\
y \qquad = -3
\end{array}
$$

6. Find the value of y by substituting for x and z in one of the original equations.

$$(2, -3, 4)$$

7. Write the solution as an ordered triple, (x, y, z).

Although substitution could be used throughout, it usually leads to fractional coefficients early in the process and is best avoided. In the next example, both addition and substitution are used.

Sometimes one or more equations may have a missing variable. This may appear confusing at first, but it actually reduces the necessary work.

EXAMPLE 2
$$
\begin{array}{l}
x + y = 6 \\
3y - 2z = -10 \\
4x + 5z = 56
\end{array}
$$

Answer

$$
\begin{array}{l}
x + y = 6 \\
y = -x + 6
\end{array}
$$

1. Solve the first equation for y.

$$
\begin{array}{l}
3y - 2z = -10 \\
3(-x + 6) - 2z = -10 \\
-3x + 18 - 2z = -10 \\
-3x - 2z = -28
\end{array}
$$

2. Substitute into the second equation and simplify.

$$
\begin{array}{rl}
-3x \ - \ 2z = -28 & \text{(5)} \\
4x \ + \ 5z = 56 & \text{(2)}
\end{array}
$$

3. The second and third equations form a system in two variables, x and z. Solve by addition.

$$
\begin{array}{r}
-15x \ - \ 10z = -140 \\
\underline{8x \ + \ 10z = 112} \\
-7x \qquad = -28 \\
x \qquad = 4
\end{array}
$$

Continued ▶

$$x + y = 6$$
$$4 + y = 6$$
$$y = 2$$

4. Substitute for x in the original first equation.

$$4x + 5z = 56$$
$$4(4) + 5z = 56$$
$$5z = 40$$
$$z = 8$$

5. Substitute for x in the original third equation.

The solution is (4, 2, 8).

6. Write the ordered triple.

Solving Systems of Three Equations in Three Variables

1. Group two pairs of equations and use the addition method to eliminate the same variable in each pair.
2. Pair the results of step 1 and use the addition method to solve the system.
3. Substitute both known values in one of the original equations to find the third variable.

You have seen from previous sections that the algebraic method of solving systems is much more accurate than the graphing method. You should strive to be as accurate as possible in your work. This applies also to life in general and your spiritual life in particular. As II Corinthians 8:21 states, a Christian should be honest in all things—to the Lord and to all men. Striving to be accurate in mathematics will help you develop the accuracy you need in everyday life.

▶ A. Exercises

Solve each system algebraically.

1. $x + y - z = -4$
   $2x + 5y + z = 25$
   $x - 2y - z = -16$

2. $y = 2x + 5$
   $3x + y - z = 8$
   $6x - 3y + z = -18$

3. $2x + 9y + 2z = 26$
   $x + y + 3z = -2$
   $3x + y - z = 30$

4. $x - y - z = -3$
   $2x + y - 6z = 20$
   $x - 2y + z = -13$

5. $x + 4y - z = -3$
   $2x - 6y + 3z = 9$
   $x + y - 2z = -6$
6. $5x + 3y = 17$
   $2x - 4z = 2$
   $3x + y - 5z = 7$
7. $x + 3y + z = -8$
   $4x - 2y - z = -9$
   $5x + 3y + 2z = -19$
8. $2x + 3y - z = 21$
   $x - y + z = 1$
   $x - 2y - z = 5$
9. $3x + y - 4z = -22$
   $2x + 3y + 4z = 32$
   $x - y + 2z = 16$
10. $x + 5y - 3z = 19$
    $2x - 3y + 4z = -11$
    $4x + y - 2z = 9$

Solve the following systems using substitution only. Notice that systems in this format are very simple to solve.

11. $x + 2y + z = 8$
    $y - 3z = 9$
    $z = -2$
12. $2x + 3y - z = 5$
    $2y + 5z = 11$
    $z = 4$

▶ B. Exercises

Solve algebraically.

13. $x + 2y - 3z = 3.9$
    $4y + 2z = 3.8$
    $3x - 5y = 23$
14. $5x - 4y = 88$
    $2x + 8z = 96$
    $2y - z = -1$
15. $2x + 5y - 3z = 21$
    $7x + 4y + 3z = -10$
    $6x + 15y - 9z = 63$

16. $2x - 3y = -1$
    $8x + 6z = 34$
    $4x - 9y + 2z = 6$

▶ C. Exercises

17. Solve the system algebraically.
    $2x + 5y - 7z + w = -28$
    $x + y + 2z + 3w = 7$
    $2x + 3y - z - w = 4$
    $3x - 2y - z + 5w = -11$
18. Solve #17 by Cramer's Rule.

▶ Dominion Modeling

19. In Emily's problem, there were criteria for fiber, protein, and the taste index. Could any of these have been omitted without changing the solution?
20. If Emily should get at least 25% of her needed calories for breakfast, did she get enough?

▊ Cumulative Review

21. Find the distance between $(2, -3)$ and $(7, 1)$.
22. Factor $16x^2 - 34x - 15$.
23. Find the zeros of $f(x) = 16x^2 - 34x - 15$.
24. Simplify $(11x^2 + x^3 - 34x + 7) - (x^3 - 5x^2 + 22)$.
25. Divide $(x^3 + 5x^2 + 3x + 2) \div (x - 2)$.

Algebra *and* Scripture

Financial Management

How can you correctly manage your finances? To manage money properly, you must implement two important principles.

One principle is that of stewardship. To be a good steward you must use math to plan a budget and keep receipts as records of spending. Investment problems can help you learn how to invest your God-given resources responsibly. You will study the stewardship principle in more detail in Chapter 9.

The other important principle of finance is that of giving. This is actually a wise investment, though many people consider it a foolish waste of money.

1. In John 12:1-6, who accused someone else of foolishly wasting financial capital?

2. According to the passage, who was misusing the funds? How was he able to do this?

> **GREATER AMPLITUDE.**
> What other evil did this man do to get money? How much did he obtain? Give the reference for the proof of your conclusion.

Read Matthew 20:1-16.

3. In verse 2 what is the value of a penny?

4. Did the householder pay everyone fairly as he had agreed?

5. Did the householder owe a penny to the men who started late in the day? Why did he give it to them?

Now read about the good Samaritan in Luke 10:25-37.

6. How much did he give the innkeeper to take care of the man who fell among thieves?

7. How much was this worth (refer to questions 3-5)?

8. At minimum wage, what is this in today's money?

Now read Mark 12:41-44 concerning a poor widow.

9. What inequality is discussed in verse 43?

10. Who gave more money? How much did the widow give?

11. What does the inequality in verses 43 and 44 refer to, since it is not strictly monetary amounts? How much did the widow give in this sense?

From the Bible, you have studied financial management in the lives of four persons: the householder, the widow, the good Samaritan, and Judas.

12. Which of these four people managed their finances well and which improperly?

13. Did those who gave give equally?

Read II Corinthians 9:6-7 which summarizes these points.

14. How much should you give according to verse 6? Explain.

15. Should we all give the same amount according to verse 7? Explain.

Knowing how to maximize your profit is important in getting the most out of what God has entrusted to you. But to be a good steward of God's money, consider what to do with the profits. You must maintain a balance between saving and giving. You must also be aware of and follow the Spirit's leading as to how much to give to further the gospel.

> ## Absolute Values
>
> For all they did cast in of their abundance; but she of her want did cast in all that she had, even all her living. ❧
>
> Mark 12:44

Chapter 6 Review

Solve graphically.

1. $2x + y = 14$
   $x - y = -5$
2. $x - y = -8$
   $3x + y = 0$

Solve algebraically. State whether the system is consistent or inconsistent.

3. $y = 3x + 9$
   $2x + 5y = 28$
4. $x + 7y = 19$
   $2x - 7y = -4$
5. $y = 2x + 8$
   $2x - y = 3$

6. $4x - y = -13$
   $x + 3y = -13$
7. $x + 3y = 12$
   $2x - 4y = 9$

8. The sum of the digits of a two-digit number is 11. If 45 is added to the number, the result is the number with its digits reversed. Find the number.

9. Evelyn invested $8400 in a certificate account and $9600 in a money market account. She expects to make $1830 annual interest. If the certificate account yields $2\frac{1}{2}\%$ more than the money market account, what rate of interest is she getting on each account?

Graph each system of inequalities.

10. $3x - y \geq -4$
    $2x + y > -1$

11. $x - 2y \leq -6$
    $4x + y > -2$

12. Maximize $z = 3x + 5y$ subject to
    $x \geq 0$
    $y \geq 0$
    $y \leq -3x + 14$
    $y \leq \frac{-1}{2}x + 4.$

Solve each system.

13. $xy = -12$
    $x + y = 1$
14. $x^2 + y = 34$
    $x^2 + y^2 = 106$
15. $x + 2y + z = 7$
    $2x - y + z = 6$
    $3x + 2y - 4z = 58$

Match the graph of each system to its type.

    A. Inconsistent

    B. Independent and consistent

    C. Dependent

16.
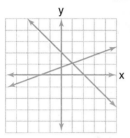

17.
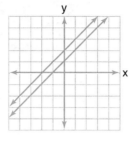

18.
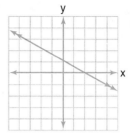

Matching.

19. A function to be maximized
20. A set of points bounded by the graphs of the conditions in a problem
21. A system with no solutions
22. A condition that a solution must meet in a problem
23. A process of maximizing a function subject to conditions represented by first-degree inequalities
24. A system with infinitely many solutions

    A. nonlinear system
    B. consistent system
    C. constraint
    D. dependent system
    E. feasible region
    F. inconsistent system
    G. linear programming
    H. objective function

25. Jay's car travels 50 mph and his plane travels 200 mph. It takes him 10 hours to travel 1100 miles. How much time did he spend in each vehicle?

26. A sporting goods store sells canoes and kayaks. They must stock at least five kayaks and at least twelve canoes each season to meet demand. They cannot stock more than twenty combined due to limited space. If they make a thirty-dollar profit per kayak and twenty-five per canoe, how many of each should be stocked to maximize profits, and what would the profit be?

27. Evaluate the usefulness of the taste index for the cereal data. Include a discussion of whether it makes sense to add the taste indexes.

28. Give the mathematical significance of Mark 12:44.

7 Radicals

$$y = \frac{a}{b}$$

Long ago when Chevrolets were invented and the *Titanic* sunk, a dollar bought more than it does today. For instance, in 1913 you would have paid 19¢ for a pound of chicken, 6¢ for a loaf of bread, and 8¢ for a quart of milk. Sears Roebuck charged $2.48 for a man's sweater and $2.89 for a lady's skirt. The Maxwell Mercury automobile sold for $1150.

Consider some typical wages before you envy the low prices. Coal miners earned 32¢ an hour, and skilled builders got 56¢ an hour. Among salaried workers, Federal civilian employees got $1169 annually, gospel ministers received salaries of $899, and teachers were paid $547.

Because the dollar fluctuates, the United States Bureau of Labor Statistics periodically reports a Consumer Price Index (CPI) for a cost comparison; something that cost an average $9.80 in 1913 would average $10.40 in 1916 and $16.50 in 1919. Exponentials, the inverse of radicals, contribute to the analysis of this data.

Year	CPI	Year	CPI	Year	CPI
1913	9.8	1943	16.9	1973	42.6
1916	10.4	1946	18.2	1976	55.6
1919	16.5	1949	24.0	1979	68.3
1922	16.9	1952	26.5	1982	94.3
1925	17.3	1955	26.7	1985	105.5
1928	17.3	1958	28.6	1988	115.7
1931	15.9	1961	29.8	1991	134.6
1934	13.2	1964	30.9	1994	146.2
1937	14.1	1967	32.9	1997	159.1
1940	13.9	1970	37.8		

After this chapter you should be able to

1. define and apply rational exponents.
2. state the exponent properties.
3. simplify radical expressions.
4. add, subtract, multiply, and divide radical expressions.
5. add, subtract, multiply, and divide exponential expressions.
6. graph radical and exponential functions.
7. solve radical equations and equations with radicals.
8. solve exponential equations and equations with exponents.

7.1 Radicals and Exponents

In Algebra 1 you learned the properties of exponents and found that they could be not only positive integers, but negative integers or rational numbers as well. This section reviews the connection between radical expressions and expressions having rational exponents. Recall that an exponent represents a repeated multiplication.

Definition

Exponent A superscript written after a term (the base) indicating the number of times the base is to be used as a factor.

For example, x^3 means $x \cdot x \cdot x$, where x is the base and 3 is the exponent. The basic exponent laws are reviewed here. Assume a and b are real numbers.

Properties of Exponents

For all $a, b \in \mathbb{R}$ and $x \neq 0$

Product property: $x^a \cdot x^b = x^{a+b}$

Quotient property: $\dfrac{x^a}{x^b} = x^{a-b}$

Power property: $(x^a)^b = x^{ab}$

Zero exponent property: $x^0 = 1$

Negative exponent property: $x^{-a} = \dfrac{1}{x^a}$

Power of a product property: $(xy)^a = x^a y^a$

Power of a quotient property: $\left(\dfrac{x}{y}\right)^a = \dfrac{x^a}{y^a}$

Substitute numbers for the variables and see if you can illustrate the properties; then look at the illustration of the next principle.

Fact: $\sqrt{3} \cdot \sqrt{3} = 3$

Fact: $3^{\frac{1}{2}} \cdot 3^{\frac{1}{2}} = 3^{\frac{1}{2} + \frac{1}{2}} = 3^1 = 3$

By the transitive property, $3^{\frac{1}{2}} \cdot 3^{\frac{1}{2}} = \sqrt{3} \cdot \sqrt{3}$

Therefore, $3^{\frac{1}{2}} = \sqrt{3}$.

Since $\sqrt{3} = \sqrt[2]{3^1} = 3^{\frac{1}{2}}$ the same type of inductive reasoning can be used in a general sense to develop the following definition.

rational exponent $x^{\frac{a}{b}} = \sqrt[b]{x^a}$ where $x > 0$, a and b are integers, and $b \neq 0$.

This means the properties of exponents also apply to radicals. The following table compares the exponential and radical forms of the properties.

Properties of Powers and Roots

	Product	Sample
Powers	$(xy)^a = x^a y^a$	$(3 \cdot 4)^2 = 12^2 = 144 = 9 \cdot 16 = 3^2 \cdot 4^2$
Roots	$\sqrt[a]{xy} = \sqrt[a]{x}\sqrt[a]{y}$	$\sqrt{4 \cdot 9} = \sqrt{36} = 6 = 2 \cdot 3 = \sqrt{4} \cdot \sqrt{9}$

	Quotient	Sample
Powers	$\left(\dfrac{x}{y}\right)^a = \dfrac{x^a}{y^a}$	$\left(\dfrac{2}{5}\right)^3 = \dfrac{8}{125} = \dfrac{2^3}{5^3}$
Roots	$\sqrt[a]{\dfrac{x}{y}} = \dfrac{\sqrt[a]{x}}{\sqrt[a]{y}}$	$\sqrt{\dfrac{16}{25}} = \dfrac{4}{5} = \dfrac{\sqrt{16}}{\sqrt{25}}$

You should become proficient at changing expressions from radical form to exponential form and vice versa. Use these properties with the definition of rational exponent to convert from either form to the other.

EXAMPLE 1   Express $\sqrt[4]{25a^3b}$ in exponential form.

Answer

$\sqrt[4]{25a^3b}$
$\sqrt[4]{5^2a^3b}$
1. Factor the numbers under the radical into prime factors.

$5^{\frac{2}{4}} a^{\frac{3}{4}} b^{\frac{1}{4}}$
2. Use the definition of rational exponent to change the radical to exponential form.

$5^{\frac{1}{2}} a^{\frac{3}{4}} b^{\frac{1}{4}}$
3. Reduce any rational exponent that can be reduced.

EXAMPLE 2   Express $2^{\frac{3}{5}} x^{\frac{4}{5}} y^{\frac{2}{5}}$ in radical form.

Answer

$2^{\frac{3}{5}} x^{\frac{4}{5}} y^{\frac{2}{5}}$
1. Make sure the denominators of the exponents are all the same.

Continued ▶

$\sqrt[5]{2^3 x^4 y^2}$	2. Use the definition of rational exponent to change the expression to radical form.
$\sqrt[5]{8x^4 y^2}$	3. Simplify where possible.

In Example 3, the same quantity is evaluated in two different ways. It is often easier to evaluate an expression in radical form.

EXAMPLE 3   Evaluate $4^{\frac{3}{2}}$.

Answer

$4^{\frac{3}{2}}$		$4^{\frac{3}{2}}$	
$\sqrt{4^3}$	1. Definition of rational exponent	$\left(4^{\frac{1}{2}}\right)^3$	1. Power property
$\sqrt{64}$	2. Evaluate the power.	$(\sqrt{4})^3$	2. Definition of rational exponent
8	3. Evaluate the radical.	2^3	3. Evaluate the radical.
		8	4. Evaluate the power.

Notice that you get the same result regardless of whether you do the power or radical first. You can choose the method you think is easier, but you should understand both. This can be expressed as $\sqrt[b]{x^a} = \left(\sqrt[b]{x}\right)^a$.

EXAMPLE 4   Evaluate $\sqrt{100,000,000}$.

Answer

$\sqrt{100,000,000}$	
$\sqrt{10^8}$	1. Express the radicand as a power.
$10^{\frac{8}{2}}$	2. Change the radical to rational exponent form.
10^4	3. Simplify the exponent.
10,000	4. Express the power as a real number.

▶ A. Exercises

Write each expression in rational exponent form. Assume variables represent positive real numbers.

1. $\sqrt{8}$

2. $\sqrt{5xy^3}$

3. $\sqrt[3]{12a^2b}$

4. $\sqrt[5]{7x^4yz^2}$

5. $\sqrt{26c^3d^2}$

6. $\sqrt[4]{16a^4b^3}$

7. $\sqrt[7]{32x^3y^2z}$

8. $\sqrt{25a^4b^3}$

9. $\sqrt[3]{27x^2z^5}$

10. $\sqrt{125a^3b^2}$

Write each expression in radical form. Assume variables represent positive real numbers.

11. $3^{\frac{2}{3}} x^{\frac{1}{3}}$

12. $5^{\frac{1}{5}} x^{\frac{3}{10}}$

13. $2^{\frac{4}{5}} a^2 b^{\frac{2}{5}}$

14. $x^{\frac{2}{3}} y^{\frac{1}{6}} z$

15. $3^{\frac{1}{4}} a^{\frac{1}{2}} b^{\frac{3}{4}}$

▶ B. Exercises

Use the exponential properties to simplify the following expressions. Leave answers in radical form if necessary. Assume variables represent positive real numbers.

16. $3^{\frac{1}{2}} \cdot 3^{\frac{3}{2}}$

17. $2^{\frac{5}{2}} \div 2^{\frac{3}{2}}$

18. $\left[5^{\frac{3}{4}} \right]^4$

19. 3^{-2}

20. $\left[2^{\frac{4}{3}}\right]^0$

21. $\left(3x^2y\right)^{\frac{1}{2}}$

22. $a^{\frac{-1}{2}}$

23. $\left(7^3a^2b^3\right)^{\frac{1}{3}}$

24. $2^3x^2y \div 2x^{\frac{1}{2}}$

Evaluate. Assume variables represent positive real numbers.

25. $\sqrt[5]{32a^{10}}$

26. $\sqrt[3]{\frac{1}{8}x^9}$

27. $\sqrt{196}$

28. $\sqrt[3]{512}$

29. $\sqrt[3]{27,000}$

30. $\sqrt[4]{16a^8b^{16}}$

31. $\sqrt{6561x^8}$

32. $\left[\frac{343}{8}\right]^{\frac{1}{3}}$

33. $\left(256a^2b^{10}\right)^{\frac{1}{2}}$

34. $\left[\frac{1728x^{12}}{125}\right]^{\frac{1}{3}}$

▶ C. Exercises

35. Express $\left(3a^2b\right)^{-\frac{2}{3}}$ as a radical in simplest form.

36. Express $\sqrt[3]{8^{-2}a^4b^{-5}}$ with positive exponents only.

▶ Dominion Modeling

37. For the inflation data, what are the variables? What variable would be a suitable independent variable? Which would be a suitable dependent variable?

38. If something cost a dollar in 1913, what would have been the expected cost in 1997?

Cumulative Review

Simplify.

39. $(5x^7y^2z)^4$

40. $(2x^2y + 3xy + 5xy^2) - (7x^2y - 3xy^2)$

41. $4xy^3(3xz - 5y + 4xyz)$

42. $(x^5 - y^5) \div (x - y)$

43. $(x + y)^4$

JOHN WALLIS

John Wallis was born in 1616 at Ashford, Kent, England. At fifteen years of age, he picked up a mathematics book and had the material mastered within two weeks. This sparked his interest in mathematics. Believing, however, that his interests would lie in the fields of medicine and theology, Wallis went to the University of Cambridge and obtained both a B.A. and an M.A. in medicine. A year later he became a chaplain in Yorkshire.

During the Civil War between the Royalists and Parliamentarians, Wallis used his mathematical reasoning ability to decipher a secret code in some Royal documents. Because of his help, Wallis was appointed the rector (church leader) of a church in London. While in London, Wallis became more and more fascinated with mathematics and began to attend some meetings of scientists that eventually became the Royal Society. Wallis educated himself in mathematics, and by the age of thirty-three his ability was so remarkable that he was appointed professor of geometry at Oxford, where he remained fifty-four years until his death in 1703.

Wallis made many mathematical contributions. He introduced the present symbol, ∞, for infinity and also worked with conic sections, equations of curves, and cycloids, as well as publishing some books. Wallis presented the meaning of fractional and negative exponents in his work of 1655, *Arithmetica Infinitorum* (The Arithmetic of Infinitesimals). His thoughts on exponents are the forerunners of our present-day exponent laws. This discovery and others made by John Wallis have further developed the fascinating study of mathematics.

Wallis' ability to perform arithmetic mentally became so developed that at one time he mentally extracted the square root of a fifty-three-digit number. Wallis was more than a good mathematician; he also applied his problem-solving skills by showing the relationship between music and math and by developing a method for teaching deaf mutes.

Wallis presented the meaning of fractional and negative exponents.

7.2 Simplifying Expressions

This first electronic telegraph, invented by Gauss, conveyed messages using impulses having a certain frequency.

Clarity of expression is necessary for effective communication, both verbal and written. It is especially important that you learn to communicate the gospel clearly to the unsaved. (In I Cor. 15:3-4 the Apostle Paul makes a plain, direct presentation of the gospel that serves as an example for Christians in witnessing.) When communicating with numbers, you should present your mathematical ideas in the most efficient way.

Simplification of radicals depends on the expression under the radical sign, called the *radicand*. You must simplify a radical expression if the radicand
1. is an exact power of the index (a square root of a square, a cube root of a cube, etc.) or contains a factor that is an exact power.
2. is a fraction.
3. is in the denominator of a fraction.

This section addresses the first type of simplification; the other two types will follow.

EXAMPLE 1   Simplify $\sqrt[3]{360a^5b^7}$. Assume $a > 0$ and $b > 0$.

Answer

$\sqrt[3]{360a^5b^7}$

$\sqrt[3]{2^3 \cdot 3^2 \cdot 5a^5b^7}$ 1. Factor the numbers into primes.

$2^{\frac{3}{3}} 3^{\frac{2}{3}} 5^{\frac{1}{3}} a^{\frac{5}{3}} b^{\frac{7}{3}}$ 2. Write the expression with rational exponents.

$2 \cdot 3^{\frac{2}{3}} 5^{\frac{1}{3}} a \cdot a^{\frac{2}{3}} b^2 b^{\frac{1}{3}}$ 3. Write each improper fraction as a mixed fraction and write two factors (having a whole number exponent and a proper rational exponent).

Continued ▶

$2ab^2 3^{\frac{2}{3}} 5^{\frac{1}{3}} a^{\frac{2}{3}} b^{\frac{1}{3}}$	4. Use the commutative and associative properties to rearrange the factors.
$2ab^2 \sqrt[3]{3^2 5 a^2 b}$	5. Convert remaining rational exponents back to radical form.
$2ab^2 \sqrt[3]{45 a^2 b}$	6. Multiply numerical factors.

There are several methods of simplifying radicals. The next example will show you the simplification of the same radical but by a different method. Decide which method seems easiest for you and use that method.

EXAMPLE 2 Simplify $\sqrt[3]{360 a^5 b^7}$. Assume $a > 0$ and $b > 0$.

Answer

$\sqrt[3]{360 a^5 b^7}$ $\sqrt[3]{2^3 \cdot 3^2 \cdot 5 a^5 b^7}$	1. Factor 360 into a product of primes.
One triple of 2s can be taken out. One triple of as can be taken out. Two triples of bs can be taken out.	2. Since the index of the radical is 3, decide how many triples of each base you can remove from the radicand and place outside the radical.
$2 \cdot a \cdot b^2 \sqrt[3]{}$	3. The exponent on the base when removed from the radicand equals the number of sets of three that can be removed.
All the 2s were removed. Two 3s are left; one 5 is left. Two as are left; one b is left. $2ab^2 \sqrt[3]{3^2 \cdot 5 a^2 b}$	4. Determine what remains under the radical by looking at the number of factors left after removing the triples.
$2ab^2 \sqrt[3]{45 a^2 b}$	5. Multiply numerical factors.

Radicals that are perfect squares are easy to simplify. If they are not obvious to you, factor the radicand into primes and simplify as shown in Example 1 or 2.

EXAMPLE 3   Simplify $\sqrt[4]{1024}$.

Answer

$\sqrt[4]{1024}$

$\sqrt[4]{2^{10}}$ 1. Factor the radicand into primes.

$2^{\frac{10}{4}}$ 2. Write with rational exponents.

$2^{\frac{5}{2}}$

$2^2 \cdot 2^{\frac{1}{2}}$ 3. Write two factors by expressing the improper fraction in the exponent as a mixed number.

$4\sqrt{2}$ 4. Convert back to radical form and simplify if necessary.

Now review the possible combinations of even and odd roots compared with positive and negative radicands.

$$\sqrt{9} = 3 \qquad\qquad \sqrt{-9} \text{ complex}$$
$$\sqrt[3]{27} = 3 \qquad\qquad \sqrt[3]{-27} = -3$$

The following table contains generalizations from the previous examples.

	Positive Radicand	Negative Radicand
Even index	positive	complex
Odd index	positive	negative

Notice that if the radicand is positive, the root is positive no matter what root is taken. Now suppose we want to simplify $\sqrt[3]{8x^5y^7}$. How do we know whether $8x^5y^7$ is positive or negative? The answer is that we do not know. But since a cube root (odd) has the same sign as the radicand, $\sqrt[3]{8x^5y^7} = 2xy^2\sqrt[3]{x^2y}$ regardless of the signs.

Now consider an even-indexed root, such as $\sqrt[4]{8x^5y^7}$. Unlike before, we know $8x^5y^7$ is positive, otherwise the radical is not a real number (complex). However x and y can be both negative or both positive and still result in a positive product $8x^5y^7$.

Therefore, in simplifying $\sqrt[4]{8x^5y^7}$ to $xy\sqrt[4]{8xy^3}$, we have assumed that $\sqrt[4]{x^4} = x$, which is only true when x is positive. For example, if $x = -2$, then $\sqrt[4]{(-2)^4} = \sqrt[4]{16} = 2$, which is the opposite of x or the absolute value of x. The precise way to write the answer is $\sqrt[4]{8x^5y^7} = |xy|\sqrt[4]{8xy^3}$, since it is valid for negative as well as positive values of x and y. In conclusion, if x is any real number, then

$$\sqrt[n]{x^n} = \begin{cases} x & \text{if } n \text{ is odd} \\ |x| & \text{if } n \text{ is even} \end{cases}$$

You must use this rule unless the exercise specifies that the variables represent positive numbers.

EXAMPLE 4 Simplify $\sqrt[6]{320x^6y^7z^{12}}$.

Answer

$\sqrt[6]{320x^6y^7z^{12}}$	
$\sqrt[6]{2^6 \cdot 5x^6y^7z^{12}}$	1. Factor into primes.
$\left\lvert 2xyz^2 \right\rvert \sqrt[6]{5y}$	2. Since the index 6 is even, absolute values are needed.
$2z^2 \lvert xy \rvert \sqrt[6]{5y}$	3. Simplify the absolute value (2 and z^2 are always positive).

▶ A. Exercises

Simplify each radical expression. Assume all variables are positive real numbers.

1. $\sqrt{225}$
2. $\sqrt[3]{2744}$
3. $\sqrt{1296}$
4. $\sqrt{25a^6b^2}$
5. $\sqrt[3]{125x^9y^{24}}$
6. $\sqrt{162a^3}$
7. $\sqrt{32x^5y}$
8. $\sqrt[3]{135a^4b^3}$

9. $\sqrt{144ab^4c}$
10. $\sqrt[5]{224x^7y^2z^8}$
11. $\sqrt[3]{1296a^4bc^3}$
12. $\sqrt{980x^5y^3}$
13. $\sqrt[4]{1296}$
14. $\sqrt{1350a^3b^5}$
15. $\sqrt{768x^{12}y^{15}}$
16. $\sqrt[4]{x^{12}y^4z^5}$

▶ B. Exercises

Simplify. (Variables may be either positive or negative.)

17. $\sqrt[4]{x^{12}y^4z^5}$
18. $\sqrt[3]{-8}$
19. $\sqrt{4x^2}$
20. $\sqrt{9z^8}$
21. $\sqrt[4]{x^4z^{12}}$

22. $\sqrt[10]{y^{20}z^{10}}$
23. $\sqrt{81x^3y}$
24. $\sqrt{20x^8y^5}$
25. $\sqrt[7]{-4y^6}$
26. $\sqrt[6]{15x^{10}}$

▶ C. Exercises

27. Explain why $\sqrt[3]{x^5} = x\sqrt[3]{x^2}$ does not require absolute value signs but $\sqrt[4]{x^6} = x\sqrt[4]{x^2}$ does.

28. Simplify $\sqrt[4]{x^4y^2 - 4x^3y^3 + 6x^2y^4 - 4xy^5 + y^6}$.

▶ Dominion Modeling

29. Generate a linear model of the inflation data from 1913-1997. (*Hint:* The data will be more manageable if you subtract 1900 from each year.)

30. Evaluate the linear model of the data.

Cumulative Review

Solve each system.

31. $x = y - 9$
$2x + 3y = 7$

32. $3x - 2y = 5$
$7x + 4y = 3$

33. $2x + y^2 = 18$
$x - y = 5$

34. $x + y + z = 7$
$x - y + z = 4$
$x + y - z = 8$

7.3 Sums and Differences

Addition is the most basic operation. Subtraction is addition of the opposite. Repeated addition results in multiplication, and repeated subtraction results in a division process. Mathematics is fascinating in how all the parts relate to one another. This interweaving of mathematical facts and their relationships is the reason each single part is so important to learn. If one part is missing, the picture will not be complete and understanding will not be clear. Here are a few basic facts that you must know to help you understand addition and subtraction of radical expressions.

To add and subtract expressions, keep the following two rules in mind:
1. Only like radical expressions may be added or subtracted.
2. Use the distributive property to add or subtract the coefficients of the like radicals.

You may be asking, "*What are like radical expressions?*" They are radicals that have the same radicand and index. For example, $\sqrt[5]{2}$ and $4\sqrt[5]{2}$ are like radical expressions, whereas $\sqrt{2}$ and $\sqrt[3]{2}$ are not like radicals and cannot be combined by addition or subtraction in their exact form.

EXAMPLE 1   Add $5\sqrt{2} + 6\sqrt{2} + \sqrt{2}$.

Answer

$5\sqrt{2} + 6\sqrt{2} + \sqrt{2}$	1. All of the radicals in this expression are like radicals.
$(5 + 6 + 1)\sqrt{2}$	2. Apply the distributive property. Remember that the coefficient on $\sqrt{2}$ is 1.
$12\sqrt{2}$	3. Add the coefficients.

Many times you will have to simplify radical expressions before you add or subtract them.

EXAMPLE 2

Find $2\sqrt{8} + \sqrt{12} - \sqrt{32}$.

Answer

$2\sqrt{8} + \sqrt{12} - \sqrt{32}$

$4\sqrt{2} + 2\sqrt{3} - 4\sqrt{2}$ 1. Simplify each radical expression.

$2\sqrt{3}$ 2. Combine like terms.

EXAMPLE 3   Find $\sqrt[3]{54} + \sqrt{20} - 5\sqrt{2} + \sqrt{45}$.

Answer

$\sqrt[3]{54} + \sqrt{20} - 5\sqrt{2} + \sqrt{45}$

$3\sqrt[3]{2} + 2\sqrt{5} - 5\sqrt{2} + 3\sqrt{5}$ 1. Simplify each term.

$3\sqrt[3]{2} + 5\sqrt{5} - 5\sqrt{2}$ 2. Combine like terms.

Just as radicals must have the same radicands and indexes to be like terms, exponential terms must have the same bases and exponents if they are to be combined. The examples below demonstrate how to simplify exponentials by combining like terms.

EXAMPLE 4   Simplify $2 \cdot 3^{51} - 5 \cdot 7^{10} + 3^{51} + 2 \cdot 7^{10}$.

Answer

$2 \cdot 3^{51} \quad 5 \cdot 7^{10} + 3^{51} + 2 \cdot 7^{10}$

$(2 \cdot 3^{51} + 3^{51}) + (2 \cdot 7^{10} - 5 \cdot 7^{10})$ 1. Group like terms.

$3 \cdot 3^{51} - 3 \cdot 7^{10}$ 2. Combine like terms using the distributive property.

$3^{52} - 3 \cdot 7^{10}$ 3. Simplify where possible using properties of exponents.

EXAMPLE 5   Simplify $5 \cdot 4^{x} + 2^{2x} + 3^{11} - 3^{10}$.

Answer

$5 \cdot 4^{x} + 2^{2x} + 3^{11} - 3^{10}$

$5(2^2)^{x} + 2^{2x} + 3^{11} - 3^{10}$
$5 \cdot 2^{2x} + 2^{2x} + 3 \cdot 3^{10} - 3^{10}$ 1. Use exponent rules to obtain like terms.

$6 \cdot 2^{2x} + 2 \cdot 3^{10}$ 2. Combine like terms.

$3 \cdot 2 \cdot 2^{2x} + 2 \cdot 3^{10}$ 3. Remove an additional factor of 2 from 6.

$3 \cdot 2^{2x + 1} + 2 \cdot 3^{10}$ 4. Simplify where possible.

▶ A. Exercises

Do the indicated operations and simplify. Variables represent positive real numbers.

1. $3\sqrt{2} - 5\sqrt{2}$
2. $7\sqrt{5} + \sqrt{15} + 3\sqrt{5}$
3. $\sqrt{45} - \sqrt{12} + \sqrt{180}$
4. $6\sqrt{8} + \sqrt{2} - 3\sqrt{32}$
5. $2\sqrt{7} - 5\sqrt{7} - \sqrt{63}$
6. $\sqrt{405} + \sqrt{180} - \sqrt[3]{135}$
7. $\sqrt{32x^2y} - x\sqrt{2y} + \sqrt{18x^2y}$
8. $\sqrt{1584a^3} + \sqrt{44a} - 6a\sqrt{11a}$
9. $\sqrt{48xy^3} - y\sqrt{147xy} + \sqrt{108xy^3}$
10. $\sqrt[5]{12a^6b} + \sqrt[3]{6a^4b} - a\sqrt[5]{12ab}$

▶ B. Exercises

Do the indicated operations and simplify. Variables represent positive real numbers.

11. $7^{36} + 8^{10} - 2 \cdot 7^{36}$
12. $3 \cdot 5^{17} - 8 \cdot 5^{17}$
13. $6^x + 6^{x+1}$
14. $5^{20} + 3 \cdot 5^{20}$
15. $\sqrt{27c^5d^2} - cd\sqrt{192c^3} + \sqrt{57c^2d}$
16. $\sqrt[3]{x^4y^2z^5} + x\sqrt[3]{xy^2z^2} - x\sqrt[3]{xy^2z^5}$
17. $\sqrt{245a^3} + \sqrt{75a^5b} - a\sqrt{980a}$
18. $\sqrt{1088x^4y} - x\sqrt{153x^2y}$
19. $\sqrt{324a^2b^4} + 5\sqrt{52ab} - ab\sqrt{1024b^2}$
20. $4 \cdot 9^{20} - 5^{30} + 3^{40} + 4 \cdot 5^{31}$
21. $8^{21} - 2^{60}$
22. $\sqrt{5x} - \sqrt{125x}$

▶ C. Exercises

Do the indicated operations and simplify. Variables represent positive real numbers.

23. $119 \cdot 10^x + 81 \cdot 10^x$
24. $5^x - 5^{x+1}$

▶ Dominion Modeling

Answer the following questions based on your linear model for the Consumer Price Index from 1913-1997. Remember that the slope of a linear model is the coefficient (or multiplier) for x and that multiplication is repeated addition.

25. What is the average annual change in prices?
26. In the graph and function rule of a linear model, what shows that it changes the same amount each year?

Cumulative Review

27. Graph $y = 2x + 5$.
28. Find the slope of the line passing through $(5, 1)$ and $(-7, 3)$.
29. Find the slope of a line perpendicular to $2x + 5y = 7$.

Find the equation of each line.

30.

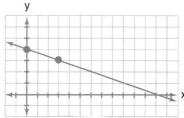

31. A line passing through $(2, 5)$ and $(1, -1)$
32. A line passing through $(1, 4)$ and parallel to $3x - y = 7$

7.4 Products

As mentioned in Section 7.1, the principle that you need to understand for multiplying radical expressions is given here.

$$\sqrt[n]{x} \cdot \sqrt[n]{y} = \sqrt[n]{xy}$$

Since $\sqrt[n]{x} = x^{\frac{1}{n}}$, $\sqrt[n]{y} = y^{\frac{1}{n}}$, and $\sqrt[n]{xy} = (xy)^{\frac{1}{n}}$, you can also substitute these expressions in the previous equation to obtain another equation in rational exponent form.

$$x^{\frac{1}{n}} \cdot y^{\frac{1}{n}} = (xy)^{\frac{1}{n}}$$

To multiply two radical expressions, you can either simplify the expressions and then multiply, or you can multiply and then simplify. Study the following examples. Both processes are given for Example 1. You may choose the process you prefer.

EXAMPLE 1 Multiply $2\sqrt{50} \cdot 4\sqrt{5}$.

Answer

Method 1

$2\sqrt{50} \cdot 4\sqrt{5}$

$2\sqrt{5^2 \cdot 2} \cdot 4\sqrt{5}$ 1. Simplify each expression.

$10\sqrt{2} \cdot 4\sqrt{5}$

$40\sqrt{10}$ 2. Multiply; then simplify again if possible.

Method 2

$2\sqrt{50} \cdot 4\sqrt{5}$ 1. Multiply the coefficients; then multiply

$8\sqrt{250}$ the radicals.

$8\sqrt{5^3 \cdot 2}$ 2. Simplify the radical expression.

$8 \cdot 5\sqrt{5 \cdot 2}$

$40\sqrt{10}$

EXAMPLE 2 Multiply $\sqrt[3]{4x^2y} \sqrt[3]{16x^2y^2}$.

Answer

$\sqrt[3]{4x^2y} \sqrt[3]{16x^2y^2}$ 1. Since neither radical can be simplified,

$\sqrt[3]{64x^4y^3}$ multiply.

$\sqrt[3]{2^6x^4y^3}$ 2. Simplify.

$2^2xy\sqrt[3]{x}$

$4xy\sqrt[3]{x}$

Sometimes you will be required to multiply radical expressions with more than one term. To multiply a multi-term radical expression by a radical, use the distributive property of real numbers. To multiply a pair of two-term radical expressions, use the FOIL method. These properties apply since radicals are real numbers.

EXAMPLE 3   Multiply $5\sqrt{7}(2 - 3\sqrt{6})$.

Answer
$$5\sqrt{7}(2 - 3\sqrt{6})$$ Distribute $5\sqrt{7}$ across the radical
$$10\sqrt{7} - 15\sqrt{42}$$ expression. Simplify if possible.

EXAMPLE 4   Multiply $2\sqrt{3}(1 + 3\sqrt{3} - 6\sqrt{7})$.

Answer
$$2\sqrt{3}(1 + 3\sqrt{3} - 6\sqrt{7})$$
$$2\sqrt{3} + 6 \cdot 3 - 12\sqrt{21}$$ Use the distributive property to
$$2\sqrt{3} + 18 - 12\sqrt{21}$$ multiply.

EXAMPLE 5   Multiply $(3 + \sqrt{2})(5 + \sqrt{3})$.

Answer
$$(3 + \sqrt{2})(5 + \sqrt{3})$$
$$15 + 3\sqrt{3} + 5\sqrt{2} + \sqrt{6}$$ Multiply by the FOIL method.

EXAMPLE 6   Multiply $(5x + \sqrt{2})(2x + 3\sqrt{2})$.

Answer
$$(5x + \sqrt{2})(2x + 3\sqrt{2})$$
$$10x^2 + 15x\sqrt{2} + 2x\sqrt{2} + 3 \cdot 2$$ 1. Multiply by FOIL.

$$10x^2 + 17x\sqrt{2} + 6$$ 2. Simplify and combine like terms.

The same principles again apply to exponentials since they are real numbers.

EXAMPLE 7   Multiply $3(3^x + 1)^2$.

Answer
$$3(3^x + 1)^2$$
$$3[(3^x)^2 + 2 \cdot 3^x + 1^2]$$ 1. Square the binomial.

$$3(3^{2x} + 2 \cdot 3^x + 1)$$ 2. Simplify.

$$3^{2x + 1} + 2 \cdot 3^{x + 1} + 3$$ 3. Distribute the 3.

▶ A. Exercises

Do the indicated operation and simplify. Assume variables are positive.

1. $\sqrt{8} \cdot \sqrt{7}$
2. $3\sqrt{5} \cdot \sqrt{6}$
3. $6\sqrt[3]{4a^4} \cdot 2\sqrt[3]{2a^2}$
4. $27^x \cdot 3^{x+1}$
5. $2^{65} \cdot 4^{10}$
6. $2^{40}(2^{11} - 3)$

7. $7(3 + \sqrt{2})$
8. $\sqrt{5}(x + 9)$
9. $\sqrt{2}(1 + \sqrt{2})$
10. $(5 - \sqrt{2})(3 + \sqrt{2})$
11. $(x + \sqrt{5})(x - \sqrt{5})$
12. $(y - \sqrt{3})^2$

▶ B. Exercises

Do the indicated operation and simplify. Assume all variables are positive.

13. $(x + 2\sqrt{6})(x + 4\sqrt{6})$
14. $(y\sqrt{3} - \sqrt{5})(y\sqrt{3} + 2\sqrt{5})$
15. $\sqrt{11}(x + \sqrt{2})(x + 3\sqrt{2})$
16. $(a + b\sqrt{7})^2$
17. $(x\sqrt{5} + \sqrt{15})(x\sqrt{3} - \sqrt{15})$
18. $(7^x - 1)(7^x + 1)$
19. $\sqrt{12a^3b}(\sqrt{3a} - 10)$

▶ C. Exercises

Do the indicated operation and simplify. Do not assume variables are positive.

20. $3\sqrt{6d^2c} \sqrt{48c^3}$
21. $\sqrt[5]{81a^4b^3} \sqrt[5]{27a^6b}$
22. $\sqrt{5xy}(3\sqrt{x} - \sqrt{5})$

▪ Cumulative Review

Factor.

23. $x^4 - 125x$
24. $6x^2 + x - 35$
25. $x^8 - 9x^4$
26. $4x^2y^3z^3 + 14x^3y^2z^3 - 6x^2y^2z^3$
27. $3x^2 + 18x - 48$
28. $x^2 + 2xy + y^2 - z^4$

Special Matrix Products

There are two types of multiplication with matrices—scalar multiplication (discussed in Chapter 3) and matrix multiplication. Let us again consider the example of the Super M grocery store chain and their inventory of soft drinks.

Super M Grocery Store 182				
Brand	Cola	Grape	Orange	Root Beer
X	9	7	5	6
Y	10	3	8	4
Z	7	6	3	5

Now suppose the manager wants to know the total amount of sales per flavor that is represented by his present inventory in store 182. Each 12-pack of brand X sells for $3.88; brand Y for $3.20; and brand Z for $2.52. To determine the total sales for cola, he will have to multiply the cost per 12-pack of each brand times the number of 12-packs of colas in each brand and then add these numbers together. He will then repeat this process for each flavor. The entire process can be done with matrix multiplication. To multiply matrices, the number of columns in the left matrix must equal the number of rows in the right matrix. For example, $(m \times n)(n \times p)$ will yield an $(m \times p)$ product. Notice that the product has the outer dimensions of the factors.

In our example, a row matrix can describe the prices of the flavors per case: [3.88 3.20 2.52]. Examine the process used to multiply the following matrices.

$$[3.88 \quad 3.20 \quad 2.52] \cdot \begin{bmatrix} 9 & 7 & 5 & 6 \\ 10 & 3 & 8 & 4 \\ 7 & 6 & 3 & 5 \end{bmatrix}$$

To find the elements of the product matrix, multiply the elements of the row matrix by the corresponding elements in the first column and find the sum of these products. Do likewise with each column. The product matrix in this example will be a 1×4 matrix since a (1×3) matrix is multiplied by a (3×4) matrix.

$$[3.88 \quad 3.20 \quad 2.52] \cdot \begin{bmatrix} 9 & 7 & 5 & 6 \\ 10 & 3 & 8 & 4 \\ 7 & 6 & 3 & 5 \end{bmatrix} = [84.56 \quad 51.88 \quad 52.56 \quad 48.68]$$

The computations for the product matrix are shown.

$a_{11} = 3.88(9) + 3.2(10) + 2.52(7)$ $a_{13} = 3.88(5) + 3.2(8) + 2.52(3)$

$a_{12} = 3.88(7) + 3.2(3) + 2.52(6)$ $a_{14} = 3.88(6) + 3.2(4) + 2.52(5)$

From this matrix the manager knows that he has $84.56 worth of cola, $51.88 worth of grape, $52.56 worth of orange, and $48.68 worth of root beer in his store.

▶ **Exercises.**

$$A = [2 \quad 3] \qquad C = \begin{bmatrix} 5 & 7 \\ 2 & 1 \end{bmatrix} \qquad D = \begin{bmatrix} 7 & 2 & 3 \\ 5 & 1 & 4 \end{bmatrix} \qquad G = \begin{bmatrix} 3 \\ 7 \end{bmatrix}$$

Find or write *impossible*.
   1. AC
   2. AD
   3. GD

Give the dimension of the product matrix MN if
   4. M is 1×7 and N is 7×5.
   5. M is $1 \times p$ and N is $p \times q$.

7.5 Quotients

Three other types of radical expressions must be simplified to obtain the simplest form. Simplifications must be made when

1. the radicand is a fraction.
2. the denominator of a fraction contains a radical.
3. the denominator of a fraction is of the form $a + b$ where a or b or both contain a radical.

You will see how to simplify each of these types. A fraction as the radicand is fairly straightforward.

$$\sqrt{\frac{1}{3}}$$

To simplify such an expression, you may apply the quotient property of roots to rewrite the radical with separate radicals in the numerator and denominator.

$$\sqrt{\frac{1}{3}} = \frac{\sqrt{1}}{\sqrt{3}} = \frac{1}{\sqrt{3}}$$

We now have the form of condition 2 in the above list. To remove the radical from the denominator, multiply the expression by 1 in the form of $\frac{\sqrt{3}}{\sqrt{3}}$.

$$\frac{1}{\sqrt{3}} \cdot \frac{\sqrt{3}}{\sqrt{3}} = \frac{\sqrt{3}}{\sqrt{9}} = \frac{\sqrt{3}}{3}$$

Notice that there is a rational number instead of a radical in the denominator. We call this the simplified form and the process of obtaining $\frac{\sqrt{3}}{3}$ from $\frac{1}{\sqrt{3}}$ is called *rationalizing the denominator*.

EXAMPLE 1   Simplify $\frac{10\sqrt{8}}{5\sqrt{10}}$.

Answer

$\frac{10\sqrt{8}}{5\sqrt{10}}$

$\frac{10}{5}\sqrt{\frac{8}{10}}$ 1. Apply the roots of quotients property and reduce the fraction outside the radical and the one under the radical. **Do not** cancel a number outside with one inside the radicand.

$2\sqrt{\frac{4}{5}}$

- -

$2\frac{\sqrt{4}}{\sqrt{5}} \cdot \frac{\sqrt{5}}{\sqrt{5}}$ 2. Apply the roots of quotients property again and rationalize the denominator.

$\frac{2 \cdot 2\sqrt{5}}{5}$

$\frac{4\sqrt{5}}{5}$

EXAMPLE 2 Simplify $\dfrac{27 \cdot 5^{100}}{12 \cdot 5^{87}}$.

Answer

$\dfrac{27 \cdot 5^{100}}{12 \cdot 5^{87}}$

$\dfrac{27}{12} \cdot \dfrac{5^{100}}{5^{87}}$

  1. Change the expression to a product of two fractions.

$\dfrac{9}{4} \cdot 5^{13}$

  2. Reduce each fraction. Do not cancel an exponent with a base.

In the following example, since the numerator and the denominator are both under the cube root symbol and both are multiples of 2, the fraction can be reduced first and then simplified.

EXAMPLE 3 Simplify $\sqrt[3]{\dfrac{2}{12}}$.

Answer

$\sqrt[3]{\dfrac{2}{12}} = \sqrt[3]{\dfrac{1}{6}} = \dfrac{\sqrt[3]{1}}{\sqrt[3]{6}} = \dfrac{1}{\sqrt[3]{6}}$

  1. Reduce the radicand and apply the quotient of roots property.

$\dfrac{1}{\sqrt[3]{6}} \cdot \dfrac{\sqrt[3]{6^2}}{\sqrt[3]{6^2}} = \dfrac{\sqrt[3]{6^2}}{\sqrt[3]{6^3}} = \dfrac{\sqrt[3]{36}}{6}$

  2. Multiply the fraction by 1 in the form of $\dfrac{\sqrt[3]{6^2}}{\sqrt[3]{6^2}}$ so that the radicand in the denominator will be a perfect cube.

Therefore the simplified form of $\sqrt[3]{\dfrac{2}{12}}$ is $\dfrac{\sqrt[3]{36}}{6}$. Notice that there are no radicals in the denominator, which is a goal when simplifying radicals.

The following example shows another type of radical expression that must be simplified because of radicals appearing in the denominator. (The form of condition 3 in the list.)

EXAMPLE 4 Simplify $\dfrac{8}{\sqrt{3} + 2}$.

Answer

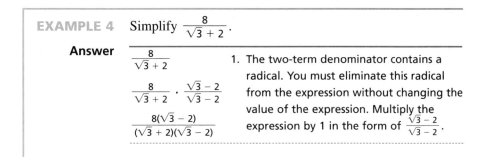

$\dfrac{8}{\sqrt{3} + 2}$

$\dfrac{8}{\sqrt{3} + 2} \cdot \dfrac{\sqrt{3} - 2}{\sqrt{3} - 2}$

$\dfrac{8(\sqrt{3} - 2)}{(\sqrt{3} + 2)(\sqrt{3} - 2)}$

  1. The two-term denominator contains a radical. You must eliminate this radical from the expression without changing the value of the expression. Multiply the expression by 1 in the form of $\dfrac{\sqrt{3} - 2}{\sqrt{3} - 2}$.

Continued ▶

$$\frac{8\sqrt{3}-16}{3-4}$$

2. Multiply in the numerator using the distributive property and in the denominator using the FOIL method.

$$\frac{8\sqrt{3}-16}{-1}$$

$$-8\sqrt{3}+16$$

3. Simplify the expression by multiplying the numerator and the denominator by -1.

The final answer in the example is an expression that has no radicals in the denominator. In a problem like the one in the example, you simplify the expression by multiplying the numerator and denominator by the *conjugate* of the denominator. To find the conjugate of a two-term radical expression, you change the sign between the terms. The expressions $a + b$ and $a - b$ are conjugates.

The common process used in simplifying expressions that contain radicals in the denominator of a fraction is to multiply the fraction by 1 in a form that will eliminate the radical.

▶ A. Exercises

Simplify each expression.

1. $\frac{2}{\sqrt{5}}$

2. $\frac{1}{\sqrt{7}}$

3. $\frac{2\sqrt{8}}{\sqrt{2}}$

4. $\sqrt{\frac{1}{5}}$

5. $\frac{5\sqrt{3}}{\sqrt{2}}$

6. $\sqrt[3]{\frac{2}{3}}$

7. $\frac{5\sqrt[3]{5}}{\sqrt[3]{15}}$

8. $\sqrt{\frac{3}{4}}$

9. $\sqrt{\frac{8}{16}}$

10. $\frac{2\sqrt{7}}{\sqrt{3}}$

▶ B. Exercises

Simplify each expression.

11. $\frac{5}{1+\sqrt{2}}$

12. $\frac{8}{\sqrt{5}-6}$

13. $\frac{4 \cdot 7^{40}}{20 \cdot 7^{29}}$

14. $\frac{6 \cdot 3^{25}}{9 \cdot 3^{11}}$

15. $\frac{2\sqrt{3}}{\sqrt{18}}$

16. $\frac{5-\sqrt{5}}{\sqrt{7}}$

17. $\frac{2}{\sqrt{6}+2}$

18. $\frac{\sqrt{3}-\sqrt{2}}{\sqrt{3}+\sqrt{2}}$

19. $\dfrac{9}{\sqrt{6} - \sqrt{3}}$

20. $\dfrac{16\sqrt{2}}{\sqrt{2} + \sqrt{5}}$

21. $\dfrac{\sqrt[4]{4}}{\sqrt[4]{8}}$

22. $\dfrac{2 + \sqrt{3}}{1 - \sqrt{2}}$

23. $\dfrac{80 \cdot 8^x}{4^x}$

▶ C. Exercises

24. Simplify $\dfrac{10\sqrt{6x^4y}}{5\sqrt{3y^3}}$. Do not assume variables are positive.

25. Simplify $\dfrac{7 \cdot 5^{3x-5}}{63 \cdot 5^{5x+2}}$; then find for what values of x the power of 5 should be put in the numerator and for what powers it should be put in the denominator.

▌Cumulative Review

Solve.

26. $2x^2 - 30 = 17x$

27. $5x + 9 = 7x + 4$

28. $x^2 + 4x - 7 = 0$

29. $(2x - 3)^2 = 45$

30. Use synthetic division and the integral root theorem to solve $x^3 + 5x^2 - 8x - 12 = 0$.

7.6 Equations with Radicals

Engineering students applied algebra to design their concrete canoes for the National Concrete Canoe Competition.

Solving equations with radicals may require factoring. Before you can solve them, you will need to know how to factor polynomials involving radicals. There are some polynomials—mainly binomials—that you could not factor in the past. For example, the binomial $x^2 - 3$ appeared not to be factorable. It looks similar to the familiar case of the difference of squares, but 3 is not a perfect square. It can however, be written as $\left(\sqrt{3}\right)^2$. Then $x^2 - 3$ is the same as $x^2 - \left(\sqrt{3}\right)^2$ or $\left(x - \sqrt{3}\right)\left(x + \sqrt{3}\right)$.

You can check this factorization by multiplying the two factors together to get the original binomial.

$$\left(x - \sqrt{3}\right)\left(x + \sqrt{3}\right) = x^2 - 3$$

You can also factor perfect square trinomials that contain radicals if you recognize them as such.

EXAMPLE 1 Factor $x^2 + 2x\sqrt{2} + 2$.

Answer $x^2 + 2x\sqrt{2} + 2$

1. Recognize this as a perfect square trinomial. The first term is a perfect square, x^2, and the last term is a perfect square, $\left(\sqrt{2}\right)^2$.

   The middle term is twice the product of the square roots of the first and last terms: $2\left(\sqrt{x^2}\right)\left(\sqrt{2}\right) = 2x\sqrt{2}$.

   $\left(x + \sqrt{2}\right)^2$

2. Thus the trinomial factors as the square of a binomial. Use the sign of the middle term in the binomial factor.

Now factor a common monomial radical.

EXAMPLE 2 Factor $\sqrt{6} - y\sqrt{3}$.

Answer

$\sqrt{6} - y\sqrt{3}$	1. Notice the common factor of $\sqrt{3}$ since $\sqrt{6} = \sqrt{2}\,\sqrt{3}$
$\sqrt{3}(\sqrt{2} - y)$	2. Factor out the common factor.

These are the only three types of polynomials containing radicals that you can factor now. There are more complicated ones that may be discussed at some future time. Always remember that you should factor common monomial factors from an expression even if it contains radicals. You will use such factoring to solve equations.

There are two types of equations using radical symbols. One is called a radical equation, and the other is called an equation with radicals. An *equation with radicals* contains radicals having only numbers as radicands. An example of such an equation is $x + \sqrt{3} = 4\sqrt{3}$. Solve this type of equation the very same way that you solve any equation that contains real numbers. The other type has variables in the radicand and is called a *radical equation*. (Discussed in Section 7.8).

People can also be classified by two types. One is the natural man; he has been born once into this world—by physical birth. This man's eternal destination is hell (Rev. 20:15). The other type of person is one who has been born twice—not only physically but also spiritually into the family of God. John tells us about this second birth in John 3:1-18. Nicodemus had to have faith in Jesus Christ to save him from eternal damnation, and so must everyone. Which type of person are you? You are one or the other.

EXAMPLE 3 Solve $x + \sqrt{3} = 4\sqrt{3}$.

Answer

$x + \sqrt{3} = 4\sqrt{3}$	
$x + \sqrt{3} - \sqrt{3} = 4\sqrt{3} - \sqrt{3}$	Subtract $\sqrt{3}$ from both
$x = 3\sqrt{3}$	sides of the equation.

EXAMPLE 4 Solve $x - 5\sqrt{2} = 3\sqrt{2} + x\sqrt{2}$.

Answer

$x - 5\sqrt{2} = 3\sqrt{2} + x\sqrt{2}$	1. Move all terms containing x to one
$x - x\sqrt{2} = 3\sqrt{2} + 5\sqrt{2}$	side of the equation and all other terms to the other side of the equation.

Continued ▶

$$x\left(1 - \sqrt{2}\right) = 8\sqrt{2}$$

2. Factor an x from each term on the left side.

$$x = \frac{8\sqrt{2}}{1 - \sqrt{2}}$$

3. Divide both sides by $1 - \sqrt{2}$.

$$x = \frac{8\sqrt{2}}{1 - \sqrt{2}} \cdot \frac{1 + \sqrt{2}}{1 + \sqrt{2}}$$

4. Simplify the radical expression. Make sure that no radicals remain in the denominator.

$$x = \frac{8\sqrt{2} + 16}{1 - 2}$$

$$x = \frac{8\sqrt{2} + 16}{-1}$$

$$x = -8\sqrt{2} - 16$$

Since the roots of positive numbers are real numbers, solving an equation containing radicals is the same as solving any other equation.

▶ A. Exercises

Factor.

1. $x\sqrt{3} - y\sqrt{3}$

2. $x^2y\sqrt{6} + \sqrt{2}$

3. $xz\sqrt{5} - z\sqrt{10}$

4. $x^2 - 7$

5. $x^2 + 2x\sqrt{5} + 5$

Solve.

6. $x + \sqrt{12} = 3\sqrt{3}$

7. $\sqrt{7} + 5y\sqrt{2} = 6\sqrt{7}$

8. $x\sqrt{20} - 3x\sqrt{5} = 8$

9. $5x\sqrt{8} - 3x\sqrt{2} = \sqrt{15}$

▶ B. Exercises

Factor.

10. $x^2 + 6x\sqrt{11} + 99$

11. $x^2 - 18$

12. $3m^2 - 51$

13. $5x^2 + 20x\sqrt{5} + 100$

14. $x^2\sqrt{7} - 6\sqrt{7}$

Solve.

15. $3x\sqrt{5} + \sqrt{15} = 9$

16. $t\sqrt{3} + 2 = \sqrt{27}$

17. $y\sqrt{6} - 3y = 2$

18. $x\left(2 + \sqrt{3}\right) + 4 = 7 + 6\sqrt{3}$

19. $4y + y\sqrt{7} = 9 + 3y$

20. $n\sqrt[3]{2} + \sqrt[3]{2} = 3\sqrt[3]{2}$

21. $3z\sqrt[3]{3} - z\sqrt[3]{3} = 4 + \sqrt[3]{6}$

22. $5x + 3x\sqrt{5} + 9 = x + 2$

23. $3x\sqrt{2} + x\left(\sqrt{2} - 4\right) = 12$

24. $2y\sqrt{147} - y\sqrt{108} = 4y\sqrt{3} + 1$

25. $4z\sqrt{12} + 6z\sqrt{2} = -1$

▶ C. Exercises

Factor. Assume all variables are positive.

26. $\sqrt{5x^3y^2} + 2\sqrt{15x^2y^2} + 3\sqrt{5xy^2}$

27. $7\sqrt{2x^3y^4} - 3\sqrt{2xz^4}$

▶ Dominion Modeling

28. Generate an exponential model of the inflation data. (Hint: The data will be more manageable if you subtract 1900 from each year.)

29. Evaluate the exponential model for the inflation data.

■ Cumulative Review

Graph.

30. $f(x) = |x|$

31. $f(x) = [x]$

32. $f(x) = 5^x$

33. $f(x) = |x - 4| - 1$

34. Give the domain and range of $f(x) = 5^x$

7.7 Radical and Exponential Functions

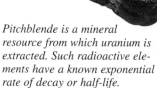

Your practice with radical and exponential expressions should make your study of radical and exponential functions easy. These functions can all be graphed by plotting points, but it is faster to make use of general patterns and translations.

Pitchblende is a mineral resource from which uranium is extracted. Such radioactive elements have a known exponential rate of decay or half-life.

Nuclear power plants, which use uranium pellets such as these, account for only 8% of the energy produced in the US.

EXAMPLE 1 Graph $f(x) = \sqrt{x}$.

Answer

x	y
0	0
1	1
2	$\sqrt{2} \approx 1.4$
3	$\sqrt{3} \approx 1.7$
4	2

1. Make a table and remember that x cannot be negative.

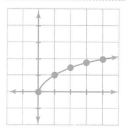

2. Graph. Notice that the domain is $\{x \mid x \geq 0\}$, so you cannot plot points to the left of the y-axis. The range will be $\{y \mid y \geq 0\}$, so the graph will lie in quadrant 1.

EXAMPLE 2   Graph $f(x) = \sqrt{x - 3} - 1$.

Answer

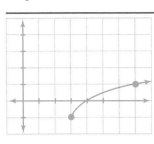

Translate the radical function $y = \sqrt{x}$ to the right 3 and down 1. (Compare with parabolic translations: $y = a(x - h)^2 + k$, which moves the function $y = x^2$ right h units and up k units.

In Example 2, the domain is $\{x \mid x \geq 3\}$, and the range is $\{y \mid y \geq -1\}$.

The *exponential function* was discussed in Chapter 2. Notice the pattern of the graphs of the following exponential functions.

$y = 2^x$

x	y
-3	$\frac{1}{8}$
-2	$\frac{1}{4}$
-1	$\frac{1}{2}$
0	1
1	2
2	4
3	8

$y = \left(\frac{1}{3}\right)^x$

x	y
-3	27
-2	9
-1	3
0	1
1	$\frac{1}{3}$
2	$\frac{1}{9}$
3	$\frac{1}{27}$

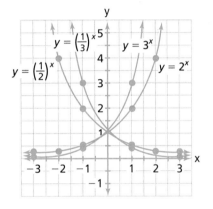

$y = \left(\frac{1}{2}\right)^x$

x	y
-3	8
-2	4
-1	2
0	1
1	$\frac{1}{2}$
2	$\frac{1}{4}$
3	$\frac{1}{8}$

$y = 3^x$

x	y
-3	$\frac{1}{27}$
-2	$\frac{1}{9}$
-1	$\frac{1}{3}$
0	1
1	3
2	9
3	27

You can see that these graphs all have the same general shape. What is true about the graph of an exponential function whose base is between 0 and 1? How does that compare to the graph when $a > 1$?

Notice the graphs of exponential functions get very close to the x-axis but do not touch or cross it. When this occurs, the line that the function approaches is called an asymptote of the graph.

EXAMPLE 3   Graph $f(x) = 4^{x-1} - 3$.

Answer

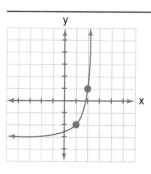

Mentally calculate points for $y = 4^x$ and translate them right 1 and down 3.

You know that $y = 5x$ is not a translation of $y = x$. Instead, the coefficient makes the graph steeper. The same is true of coefficients of radical and exponential functions. The following example shows that $f(x) = 3(2^x)$ is not a translation of $f(x) = 2^x$, but is steeper.

EXAMPLE 4   Graph $f(x) = 3(2^x)$.

Answer

x	$f(x)$
0	3
1	6
−1	$\frac{3}{2}$

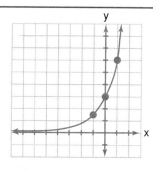

1. Find 3 points.

2. Plot the 3 points and sketch an exponential function through them.

The general exponential function $f(x) = ca^x$ ($a > 0$) includes a coefficient. You will use this general form for interest applications in Chapter 12.

▶ **A. Exercises**

Graph.

1. $y = 4^x$
2. $y = \left(\frac{1}{4}\right)^x$
3. $f(x) = \sqrt{x} + 3$

4. $f(x) = \sqrt{x + 1}$
5. $f(x) = 2^{x-2}$

Give the domain and range of each function.

6. $f(x) = \sqrt{x}$
7. $f(x) = 10^x$
8. $f(x) = \sqrt{x - 4}$
9. $f(x) = 2^x - 3$

▶ B. Exercises

Graph.

10. $f(x) = 4\left(\dfrac{1}{2}\right)^x$

11. $f(x) = \sqrt{x - 3} + 1$

12. $f(x) = \left(\dfrac{1}{5}\right)^x + 2$

13. $f(x) = -3^x$

14. $f(x) = -2\sqrt{x}$

Give the domain and range of each function.

15. $f(x) = \sqrt{x - h} + k$
16. $f(x) = ca^x$ if $a > 0$ and $c > 0$

Find $f(-3)$ and $f(x + 1)$ for each function.

17. $f(x) = \sqrt{x + 3}$

18. $f(x) = 2^x$

Use $f(x) = \sqrt[3]{x}$.

19. Graph it by plotting points.

20. Find the domain and range.

▶ C. Exercises

21. For the exponential function $f(x) = 2^x$, find the value of the function as x decreases ($x = 0, -1, -2, -10, -20, -100$).

22. As the x decreases from 0 to negative infinity, what happens to the value of the function?

23. At what value of x is $2^x = 0$?

24. As a increases, what happens to the graph of the exponential function $f(x) = a^x$?

▶ Dominion Modeling

Reconsider the CPI data. An exponential model repeatedly *multiplies* the same number by a starting amount to get a new value. So in $y = A(1 + r)^t$, the starting amount A is multiplied by $100\% + r\%$ for t times to get the final amount y. (*Hint:* Also, in this case r is not a measure of how well the model fits the data; it is a measure of growth.)

25. According to this model, what is the value of r from 1979 to 1982? From 1982 to 1985?

26. How could you explain the change in average inflation rates during these two times in history ?

Find the zeros of each function.

27. $f(x) = 4x + 8$
28. $f(x) = x^2 + 3x - 28$
29. $f(x) = |x| - 3$
30. $f(x) = x^3 + 3x^2 - 6x - 8$
31. $f(x) = \sqrt{x - 1} - 2$
32. $f(x) = 3\left(\frac{1}{2}\right)^x$

7.8 Radical Equations

When one or more radicands in an equation contain the variable, the equation is called a *radical equation*. An example of a radical equation is $\sqrt{x} + 2 = 18$. This equation is quite different from $\sqrt{2} + x = 18$, which is an equation with a radical.

To solve a radical equation, you must isolate the radical on one side of the equation and remove it by raising both sides of the equation to the appropriate power needed to eliminate the radical. After the radicals are removed, solve the equation. When you raise both sides of the equation to a power, you often introduce answers that are not true solutions, which are called *extraneous*. Because of this, you *must* check each solution in the original equation to determine whether the answer is correct.

Many hucksters and charlatans offer answers to daily problems. But Scripture admonishes every Christian to "prove all things" (I Thess. 5:21). You must check every idea or action against God's Word, the Bible, just as you must test your solutions to radical equations against the original equation. There are many solutions to life's problems advocated by the world that are not God's answers to our problems.

Look at the following examples of solving radical equations.

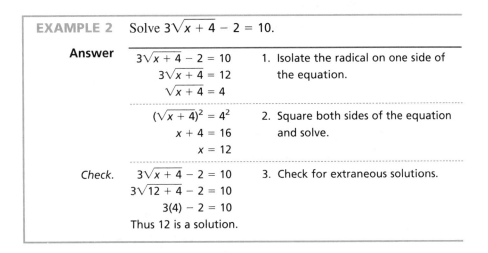

EXAMPLE 1   Solve $\sqrt{x} + 5 = 3$.

Answer

$\sqrt{x} + 5 = 3$

$\sqrt{x} = -2$ 1. Isolate the radical on one side of the equation.

$(\sqrt{x})^2 = (-2)^2$ 2. Square both sides of the equation.
$x = 4$

$\sqrt{4} + 5 = 7 \neq 3$ 3. Check for an extraneous solution. When finding the $\sqrt{4}$ in this check, always use the principal square root. The solution $x = 4$ is extraneous.

You could have recognized that there are no solutions to Example 1 at step 1, since $\sqrt{x}$ always refers to the positive root. This is why the range of $f(x) = \sqrt{x}$ consists only of the non-negative real numbers ($f(x) \geq 0$).

EXAMPLE 2   Solve $3\sqrt{x + 4} - 2 = 10$.

Answer

$3\sqrt{x + 4} - 2 = 10$ 1. Isolate the radical on one side of
$3\sqrt{x + 4} = 12$ the equation.
$\sqrt{x + 4} = 4$

$(\sqrt{x + 4})^2 = 4^2$ 2. Square both sides of the equation
$x + 4 = 16$ and solve.
$x = 12$

Check. $3\sqrt{x + 4} - 2 = 10$ 3. Check for extraneous solutions.
$3\sqrt{12 + 4} - 2 = 10$
$3(4) - 2 = 10$
Thus 12 is a solution.

The distinction between radical equations and equations with radicals should help you see the difference between exponential equations and equations with exponents. An equation with exponents can be solved in the same way as equations with radicals.

EXAMPLE 3   Solve $5x - 2 \cdot 5^{43} = 7 \cdot 5^{43}$.

Answer $5x - 2 \cdot 5^{43} = 7 \cdot 5^{43}$

$$5x = 7 \cdot 5^{43} + 2 \cdot 5^{43}$$
$$5x = 9 \cdot 5^{43}$$
$$x = 9 \cdot 5^{42}$$

To solve an exponential equation, however, you must find a missing exponent. For instance to solve $2^x = 32$ you must find the power of 2 which yields 32. Since 32 is 2^5, you can see from $2^x = 2^5$ that $x = 5$. In other words, if you can get the same base on both sides you can set the exponents equal.

If $a^x = a^b$ then $x = b$.

In Chapter 12 you will learn to solve exponential equations that have different bases on each side.

EXAMPLE 4   Solve $3^{4x} = 81$.

Answer $3^{4x} = 81$

$3^{4x} = 3^4$ 1. Factor each base into its prime factors.

$4x = 4$ 2. Set the exponents equal to each other
$x = 1$ and solve.

EXAMPLE 5   Solve $4^x = 32$.

Answer $4^x = 32$

$(2^2)^x = 2^5$ 1. Factor all bases into a product of primes.

$2^{2x} = 2^5$ 2. Use the laws of exponents to simplify.

$2x = 5$ 3. Set the exponents equal to each other
$x = \frac{5}{2}$ and solve.

EXAMPLE 6   Solve $25^x = \frac{1}{125}$.

Answer $25^x = \frac{1}{125}$

$(5^2)^x = \frac{1}{5^3}$ 1. Simplify each side of the equation to
$5^{2x} = 5^{-3}$ expressions having like bases.

$2x = -3$ 2. Set the exponents equal to each other
$x = \frac{-3}{2}$ and solve.

▶ A. Exercises

Solve and check.

1. $2^x = 16$
2. $4^{3x} = 64$
3. $9^x = 27$
4. $5^{3x + 1} = 25$
5. $8^x = 32$

6. $8\sqrt{x} = 40$
7. $\sqrt{x} + 2 = 9$
8. $\sqrt{x} + 4\sqrt{x} - 8 = 37$
9. $\sqrt{y + 6} + 3 = 14$
10. $\sqrt{x - 8} + 9 = 2$

▶ B. Exercises

Solve. You do not need to show your check but do not include extraneous solutions in your answers.

11. $4^{3x} = \frac{1}{4}$
12. $9^x = \frac{1}{81}$
13. $25^x = \frac{1}{5}$
14. $4^{2x - 5} = 32$
15. $6^{3x - 6} = 216$
16. $3\sqrt{x} + 5 = \sqrt{x} + 8$
17. $\sqrt{y - 3} + 6 = 3\sqrt{y - 3} + 8$
18. $5\sqrt{2x + 1} + 8 = 23$
19. $26 + 3\sqrt{4y - 5} = 2\sqrt{4y - 5} + 7$
20. $4 - 2\sqrt{x + 6} = -16$
21. $3^{x + 4} = \frac{1}{9}$
22. $27^{x - 1} = \frac{1}{81}$
23. $25^{3x} = 625$
24. $2^x = 0.5$
25. $3^{x + 6} = 243$
26. $4.5 + \sqrt{x + 3} = 6.2$
27. $4\sqrt{8y - 5} + 2\sqrt{8y - 5} = 18$
28. $\sqrt{3x + 7} - 15 = 2\sqrt{3x + 7} + 6$
29. $2\sqrt{y + 5} + 18 = 22$
30. $7 + \sqrt{3y + 4} = 8\sqrt{3y + 4} - 14$

▶ C. Exercises

Solve.

31. $3^{-5x}(6^{-2})^3 = \left(\frac{1}{2^{-x}}\right)^5$

32. $\sqrt{2x + 5} + 7 = \dfrac{3}{(2x + 5)^{-\frac{1}{2}}}$

▶ Dominion Modeling

33. According to the *exponential* model for the CPI data, when might we expect the Consumer Price Index to be twice the value in 1943? Is the exponential model useful here?

34. According to the *linear* model for the CPI data, when might we expect the Consumer Price Index to be twice the value in 1943? Is the linear model useful here?

Cumulative Review

If $f(x) = 2(x - 1)^2 + 4$.

35. Find the minimum point.

36. Graph $f(x)$.

37. Find the y-intercept.

38. Find the discriminant.

39. Find the zeros.

 MIND OVER MATH

Make this equation true by moving one digit to the other side of the equal sign.

$$\sqrt{2187} = 37$$

7.9 More Radical Equations

In this section you will study radical equations that have more than one radical expression. You will also study radical equations that contain more than one variable. These literal equations are often seen and used in the sciences. It is important that you learn how to work with this type of equation.

EXAMPLE 1   Solve $\sqrt{x} + 6 = \sqrt{x - 12}$.

Answer

$\sqrt{x} + 6 = \sqrt{x - 12}$ $(\sqrt{x} + 6)^2 = (\sqrt{x - 12})^2$	1. One of the radicals is already isolated. Square both sides.
$x + 12\sqrt{x} + 36 = x - 12$ $12\sqrt{x} = -48$	2. Simplify this equation. Notice it still has a radical in it. Isolate the radical and square both sides.
$\sqrt{x} = -4$ There is no solution.	3. This equation has no solution since the principal square root cannot be negative. If you do not notice this, you would square to obtain $x = 16$, which is extraneous (does not check).

EXAMPLE 2   Solve $\sqrt{x} - \sqrt{x + 32} = -2$.

Answer

$\sqrt{x} - \sqrt{x + 32} = -2$ $-\sqrt{x + 32} = -2 - \sqrt{x}$	1. Isolate the most complicated radical.
$\sqrt{x + 32} = 2 + \sqrt{x}$	2. Multiply both sides by -1 to eliminate the negatives.
$\left(\sqrt{x + 32}\right)^2 = \left(2 + \sqrt{x}\right)^2$ $x + 32 = 4 + 4\sqrt{x} + x$	3. Square both sides.
$-4\sqrt{x} = -28$ $\sqrt{x} = 7$ $\left(\sqrt{x}\right)^2 = 7^2$ $x = 49$	4. Isolate the radical again and repeat the process.

Continued ▶

Check.

$$\sqrt{x} - \sqrt{x + 32} = -2$$
$$\sqrt{49} - \sqrt{49 + 32} = -2$$
$$7 - \sqrt{81} = -2$$
$$7 - 9 = -2$$
$$-2 = -2$$

$x = 49$ is the solution.

5. Check for an extraneous solution.

Examine the reasons for extraneous solutions. There are two cases in which extraneous roots appear. The first occurs when the equation contains a term that is undefined. The domain of $f(x) = \sqrt{x}$ is $x \geq 0$, and the domain of $f(x) = \sqrt{x + 32}$ is found by solving $x + 32 \geq 0$, giving $x \geq -32$. Since the solution in Example 2, 49, is greater than both 0 and -32, the radicals $\sqrt{x}$ and $\sqrt{x + 32}$ are defined when $x = 49$.

The second reason for extraneous roots is that the solution is not in the range of the function. The ranges of $f(x) = \sqrt{x}$ and $f(x) = \sqrt{x + 32}$ are both $f(x) \geq 0$. Since $49 > 0$, no range violations exist and we conclude 49 is a root of the equation. If there had been a range violation, we would have seen a radical equal to a negative number. Recall Example 1 where $\sqrt{x} = -4$ occurred in the solution.

EXAMPLE 3   Solve $x = \sqrt{3x^2 + 9x - 5} - 3$.

Answer

$x = \sqrt{3x^2 + 9x - 5} - 3$ $x + 3 = \sqrt{3x^2 + 9x - 5}$ $(x + 3)^2 = \left(\sqrt{3x^2 + 9x - 5}\right)^2$	1. Isolate the radical and square both sides.
$x^2 + 6x + 9 = 3x^2 + 9x - 5$ $0 = 2x^2 + 3x - 14$ $0 = (2x + 7)(x - 2)$	2. Solve this quadratic equation.
$2x + 7 = 0$ or $x - 2 = 0$ $2x = -7 \qquad\qquad x = 2$ $x = \frac{-7}{2}$	3. Set the radicand ≥ 0 and solve the quadratic inequality (using the quadratic formula) to obtain $x \leq -3.48$ or $x \geq 0.48$. Also, since the radical equals $x + 3$ (step 1), $x \geq -3$. Thus, $x = 2$ satisfies all the conditions but $x = -\frac{7}{2}$ is extraneous since it does not satisfy $x \geq -3$.
Check.	4. The checks below verify the conclusions in step three and illustrate checks with fractions. Which way is easier?

Continued ▶

$$x = \sqrt{3x^2 + 9x - 5} - 3$$

$$\frac{-7}{2} = \sqrt{3\left(\frac{-7}{2}\right)^2 + 9\left(\frac{-7}{2}\right) - 5} - 3$$

$$\frac{-7}{2} = \sqrt{\frac{147}{4} - \frac{63}{2} - 5} - 3$$

$$\frac{-7}{2} = \sqrt{\frac{147}{4} - \frac{126}{4} - \frac{20}{4}} - 3$$

$$\frac{-7}{2} = \sqrt{\frac{1}{4}} - 3$$

$$\frac{-7}{2} = \frac{1}{2} - \frac{6}{2}$$

$$\frac{-7}{2} = \frac{-5}{2}$$

Therefore $\frac{-7}{2}$ is not a solution.

$$x = \sqrt{3x^2 + 9x - 5} - 3$$

$$2 = \sqrt{3(2)^2 + 9(2) - 5} - 3$$

$$2 = \sqrt{12 + 18 - 5} - 3$$

$$2 = \sqrt{25} - 3$$

$$2 = 5 - 3$$

$$2 = 2$$

Therefore 2 is a solution.

The next example shows a literal equation that contains a radical expression.

EXAMPLE 4   Solve $v = \sqrt{\dfrac{e^2}{4\pi e_0 mr}}$ for m.

Answer

$$v = \sqrt{\frac{e^2}{4\pi e_0 mr}}$$

$$v^2 = \left[\sqrt{\frac{e^2}{4\pi e_0 mr}}\right]^2$$ 1. Square both sides, since the radical is isolated on one side of the equation.

$$v^2 = \frac{e^2}{4\pi e_0 mr}$$ 2. Solve for m.

$$4\pi e_0 mr v^2 = e^2$$

$$m = \frac{e^2}{4\pi e_0 r v^2}$$

▶ **A. Exercises**

Solve.

1. $\sqrt{x + 3} - 1 = \sqrt{x - 6}$

2. $\sqrt{x} = \sqrt{x - 9} + 3$

3. $\sqrt{2x + 5} + 4 = \sqrt{2x + 69}$

4. $\sqrt{x - 5} - 5 - \sqrt{x + 100} = 0$

5. $2x + 3 = \sqrt{5x^2 + 8x - 36}$

6. $x - \sqrt{3x^2 + 9x + 7} = -2$

7. $\sqrt{10x^2 - 29x + 2} = 3x - 4$

8. $\sqrt{x - 21} - \sqrt{x} = 1$

9. $\sqrt{3x + 8} + 3 = \sqrt{3x + 35}$

10. $2x = \sqrt{5x^2 + 21x + 10} - 4$

▶ B. Exercises

Solve for the indicated variable.

11. $v = \sqrt{\dfrac{2k}{m}}$ for m

12. $P = \sqrt{2mE}$ for E

13. $E_1 = \sqrt{E_2{}^2 + E_3{}^2}$ for E_2

14. $d = a\sqrt{h^2 + k^2}$ for h

15. $t = \dfrac{2d}{\sqrt{c^2 - u^2}}$ for c

16. $R = \sqrt{RS + T}$ for R

17. $\sqrt{P - rP} = N$ for P

Use the equation $\sqrt{Ax + B} = C$ and assume $A \neq 0$.

18. For what values of C does the equation have solutions?

19. What is the domain of the radical?

20. Under the conditions above, what is the solution to the radical equation?

▶ C. Exercises

Solve each equation. Use the domains and ranges of the radicals to check your solutions.

21. $\sqrt{x^2 + 9} = \sqrt{3x^2 - x - 6}$

22. $\sqrt{x - 5} + 2 = 3\sqrt{x + 1}$

23. $\sqrt{x + 5} - 3 = \sqrt{x + 1}$

24. Five less than the square of a number is eleven. Find the number.

25. Jessica biked to Gettysburg and returned in 5 hours. If she averaged 4 mph going and 6 mph returning, how far is Gettysburg from her home?

26. A sand box covers 10 square feet. Find its width if its length is 2 feet longer than its width.

27. The sum of the squares of two consecutive integers is 313. Find the integers.

28. The perimeter of a rectangle is 180 feet. If the width is the square root of the length, find the dimensions.

Algebra *and* Scripture

Number Types

Knowing the types of numbers is essential to algebra. The only difference between factoring $x^2 - 3$ and $x^2 - 4$ is in the type of numbers used for factoring.

1. Read Numbers 1:2-3. What did God command Moses to do and what kind of numbers would Moses need to use?
2. Read Leviticus 6:20. What did God instruct Aaron and his sons to do? What kind of numbers did they use?

Radicals such as $\sqrt{5}$ are irrational numbers. You know that π is also irrational, but there is a difference. $\sqrt{5}$ is the zero of a polynomial with integer coefficients—it is the solution to $x^2 - 5 = 0$. On the other hand, no polynomial with integer coefficients has π as a solution. This suggests a classification.

> **Definitions**
>
> **Algebraic number**   A number that is a solution to a polynomial equation with integral coefficients.
>
> **Transcendental number**   A real number that is not algebraic.

You can show that all integers, rational numbers, and radicals are algebraic. Set the number equal to x and undo operations until you get a polynomial in integers. Use exponents to undo radicals; you may need to clear fractions also.

$x = -3$ is algebraic, since $x + 3 = 0$ is a polynomial equation with -3 as a solution.

$x = \frac{2}{5}$ is algebraic, since $5x = 2$ or $5x - 2 = 0$ is a polynomial equation with $\frac{2}{5}$ as a solution.

$x = \sqrt{3}$ is algebraic since $x^2 = 3$ or $x^2 - 3 = 0$ is a polynomial equation with $\sqrt{3}$ as a solution.

Can you show that the following numbers are algebraic by providing the polynomial equation with integer coefficients?

3. $\frac{-17}{3}$ 4. $\sqrt[3]{5}$ 5. $-5\frac{1}{2}$

GREATER AMPLITUDE
Is $2 + 3\sqrt{7}$ algebraic? Why?

All of the numbers in the Bible are rational numbers. However algebraic numbers that are irrational (such as radicals) and transcendental numbers (all irrational) are implied by various measurements.

6. Give the dimensions of the base of the ark of the covenant (Exodus 25:10).

7. What is the length of a diagonal across the base?

8. What type of number is this length?

9. In I Kings 7 what number can be approximated from the circular dimensions given (the brim width of one handbreadth would have to be taken into account).

10. What kind of number is it?

The commands to count and measure in the Bible require a knowledge of the number system.

> ## Absolute Values
>
> FROM TWENTY YEARS OLD and upward, all that are able to go forth to war in Israel: thou and Aaron shall number them by their armies.
>
> NUMBERS 1:3 ಏ

Chapter 7 Review

Write each expression in rational exponent form.

1. $\sqrt{7xy^5}$

2. $\sqrt[5]{25a^3b^2}$

Write each expression in radical form.

3. $2^{\frac{4}{3}}a^{\frac{1}{6}}$

4. $x^{\frac{2}{5}}y^{\frac{1}{5}}$

Perform the indicated operations and simplify. Leave answers in radical form.

5. $\left(3a^2b^3\right)^{\frac{1}{3}}$

6. $(5x^4y)^0$

7. $2^{\frac{1}{3}} \cdot 2^{\frac{3}{4}}$

8. $3^{\frac{4}{3}} \div 3$

Simplify.

9. $\sqrt{27a^5b}$

10. $\sqrt[3]{125x^4y^6}$

11. $\sqrt{180a^3b^2c^5}$

12. $3^{20}(27^4 - 9^5)$

Do the indicated operations and simplify. Assume variables represent positive numbers.

13. $7\sqrt{18} - 3\sqrt{2}$

14. $\sqrt{x^4y^3z} + xy\sqrt{x^2yz} + 6x\sqrt{x^2yz}$

15. $\sqrt[3]{135a^3b^6} - 2ab\sqrt[3]{5b^3} + a\sqrt[3]{1080b^6}$

16. $\dfrac{\sqrt{3}}{\sqrt{18}}$

17. $\sqrt{6a^2b^3}\,\sqrt{3ab}$

18. $\sqrt{4z}\left(1 + \sqrt{2z}\right)$

19. $\left(1 + \sqrt{3}\right)\left(1 - \sqrt{3}\right)$

20. $\left(x + \sqrt{5}\right)\left(2x - \sqrt{5}\right)$

21. $\left(3x + \sqrt{7}\right)^2$

22. $\dfrac{10 \cdot 7^{15}}{35 \cdot 7^8}$

23. $\dfrac{4}{1 + \sqrt{5}}$

Evaluate for $x = 0, -1,$ and 5.

24. $f(x) = \sqrt{x + 4}$ 25. $g(x) = 2^x - 7$

Graph.

26. $f(x) = \sqrt{x - 1}$ 27. $g(x) = 3^x$

Factor.

28. $x^2 - 7$

29. $x^2y\sqrt{3} - xy\sqrt{75}$

Solve.

30. $8^x = 32$

31. $y\sqrt{7} + 8y = 6$

32. $\sqrt{3x - 6} + 2 = \sqrt{3x + 26}$

33. $\sqrt{x} + 5 = 4$

34. $6^{11}x - 3^{10} = 3^8$

35. $d = \sqrt{D(D - 4f)}$ for f

36. Evaluate the exponential model of the inflation data.
37. Give the mathematical significance of Numbers 1:3.

8 Complex Numbers

It's a swing—crack!—and the ball flies into center field. Two hundred twenty feet from home plate, the ball takes one hop before the center fielder snags it and fires it home. In the stands, gawking spectators wonder if the speedster on third base can score.

Even as far back as 1744, boys played baseball. During the Civil War, many soldiers sharpened their baseball skills when they were not fighting. From the battlefields of the 1860s, baseball exploded to become one of America's favorite pastimes.

Here is the data for the long throw from center field to home plate, 220 feet away. In this case, the fielder threw the ball from 6.0 feet high, and the catcher caught it when it was half a foot off the ground. Units are in seconds and feet.

Time	Height	Distance	Time	Height	Distance
0.0	6.0	220.0	0.9	16.2	109.8
0.1	8.4	207.8	1.0	15.7	97.5
0.2	10.5	195.5	1.1	14.9	85.3
0.3	12.3	183.3	1.2	13.8	73.1
0.4	13.7	171.0	1.3	12.4	60.8
0.5	14.9	158.8	1.4	10.6	48.6
0.6	15.7	146.5	1.5	8.5	36.3
0.7	16.2	134.3	1.6	6.1	24.1
0.8	16.3	122.0	1.7	3.4	11.8

After this chapter you should be able to

1. define imaginary numbers and complex numbers.

2. perform the four basic operations of addition, subtraction, multiplication, and division with complex numbers.

3. solve quadratic equations that have complex numbers as roots.

4. graph complex numbers on a complex plane.

5. use vectors to represent and add complex numbers.

8.1 Pure Imaginary Numbers

You have studied the set of real numbers in most of your previous courses in math and science. The set of real numbers is made of subsets such as integers, natural numbers, whole numbers, rational, and irrational numbers. The set broader than the set of real numbers is called the set of complex numbers. You can see the value of complex numbers by solving the equation $x^2 + 1 = 0$. One way to solve this is to take square roots.

$$x^2 + 1 = 0$$
$$x^2 = -1$$
$$\sqrt{x^2} = \pm\sqrt{-1}$$
$$x = \pm\sqrt{-1}$$

Electrical distribution stations re-direct the electricity from a central generator to various districts and neighborhoods. Electrical engineers must use complex numbers.

By the quadratic formula you obtain the same result.

$$x^2 + 1 = 0$$
$$x = \frac{0 \pm \sqrt{0-4}}{2}$$
$$x = \pm\frac{\sqrt{-4}}{2}$$
$$x = \pm\frac{\sqrt{4}\sqrt{-1}}{2}$$
$$x = \pm\frac{2\sqrt{-1}}{2}$$
$$x = \pm\sqrt{-1}$$

Since the square root of a negative number is not a real number, it is designated by the term *imaginary*. Imaginary quantities were first introduced by Tartaglia, an Italian mathematician of the 1500s. He used them to describe solutions to cubic equations. Cardan, another Italian mathematician, named these numbers *fictitious numbers*. It was not until 1777 that Leonhard Euler first used the *i* to denote the square root of negative one. The understanding that we have today is based on Euler's work. Imaginary numbers complement the real numbers to form the complex number system, just as irrational numbers complement the rational numbers to form the real numbers.

Definition

Imaginary unit i, where $i^2 = -1$ or $i = \sqrt{-1}$.

The solution to the equation $x^2 + 1 = 0$ is not written $\pm\sqrt{-1}$ but is written $\pm i$. It is necessary that you know how to simplify powers of i so that if they appear in an expression, you can change the expression to simplest form.

$$i^1 = \sqrt{-1} = i$$
$$i^2 = \sqrt{-1} \cdot \sqrt{-1} = -1$$
$$i^3 = i^2 \cdot i = (-1)i = -i$$
$$i^4 = i^2 \cdot i^2 = (-1)(-1) = 1$$
$$i^5 = i^4 \cdot i = (1)i = i$$
$$i^6 = i^4 \cdot i^2 = (1)(-1) = -1$$

etc.

Notice that the pattern starts repeating after i^4. To what do i^7, i^8, i^9, and i^{10} simplify? To simplify an imaginary expression with a large exponent, divide the exponent by 4 (the number of different values before the pattern starts repeating). The remainder is the power of i equivalent to the original power. Look at Example 1.

EXAMPLE 1 Simplify i^{57}.

Answer i^{57}

$$\begin{array}{r} 14 \\ 4\overline{)57} \\ \underline{4} \\ 17 \\ \underline{16} \\ 1 \end{array}$$

1. Divide the exponent 57 by 4 to determine the number of cycles of 4 powers of i and any amount left over.

$$i^{57} = i^{4 \cdot 14 + 1} = (i^4)^{14}\, i^1 = (1)^{14}\, i^1 = i$$
$$i^{57} = i$$

2. The exponent on the simplification is the remainder from the division.

Definition

Pure imaginary number the product of a real number and i, written in the form ai, where $a \in \mathbb{R}$, $a \neq 0$, and i is the imaginary unit.

Some examples are $-3i$, $\sqrt{5}i$ and $\frac{5}{2}i$. The imaginary unit, i, is also a pure imaginary number where $a = 1$.

You should always simplify any radical expression that has a negative under the radical sign to an expression containing the imaginary unit i.

EXAMPLE 2   Simplify $\sqrt{-32}$.

Answer $\sqrt{-32}$

$\sqrt{32}\sqrt{-1}$ 1. Factor the imaginary unit from the expression.

$\sqrt{32}i$ 2. Replace $\sqrt{-1}$ with i.

$4\sqrt{2}i$ 3. Simplify the radical expression.

Remember that pure imaginary numbers are not part of the real number system. $\sqrt{-1}$ does not have meaning in the real number system. Whenever you see $\sqrt{-n}$ be sure to replace it with $\sqrt{n}i$ since $\sqrt{-n} = \sqrt{n}\sqrt{-1}$. The properties of real numbers apply to imaginary numbers as long as you are careful to write them in terms of i.

EXAMPLE 3   Simplify $\sqrt{-2}\sqrt{-3}$.

Answer $\sqrt{-2}\sqrt{-3}$

$\left(\sqrt{2}i\right)\left(\sqrt{3}i\right)$ 1. Replace $\sqrt{-n}$ with $\sqrt{n}i$.

$\sqrt{6}i^2$ 2. Multiply.

$\sqrt{6}(-1) = -\sqrt{6}$ 3. Simplify by substituting -1 for i^2.

Recall that in the set of real numbers $\sqrt{a}\sqrt{b} = \sqrt{ab}$. However, in the set of complex numbers $\sqrt{-1}\sqrt{-1} \neq 1$, but instead $\sqrt{-1}\sqrt{-1} = i(i) = i^2 = -1$.

EXAMPLE 4   Solve $x^2 + 45 = 0$.

Answer $x^2 + 45 = 0$

$x^2 = -45$ 1. Move the constant term to the right
$x = \pm\sqrt{-45}$ and find the square root of both sides.

$x = \pm\sqrt{45}i$ 2. Simplify the expression.
$x = \pm3\sqrt{5}i$

▶ A. Exercises

Simplify. Variables represent positive real numbers.

1. $\sqrt{-2}$
2. $\sqrt{-9}$
3. $\sqrt{-16}$
4. $\sqrt{-20}$
5. $\sqrt{-48}$
6. $-\sqrt{-9}$
7. $\sqrt{-175}$
8. $\sqrt{-25x^2}$
9. i^8
10. $\sqrt{-24x}$
11. i^{26}
12. $\sqrt{-121a^2b}$
13. $-\sqrt{36}$
14. $-\sqrt{-135}$
15. i^{83}
16. i^{359}

▶ B. Exercises

Simplify. Variables represent positive real numbers.

17. $\sqrt{-a^3b^4}$
18. $\sqrt{-675x^3y}$
19. $\sqrt{-24a^5b^3}$
20. $\sqrt{-252x^6y}$

Solve.

21. $x^2 + 4 = 0$
22. $x^2 + 49 = 0$
23. $x^2 + 126 = 0$
24. $x^2 + 200 = 0$
25. $x^2 + 75 = 0$

▶ C. Exercises

26. Simplify $\sqrt{-98x^3y^5z^7}$. Do not assume variables are positive.

27. Solve $\frac{3}{4}x^2 + 29 = 0$.

▶ Dominion Modeling

28. Would a linear or exponential model be appropriate for the baseball data (time and height)?

29. From the shape of the baseball data, a quadratic function seems to be appropriate (for time and height). Find a quadratic model.

▮ Cumulative Review

Simplify.

30. $(5x^2 - 3x - 7) - (2x^2 - x + 4)$
31. $5\sqrt{7} - \sqrt{28}$
32. $(x^3 + 5x) + (x^2 - 3x)$
33. $4^{11} + 3 \cdot 2^{19}$
34. $xy + x\sqrt{y} + 3xy - 2x\sqrt{y}$

8.2 Adding Complex Numbers

The sum of a real number and a pure imaginary number is called a *complex number*. You may think all of math is complex, but don't give up. The Lord has given you a sound mind, and He expects you to learn to reason with that mind and use your talents for Him. II Timothy 1:7 states "For God hath not given us the spirit of fear; but of power, and of love, and of a sound mind." If God has given you talent in mathematics, you are responsible to use that talent to honor and glorify the Lord. Learn this material to the best of your ability so that you can apply your knowledge to the math and science that you study in the future.

Over 84% of the energy produced in the US comes from fossil fuels (coal, natural gas, oil). This Florida generator is among the most fuel-efficient of its type.

Definition

Complex number   a number that can be expressed in the *standard form* $a + bi$, where $a, b \in \mathbb{R}$ and $i = \sqrt{-1}$.

In $a + bi$, a is known as the *real part* and b as the *imaginary part*. A complex number is never left in the form $\frac{a + bi}{c}$ but is written in standard form as $\frac{a}{c} + \frac{b}{c}i$. *Note:* Any complex number that is not a real number is called *imaginary* whether it is of the form $a + bi$ or just bi.

Are the numbers 5 and $-7i$ complex numbers? Yes, because you can write both the real number 5 and the pure imaginary number $-7i$ in the standard form of a complex number, $a + bi$. For the number 5, let $a = 5$ and $b = 0$ to write $5 + 0i$. For the number $-7i$, let $a = 0$ and $b = -7$ to write $0 - 7i$. The set of complex numbers is the broadest set of numbers studied thus far. The diagram shown here summarizes the relationship between types of numbers.

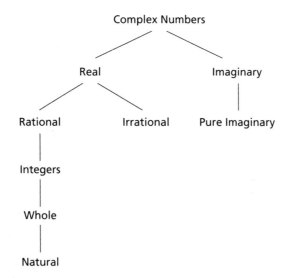

Two complex numbers, $z = a + bi$ and $w = c + di$, are equal if $a = c$ and $b = d$.

Add complex numbers as illustrated. If $z = a + bi$ and $w = c + di$, then $z + w = (a + c) + (b + d)i$.

See the examples that follow.

EXAMPLE 1   Add $(3 + 2i) + (5 - 4i)$.

Answer $(3 + 2i) + (5 - 4i)$
$(3 + 5) + (2 - 4)i$
$8 - 2i$

Notice that the same answer would be obtained in Example 1 by removing the parentheses and combining like terms. Example 2 illustrates both methods for a subtraction problem. In method one, subtract the corresponding real parts and imaginary parts. In method two, remove parentheses and then combine like terms.

EXAMPLE 2   Subtract $(5 - 3i) - (2 + 6i)$.

Answer

Method 1	Method 2
$(5 - 3i) - (2 + 6i)$	$(5 - 3i) - (2 + 6i)$
$(5 - 2) + (-3 - 6)i$	$5 - 3i - 2 - 6i$
$3 - 9i$	$3 - 9i$

▶ A. Exercises

Write each number in complex number form $a + bi$.

1. 7
2. $4i$
3. $-\sqrt{-9}$
4. $8 + \sqrt{-8}$
5. $-6i$
6. $\dfrac{2 - 6i}{3}$

Give the real part and the imaginary part of each complex number.

7. $5 + 11i$
8. $3 - 6i$
9. $10i$
10. -5
11. $i + 2$
12. $\dfrac{3 + 12i}{9}$

▶ B. Exercises

Do the indicated operation.

13. $(9 - 4i) - (3 + 2i)$
14. $(3 + 4i) + (6 + i)$
15. $(1 - 6i) + (3 - 2i)$
16. $(9 + 2i) + (-6 + 3i)$
17. $(28 - 5i) + (3 - i)$
18. $(-6 + 2i) - (2 + i)$
19. $(5 - 8i) - (-2 - i)$
20. $(-3 + 2i) - (-7 + 6i)$

Simplify.

21. $5i - (4 + 6i)$
22. $(i + 7) + (3 - 4i)$
23. $\dfrac{18 - 5i}{6} - \dfrac{2i - 7}{5}$
24. $i^7 - i^6$
25. $\left(\sqrt{3} - \sqrt{6i}\right) + \left(\sqrt{27} + \sqrt{54i}\right)$
26. $5i - 3 + i^4 + i$

▶ C. Exercises

Compute and simplify.

27. $\left(\sqrt{3} - 2i\right) - \left(5 + \frac{2}{3}i\right) - \left(-4 - \frac{7}{5}i\right)$
28. Demonstrate the associative property of complex numbers using $(3 + 4i) + (2 - 5i) + (6 - 3i)$.

▮ Cumulative Review

Simplify.

29. $(x - 3)(x + 8)$
30. $(5x - 7)(5x + 7)$
31. $3x(2x - 5)^2$
32. $\sqrt{7}\,(5 - \sqrt{7})$
33. $(2 + \sqrt{3})(2 - \sqrt{3})$

8.3 Multiplying Complex Numbers

To multiply two complex numbers, you apply the distributive property or the FOIL method. After performing the multiplication, you should always simplify the result to the standard form $a + bi$. This is done by combining like terms and substituting for higher powers of i.

EXAMPLE 1	Multiply $5(3 + 2i)$.	
Answer	$5(3 + 2i)$	
	$15 + 10i$	Multiply by applying the distributive property.

EXAMPLE 2	Multiply $(4 - 2i)(2 + 3i)$.	
Answer	$(4 - 2i)(2 + 3i)$	
	$8 + 12i - 4i - 6i^2$	1. Multiply by the FOIL method.
	$8 + 12i - 4i - 6(-1)$ $8 + 12i - 4i + 6$	2. Since $i^2 = -1$, substitute it for i^2 and simplify.
	$14 + 8i$	3. Combine like terms.

EXAMPLE 3	Multiply $\left(3 + \sqrt{2}\,i\right)\left(3 - \sqrt{2}\,i\right)$.	
Answer	$\left(3 + \sqrt{2}\,i\right)\left(3 - \sqrt{2}\,i\right)$	
	$9 - 3\sqrt{2}\,i + 3\sqrt{2}\,i - 2i^2$ $9 - 2(-1)$	1. Multiply by FOIL, recognizing that the outer and inner products add to zero.
	11	2. Combine like terms.

▶ A. Exercises

Multiply and simplify.

1. $-3(2 + 5i)$
2. $12(7 + 3i)$
3. $-2(6 - i)$
4. $9(2 + i)$
5. $(3 + i)(2 - i)$
6. $(1 + 6i)(3 - 2i)$
7. $(-2 - 6i)(1 + i)$
8. $(4 - 6i)(3 - 5i)$
9. $(7 + 2i)(1 + 4i)$
10. $(4 - 9i)(10 + i)$
11. $(2 - 5i)(3 - 8i)$
12. $(7 - i)(1 - i)$
13. $(12 + 5i)(6 + 8i)$

▶ B. Exercises

Perform the indicated operations and simplify.

14. $\left(2 + \frac{1}{3}i\right)i$
15. $4i\left(\frac{1}{2} - \frac{3}{2}i\right)$
16. $\frac{4}{5}i\left(\frac{2}{3}i\right)$
17. $\frac{5}{6}i(12 - 13i)$
18. $\left(5 - \frac{4}{3}i\right)\left(\frac{1}{2} + \frac{5}{6}i\right)$
19. $(2 - 0.5i)(3 - 0.42i)$
20. $\left(\frac{1}{2} - \frac{5}{2}i\right)\left(\frac{1}{3} + \frac{2}{3}i\right)$
21. $\left(\sqrt{3}i - 4\right)\left(\sqrt{3} + 4i\right)$
22. $\left(\sqrt{2}i\right)^3$
23. $\left(4 - \sqrt{3}i\right)^2$

▶ C. Exercises

Perform the indicated operation and simplify.

24. $(1 + 2i)^3$
25. $(5 - 3i)^4$
26. Look for a pattern when multiplying two complex numbers. Multiply to find zw, where $z = a + bi$ and $w = c + di$.

▶ Dominion Modeling

27. Using the baseball data, if the runner on third base starts for home just when the center fielder throws toward home, how fast would the runner have to run to beat the throw? Would it be reasonable to expect the runner to beat the throw home? (*Hint:* The distance from home plate to first or third base is **90** feet.)

28. Suppose that the ball passed over second base on its way to home plate. Would it be reasonable to expect the second baseman to catch it, or would the ball be too high?

■ Cumulative Review

Simplify.

29. $\dfrac{3x^2 + 12x - 9}{3}$

31. $\dfrac{3\sqrt{5}}{8\sqrt{3}}$

30. $\dfrac{4 \pm \sqrt{8}}{6}$

32. $\dfrac{6}{5 - \sqrt{3}}$

Divide.

33. $(x^2 + 3x - 7) \div (x - 2)$

Matrix Products

Recall the method for finding special matrix products in Chapter 7. You can extend that principle to multiply two matrices. Multiply each row by each column.

EXAMPLE 1. Multiply $\begin{bmatrix} 3 & 2 \\ 7 & 1 \end{bmatrix} \begin{bmatrix} 3 & 8 & 0 \\ 4 & -2 & 2 \end{bmatrix}$.

Answer

$\begin{bmatrix} 3 & 2 \\ 7 & 1 \end{bmatrix} \begin{bmatrix} 3 & 8 & 0 \\ 4 & -2 & 2 \end{bmatrix}$

$\begin{bmatrix} (3)(3) + (2)(4) & (3)(8) + (2)(-2) & (3)(0) + (2)(2) \\ (7)(3) + (1)(4) & (7)(8) + (1)(-2) & (7)(0) + (1)(2) \end{bmatrix}$

1. To find the row 1, column 1, entry of the product matrix, multiply row 1 of the first matrix times column 1 of the second matrix as shown.

   $3 \cdot 3 + 2 \cdot 4 = 9 + 8 = 17$

$\begin{bmatrix} 17 & 20 & 4 \\ 25 & 54 & 2 \end{bmatrix}$

2. Continue this process to find each entry of the product matrix.

To multiply two matrices, the number of columns of the first matrix must be the same as the number of rows of the second matrix.

$$(m \times \boxed{n)(n} \times p)$$

In this case, the product is a matrix with dimensions $m \times p$.

Remember also that powers are repeated multiplication.

$$A^2 = AA$$

To find powers of a matrix A, the matrix must be square (same number of columns as rows). For an $n \times n$ matrix A, the powers $A^2, A^3, \ldots$ will also be $n \times n$ matrices.

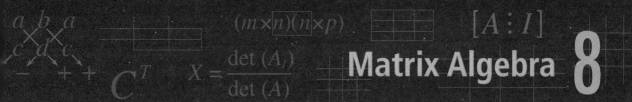
▶ Exercises

$$A = \begin{bmatrix} 1 & 7 \\ 3 & -4 \end{bmatrix} \quad B = \begin{bmatrix} 1 & 0 \\ 0 & 1 \end{bmatrix} \quad C = \begin{bmatrix} 5 & 3 & 0 \\ -4 & 1 & 7 \end{bmatrix} \quad D = \begin{bmatrix} 5 & -5 \\ 1 & 7 \\ 8 & -4 \end{bmatrix}$$

Find the products using the above matrices. Give the dimension of each product before multiplying.

1. AC
2. CD
3. DC
4. A^3
5. What can you conclude from the results of exercises 2 and 3?

8.4 Dividing Complex Numbers

Division of complex numbers is accomplished by writing the dividend over the divisor and simplifying the fraction. The simplification of a division problem that contains an imaginary number in the denominator is similar to rationalizing a denominator that contains a radical. This should seem reasonable to you because according to the definition of an imaginary number, it either is a radical or contains a radical. Remember that $i = \sqrt{-1}$. Also remember that you can never leave a radical in the denominator of a fraction. Therefore you can never leave an imaginary number in the denominator of a fraction.

There are two main types of division using imaginary numbers. Sometimes the divisor is a pure imaginary number, and sometimes the divisor is a complex number of the form $a + bi$, where $a, b \in \mathbb{R}$. Each division problem can be expressed as a fraction. For example $3 \div 4 = \frac{3}{4}$, $10 \div 9 = \frac{10}{9}$, and $(3 + 2i) \div (3i) = \frac{3 + 2i}{3i}$. The basic goal when dividing complex numbers is to eliminate all imaginary numbers from the denominator of the fraction.

Just as the product of complex numbers must be simplified to $a + bi$ form, so division must be simplified. As mentioned in Section 8.2, an answer is never left in $\frac{a + bi}{c}$ form but is written as $\frac{a}{c} + \frac{b}{c}i$.

EXAMPLE 1 Divide $(2 + 6i) \div 3i$.

Answer $(2 + 6i) \div 3i$

$\dfrac{2 + 6i}{3i}$ 1. Change the division to fractional form.

$\dfrac{2 + 6i}{3i} \cdot \dfrac{i}{i}$ 2. To divide, you must eliminate the pure imaginary number in the denominator. To do this, multiply the fraction by 1 in the form of $\frac{i}{i}$.

$\dfrac{2i + 6i^2}{3i^2}$

$\dfrac{2i + 6(-1)}{3(-1)}$ 3. Simplify the expression by changing i^2 to -1.

$\dfrac{-6 + 2i}{-3}$

$\dfrac{-6}{-3} + \dfrac{2}{-3}i$ 4. Change to $a + bi$ form.

$2 - \dfrac{2}{3}i$

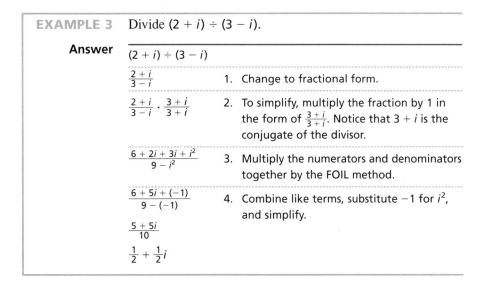

EXAMPLE 2   Divide $(42 - 30i) \div \sqrt{6}i$.

Answer

$(42 - 30i) \div \sqrt{6}i$

$\dfrac{42 - 30i}{\sqrt{6}i}$

$\dfrac{42 - 30i}{\sqrt{6}i} \cdot \dfrac{\sqrt{6}i}{\sqrt{6}i}$

$\dfrac{42\sqrt{6}i - 30\sqrt{6}i^2}{6i^2}$

1. Eliminate the imaginary number in the denominator by multiplying by 1 in the form of $\frac{i}{i}$. Rationalize the denominator as well.

$\dfrac{42\sqrt{6}i - 30\sqrt{6}(-1)}{6(-1)}$

2. Simplify the expression.

$\dfrac{30\sqrt{6} + 42\sqrt{6}i}{-6}$

$\dfrac{30\sqrt{6}}{-6} + \dfrac{42\sqrt{6}}{-6}i$

$-5\sqrt{6} - 7\sqrt{6}i$

Recall that real numbers $2 + \sqrt{7}$ and $2 - \sqrt{7}$ are conjugates of one another. Likewise the conjugate of a complex number $3 - i$ is $3 + i$. In general $a + bi$ and $a - bi$ are conjugates, so you can always obtain the conjugate by changing the sign of the imaginary part. Look at Example 3 to see how you use the conjugate to simplify this type of division problem.

EXAMPLE 3   Divide $(2 + i) \div (3 - i)$.

Answer

$(2 + i) \div (3 - i)$

$\dfrac{2 + i}{3 - i}$

1. Change to fractional form.

$\dfrac{2 + i}{3 - i} \cdot \dfrac{3 + i}{3 + i}$

2. To simplify, multiply the fraction by 1 in the form of $\frac{3 + i}{3 + i}$. Notice that $3 + i$ is the conjugate of the divisor.

$\dfrac{6 + 2i + 3i + i^2}{9 - i^2}$

3. Multiply the numerators and denominators together by the FOIL method.

$\dfrac{6 + 5i + (-1)}{9 - (-1)}$

4. Combine like terms, substitute -1 for i^2, and simplify.

$\dfrac{5 + 5i}{10}$

$\dfrac{1}{2} + \dfrac{1}{2}i$

We can also find reciprocals of complex numbers. Once again we must simplify the result.

EXAMPLE 4 Find the reciprocals of $5i$ and of $4 - 7i$.

Answer $\frac{1}{5i} = \frac{1}{5i} \cdot \frac{i}{i} = \frac{i}{5i^2} = \frac{i}{5(-1)} = -\frac{1}{5}i$

$\frac{1}{4-7i} = \frac{1}{4-7i} \cdot \frac{4+7i}{4+7i} = \frac{4+7i}{16-49i^2} = \frac{4+7i}{16+49} = \frac{4}{65} + \frac{7}{65}i$

▶ A. Exercises

Give the conjugate of each number.

1. $3 - 4i$
2. $2i - 5$
3. 7
4. $-6i$

Write in $a + bi$ form.

5. $\frac{5 + 8i}{4}$
6. $\frac{-3i + 7}{5}$

Perform the indicated operation and simplify.

7. $\frac{5}{2i}$
8. $\frac{7}{3i}$
9. $\frac{4i}{2i}$
10. $\frac{19i}{7i}$

▶ B. Exercises

Simplify.

11. $\frac{18i}{6}$
12. $\frac{4 - 2i}{2}$
13. $\frac{5 + 15i}{5}$
14. $\frac{2 - 5i}{i}$
15. $\frac{6 + 3i}{4i}$
16. $\frac{-2 + 7i}{-2i}$
17. $\frac{4 + 3i}{1 - i}$
18. $\frac{5 - 2i}{3 + i}$
19. $\frac{8 - i}{2 + 5i}$

20. $\frac{-3 + 9i}{2 + i}$

21. $\frac{6 - 4i}{7 + 2i}$

Find the reciprocal of each and put your answers in $a + bi$ form.

22. $4i$

23. $2 - 3i$

24. $\frac{5}{3} + \frac{2}{3}i$

▶ C. Exercises

25. Find a formula for $z \div w$ if $z = a + bi$ and $w = c + di$.

26. Perform the division $(7 + i) \div (1 - 2i)$ by finding the reciprocal of $1 - 2i$ and multiplying. Then perform the division by the method of the lesson.

◾ Cumulative Review

Solve each equation.

27. $x^2 + 3x - 1 = 0$

28. $2x - 3 = 5x^2 - 7$

29. $x^2 + 2(x - 5) = 3 - x(x + 1)$

Give the discriminant of each equation and use it to classify the solutions.

30. $x^2 + 2x - 5 = 0$

31. $x^2 + 2x + 5 = 0$

EMMY NOETHER

Amalie Emmy Noether was born in the small university town of Erlangen, Germany, on March 23, 1882. Her father was a distinguished mathematician and a professor at the University of Erlangen. Emmy grew up in a family that was frequently engaged in thought-provoking questions and discussions, and consequently her young mind was constantly challenged. Because of this stimulating home life, she became very interested in the field of mathematics. Eventually Emmy and her brother, Fritz, both pursued careers in this field.

Although it was unusual and considered shameful in her time for a woman to seek higher education, Emmy formally entered Erlangen University in 1904, after having attended lectures there for four years. She was a personal student of Paul Gordon, a friend of the family who taught at the university. Emmy wrote her doctoral dissertation, "On Complete Systems of Invariants for Ternary Biquadratic Forms," under Gordon's direction in 1907 and received her Ph.D. in December of that same year.

Emmy soon began to realize that her greatest talent lay in the conceptual approach to thinking, rather than in the formalist approach held by Gordon. She gradually left Gordon's approach and chose algebraists Ernst Fisher and Erhard Schmidt as tutors for her future mathematical training. Under their direction Emmy studied the methods and research of the great mathematician David Hilbert, whose interests were close to her own. Hilbert found that Emmy's knowledge of invariant theory proved to be useful to him in his study of the theory of relativity, and he persuaded Emmy to move to the university at Göttingen in 1915.

Emmy applied for a position as lecturer at the University of Göttingen. She was denied because of the social stigma against women lecturers of the day. Hilbert explained Emmy's qualifications to the philosophical faculty, but they too refused her admittance. Emmy got around the system by presenting lectures under Hilbert's name until after World War I, when she finally obtained a low-paying position. Emmy loved her subject as well as her students. Her warmth and imagination constantly sparked creative ideas in the minds of her students. Therefore she contributed greatly to the field of mathematics by influencing others to reach their potential.

Emmy Noether, cited by Albert Einstein as "the most significant creative mathematical genius thus far produced since the higher education of women began," contributed to the development of modern algebra. In 1920 she began unifying key concepts into a general theory of commutative rings and noncommutative algebra. Examples of rings in algebra include the integers, the real numbers, square matrices of a given size, and the complex numbers. The complex numbers are especially important since all roots of quadratic equations are complex numbers.

Emmy continued lecturing, teaching, and writing articles at Göttingen until the National Socialist party rose to power in Germany in 1933. She and other scholars at the university were then dismissed. Emmy had several strikes against her when this party came into existence. Besides being an intelligent female, she was also a Jew. Fortunately, Emmy was able to take refuge in America and to teach and lecture at Bryn Mawr College and Princeton University. On April 14, 1935, the greatest woman mathematician in history died unexpectedly after an operation, having taught in America for only a year and a half.

She contributed greatly to the field of mathematics by influencing others to reach their potential.

8.5 Quadratic Equations

All roots of a quadratic equation are contained in the set of complex numbers. Real roots are just complex numbers of the form $a + bi$ where $b = 0$. We now turn our attention to solving quadratics whose solutions are not real ($b \neq 0$). Remember that to solve a quadratic equation, you can use the quadratic formula.

If $ax^2 + bx + c = 0$

then $x = \dfrac{-b \pm \sqrt{b^2 - 4ac}}{2a}$

EXAMPLE   Solve $3x^2 - 2x + 1 = 0$.

Answer

$3x^2 - 2x + 1 = 0$

$a = 3, b = -2, c = 1$ 1. Determine the values of a, b, and c.

$x = \dfrac{-b \pm \sqrt{b^2 - 4ac}}{2a}$

$x = \dfrac{-(-2) \pm \sqrt{(-2)^2 - 4(3)(1)}}{2(3)}$ 2. Substitute these values in the quadratic formula.

$x = \dfrac{2 \pm \sqrt{4 - 12}}{6}$ 3. Simplify and change to standard form.

$x = \dfrac{2 \pm \sqrt{-8}}{6}$

$x = \dfrac{2 \pm 2\sqrt{2}i}{6}$

$x = \dfrac{2}{6} \pm \dfrac{2\sqrt{2}}{6}i$

$x = \dfrac{1}{3} \pm \dfrac{\sqrt{2}}{3}i$

There are two solutions in this example. They are $\frac{1}{3} + \frac{\sqrt{2}}{3}i$ and $\frac{1}{3} - \frac{\sqrt{2}}{3}i$. Recall that the solutions of a quadratic equation are the zeros of a quadratic function. The fact that this equation has complex roots parallels the fact that the quadratic function $y = 3x^2 - 2x + 1$ has no real zeros and its graph does not cross the x-axis.

You can determine if the solutions to any quadratic equation are real by looking at the discriminant (radicand) in the quadratic formula.

The quadratic equation $ax^2 + bx + c = 0$, where $a, b, c \in \mathbb{R}$ and $a \neq 0$, has
2 real solutions if $b^2 - 4ac > 0$
1 real solution if $b^2 - 4ac = 0$ (The two solutions are equal.)
2 imaginary solutions if $b^2 - 4ac < 0$ (The two solutions are conjugates.)

In the case where $d = b^2 - 4ac > 0$, the solutions can be classified more specifically. If d is a perfect square, both solutions are rational; if it is not a perfect square, both solutions are irrational.

▶ A. Exercises

Give the value of the discriminant and determine the number and nature of the solutions in each quadratic equation. Be as specific as possible.

1. $x^2 + 3x - 1 = 0$
2. $2x^2 + 3x + 4 = 0$
3. $x^2 - 5x + 8 = 0$
4. $x^2 - 4x + 4 = 0$
5. $3x^2 + 2x - 5 = 0$

▶ B. Exercises

Solve.

6. $x^2 + 3x - 5 = 0$
7. $3x^2 + 4x + 8 = 0$
8. $2x^2 - x + 1 = 0$
9. $5x^2 + 3x - 2 = 0$
10. $4z^2 - 2z + 3 = 0$
11. $x^2 + 5x + 6 = 0$
12. $2x^2 + 3x + 5 = 0$
13. $z^2 + 4z - 6 = 0$
14. $3x^2 - 2x + 1 = 0$
15. $5q^2 + 4q + 3 = 0$
16. $5x^2 + 11 = 0$
17. $x^2 + 3 = x$
18. $t(t - 1) = 4 - t$
19. $w^2 - 2w + 4 = w - 1$
20. $3 - 7a^2 = 4a - 5a^2$

Solve.

21. $\frac{2}{3}c^2 - \sqrt{3}c - 5 = 0$
22. $\frac{3}{4}p^2 - \sqrt{2}p + 6 = 0$

► **Dominion Modeling**

23. How high is the ball after 2.5 seconds?
24. When is the ball 20 feet off the ground?
25. When did the ball reach its maximum height?

Cumulative Review

Graph.

26. $y = x^2 - 3$
27. $y = -x^2 + 1$
28. $y = x^2 + 4x + 5$
29. $y \leq (x - 1)^2$
30. $y > \frac{5}{7}x - 3$

8.6 Graphing Complex Numbers

The Cartesian plane on which you graph ordered pairs such as (3, 2) is a plane that represents ordered pairs of real numbers. The Cartesian plane is the cross product of the set of real numbers, $\mathbb{R} \times \mathbb{R}$. Since it has only points corresponding to ordered pairs of real numbers on it, you cannot graph a complex number on a Cartesian plane. To graph a complex number, you must use a *complex plane*. A complex plane looks similar to the Cartesian plane, but the axes represent different things. Look at the complex plane shown here.

imaginary

real

The horizontal axis represents the real part of the complex number and the vertical axis represents the imaginary part. To graph a complex number such as 3 + 2*i*, graph the real part along the horizontal axis and the imaginary part along the vertical axis.

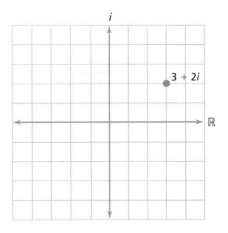

The complex number 3 + 2*i* is represented by the point that is 3 units right and 2 units up from the origin.

Do you remember the informal definition for the absolute value of a number? It is informally defined as the distance of the number from 0 on the number line. Likewise the absolute value of a complex number is the distance from the origin to the point that represents it. Find $|3 + 2i|$ by applying the Pythagorean theorem.

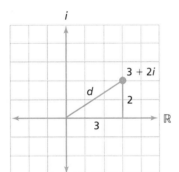

The distance from 3 + 2*i* to the origin is found by

$$d^2 = 3^2 + 2^2$$
$$d^2 = 9 + 4$$
$$d^2 = 13$$
$$d = \sqrt{13}$$
$$|3 + 2i| = \sqrt{13}$$

If the complex number is in the general form *a* + *bi*, a formula can be developed to find the absolute value (sometimes called the modulus) of any complex number.

$$|a + bi| = \sqrt{a^2 + b^2}$$

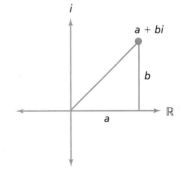

EXAMPLE   Graph $-6 + i$ and find its absolute value.

Answer

Determine a and b.

$a \quad = -6$

$b \quad = 1$

Use the formula $|a + bi| = \sqrt{a^2 + b^2}$.

$\begin{aligned} |-6 + i| &= \sqrt{(-6)^2 + (1)^2} \\ &= \sqrt{36 + 1} \\ &= \sqrt{37} \end{aligned}$

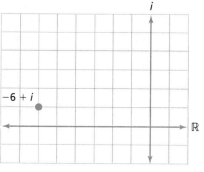

► A. Exercises

Graph.

1. $4 + 3i$
2. $-6 + 5i$
3. $-2 - 3i$
4. $7 - 4i$
5. $5 + 3i$
6. $7 + 2i$
7. $1 + 4i$
8. 9
9. $5i$
10. $-6i$
11. Give the complex number represented by each letter plotted on the complex plane.

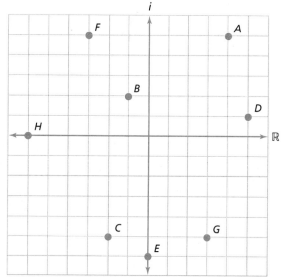

► B. Exercises

Find the absolute value of each number.

12. $|3i|$
13. $|1 - 7i|$
14. $|5 + 2i|$
15. $|-6 - 4i|$
16. $|3 + 6i|$
17. $|-7 - 8i|$
18. $|2 + i|$
19. $|-12|$
20. $|4 - 9i|$

Graph and find the absolute value to the nearest hundredth.

21. $2\sqrt{3} - \pi i$

22. $\frac{-18}{7} + \frac{\sqrt{5}}{7} i$

▪ Cumulative Review

23. Find the distance between (0, 0) and (−4, 1).

24. Find the midpoint of the segment joining (0, 0) and (2, 5).

25. Find the slope of the line joining (2, 0) and (0, −4).

Find the length, midpoint, and slope of the segment joining each pair of points

26. (−5, 3) and (2, 7)

27. (−3, −1) and (2, −5)

Divide 12 into two parts such that their product is 45.

8.7 Vectors

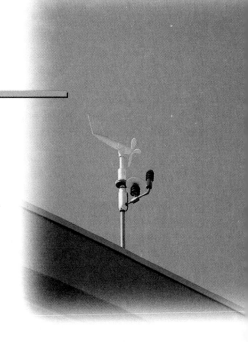

Often there are many ways to represent the same thing. Although there is only one way of salvation, you should know many ways to explain the gospel to people whom you meet. Likewise, there are several ways to explain or represent complex numbers.

The wind is out of the southwest at 15 mph; the temperature is 75°F at the airport. Weather reports depend on an anemometer, such as this one at Torrance municipal airport in California, which measures both the speed and direction of the wind vector.

In the last section you saw how to represent complex numbers in the complex plane by a point, similar to the way we represent an ordered pair in the Cartesian plane. Vectors can also represent complex numbers. A *vector* is a directed segment, which means its length and direction are important. Vectors are used in many areas other than with complex numbers, but in this section you will be introduced to vectors only as related to complex numbers.

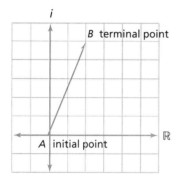

Each vector has an *initial point* and a *terminal point*. In the vector representation of 2 + 5i shown here, the initial point is the origin and the terminal point is (2, 5). Notice that this terminal point has coordinates that originate from the ordered pair formed from the real and imaginary parts of the complex number.

This vector is represented by $\overrightarrow{AB}$. Notice the half-arrow that is used in the notation. Remember that both the length and the direction of a vector are important. You can determine the direction either by measuring the angle it forms with the positive x-axis or by calculating the slope of its line and specifying direction (a vector with $m = 2$ could go up to the right or down to the left). The slope may be found either algebraically or from its graph. Recall that to find the slope, you must divide the change in y by the change in $x \left(m = \frac{\Delta y}{\Delta x} \right)$. To determine the length of a vector such as 2 + 5i, find its absolute value (modulus).

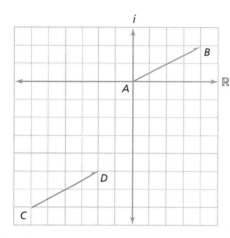

A vector's initial point does not have to be the origin. It can be any point of the complex plane.

Notice that $\overrightarrow{AB}$ and $\overrightarrow{CD}$ are the same length, point the same direction, and have the same slope. $\overrightarrow{AB}$ and $\overrightarrow{CD}$ are equivalent vectors,

Definition

Equivalent vectors   two vectors that have equal length and the same direction.

EXAMPLE 1 Determine the complex number represented by each vector and find its length.

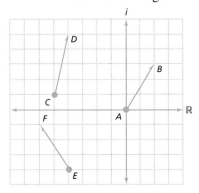

Answer

The complex number for $\overrightarrow{AB}$ is $2 + 3i$. The complex numbers represented by $\overrightarrow{CD}$ and $\overrightarrow{EF}$ are $1 + 4i$ and $-2 + 3i$ respectively.

1. Find the complex number represented by $\overrightarrow{AB}$ by starting at the initial point and moving horizontally and then vertically to the terminal point. From A to B move right 2 units on the real axis and up 3 units parallel to the imaginary axis.

$$AB = |2 + 3i|$$
$$= \sqrt{2^2 + 3^2}$$
$$= \sqrt{4 + 9}$$
$$= \sqrt{13}$$

2. The length of $\overrightarrow{AB}$ is represented by $|2 + 3i|$.

$$CD = |1 + 4i|$$
$$= \sqrt{1^2 + 4^2}$$
$$= \sqrt{1 + 16}$$
$$= \sqrt{17}$$
$$EF = |-2 + 3i|$$
$$= \sqrt{(-2)^2 + 3^2}$$
$$= \sqrt{4 + 9}$$
$$= \sqrt{13}$$

3. Find the lengths of $\overrightarrow{CD}$ and $\overrightarrow{EF}$.

To find the complex number represented by a particular vector, you can subtract the real part of the initial point from the real part of the terminal point to find *a*, and then do the same with the imaginary parts to find *b*. You could find $\overrightarrow{CD}$ in the previous example by determining the complex number associated with the ordered pairs of the initial and terminal points, $C(-5, 1)$ and $D(-4, 5)$. Subtract the real and imaginary parts to obtain the ordered pair (1, 4) or the complex number $1 + 4i$.

EXAMPLE 2   Determine the complex number represented by the vector and find its direction

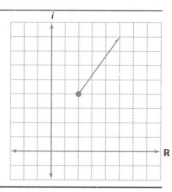

Answer	$(5 - 2, 8 - 4)$	1. Subtract the coordinates of the initial point (2, 4) from the coordinates of the terminal point (5, 8).
	$(3, 4)$	
	$3 + 4i$	2. Change this ordered pair to complex number form.
	$m = \dfrac{\Delta y}{\Delta x} = \dfrac{4}{3}$ up to the right	3. Find the direction from the graph.

Since vectors can represent complex numbers and complex numbers can be added together, the addition of complex numbers can be represented graphically by vector addition. To add two vectors graphically, place the first vector on the graph using the origin as the initial point. Graph the second vector by placing its initial point at the terminal point of the first vector. Find the sum by drawing a vector from the origin to the terminal point of the second vector. This method is called the *triangular law of vectors*. See the following example for a better understanding of this procedure.

EXAMPLE 3   Add $(4 + 3i) + (-6 + i)$ graphically.

Answer

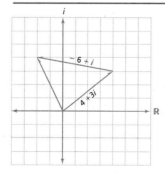

1. Use the origin as the initial point and graph a vector to represent $4 + 3i$.

2. Using the terminal point (4, 3) as the initial point for the next vector, graph $-6 + i$.

3. Draw the vector whose initial point is (0, 0) and whose terminal point is the terminal point of the second vector drawn.

Continued ▶

$$-2 + 4i$$

4. Determine the complex number described by the last vector drawn.

Now compare the graphic addition of the vectors to the algebraic addition, noting the same result.

$$(4 + 3i) + (-6 + i) = (4 - 6) + (3 + 1)i = -2 + 4i$$

You may not always start the addition of vectors at the origin. The basic principle remains the same, however. Graph the first vector. Graph the second vector, using the terminal point of the first vector as the initial point of the second vector. Find the sum by drawing a vector from the initial point of the first vector to the terminal point of the second and determining the complex number it describes.

▶ A. Exercises

Using the origin as the initial point, draw the vector that represents each complex number.

1. $5i$

2. $-4 - i$

3. $3 + 5i$

4. 6

Give the length and direction of the vector represented by each complex number.

5. $2 - 4i$

6. $-4 - 3i$

Using $(-3, -2)$ as the initial point, draw the vector that represents each complex number.

7. $4 + 7i$

8. $2 - 9i$

9. $-3i$

10. 8

Give the complex number form of the vector with the given initial and terminal points respectively.

11. $(4, 7)$ and $(-3, 1)$

12. $(-2, 5)$ and $(1, 3)$

Find the complex number and length of each vector represented here.

13.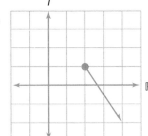

14.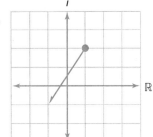

15.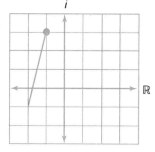

17.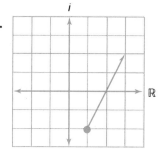

16.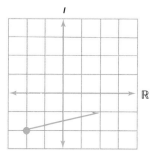

18.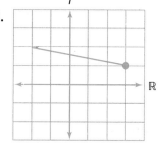

▶ B. Exercises

Write the addition problem described by each graph. Give the final sum.

19.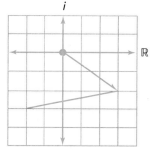

21.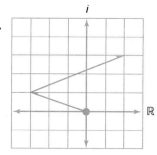

20.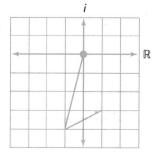

22.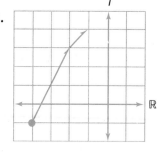

Use vectors to show the vector addition of the following complex numbers.

23. $(2 - i) + (5 + 3i)$
24. $(-1 + 3i) + (3 - 4i)$
25. $(3 + 2i) + (-7 - 3i)$
26. $(-5 - 2i) + (-2 + 3i)$
27. $(6 + 4i) + (-6 + i)$
28. $(5 - 3i) + 4i$

▶ C. Exercises

29. Is vector addition commutative? Why or why not?
30. How could you define vector subtraction: $(a + bi) - (c + di)$?

▪ Cumulative Review

Give the equation of each line.

31. The line graphed at right
32. A line passing through (3, 1) and (4, −1)
33. A line perpendicular to $y = \frac{2}{3}x - 1$ at (3, 1)
34. A line parallel to $4x - 3y = 2$ and passing through (6, 3)
35. Two investments total $1000. If the combined annual interest is $68, how much was invested at 8% and how much at 5%?

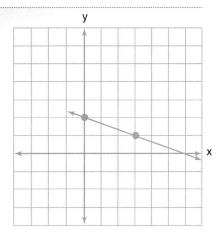

Algebra *and* Scripture

Numbers in Contexts

Classifying contexts of numbers can help you interpret the Bible. The most basic and frequent usage is *literal*. When you say, "Dan, I saw eight deer in a field today," you mean that you saw exactly eight of them. If a friend interprets your words, thinking that you are communicating a secret message, the obvious literal meaning is ignored and replaced.

1. If someone is always looking for hidden meanings in your words, can you share your excitement at spotting the deer?

> **GREATER AMPLITUDE.**
> God wrote the Bible to communicate in everyday language. In what kind of Greek did He write the New Testament?

The next usage is *rounding*. An estimate is not a lie—the significant figures are accurate.

2. How can you tell when an integer is rounded? Give examples.

Another usage involves *idioms*. Suppose your mom tells you "Run to the store and get two or three good green peppers."

3. What does she mean, and why didn't she specify an exact amount?

The use of numbers for *climax* is common in English. "There were millions of 'em!" describes an anthill by expressing a number beyond your ability to count. A more poetic example builds suspense through a sequence of numbers: "The bulging snake continued feasting on the little frogs in Joey's terrarium: four, five, six."

4. Use a dictionary to define *hyperbole*. Which of the above two illustrations of climax does it describe?

Suppose the sentence, "Thirteen black cats crossed my path as I hurried through the dark streets." appeared in a story called *Horror in the Graveyard*. This illustrates the least frequent use of numbers, the *symbolic*. If a writer intends number symbolism, he must provide many contextual clues.

5. List 3 clues alerting you to symbolism in *Horror in the Graveyard* that are absent when you say you saw 13 deer.

The primary number symbol in the Bible is *seven*, but do not assume that every seven is symbolic. God makes it clear when He intends symbolism.

6. Read Revelation 1:12-20. It is clear that the Lord is using symbols here. (See verse 20.) Is the number seven symbolic?

Just as you are offended when people twist your words, God forbids twisting His Word (Rev. 22:18-19). It is a serious mistake to seek symbols in Scripture where none were intended or to ignore a symbol where it was intended.

For each of the five uses of numbers in Scripture, identify the verse that illustrates it.

7. Literal   A. Amos 1:9-10
8. Rounding   B. John 2:6*b*
9. Idiom   C. John 6:9
10. Climax   D. Acts 2:41
11. Symbol   E. Revelation 5:6

12. Which use is displayed in Matthew 18:20?

> ## Absolute Values
>
> **F**OR WHERE TWO OR THREE are gathered together in my name, there am I in the midst of them. ❧
>
> MATTHEW 18:20

Chapter Review

Simplify.

1. $\sqrt{-32}$
2. $\sqrt{-25}$
3. $\sqrt{-48}$
4. $\sqrt{-a^5b^8}$

Perform the indicated operation.

5. $(1 + 7i) + (-5 + i)$
6. $(-4 + 2i) - (-2 - 6i)$
7. $12i - (3 + 2i)$
8. $9 + (6 - i)$
9. $3(4 + 2i)$
10. $6i(1 - 3i)$
11. $(2 + i)(3 - 4i)$
12. $(9 - 2i)(1 - i)$
13. $(-7 - 3i)(2 - 5i)$
14. $\frac{6}{3i}$
15. $\frac{-4}{5i}$
16. $\frac{3}{2 + i}$
17. $\frac{4 + 2i}{1 - 4i}$

Graph and find the absolute value of each complex number.

18. $5i$
19. $3 - 7i$
20. $-6 + 5i$

Graph the vector described by each complex number. Use the origin as the initial point.

21. $4 + 2i$
22. $-3 + i$

Use vectors to show the addition of the following complex numbers.

23. $(-1 + i) + (3 + 2i)$
24. $(5 + 2i) + (1 + 3i)$

Solve.

25. $x^2 + 3x - 2 = 0$
26. $2x^2 - 4x + 1 = 0$
27. $x^2 + 5x + 8 = 0$

28. Give the complex number representing the vector with initial point (2, 7) and terminal point (−1, 4).

Give the magnitude and direction (include slope) of the vector
29. represented by $4 - i$.
30. going from (2, −1) to (4, 4).
31. Evaluate the model for the baseball data.
32. Give the mathematical significance of Matthew 18:20.

9 Rational Expressions and Equations

$y = mx + b$

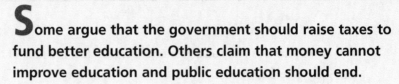

Some argue that the government should raise taxes to fund better education. Others claim that money cannot improve education and public education should end.

Rational expressions will help you study whether government spending improves SAT scores. Consider the 76 data pairs from a 1992 report on Massachusetts schools by the Beacon Hill Institute.

Spending	SAT	Spending	SAT	Spending	SAT	Spending	SAT
3260	907	3012	905	5021	963	3695	884
3814	990	2979	924	3452	893	3292	995
4496	895	3528	931	4112	953	4336	851
4616	853	3876	920	3608	902	3239	890
4832	994	3266	909	3165	918	3723	961
4195	984	3540	895	3746	908	2825	865
3730	902	3341	896	3902	993	4194	935
3411	950	4597	1029	3560	921	3613	944
4340	787	3073	903	3452	837	5348	886
4044	890	3981	955	2698	886	4705	1024
3290	833	3372	973	3218	886	4894	976
5134	986	3386	919	4314	987	4289	944
5968	859	3631	947	3528	911	3257	939
3847	939	3599	918	4448	998	5616	1031
3516	965	3506	722	3205	935	5285	965
3885	987	4687	1014	3748	897	4067	867
4192	967	4212	917	4210	873	4728	1018
3809	942	4047	917	3405	845	3947	914
3618	919	3886	816	3342	939	4536	862

After this chapter you should be able to

1. simplify rational expressions.
2. perform the four basic operations with rational expressions.
3. graph rational functions.
4. solve rational equations.
5. solve problems using rational equations.
6. use direct and inverse variations to solve problems.

9.1 Simplifying Rational Expressions

A *rational expression* is an algebraic expression that is a ratio of two polynomials, $\frac{P(x)}{Q(x)}$, where $Q(x) \neq 0$.

When working with rational expressions you will be required to simplify your answers. This is similar to reducing a fraction to lowest terms. The basic procedure is to factor both the numerator and the denominator and then cancel any common factors. Remember that factors are multiplied together; you cannot cancel terms in addition.

EXAMPLE 1   Simplify $\dfrac{5x^2 + 40x}{5xy + 40y}$ and leave the answer in factored form.

Answer $\dfrac{5x^2 + 40x}{5xy + 40y}$

$\dfrac{5x(x + 8)}{5y(x + 8)}$ 1. Factor both the numerator and the denominator.

$\dfrac{x}{y}$ 2. Cancel common factors.

EXAMPLE 2   Simplify $\dfrac{126a^3 - 126a^2b}{84a^2 + 84ab}$ and leave the answer in factored form.

Answer $\dfrac{126a^3 - 126a^2b}{84a^2 + 84ab}$

$\dfrac{\overset{3}{\cancel{126}}\,\cancel{a^2}(a - b)}{\underset{2}{\cancel{84a}}\,a(a + b)}$ 1. Factor both the numerator and the denominator.

$\dfrac{3a(a - b)}{2(a + b)}$ 2. Cancel common factors. The GCF of 126 and 84 is 42.

EXAMPLE 3   Simplify $\dfrac{x^4 + x^3 - 6x^2}{x^2 - 2x}$.

Answer $\dfrac{x^4 + x^3 - 6x^2}{x^2 - 2x}$

$\dfrac{x^2(x^2 + x - 6)}{x(x - 2)}$ 1. Factor both the numerator and the denominator.

$$\frac{\cancel{x}(x+3)(x-2)}{\cancel{x}(x-2)}$$

$x(x+3)$

$x^2 + 3x$

2. Cancel common factors and multiply remaining factors.

▶ A. Exercises

Simplify. Leave answers in factored form.

1. $\dfrac{3a^2b}{9ab}$

2. $\dfrac{18x^3y}{4x^4y}$

3. $\dfrac{5x^2 + 5xy}{2x + 2y}$

4. $\dfrac{147a^3 + 147a^2b}{14a^2 + 14ab}$

5. $\dfrac{30 + 42n}{9mn}$

6. $\dfrac{x^2 + 2xy + y^2}{y^2 + 2xy + x^2}$

7. $\dfrac{x^2 - y^2}{y^2 - x^2}$

8. $\dfrac{2x^2 + xy - y^2}{3x^2 + 3xy}$

▶ B. Exercises

Simplify. Leave answers in factored form.

9. $\dfrac{3a^2 + 7ab + 2b^2}{a^2 + ab - 2b^2}$

10. $\dfrac{3c^2 + 8cd + 5d^2}{c^2 - d^2}$

11. $\dfrac{2x^2 + 5xz - 3z^2}{x^2 + 2xz - 3z^2}$

12. $\dfrac{30a^4 - 20a^3b - 10a^2b^2}{15a^3 + 20a^2b + 5ab^2}$

13. $\dfrac{3a^3 + 6a^2b + 3ab^2}{6a^2b + 6ab^2}$

14. $\dfrac{z^3 - 4z^2 + 4z}{z^2 + z - 6}$

Simplify. Multiply factors out.

15. $\dfrac{6a^3 + 3a^2b - 3ab^2}{30a^3 - 45a^2b + 15ab^2}$

16. $\dfrac{a^2 + 2ab + b^2}{4a^2 + 2ab - 2b^2}$

17. $\dfrac{40x^3 + 80x^2y - 120xy^2}{5x^2y + 25xy^2 + 30y^3}$

18. $\dfrac{x^2 - 4xy + 3y^2}{x^3 - 2x^2y + xy^2}$

▶ C. Exercises

Simplify.

19. $\dfrac{x^3 - xy^2 + x^2y - y^3}{x^2 - y^2}$

20. $\dfrac{x^2 - y^2}{x^3 - y^3}$

▶ Dominion Modeling

21. For the educational data, what are the variables? What variable would be a suitable independent variable? Which would be a suitable dependent variable?

Cumulative Review

22. Simplify $8(3x - 7)$.
23. Solve $8 = 3x - 7$.
24. Graph $y = 3x - 7$.
25. Find the minimum point by completing the square. $y = x^2 + 8x - 1$
26. Reversing the digits of a two-digit number reduces the original number by 18. Find the number if the sum of the original digits is 12.

9.2 Multiplying Rational Expressions

Learning mathematics is not the only benefit you receive from math class. By working the problems you are learning to be diligent and to persevere in a difficult task. You need to learn not to "faint in the face of adversity" (Prov. 24:10). Second Thessalonians 3:13 says, "But ye, brethren, be not weary in well doing." The lessons you learn in math class should prepare you to serve the Lord throughout your life. Perseverance is one such lesson developed by tackling tough problems.

Multiplying rational expressions depends upon the same properties used in multiplying rational numbers. Factor all numerators and denominators, cancel like factors, and then multiply the remaining factors in the numerators together and the remaining factors in the denominators together. A few examples will clarify this process for you.

EXAMPLE 1 Multiply $\dfrac{5x^2 - 5x - 100}{3x^2 + 6x - 24} \cdot \dfrac{3x - 6}{3x}$. Leave your answer in factored form.

Answer

$$\dfrac{5x^2 - 5x - 100}{3x^2 + 6x - 24} \cdot \dfrac{3x - 6}{3x}$$

$$\dfrac{5(x^2 - x - 20)}{3(x^2 + 2x - 8)} \cdot \dfrac{3(x - 2)}{3x}$$ 1. Factor all numerators and denominators.

$$\dfrac{5(x - 5)(x + 4)}{3(x + 4)(x - 2)} \cdot \dfrac{3(x - 2)}{3x}$$ 2. Cancel common factors. Multiply the remaining factors in the numerators and the remaining factors in the denominators.

$$\dfrac{5(x - 5)}{3x}$$

EXAMPLE 2 Multiply $\dfrac{8a^3b}{5abc^4} \cdot \dfrac{25a^2c^3x}{2a^4xy}$.

Answer

$$\dfrac{8a^3b}{5abc^4} \cdot \dfrac{25a^2c^3x}{2a^4xy}$$

$$\dfrac{\overset{4}{8}\overset{a}{a^3}b}{5abc^4_c} \cdot \dfrac{\overset{5}{25}\overset{a^2}{a^2}\overset{c^3}{c^3}x}{2a^4xy}$$ 1. Cancel.

$$\dfrac{20}{cy}$$ 2. Multiply remaining factors.

► A. Exercises

Multiply. Leave your answers in factored form.

1. $\dfrac{9xy^4}{4x^2y} \cdot \dfrac{2x^3}{15x}$

2. $\dfrac{5a^3b^6}{10a^2b^4} \cdot \dfrac{6a^4}{2b^2}$

3. $\dfrac{8a^3b}{7ac^5} \cdot \dfrac{21ac^4}{4a^4}$

4. $\dfrac{x^2 - xy - 2y^2}{x^2 - y^2} \cdot \dfrac{3x^2 + 6xy + 3y^2}{x + y}$

5. $\dfrac{a^2 + 2a - 15}{a^2 - 6a + 9} \cdot \dfrac{a^2 + 3a - 18}{a^2 + 11a + 30}$

6. $\dfrac{x^2 + 9x + 18}{x^2 + 5x + 6} \cdot \dfrac{x^2 + 4x + 4}{x^2 - 36}$

7. $\dfrac{4a - 12}{a^2 + 9a + 14} \cdot \dfrac{a^2 + a - 42}{8a - 48}$

8. $\dfrac{a^2 - 3ab - 10b^2}{a^2 + 2ab + b^2} \cdot \dfrac{a^2 - b^2}{a^2 - 2ab + b^2}$

9. $\dfrac{x^2 + xy - 6y^2}{x^2 - 2xy - 15y^2} \cdot \dfrac{9x - 45y}{3x^2 - 6xy}$

10. $\dfrac{a^2 - 4a - 32}{a^2 - 10a + 16} \cdot \dfrac{a^2 + 8a + 16}{a^2 - 1}$

11. $\dfrac{a^2 - 2a - 15}{a^2 - 3a - 10} \cdot \dfrac{a^2 + 4a + 3}{a^2 + 5a + 6}$

▶ B. Exercises

Multiply. Leave your answers in factored form.

12. $\dfrac{8a^3b - 20a^2b^2 - 12ab^3}{8a^2 - 2ab} \cdot \dfrac{12ab - 6b^2}{4a^2 - b^2}$

13. $\dfrac{15x^3z - 30x^2z^2 + 15xz^3}{3x^2 - 6xz + 3z^2} \cdot \dfrac{x^2 + 2xz + z^2}{15x^2 + 20xz + 5z^2}$

14. $\dfrac{7x^2 + 70x + 112}{4x + 8} \cdot \dfrac{x^2 - 9x + 18}{7x^2 + 14x - 336}$

15. $\dfrac{x^2 + 2x - 8}{x + 5} \cdot \dfrac{x^2 + 6x + 5}{x - 2} \cdot \dfrac{x^2 + 3x - 4}{x^2 + x - 2}$

16. $\dfrac{a^2 + 5ab + 4b^2}{a^2 - 2ab + b^2} \cdot \dfrac{a - b}{a^2 + 2ab + b^2} \cdot \dfrac{a^2 - b^2}{a + 4b}$

17. $\dfrac{a^2 + 9a + 14}{2a + 12} \cdot \dfrac{4a + 24}{2a^2 + 8a - 42} \cdot \dfrac{a^2 - 6a + 9}{a^2 + a - 2}$

18. $\dfrac{x^2 + x - 20}{x^2 - 7x + 6} \cdot \dfrac{x^2 - 5x + 4}{x^2 + 7x + 10} \cdot \dfrac{x^2 - 4x - 12}{x + 2}$

▶ C. Exercises

Multiply.

19. $\dfrac{m - n}{m^2 - n^2} \cdot \dfrac{m^4 - n^4}{m^3 - n^3}$

20. $\dfrac{7m^3}{21n^2 + 84n} \cdot \dfrac{9n^4 + 12n^3 - 81n^2 + 60n}{m^4n - m^4 - m^3n + m^3}$

▶ Dominion Modeling

21. Researchers at the Beacon Hill Institute at Suffolk University proposed that we use a *rational* model for the educational data. That is, for dollars d and SAT scores s, model the data with the rule $s(d) = m \cdot \left(\dfrac{1}{d}\right) + b$. This should look somewhat like the familiar linear model $f(x) = mx + b$. What independent and dependent variables would correspond to the

Beacon Hill Institute's analysis? (*Hint:* Transform one of your original variables to fit the rational model.)

22. With these transformed variables, make a new data table.

Cumulative Review

23. Simplify $\sqrt{3x} - \sqrt{12x} + \sqrt{3x^5}$.
24. Solve $x^2 + 5 = x$.
25. Graph $y = x^2$.
26. Use long division. $(x^2 + 7x - 3) \div (x + 2)$
27. The length of a rectangular garden is 10 feet longer than twice the width. Give the dimensions if the area is 132 square feet.

Multiply and simplify $\dfrac{3x^3 - 5x^2 - 6x + 10}{(3x - 5)(x + i)} \cdot \dfrac{x^3 + 4x^2 + x + 4}{2x^4 + 7x^3 - 8x^2 - 14x + 8}$.

9.3 Dividing Rational Expressions

Division of rational expressions follows the same principle as dividing fractions. Recall that $\frac{2}{5} \div \frac{3}{5} = \frac{2}{5} \cdot \frac{5}{3}$.

You must multiply by the reciprocal (multiplicative inverse) of the divisor. To divide rational expressions, use the same process.

EXAMPLE 1 Divide $\dfrac{x^2 + x - 6}{x - 6} \div \dfrac{x + 3}{x^2 - 7x + 6}$. Leave your answer in factored form.

Answer $\dfrac{x^2 + x - 6}{x - 6} \div \dfrac{x + 3}{x^2 - 7x + 6}$

$\dfrac{x^2 + x - 6}{x - 6} \cdot \dfrac{x^2 - 7x + 6}{x + 3}$ 1. Multiply the first term by the reciprocal of the second term.

$\dfrac{(x + 3)(x - 2)}{x - 6} \cdot \dfrac{(x - 6)(x - 1)}{x + 3}$ 2. Factor and cancel.

$(x - 2)(x - 1)$

EXAMPLE 2 Divide $\dfrac{6x^2 + 48x + 96}{2x^2 + 8x - 10} \div \dfrac{5x^2 + 10x - 40}{10x^2 + 80x + 150}$. Leave your answer in factored form.

Answer $\dfrac{6x^2 + 48x + 96}{2x^2 + 8x - 10} \div \dfrac{5x^2 + 10x - 40}{10x^2 + 80x + 150}$

$\dfrac{6x^2 + 48x + 96}{2x^2 + 8x - 10} \cdot \dfrac{10x^2 + 80x + 150}{5x^2 + 10x - 40}$ 1. Multiply by the reciprocal of the divisor.

$\dfrac{6(x^2 + 8x + 16)}{2(x^2 + 4x - 5)} \cdot \dfrac{10(x^2 + 8x + 15)}{5(x^2 + 2x - 8)}$ 2. Factor and cancel.

$\dfrac{6(x + 4)(x + 4)}{2(x + 5)(x - 1)} \cdot \dfrac{10(x + 5)(x + 3)}{5(x + 4)(x - 2)}$

$\dfrac{6(x + 4)(x + 3)}{(x - 1)(x - 2)}$

Division problems can be expressed as fractions. For example, $3 \div 4$ can be written $\frac{3}{4}$. When the numerator or denominator are rational expressions, the entire problem is called a *complex rational expression* and can be thought of as a division problem.

EXAMPLE 3 Simplify $\dfrac{\frac{1}{x^2 - x - 6}}{\frac{x + 3}{x^2 - 9}}$.

Answer $\dfrac{\frac{1}{x^2 - x - 6}}{\frac{x + 3}{x^2 - 9}}$

$\dfrac{1}{x^2 - x - 6} \div \dfrac{x + 3}{x^2 - 9}$ 1. Change the complex rational expression to division.

Continued ▶

$$\frac{1}{x^2 - x - 6} \cdot \frac{x^2 - 9}{x + 3}$$ 2. Write the division as multiplication.

$$\frac{1}{(x - 3)(x + 2)} \cdot \frac{(x - 3)(x + 3)}{x + 3}$$ 3. Simplify.

$$\frac{1}{x + 2}$$

▶ A. Exercises

Divide. Leave your answers in factored form.

1. $\dfrac{4a}{5} \div \dfrac{a}{5}$

2. $\dfrac{9x^2yz}{2xy} \div \dfrac{3xy^2}{6xz^2}$

3. $\dfrac{2x + 6}{x - 2} \div \dfrac{4x^2}{5x - 10}$

4. $\dfrac{5a^2 - 5b^2}{a + b} \div \dfrac{a^2 - 2ab + b^2}{3a + 3b}$

5. $\dfrac{x^2 - 5x + 6}{x + 4} \div \dfrac{x - 3}{x^2 + 3x - 4}$

6. $\dfrac{4a + 28}{2a^2 + 8a - 42} \div \dfrac{2a^2 - 4a - 6}{a^2 - 5a - 6}$

7. $\dfrac{c^2 + 4cd + 3d^2}{c^2 - d^2} \div \dfrac{c^2 + 5cd + 6d^2}{c^2 - 2cd + d^2}$

8. $\dfrac{a^2 - 4}{a^2 - 5a + 6} \div \dfrac{a^2 + 4a + 4}{a^2 + 9a + 14}$

9. $\dfrac{6d^2 - 11d + 4}{10d^2 + 29d - 21} \div \dfrac{12d^2 - 31d + 20}{8d^2 + 34d + 21}$

10. $\dfrac{4z - 6}{z^3 + 4z^2 + z + 4} \div \dfrac{4z^2 - 9}{2z^2 + 11z + 12}$

11. $\dfrac{x^2 - 5x - 6}{x^2 - 10x + 16} \div \dfrac{x^2 - 3x - 18}{x - 2}$

12. $\dfrac{a^2 + 2a + 1}{a^5 + a^4 - 6a^3} \div \dfrac{a^2 - 1}{a^3 + 3a^2}$

▶ B. Exercises

Divide. Leave your answers in factored form.

13. $\dfrac{x^4y + 3x^3y - 4x^2y}{x^3 + 2x^2 - 3x} \div \dfrac{x^2 - x - 20}{x + 3}$

14. $\dfrac{x^3 - x}{4x^3 - 4x^2 - 24x} \div \dfrac{x^2 - 6x + 5}{8x^2 - 24x}$

Simplify the following complex rational expressions. Leave your answers in factored form.

15. $\dfrac{\frac{x^2 - 1}{5x}}{\frac{x + 1}{10x}}$

16. $\dfrac{\frac{1}{a + b}}{\frac{a + 3b}{a^2 + 4ab + 3b^2}}$

17. $\dfrac{\frac{c^2 + 6c + 8}{c^2 + 7c + 12}}{\frac{c + 5}{c^2 + 2c - 3}}$

18. $\dfrac{\frac{x^2 - xy - 2y^2}{x^2 + xy}}{\frac{x}{x^2 - y^2}}$

19. $\dfrac{\frac{5x}{3x - 9}}{x}$

20. $\dfrac{\frac{5x}{3x - 9}}{x}$

▶ C. Exercises

21. Explain why you invert and multiply when dividing rational expressions.

22. Simplify $1 + \dfrac{1}{x + \frac{1}{x + 1}}$.

▶ Dominion Modeling

23. Consider the transformed table of educational data. What is an appropriate linear model? Note that this is actually a *rational* model.

Cumulative Review

24. Simplify $(5 - 3i)(2 + 4i)$.
25. Solve $(x - 5)(x - 1) = 2x - 9 + x$.
26. Graph $f(x) = |x|$.
27. Factor $16x^3 - 54$.
28. Marvin has a $500 CD that earns 8% interest. How much must he invest in a savings account earning 5% interest to earn a total of $56 annually in interest?

a b a
c d c

$(m \times n)(n \times p)$

C^T $X = \dfrac{\det(A_i)}{\det(A)}$

$[A : I]$

Matrix Algebra 9

Matrix Division

Remember that division is multiplying by the multiplicative inverse:
$\frac{2}{7} \div \frac{5}{9} = \frac{2}{7} \cdot \frac{9}{5}$. Division of matrices can also be done by finding an *inverse matrix* and multiplying. Two real numbers are multiplicative inverses when their product is the multiplicative identity, 1. Two matrices are inverses when their product is the identity matrix. The 2 × 2 and 3 × 3 identity matrices

are $I = \begin{bmatrix} 1 & 0 \\ 0 & 1 \end{bmatrix}$, $I = \begin{bmatrix} 1 & 0 & 0 \\ 0 & 1 & 0 \\ 0 & 0 & 1 \end{bmatrix}$. Notice all entries are zero except the *main*

diagonal. The notation used for the inverse of matrix A is A^{-1} and

$$A^{-1}A = I = AA^{-1}.$$

Fortunately there is a simple formula for finding the inverse of a 2 × 2 matrix. You will learn to find inverses for larger matrices in Chapter 12.

If $A = \begin{bmatrix} a & b \\ c & d \end{bmatrix}$, then $A^{-1} = \dfrac{1}{\det(A)} \begin{bmatrix} d & -b \\ -c & a \end{bmatrix}$

In other words, to find the inverse switch the elements in the main diagonal, take the opposite of the other elements, and multiply the result by the reciprocal of the determinant of the original matrix.

If $A = \begin{bmatrix} 2 & 4 \\ 5 & 7 \end{bmatrix}$, then $A^{-1} = \dfrac{1}{14-20} \begin{bmatrix} 7 & -4 \\ -5 & 2 \end{bmatrix} = -\dfrac{1}{6} \begin{bmatrix} 7 & -4 \\ -5 & 2 \end{bmatrix} = \begin{bmatrix} -\frac{7}{6} & \frac{2}{3} \\ \frac{5}{6} & -\frac{1}{3} \end{bmatrix}$

To verify that this is the inverse, multiply A^{-1} by A to obtain I.

$A^{-1}A = \begin{bmatrix} -\frac{7}{6} & \frac{2}{3} \\ \frac{5}{6} & -\frac{1}{3} \end{bmatrix} \begin{bmatrix} 2 & 4 \\ 5 & 7 \end{bmatrix} = \begin{bmatrix} -\frac{7}{3} + \frac{10}{3} & \frac{-14}{3} + \frac{14}{3} \\ \frac{5}{3} - \frac{5}{3} & \frac{10}{3} - \frac{7}{3} \end{bmatrix} = \begin{bmatrix} 1 & 0 \\ 0 & 1 \end{bmatrix} = I$

Matrices can be used to solve a system of equations. Write the *coefficient matrix A* times a *variable matrix X* and set the product equal to a *constant matrix B* as shown. Any matrix such as X or B that has only one column is called a column matrix.

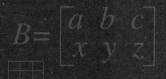

EXAMPLE Solve the system by setting up a matrix equation $AX = B$.

$$2x + 4y = 5$$
$$5x + 7y = 3$$

Answer

$$\begin{bmatrix} 2 & 4 \\ 5 & 7 \end{bmatrix}\begin{bmatrix} x \\ y \end{bmatrix} = \begin{bmatrix} 5 \\ 3 \end{bmatrix}$$

Solve the system by multiplying by A^{-1} on the left.

$$AX = B$$
$$A^{-1}(AX) = A^{-1}B \qquad \text{Multiplication property of equality}$$
$$(A^{-1}A)X = A^{-1}B \qquad \text{Associative property of multiplication}$$
$$IX = A^{-1}B \qquad \text{Inverse property of matrices}$$
$$X = A^{-1}B \qquad \text{Identity property of matrices}$$

Using the inverse matrix found earlier,

$$X = \begin{bmatrix} x \\ y \end{bmatrix} = \begin{bmatrix} -\frac{7}{6} & \frac{2}{3} \\ \frac{5}{6} & -\frac{1}{3} \end{bmatrix}\begin{bmatrix} 5 \\ 3 \end{bmatrix} = \begin{bmatrix} -\frac{35}{6} + 2 \\ \frac{25}{6} - 1 \end{bmatrix} = \begin{bmatrix} -\frac{23}{6} \\ \frac{19}{6} \end{bmatrix}$$

Therefore the solution to the system is $\left(-\frac{23}{6}, \frac{19}{6}\right)$.

▶ Exercises

Find each inverse.

1. $\begin{bmatrix} -3 & -2 \\ 5 & -1 \end{bmatrix}$

2. $\begin{bmatrix} 5 & 8 \\ 3 & 4 \end{bmatrix}$

3. What is the significance of having $\det(A) = 0$?

Solve the systems by using an inverse matrix.

4. $\begin{bmatrix} 8 & -5 \\ -4 & 3 \end{bmatrix}\begin{bmatrix} x \\ y \end{bmatrix} = \begin{bmatrix} 21 \\ -11 \end{bmatrix}$

5. $\begin{bmatrix} 3 & 2 \\ 4 & 3 \end{bmatrix}\begin{bmatrix} x & y \\ z & w \end{bmatrix} = \begin{bmatrix} 4 & -5 \\ 2 & 3 \end{bmatrix}$

9.4 Adding and Subtracting Rational Expressions

$\mathbf{P}$roverbs 14:6 says, "knowledge is easy unto him that understandeth." Understanding why to use certain procedures in algebra is very important. Knowing merely how to do a problem is not nearly as satisfying or beneficial as knowing why you should do it in a particular way.

Adding and subtracting rational expressions follows the same process as adding and subtracting fractions. You can see that the mathematical basis for algebra was established in elementary school. Before adding and subtracting rational expressions, look at the problems below to review addition and subtraction of fractions.

$$\frac{5}{3} + \frac{2}{3} = \frac{7}{3} \qquad\qquad \frac{3}{5} - \frac{2}{7} = \frac{21}{35} - \frac{10}{35} = \frac{11}{35}$$

To add or subtract fractions and rational expressions:

1. Make sure that the expressions have a common denominator before you perform the operation.
2. Add or subtract the numerators and place the result over the denominator.
3. Simplify the resulting expressions.

EXAMPLE 1	Subtract $\frac{2x + 5}{x - 1} - \frac{6x - 3}{x - 1}$.
Answer	$\frac{2x + 5}{x - 1} - \frac{6x - 3}{x - 1}$ 1. Before performing the operation, check to see whether the expressions have common denominators.
	$\frac{(2x + 5) - (6x - 3)}{x - 1}$ 2. Subtract the numerators.
	$\frac{2x + 5 - 6x + 3}{x - 1}$ 3. Simplify, making sure to check that the answer is reduced.
	$\frac{-4x + 8}{x - 1}$

Sometimes you must make adjustments in the denominators. For example, one denominator may be $y - 1$ while the other is $1 - y$. Although these are similar, they are not equal. Notice that $-1(1 - y) = -1 + y = y - 1$. To change the order of a difference, multiply the entire rational expression by 1 in the form of $\frac{-1}{-1}$. This changes the form of the expression but not its value.

EXAMPLE 2 Add $\frac{5x + 4}{x - 3} + \frac{3x - 1}{3 - x}$.

Answer

$\frac{5x + 4}{x - 3} + \frac{3x - 1}{3 - x}$

$\frac{5x + 4}{x - 3} + \frac{-1}{-1} \cdot \frac{(3x - 1)}{(3 - x)}$ 1. To add these expressions, you must change the expression $3 - x$

$\frac{5x + 4}{x - 3} + \frac{-3x + 1}{x - 3}$ to $x - 3$ by multiplying the expression by $\frac{-1}{-1}$.

$\frac{5x + 4 - 3x + 1}{x - 3}$ 2. Having obtained common denominators, add the numerators and simplify.

$\frac{2x + 5}{x - 3}$

To add or subtract rational expressions with different denominators, obtain the common denominator by multiplying by the appropriate forms of 1.

Finding the common denominator

1. Factor each denominator into prime factors.
2. Use the least common multiple as the common denominator.

EXAMPLE 3 Add $\frac{5x}{x^2 + x - 6} + \frac{x + 7}{x^2 - 4x + 4}$. Leave your answer in factored form.

Answer

$\frac{5x}{x^2 + x - 6} + \frac{x + 7}{x^2 - 4x + 4}$ 1. A common denominator is needed.

$\frac{5x}{(x + 3)(x - 2)} + \frac{x + 7}{(x - 2)^2}$ 2. Factor. LCM is $(x + 3)(x - 2)^2$.

$\frac{5x}{(x + 3)(x - 2)} \cdot \frac{x - 2}{x - 2} + \frac{x + 7}{(x - 2)^2} \cdot \frac{x + 3}{x + 3}$ 3. Multiply each term by the appropriate form of 1 to obtain common denominators.

$\frac{5x^2 - 10x}{(x + 3)(x - 2)^2} + \frac{x^2 + 10x + 21}{(x + 3)(x - 2)^2}$

$\frac{6x^2 + 21}{(x + 3)(x - 2)^2}$ 4. Add and simplify if possible. Factor out 3 in the numerator.

$\frac{3(2x^2 + 7)}{(x + 3)(x - 2)^2}$

EXAMPLE 4   Subtract $\dfrac{4x + 2}{x^2 + 11x + 30} - \dfrac{x - 1}{x^2 + 2x - 24}$. You may leave your

answer in factored form.

Answer

$$\dfrac{4x + 2}{x^2 + 11x + 30} - \dfrac{x - 1}{x^2 + 2x - 24}$$

$$\dfrac{4x + 2}{(x + 6)(x + 5)} - \dfrac{x - 1}{(x + 6)(x - 4)}$$

1. Factor each denominator. The LCM of the two denominators is $(x + 6)(x + 5)(x - 4)$.

$$\dfrac{4x + 2}{(x + 6)(x + 5)} \cdot \dfrac{x - 4}{x - 4} - \dfrac{x - 1}{(x + 6)(x - 4)} \cdot \dfrac{x + 5}{x + 5}$$

$$\dfrac{(4x + 2)(x - 4)}{(x + 6)(x + 5)(x - 4)} - \dfrac{(x - 1)(x + 5)}{(x + 6)(x + 5)(x - 4)}$$

2. Multiply each term by the appropriate form of 1.

$$\dfrac{(4x^2 - 14x - 8) - (x^2 + 4x - 5)}{(x + 6)(x + 5)(x - 4)}$$

3. Subtract.

$$\dfrac{4x^2 - 14x - 8 - x^2 - 4x + 5}{(x + 6)(x + 5)(x - 4)}$$

$$\dfrac{3x^2 - 18x - 3}{(x + 6)(x + 5)(x - 4)}$$

4. Give the answer in factored form as instructed.

$$\dfrac{3(x^2 - 6x - 1)}{(x + 6)(x + 5)(x - 4)}$$

In Section 9.3, Example 3, division was used to simplify a complex fraction. Now consider another way to simplify a complex rational expression.

EXAMPLE 5   Simplify $\dfrac{5 + \frac{1}{x}}{25 - \frac{1}{x^2}}$.

Answer

$$\dfrac{5 + \frac{1}{x}}{25 - \frac{1}{x^2}}$$

1. Notice that x^2 is the LCM of the fractions contained in the complex rational expression.

$$\dfrac{\left[5 + \frac{1}{x}\right]x^2}{\left[25 - \frac{1}{x^2}\right]x^2}$$

2. Multiply the numerator and denominator by x^2.

$$\dfrac{5x^2 + x}{25x^2 - 1}$$

$$\dfrac{x(5x + 1)}{(5x + 1)(5x - 1)}$$

3. Simplify the resulting expression.

$$\dfrac{x}{5x - 1}$$

EXAMPLE 6 Simplify $\dfrac{\dfrac{1}{x^2 - x - 6}}{\dfrac{x + 3}{x^2 - 9}}$.

Answer

$\dfrac{\dfrac{1}{x^2 - x - 6}}{\dfrac{x + 3}{x^2 - 9}}$

$\dfrac{\dfrac{1}{(x + 2)(x - 3)}}{\dfrac{x + 3}{(x - 3)(x + 3)}}$ 1. Factor to find the common denominator.

$\dfrac{\dfrac{1}{(x + 2)(x - 3)}}{\dfrac{x + 3}{(x - 3)(x + 3)}} \cdot \dfrac{(x + 2)(x - 3)(x + 3)}{(x + 2)(x - 3)(x + 3)}$ 2. Multiply the numerator and the denominator of the complex expression by the common denominator.

$\dfrac{x + 3}{(x + 3)(x + 2)}$ 3. Simplify.

$\dfrac{1}{x + 2}$

▶ A. Exercises

Perform the indicated operation. Leave your answers in reduced factored form.

1. $\dfrac{7}{5y} + \dfrac{6}{5y}$

2. $\dfrac{a}{a^2 - 1} + \dfrac{1}{a^2 - 1}$

3. $\dfrac{x^2}{3} - \dfrac{2}{-3}$

4. $\dfrac{4}{z^2} + \dfrac{6}{z}$

5. $\dfrac{5a}{a + b} - \dfrac{6}{a}$

6. $\dfrac{3x}{x + 2} + \dfrac{5x}{x - 6}$

7. $\dfrac{5}{m - 5} + \dfrac{2}{5 - m}$

8. $\dfrac{3t}{t + 6} - \dfrac{4t}{6 + t}$

9. $\dfrac{c}{c - 6} - \dfrac{6}{6 - c}$

10. $\dfrac{x^2 + 5x - 7}{x^2 + 3x - 28} - \dfrac{x^2 + 4x - 3}{x^2 + 3x - 28}$

11. $\dfrac{6r}{r + 3} - \dfrac{9r}{r + 8}$

12. $\dfrac{a + 2}{a - 6} + \dfrac{a + 8}{a - 2}$

▶ B. Exercises

Perform the indicated operation. (*Hint:* simplify both rational expressions before adding or subtracting.)

13. $\dfrac{2x - 6}{x^2 + x - 12} + \dfrac{x^2 - 36}{x^2 - 2x - 24}$

14. $\dfrac{3x + 5}{9x^2 - 25} - \dfrac{15x}{25x - 15x^2}$

Do the indicated operations. Leave your answer in reduced factored form.

15. $\dfrac{6x}{x^2 - x - 12} - \dfrac{9x}{x^2 - 6x + 8}$

16. $\dfrac{y + 2}{y^2 + 5y - 6} - \dfrac{y - 6}{y^2 + 10y + 24}$

17. $\dfrac{a}{a^2 - 5a - 14} + \dfrac{5}{a^2 - 10a + 21}$

18. $\dfrac{4x}{x^2 - 5x - 36} + \dfrac{12}{x^2 - 7x - 18}$

19. $\dfrac{5n}{n^2 + 4n + 3} + \dfrac{n - 6}{n^2 + 8n + 7}$

20. $\dfrac{6}{a^2 + 6a + 8} - \dfrac{8}{a^2 - 6a + 8}$

Simplify.

21. $\dfrac{\frac{x}{y} + 1}{\frac{x}{y} - \frac{y}{x}}$

22. $\dfrac{\frac{2x}{y} + 1}{\frac{2x + y}{y^3}}$

23. $\dfrac{\frac{2}{t} - \frac{3}{t^2}}{\frac{5}{t^2} + \frac{1}{t}}$

24. $\dfrac{\frac{6}{x + 1} - \frac{4}{x + 2}}{\frac{2}{x} - \frac{2}{x + 1}}$

▶ C. Exercises

Perform the indicated operation; do not attempt to simplify.

25. $\dfrac{1}{x^3 - 1} + \dfrac{2}{x^2 + x + 1} + \dfrac{3}{x^2 - x + 1}$

26. $\dfrac{x^6 - 1}{x^2 + x + 1} - \dfrac{x^6 - 1}{x^2 - 1}$

▶ Dominion Modeling

27. For the educational data, what mathematical features will a rational model have?

28. What political messages might one take from this?

▪ Cumulative Review

29. Simplify $\dfrac{2 + 3i}{6 + 5i}$.

30. Graph $f(x) = 2^x$.

31. Solve $4 + \sqrt{3x - 2} = 12$.

32. Graph $y = -3(x - 1)^2 + 5$.

33. Find the zeros and give their multiplicities if $f(x) = x^3 + 2x^2 - 7x + 4$.

NORTH AMERICAN MATH

Are you surprised that mathematics developed in both ancient and modern America? Before discussing mathematics in the United States, consider the Mayas.

Maya

The Mayas left behind astounding architectural achievements in Mexico and Central America. They also developed a remarkable calendar because of their religious beliefs. To the Mayas, time was an ever-recurring cycle, and they thought if the priests could determine what happened in a previous cycle, they could predict events in the current cycle.

The complex calendar system shows that they understood math and astronomy. Their numeration system used a base of 20 and three numerals: ⊖ for zero, ● for one, and ▬▬ for five. Numerals were usually expressed vertically, with the larger place values at the top and the smaller place values at the bottom.

Scholars among the Mayas could add, subtract, multiply, and maybe even divide. They apparently used only whole numbers, so any divisions had to involve least common multiples or be expressed as a whole number plus a remainder.

The precision of the Maya calendar required not only good mathematics but also a careful attention to astronomical data. For example, by observation and calculation, Maya astronomers determined the length of the earth's solar year, of the synodic revolution of Venus, and of the lunar month.

The glyphs carved on the Hieroglyphic Stairway at Copan, Honduras, tell the entire history of the Mayas.

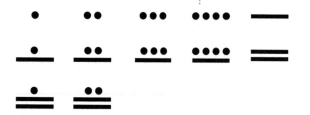

United States

In modern times, the United States has contributed directly to the history of mathematics even though its own history is comparatively brief. America has provided refuge for mathematicians escaping political strife in Europe and has also produced several noted mathematicians of its own.

The Institute for Advanced Study opened in Princeton, New Jersey, in 1933. Several mathematicians came from Europe to research and teach at the new institute. One of these was Austrian by birth Kurt Gödel (1906-1978), who had achieved fame two years earlier for his theorem on logical systems. John von Neumann (1903-1957) came over from Hungary and made advances in algebra, computers, quantum physics, and the atomic bomb. Two others were German: Herman Weyl (1885-1955), researching in modern algebra and quantum physics, and Albert Einstein (1879-1955), contributing both mathematical research and his famous theory of relativity.

Europeans gravitated to other American institutions as well. Emmy Noether (1882-1935) and Norbert Weiner (1894-1964), both Germans, taught in Bryn Mawr, Pennsylvania, and Cambridge, Massachusetts (MIT), respectively. Two British logicians also arrived in America: Bertrand Russell (1872-1970) to Los Angeles (UCLA) and Alfred North Whitehead (1861-1947) to Cambridge (Harvard). James Joseph Sylvester (1814-1897) came twice from Britain to do research in matrix algebra. He settled the first time at Richmond, Virginia, and later at Baltimore, Maryland.

As for American-born mathematicians, Benjamin Peirce (1809-1880) and his son Charles S. Peirce (1839-1914) from Massachusetts contributed to the development of matrix algebra. Americans have also contributed to many applied fields such as computers, statistics, and numerical approximation. In mathematical theory, Americans have contributed much research in topology, especially algebraic topology.

The great mathematicians on the faculty of the Institute for Advanced Study in Princeton, New Jersey, moved into Fuld Hall, the institute's first building, in 1939.

Fuller Lodge is the building where John von Neumann probably lived while working at Los Alamos during World War II.

9.5 Rational Functions

A *rational function* is defined by $f(x) = \frac{P(x)}{Q(x)}$, where $Q(x) \neq 0$ and $P(x)$ and $Q(x)$ are polynomial functions.

To evaluate a rational function, substitute the value of the variable and simplify.

EXAMPLE 1   If $f(x) = \frac{x - 3}{x^2 + 4x + 3}$, find $f(0)$, $f(3)$, $f(-1)$, $f(-2)$, and $f(-4)$.

Answer

$$f(0) = \frac{0 - 3}{0^2 + 4 \cdot 0 + 3} = \frac{-3}{3} = -1$$

$$f(3) = \frac{3 - 3}{3^2 + 4 \cdot 3 + 3} = \frac{0}{24} = 0$$

$$f(-1) = \frac{-1 - 3}{(-1)^2 + 4(-1) + 3} = \frac{-4}{0} \text{ undefined}$$

$$f(-2) = \frac{-2 - 3}{(-2)^2 + 4(-2) + 3} = \frac{-5}{-1} = 5$$

$$f(-4) = \frac{-4 - 3}{(-4)^2 + 4(-4) + 3} = \frac{-7}{3}$$

You can also graph rational functions.

EXAMPLE 2   Graph $f(x) = \frac{1}{x}$.

Answer

x	$f(x)$
-3	$\frac{-1}{3}$
-2	$\frac{-1}{2}$
-1	-1
0	undefined
1	1
2	$\frac{1}{2}$
3	$\frac{1}{3}$

1. Find ordered pairs.

Continued ▶

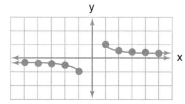

2. Plot them.

x	f(x)
$\frac{3}{4}$	$\frac{4}{3}$
$\frac{1}{2}$	2
$\frac{1}{4}$	4

x	f(x)
$\frac{-3}{4}$	$\frac{-4}{3}$
$\frac{-1}{2}$	−2
$\frac{-1}{4}$	−4

3. f(0) is undefined, so substitute fractions to find out what happens between −1 and 0 and 0 and 1.

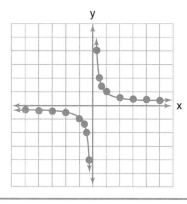

4. Finish the graph by plotting these points.

There is a faster method for graphing these functions if you recognize some common patterns. In Example 2, the graph of $f(x) = \frac{1}{x}$ gets closer and closer to both axes. When a graph approaches a line in this way, the line is called an *asymptote*. The y-axis is a *vertical asymptote* and the x-axis is a *horizontal asymptote* of f(x). Asymptotes provide a guide for graphing.

As you substitute larger numbers into the denominator, the resulting fractions approach zero. Since the y-values approach zero, y = 0 (the x-axis) is an asymptote. For this reason the x-axis is always a horizontal asymptote when the denominator has a higher degree than the numerator. In Example 2 the degree of the denominator is one and the degree of the numerator is zero.

As in Example 2, vertical asymptotes occur where the function is undefined. This happens when the denominator is zero since the values of x that make the denominator zero are not in the domain of the function.

EXAMPLE 3 Graph $f(x) = \dfrac{1}{x^2 + 3x}$.

Answer

$x^2 + 3x = 0$

$x(x + 3) = 0$

$x = 0$ or $x = -3$

1. Find where the denominator is zero. These values determine vertical asymptotes. Since the function is undefined here, the domain is $D = \{x \mid x \neq 0 \text{ and } x \neq -3\}$.

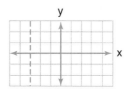

2. Graph the vertical asymptotes and remember that $y = 0$ is a horizontal asymptote (since the constant numerator has a lower degree than the denominator).

x	$f(x) = \dfrac{1}{x^2 + 3x}$
1	$\dfrac{1}{1^2 + 3(1)} = \dfrac{1}{4}$
-1	$\dfrac{1}{(-1)^2 + 3(-1)} = \dfrac{-1}{2}$
-4	$\dfrac{1}{(-4)^2 + 3(-4)} = \dfrac{1}{4}$
-2	$\dfrac{1}{(-2)^2 + 3(-2)} = -\dfrac{1}{2}$

3. Select values on each side of the vertical asymptotes to evaluate.

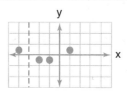

4. Plot these points.

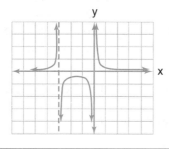

5. Sketch the graph by approaching each of the three asymptotes without crossing any of them.

Finding the intercepts can help you graph rational functions. Find $f(0)$ to locate the y-intercept; then find any x-intercepts by solving $f(x) = 0$. When the function has zeros (x-intercepts), the graph may cross the horizontal asymptote, but the ends of the graph will still get closer and closer to the asymptote. Even in Example 3, the fact that there are no intercepts shows that no points should lie on the x-axis. Example 4 illustrates a rational function with intercepts.

EXAMPLE 4   Graph $f(x) = \dfrac{x^2 - 4}{x^3 - 1}$.

Answer

$f(0) = \dfrac{0^2 - 4}{0^3 - 1} = \dfrac{-4}{-1} = 4$	1. Find the y-intercept.
$x^2 - 4 = 0$ when $x = \pm 2$	2. Find the x-intercept by setting the numerator equal to zero.
$x^3 - 1 = 0$ when $x = 1$	3. Find the vertical asymptote(s) by setting the denominator equal to zero (any complex solutions are irrelevant to the graph).
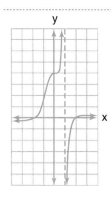	4. Graph the asymptotes and intercepts as guides.
	5. You may be able to sketch the graph, but if in doubt plot more points. Since $f(3) = \frac{5}{26}$, you can see that the graph approaches the horizontal asymptote from above (positive side).

Notice from the graph that the domain is $\{x \mid x \neq 1\}$ and the range is $\mathbb{R}$.

▶ A. Exercises

Find $f(-2)$, $f(0)$, and $f(3)$ for each function.

1. $f(x) = \dfrac{x + 1}{x^2}$

2. $f(x) = \dfrac{4}{x - 1}$

3. $g(x) = \dfrac{-2}{x - 3}$

4. $h(x) = \dfrac{6x}{x^2 - 1}$

Find the vertical asymptotes for each function.

5. $f(x) = \frac{2}{x^3}$

6. $g(x) = \frac{5x}{x^2 - 1}$

7. $f(x) = \frac{-2}{x + 4}$

8. $g(x) = \frac{6x + 1}{x^2 - 5x + 6}$

Find any intercepts for each rational function.

9. $f(x) = \frac{x - 8}{x^2 - 4}$

10. $g(x) = \frac{2x - 10}{x^2 + x - 2}$

11. $h(x) = \frac{9}{x + 3}$

12. $f(x) = \frac{x - 1}{x^2 + x}$

▶ B. Exercises

Graph each function.

13. $f(x) = \frac{1}{x^3}$

14. $g(x) = \frac{1}{x^2 - 2x}$

15. $h(x) = -\frac{2}{x}$

16. $f(x) = \frac{1}{x^2}$

17. $g(x) = \frac{6}{x^2 - 5x}$

Give the domain of each function.

18. $f(x) = \frac{3}{x + 1}$

19. $h(x) = \frac{x - 2}{x^3}$

20. $k(x) = \frac{x - 1}{x^2 - 2x - 3}$

21. $g(x) = \frac{x^2 + 3x + 2}{x + 1}$

Graph each rational function.

22. $f(x) = \frac{5}{x - 4}$

23. $k(x) = \frac{x - 1}{x^2}$

24. $g(x) = \frac{x + 1}{x^2 - 3}$

25. $h(x) = \frac{2 - x}{x^2 + 6x + 9}$

26. If $f(x) = \frac{2x + 1}{x}$, change its form by assuming $x \neq 0$ and dividing each term in the numerator by x. Then discuss its graph in terms of translation of a rational function.

27. How do the graphs of $g(x) = \frac{x^2 - 9}{x + 3}$ and $h(x) = x - 3$ differ? Do not graph them.

28. Give the domain and range of $g(x) = \frac{1}{x^3 - 9x}$.

▶ Dominion Modeling

29. In the SAT data, what is the highest SAT score the rational model permits? (Note: A perfect score is 1600.)

30. Combining the verbal and mathematical tests, the lowest possible score was 400. How much money does the model say could be spent to get this horrible score? How reliable is the model for this question?

Cumulative Review

31. Simplify $\frac{x^2 - 1}{x^2 - x} \cdot \frac{x^2 + x}{x^3 + 1}$.

32. Solve $x^2 + 3x + 2 < 0$.

33. Graph $f(x) = (x - 1)(x + 2)(x - 3)$.

34. Factor $15x^2 - 11x - 14$.

35. A company makes $3 profit per CD and $2 per cassette. Write the objective function. Subject to the graphed constraints, how many of each will maximize their profit?

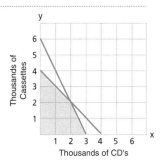

9.6 Rational Equations

A *rational equation* is an equation that contains at least one rational expression. To solve a rational equation, determine the common denominator of all the fractional expressions in the equation and multiply both sides by it, thus eliminating all numerical fractions and rational expressions. After this, solve the resulting equation that may be linear or quadratic. You know how to solve both of these types already.

You must also check for extraneous solutions in this type of equation. Any time you multiply an equation by an expression containing variables there is a possibility that you will introduce some answers that are not solutions, so all of them *must* be checked.

EXAMPLE 1   Solve $\dfrac{18}{x-6} = 6$.

Answer

$$\dfrac{18}{x-6} = 6$$

$$(x-6)\left(\dfrac{18}{x-6}\right) = 6(x-6)$$ 1. The common denominator is $x-6$. Multiply both sides of the equation by this common denominator.

$$18 = 6x - 36$$ 2. Solve this linear equation.
$$54 = 6x$$
$$x = 9$$

Check.

$$\dfrac{18}{x-6} = 6$$

$$\dfrac{18}{9-6} = 6$$

$$\dfrac{18}{3} = 6$$

The solution to the equation is $x = 9$.

Notice that 9, our solution, is in the domain of the rational expression on the left side of the equation. In the future, you may check your answers in the domain rather than by substituting them into the equation.

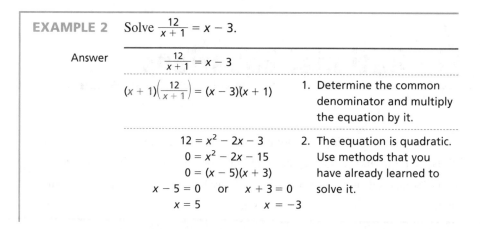

EXAMPLE 2   Solve $\dfrac{12}{x+1} = x - 3$.

Answer

$$\dfrac{12}{x+1} = x - 3$$

$$(x+1)\left(\dfrac{12}{x+1}\right) = (x-3)(x+1)$$ 1. Determine the common denominator and multiply the equation by it.

$$12 = x^2 - 2x - 3$$ 2. The equation is quadratic. Use methods that you have already learned to solve it.
$$0 = x^2 - 2x - 15$$
$$0 = (x-5)(x+3)$$
$$x - 5 = 0 \quad \text{or} \quad x + 3 = 0$$
$$x = 5 \qquad\qquad x = -3$$

Continued ▶

Check.
Since $x + 1 = 6$ when $x = 5$ and $x + 1 = -2$ when $x = -3$,
$\frac{12}{x+1}$ is defined for both values. Therefore 5 and -3 are in
the domain and both are solutions.

EXAMPLE 3   Solve $\frac{x+2}{x-4} = \frac{30}{(x-4)(x+1)} + \frac{4}{x+1}$.

Answer

$$\frac{x+2}{x-4} = \frac{30}{(x-4)(x+1)} + \frac{4}{x+1}$$

1. Determine the common denominator and multiply the equation by it.

$$(x-4)(x+1)\left(\frac{x+2}{x-4}\right) = (x-4)(x+1)\left(\frac{30}{(x-4)(x+1)}\right) + (x-4)(x+1)\left(\frac{4}{x+1}\right)$$

$$(x+2)(x+1) = 30 + 4(x-4)$$
$$x^2 + 3x + 2 = 30 + 4x - 16$$
$$x^2 - x - 12 = 0$$
$$(x-4)(x+3) = 0$$
$$x - 4 = 0 \quad \text{or} \quad x + 3 = 0$$
$$x = 4 \qquad\qquad x = -3$$

2. Simplify the resulting equation and solve.

Check.
When $x = 4$, the left side of the original equation is undefined, so it is extraneous.
When $x = -3$, all three expressions are defined.
Therefore, $x = -3$ is the only solution.

3. Are both results in the domains of the original rational expressions?

▶ **A. Exercises**

Solve and check.

1. $\frac{9}{a} = 3$

2. $\frac{16}{x+2} = 4$

3. $\frac{25}{a+4} = 5$

4. $\frac{7}{x+9} = \frac{1}{2}$

5. $\frac{x+24}{x} = \frac{x}{4}$

6. $\frac{1}{x+6} = \frac{2}{x+9}$

7. $\frac{a+8}{5} = \frac{3a}{7}$

8. $\dfrac{x+6}{x+16} = \dfrac{3}{5}$

9. $\dfrac{a-4}{8} + \dfrac{a}{16} = \dfrac{11}{a+3}$

10. $\dfrac{c+9}{c-9} - \dfrac{24}{c} = 5$

11. $\dfrac{x+6}{x-8} = \dfrac{x+3}{x+10}$

12. $\dfrac{8}{y(y-2)} = \dfrac{y}{3y}$

▶ B. Exercises

Solve and check.

13. $\dfrac{6x}{x^2 - 3x - 18} = \dfrac{5x}{x^2 - 4x - 12}$

14. $\dfrac{8}{a^2 - 2a - 8} = \dfrac{16}{a^2 - a - 6}$

15. $\dfrac{3t}{t^2 - t - 20} = \dfrac{-6t}{t^2 - 7t + 10}$

16. $\dfrac{6}{x} - \dfrac{5}{x+1} = \dfrac{3}{x}$

17. $\dfrac{7}{9x} - \dfrac{1}{18} = \dfrac{3}{4x}$

18. $\dfrac{2x}{x^2 - 1} + \dfrac{5}{x+1} = \dfrac{3}{x-1}$

19. $\dfrac{x}{x+5} - \dfrac{3x}{x+2} = \dfrac{4}{x^2 + 7x + 10}$

20. $\dfrac{4}{x-1} = \dfrac{x}{x+2} - \dfrac{6}{x^2 + x - 2}$

▶ C. Exercises

Solve and check.

21. $\dfrac{1}{x} + \dfrac{2x}{x+3} = \dfrac{5}{x-2} - \dfrac{12x+14}{x^3 + x^2 - 6x}$

22. $\dfrac{1}{x-a} + \dfrac{2}{x+b} = \dfrac{3}{x^2 - ax + bx - ab}$

▶ Dominion Modeling

23. Recall the SAT data. Without any transformation, how would a linear model work with this data? What benefits or weaknesses would this model have? What are the political consequences of an untransformed linear model? Explain.

24. Simplify $\dfrac{4}{x-3} - \dfrac{7x}{x+2}$.

25. Solve $4x + 7 = 5x^2 + 5x$.

26. Graph the system.

$$x + y < 4$$
$$2x - 3y \geq 9$$

27. Find $(f \circ g)(x)$ if $f(x) = \sqrt{2x + 1}$ and $g(x) = 3x - 4$.

28. Ayer's Freezer Co. wants to know how many freezers to produce to minimize costs. They have found that the function $C(x)$ represents the cost to produce x freezers. If $C(x) = x^2 - 80x + 5800$, how many freezers should they produce?

9.7 Variations

Quadratic equations often occur in *variations*. The first of the three types of variations that you will study in this section is *direct variation*. We say that y varies directly as x if $y = kx$, where k is a positive constant known as the constant of variation. Notice that as x increases, so does y, and the increase in y is directly proportional to that of x. This is true of all direction variations.

While $y = kx$ is the general form for direct variation, you should recognize that other expressions can be substituted for either variable. For instance, if y varies directly as the square of x, then the direct variation has the quadratic form, $y = kx^2$, which you know is the standard form of a parabola with its vertex at the origin.

Many physical phenomena can be expressed in terms of direct variations. Look at the following examples.

EXAMPLE 1   The area of a circle varies directly as the square of the radius. Write the equation of this variation and give the constant of variation.

Answer	Let A = area of the circle and r = radius.	1. Define the variables.
	$A = kr^2$	2. Write the equation described above, using k as the constant of variation.
	$k = \pi$	3. What is the area of a circle? Since you know the formula $A = \pi r^2$, find k by comparison.

EXAMPLE 2   If y varies directly as x and $y = 8$ when $x = \frac{1}{2}$, find y when $x = 4$.

Answer	$y = kx$	1. Write the general equation for this direction variation.
	$8 = k\left(\frac{1}{2}\right)$	2. Substitute the given values for x and y.
	$2(8) = k\left(\frac{1}{2}\right)(2)$ $16 = k$	3. Solve for k.
	$y = 16x$	4. Substitute $k = 16$ into your general equation.
	$y = 16(4)$ $y = 64$	5. Substitute $x = 4$ and find y.

Often two variables are not related directly, but inversely. This means as x increases, y decreases. The general form is $y = \frac{k}{x}$. As in the case of direct variation, the decrease in y is proportional to the increase in x. The equation $F = \frac{k}{r^2}$ describes the *inverse variation* of the gravitational force F between spherical objects and the square of the distances between their centers of gravity. In this equation, F varies inversely as the square of r.

EXAMPLE 3   If y varies inversely as x^3 and $y = 16$ when $x = 2$, find y when $x = 8$.

Answer

$y = \frac{k}{x^3}$

1. Write the general equation of the given inverse variation.

$16 = \frac{k}{2^3}$

$16 = \frac{k}{8}$

$128 = k$

2. Substitute the given values for x and y to find k.

$y = \frac{128}{x^3}$

3. Write the general equation for this particular variation using $k = 128$.

$y = \frac{128}{8^3}$

$y = \frac{128}{512}$

$y = \frac{1}{4}$

4. Using this equation, find the value of y when $x = 8$.

EXAMPLE 4   If the temperature remains constant, the volume of a gas varies inversely with its pressure. If a certain gas has a volume of 25 cubic inches at 15 pounds per square inch (psi) and the pressure is increased to 20 psi, what is the volume of the gas after the pressure increase?

Answer

V = volume of the gas
P = pressure in psi

1. Assign variables.

$V = \frac{k}{P}$

2. Write the general equation.

$25 = \frac{k}{15}$

$375 = k$

3. Find the value of the constant k by substituting known values for V and P.

$V = \frac{375}{P}$

4. Write the general equation for this variation.

$V = \frac{375}{20}$

$V = 18.75$

5. Find V when $P = 20$.

The volume of the gas at 20 psi is 18.75 cubic inches.

Sometimes variations involve more than two variables; they are called *combined* or *joint variations*. If z varies jointly as x and y, the joint variation is given by $z = kxy$. However, a joint variation may also mix direct and inverse variation as in Example 5.

EXAMPLE 5   Write the general equation for this statement: y varies directly as the sum of x and z and inversely as the square of x.

Answer $y = k(x + z)$

1. Write the direct variation: "y varies directly as the sum of x and z".

$y = \dfrac{k(x + z)}{x^2}$

2. Combine the information that y also varies inversely as x^2 with the equation already written to obtain the joint variation.

▶ A. Exercises

1. If y varies directly as x and $y = 30$ when $x = 5$, find y when $x = 8$.
2. If y varies inversely as x and $y = 16$ when $x = 2$, find y when $x = 8$.
3. If y varies directly as the cube of x and $y = 108$ when $x = 3$, find y when $x = 1$.
4. If y varies jointly as the product of x and z and $y = 40$ when $x = 1$ and $z = 5$, find y when $x = 4$ and $z = 2$.
5. If y varies inversely as the square of x and $y = 2$ when $x = 3$, find y when $x = 6$.
6. If y varies directly as x and inversely as z and $y = 2$ when $x = 2$ and $z = 4$, find y when $x = 6$ and $z = 2$.
7. The formula for finding simple annual interest, given the principal and the rate, is $I = pr$. State this in variation terminology.
8. Find I when $p = \$12{,}000$ and $r = 0.07$.

▶ B. Exercises

9. The speeds of two meshed gears as they revolve vary inversely as the number of teeth they have. One gear has **48** teeth and revolves at a rate of **810** revolutions per minute. If the other gear has **45** teeth, how fast is it driven to work properly with the other gear?
10. Kinetic energy is described by a joint variation. Kinetic energy varies jointly as the mass and the square of the velocity. If a certain body that has a mass of **3** grams has energy of **6** joules at a velocity of **2** meters per second, what is the velocity of the body when its energy is **24** joules?

11. The weight of an object varies inversely as the square of its distance from the center of the earth. If the radius of the earth is assumed to be 6370 kilometers and a boy on the surface of the earth weighs 55 kg, how much will he weigh if he is 630 kilometers above the earth's surface?

12. The resistance of an electrical wire depends on its length and diameter. The resistance varies directly as the length and inversely as the square of the diameter. If the resistance of 55 m of wire that has a radius of 1.5 millimeters is 10 ohms, what is the resistance of 27.5 m of this same type of wire if the diameter of the wire is 5 millimeters?

13. From geometry we know that the area of a regular polygon varies jointly with the apothem (a) and the perimeter (p). Write the equation for this area and identify k.

14. Write the equation for the area of an equilateral triangle of side length s. Give the type of variation and identify k.

► C. Exercises

15. Show by numerical example that the volume of a cube ($V = e^3$) is not directly proportional to its surface area ($S = 6e^2$).

16. Identify the type of variation represented by $xy = 4$ and sketch a first quadrant graph of it.

► Dominion Modeling

17. According to the rational model of the SAT data, how much money must be spent to achieve a perfect score of 1600? How much must be spent according to the linear (untransformed) model? Explain why the models give similar or different answers.

Cumulative Review

18. Simplify $(8 - 5i) + (7 + 2i)$.

19. Solve $\frac{3}{4x} + 4 = \frac{5}{6x}$.

20. Write the equation of the line through (5, 7) and (1, −3).

21. Factor $x^5 - 3x^4 + 8x^2 - 24x$.

22. The sum of a number and one-half of its reciprocal is $\frac{57}{40}$. Find the number.

9.8 Work Problems

Proverbs 13:11 says "He that gathereth by labour shall increase." Work is a God-given command. Christians should be willing to work as hard as they can to

Five of these pineapple pickers pick at the same rate. Another picker is an hour faster at filling the truck; the other two are each an hour slower. How long does it take each if together it takes them 1 hour?

please the Lord. You cannot work for your salvation, but after you are saved you should work to be a good testimony to those around you. (See Eph. 2:8-10.)

In this section you will learn to solve *work problems*. The basic idea behind them is that it will take a certain amount of time for one machine or person to do a job and a different amount of time for another machine or person to do the same job. But if two machines or two people are working together on a project, the job should get done more quickly. The relevant information can be summarized using a table as in Example 1.

EXAMPLE 1 A large water tank can be filled in **8** hours of continuous pumping using pump *A*. If a smaller pump *B* works with pump *A*, it takes only **6** hours to fill the tank. How long would it take to fill the tank using only pump *B*?

Answer

	Hours for Entire Job	Part of work Done in 1 Hour
Pump A	8	$\frac{1}{8}$
Pump B	x	$\frac{1}{x}$
Together	6	$\frac{1}{6}$

1. **Read.** What are you looking for in this problem? Let x = the time for pump *B* to fill the tank alone.

2. **Plan.** Make a table to summarize the information.

$$\frac{1}{8} + \frac{1}{x} = \frac{1}{6}$$
$$24x\left(\frac{1}{8} + \frac{1}{x}\right) = 24x\left(\frac{1}{6}\right)$$
$$3x + 24 = 4x$$
$$x = 24$$

3. **Solve.** Write an equation from the last column and solve for x. (The total work done separately equals the work done together.)

It would take pump *B* 24 hours to fill the tank.

4. **Check.** Interpret the answer in context.

Do you understand why $\frac{1}{8}$ represents the part of the job done by pump *A* in 1 hour? If you can get your homework done in 2 hours, then you can get $\frac{1}{2}$ of the work done in 1 hour? *Right?*

EXAMPLE 2   Teresa and John are going to work together to paint their living room. John can paint it in **8** hours and Teresa can paint the room in **10** hours. How long will it take them to paint the room if they work together?

Answer

	Hours for Entire Job	*Part of work Done in 1 Hour*
Teresa	10	$\frac{1}{10}$
John	8	$\frac{1}{8}$
Together	x	$\frac{1}{x}$

1. **Read.** Determine what you are looking for. Let x = the time it takes them when working together.

2. **Plan.** Complete a table to summarize the information.

$$\frac{1}{10} + \frac{1}{8} = \frac{1}{x}$$

$$40x\left(\frac{1}{10} + \frac{1}{8}\right) = 40x\left(\frac{1}{x}\right)$$

$$4x + 5x = 40$$

$$9x = 40$$

$$x = \frac{40}{9} = 4\frac{4}{9}$$

3. **Solve.** Write an equation from the last column and solve for x.

It will take them $4\frac{4}{9}$ hours to paint the room.

4. **Check.** Interpret the answer in the context.

▶ A. Exercises

How much of the job can Mary complete in one hour if the whole job takes
1. 4 hours.
2. 5 hours.
3. $2\frac{1}{2}$ hours.
4. 20 minutes.

Given the portion of the job Bob and Fred each complete in one hour, how much will they complete in one hour working together?

5. Bob: $\frac{2}{9}$ and Fred: $\frac{5}{9}$

6. Bob: $\frac{3}{8}$ and Fred: $\frac{1}{8}$

7. Bob: $\frac{1}{10}$ and Fred: $\frac{1}{4}$

8. Bob: $\frac{2}{7}$ and Fred: $\frac{5}{8}$

9. In 6 hours Paul can weed his Mom's flower gardens. If Paul's friend Bill comes to help him, they can do the gardens in 4 hours. How long would it take Bill to do the job by himself?

10. One pipe can drain a large swimming pool in 28 hours, whereas a larger pipe could drain the pool in 7 hours. If both pipes are opened, how long will it take for the pool to drain completely?

11. Dave is adding a room to his home. If he does the job alone he can finish it in 16 days. If his brother, who is a master carpenter, helps him, they can finish the room in 4 days. How long would it take Dave's brother to add the room by himself?

12. Debbie can completely set the tables for a banquet in 32 minutes. If Julie helps her they can do it in 14 minutes. How long would it take Julie to set the tables by herself?

▶ B. Exercises

Express your answers in hours and minutes.

13. Judy, Karen, and Susan must work together on stuffing advertising envelopes for an uptown business. If Judy did them by herself it would take her 12 hours. It would take Karen 24 hours alone and Susan 8 hours. How long will it take them if they all work together?

14. Jerry can put a puzzle together in 5 hours, and Kathy can put it together in 7 hours. If they both worked on the puzzle, how long would it take them to put it together?

15. Faith Christian School has two computers that will help with the scheduling of classes. One computer could do the whole job alone in $\frac{1}{2}$ hour, while the other computer would take $\frac{2}{3}$ of an hour. If the computers work on the job together, how long will it take them to finish the scheduling?

16. A swimming pool has two fill pipes and one drainpipe. Pipe *A* will fill the pool in 6 hours and pipe *B* will fill it in 8 hours. Pipe *C* will drain the pool in 10 hours. Find how long it will take to fill the pool if both pipe *A* and *B* are used, but the drainpipe is left open.

▶ C. Exercises

17. Rework problem 16, given that the open drain is discovered and closed after 2 hours.

18. Sam, Bill, and Joe are making phone solicitations on a rotary phone and a push button phone. They want to make 110 calls. Sam can make a call and solicitation on the average in 4 minutes and Bill and Joe can do it on the average in 3 minutes. If Sam and Bill make the calls together, how long will it take them to make them? How long will it take Bill and Joe working together? How long if all three work together?

▶ Dominion Modeling

19. Find and evaluate a quadratic model of the SAT data.
20. Find and evaluate an exponential model of the SAT data.

■ Cumulative Review

21. Simplify $\dfrac{6x^3}{\sqrt[3]{x^2y}}$.

22. Solve the system.

    $4x + 3y = 13$
    $5x - 2y = 22$

23. Graph $f(x) = \dfrac{3}{x - 4}$.

24. Find the distance from $(3, 6)$ to $(7, -1)$.

25. If y varies inversely with the cube of x and y is 125 when $x = 0.2$, find k and find y when $x = 2$.

Algebra *and* Scripture

Investments

You have already studied debt and profit in the Bible.

1. Review the Absolute Values verse for Chapter 4, Romans 13:8. What does it teach about debt?

2. Review the Absolute Values verse for Chapter 6, Mark 12:44. What does it teach about profit?

Another important principle of investment is stewardship. The three key aspects of stewardship involve ownership, operation, and focusing on the objective.

Ownership

3. What is a steward? Use a dictionary or Bible dictionary.

4. Why is a steward mentioned in Matthew 20:8?

5. Who is the owner of your body and who is its steward (I Cor. 6:19-20)?

6. Who owns your money and possessions (Ps. 24:1; I Cor. 4:7), and who is the steward?

7. What are you a steward of according to I Corinthians 4:1-2 and what is your responsibility to the owner?

Operation

8. What did the owner expect of his stewards in Luke 12:42-48? (Notice especially verses 42 and 47.)

9. How should business be conducted according to Luke 14:29-30?

10. What did the owner expect of his steward in Matthew 25:14-30?

11. What mistake did the stewards of the vineyard make in Luke 20:9-16?

12. What mistake did the unjust steward make that got him fired (Luke 16:1-8)?

13. Though wicked, the unjust steward understood one principle of financial stewardship. What was it?

Objective

14. How is the above principle expressed as an objective of stewardship in the next verses (Luke 16:9-13)?

15. What is more important than possessions like food and clothing (Luke 12:16-23)?

16. How can you be a good steward of your body (I Tim. 4:8 and Rom. 12:1)?

GREATER AMPLITUDE.
  What is every believer a steward of according to I Peter 4:10?

17. What should be your objectives as you invest your possessions as a steward (Luke 12:33-34, Luke 18:22, I Corinthians 10:31)?

Luke 14:28 mentions the value of mathematical planning for financial stewardship.

Absolute Values

FOR WHICH OF YOU, intending to build a tower, sitteth not down first, and counteth the cost, whether he have sufficient to finish it?

LUKE 14:28

Chapter Review

Find $f(2)$ and $f(-3)$.

1. $f(x) = \frac{x+1}{x-3}$

2. $f(x) = \frac{x+8}{x^2-9}$

If $f(x) = \frac{x-8}{x^2-4}$, find any

3. y-intercepts.

4. x-intercepts.

5. vertical asymptotes.

6. horizontal asymptotes.

Give the domain of each rational function.

7. $f(x) = \frac{x-3}{x-1}$

8. $g(x) = \frac{4}{x^2-8x-20}$

Graph.

9. $k(x) = \frac{2}{x+1}$

10. $h(x) = \frac{x-1}{x^2-x-6}$

Simplify.

11. $\frac{15x^2y}{27xy^3}$

12. $\frac{x^2-5x+6}{x} \cdot \frac{x^2+2x}{x-3}$

13. $\frac{5x-15}{3x^2+9x} \div \frac{x-3}{3x^2}$

14. $\frac{x+7}{3x} + \frac{x-2}{3x}$

15. $\frac{2x^2+5x-12}{3x^2+7x-20}$

16. $\frac{5}{x+1} - \frac{3}{x}$

17. $\frac{\frac{1}{x}+\frac{3}{x}}{\frac{5}{x^2}+\frac{2}{x}}$

18. $\frac{7x}{x-2} + \frac{x}{2-x}$

19. $\frac{4x+4}{10x^3} \cdot \frac{5x^2}{x+1}$

20. $\frac{x^2-1}{x^2+x-2} \div \frac{x^2+2x+1}{x+2}$

Solve.

21. $\dfrac{4}{x-3} = 7$

22. $\dfrac{x}{x-4} = \dfrac{x+2}{x-6}$

23. $\dfrac{3}{5x} + \dfrac{1}{6} = \dfrac{7}{10x}$

24. $\dfrac{3}{2x-2} + \dfrac{5}{4x} = \dfrac{7}{x^2-x}$

25. $\dfrac{x^2}{4x-12} = \dfrac{-9}{3-x}$

26. $\dfrac{x^2+x}{x-2} + \dfrac{2x}{x-2} = \dfrac{10}{x-2}$

27. $\dfrac{5}{3x^2-x-10} = \dfrac{4}{2x^2-7x+6} - \dfrac{1}{6x^2+x-15}$

28. Pam can do the gardening in 40 minutes, but Karen can do it in 30 minutes. How long will be take them if they work together?

29. If 8 is reduced by the reciprocal of a number, the result is the same as the quotient of 3 and the number. Find the number.

30. Evaluate the rational model for the educational data. What other variables might influence SAT scores?

31. Give the mathematical significance of Luke 14:28.

10 Trigonometry

Kayakers recognize St. John, New Brunswick, for its Reversing Falls, which earn the treacherous Class V-VI rating. The falls consist of rapids and whirlpools that limit navigation upriver.

The rapids are dangerous because the water flow changes directions. For over 6 hours, the St. John River drops 14 feet over the Reversing Falls into the Bay of Fundy until the bay rises, balancing the riverflow. All is quiet for about ten minutes. Then the thundering begins again as the bay forces itself up the river for over 6 hours reaching 80 miles upstream. Every 24 hours and 55 minutes the moon completes a revolution, and the cycle of tides repeats. Boaters who use the ten-minute "slack tides" must time their trips carefully.

Trigonometry provides a means for describing and analyzing tidal data. Projected tides for St. John, New Brunswick, on Monday, April 11, 2011, follow. The height is in meters; the time is military style.

Time	Height	Time	Height	Time	Height
0	2.65	8	4.37	16	6.29
1	3.81	9	3.12	17	6.81
2	5.12	10	2.10	18	6.69
3	6.27	11	1.62	19	5.99
4	7.03	12	1.88	20	4.95
5	7.19	13	2.79	21	3.81
6	6.66	14	4.04	22	2.76
7	5.63	15	5.28	23	2.07

After this chapter you should be able to

1. define and approximate the six trigonometric ratios.
2. give exact trigonometric ratios for special angles.
3. solve right triangles.
4. solve problems using trigonometric ratios.
5. convert between radians and degrees.
6. graph trigonometric functions using amplitude and periods.

10.1 Right-Triangle Trigonometry

The basic meaning of *trigonometry* is "triangle measure." The study of trigonometry will begin with the study of right triangles, but trigonometry is not limited to right triangles. In fact, the study of advanced topics in trigonometry may not even involve the use of a triangle.

Right-triangle trigonometry is based on ratios or comparisons of different sides of a right triangle. Before looking at the basic ratios, you need to have a complete understanding of the parts of a right triangle.

In $\triangle ABC$ the side c, opposite the right angle, is called the *hypotenuse* and the other two sides are called the *legs*. If you consider $\angle B$, then a is the leg adjacent to $\angle B$ and b is the leg opposite $\angle B$. The uppercase letters represent both the angles and their measures, while the lowercase letters represent both the sides and their lengths. Uppercase designation $\overline{AB}$ is also used to represent a side where AB refers to its length.

The study of trigonometry is based on the following three basic trigonometric ratios.

Definitions

Sine of an angle   the ratio of the length of the leg opposite the angle to the length of the hypotenuse.

Cosine of an angle   the ratio of the length of the leg adjacent to the angle to the length of the hypotenuse.

Tangent of an angle   the ratio of the length of the leg opposite the angle to the length of the leg adjacent to the angle.

The trigonometric ratios of $\triangle ABC$ illustrated in this section are summarized in the following table.

Trigonometric Ratios			
Name	Abbreviation	Meaning	Side Ratio
sine of A	sin A	$\dfrac{opp.}{hyp.}$	$\dfrac{a}{c}$
cosine of A	cos A	$\dfrac{adj.}{hyp.}$	$\dfrac{b}{c}$
tangent of A	tan A	$\dfrac{opp.}{adj.}$	$\dfrac{a}{b}$

Remember that you are dealing with a right triangle, so you can apply the Pythagorean theorem when needed.

EXAMPLE 1 Give the exact value of the three basic trigonometric ratios for the two acute angles in the triangle shown here.

Answer

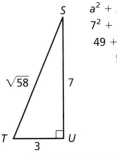

$$a^2 + b^2 = c^2$$
$$7^2 + 3^2 = c^2$$
$$49 + 9 = c^2$$
$$58 = c^2$$
$$c = \sqrt{58}$$

1. Find the length of the hypotenuse by using the Pythagorean theorem.

$$\sin \angle T = \frac{opp.}{hyp.} = \frac{7}{\sqrt{58}} \cdot \frac{\sqrt{58}}{\sqrt{58}} = \frac{7\sqrt{58}}{58}$$

2. Find the trigonometric ratios for $\angle T$ and $\angle S$.

$$\cos \angle T = \frac{adj.}{hyp.} = \frac{3}{\sqrt{58}} \cdot \frac{\sqrt{58}}{\sqrt{58}} = \frac{3\sqrt{58}}{58}$$

$$\tan \angle T = \frac{opp.}{adj.} = \frac{7}{3}$$

$$\sin \angle S = \frac{opp.}{hyp.} = \frac{3}{\sqrt{58}} \cdot \frac{\sqrt{58}}{\sqrt{58}} = \frac{3\sqrt{58}}{58}$$

Continued ▶

$$\cos \angle S = \frac{adj.}{hyp.} = \frac{7}{\sqrt{58}} \cdot \frac{\sqrt{58}}{\sqrt{58}} = \frac{7\sqrt{58}}{58}$$

$$\tan \angle S = \frac{opp.}{adj.} = \frac{3}{7}$$

Given the measure of a certain angle, you can find the approximate value of the sine, cosine, or tangent ratios without finding the side lengths of a triangle. The ratio calculations for degrees have already been done for you and summarized in a trigonometric table on pages 612–17. Degrees are often broken down into minutes with **60** minutes in a degree. The angle **36°40′** is read as "thirty six degrees forty minutes." Minutes are sometimes further divided into seconds with **60** seconds per minute, for example, **36°40′19.″**

Calculators can give these trigonometric values with more precision than the tables. Calculators express angles using decimal parts of a degree as well as degrees and minutes. You may use either to calculate the trigonometric ratios.

Learn to use a calculator correctly. It will be a valuable tool for you in mathematics. Wise use of tools is important in all walks of life. The Christian's most valuable tool is the Word of God. Learn to use it well and wisely. The only way to be confident in using the Bible is to study it and become so familiar with it that you can comfortably use it.

Find the following ratios:
a. sin 58°
b. tan 27°40′
c. cos 83°10′

Answer   a. sin 58° = 0.8480
b. tan 27°40′ = 0.5243
c. 83°10′ = 0.1190

Find the exact value of the three basic trigonometric ratios for the acute angles of each triangle.

1.

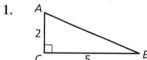

2.

3.

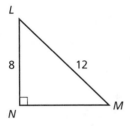

Find the approximate decimal value of the three basic trigonometric ratios for each acute angle of each triangle.

4.

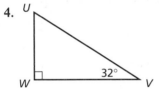

5.

Use a calculator to find these ratios.

6. sin 38°10′
7. cos 12°
8. tan 42°50′
9. cos 57°20′
10. sin 82°30′
11. tan 27°40′
12. tan 76°17′
13. cos 14°20′
14. sin 64°50′
15. tan 3°20′

▶ B. Exercises

Assuming ∠C is the right angle, give sin A, using the given information.
16. $a = 5, c = 10$
17. $A = 45°$
18. $a = 2, b = 5$
19. $B = 33°$
20. $b = 3, c = 4$
21. Change 75.28° to degrees, minutes, and seconds.
22. Find sin 32°29′41″ to five decimal places.

▶ C. Exercises

Answer the following questions about trig ratios (*Hint:* study the table).
23. For what angle measure would sin $x \approx \frac{1}{3}$?
24. What is the relation between two angles A and B if sin A = cos B?

▶ Dominion Modeling

25. Make a scatterplot of the tidal data. Would a linear model be useful? Explain.

▦ Cumulative Review

Find $f(0.1)$ if
26. $f(x) = [x]$.
27. $f(x) = 5x + 1$.
28. $f(x) = \frac{4}{x}$.
29. $f(x) = x^2 + x - 1$.
30. $f(x) = \sqrt{x - x^2}$.

10.2 Problem Solving

Given the value of a trigonometric ratio, you can find the corresponding angle. Reversing the relation between angles and ratios will permit you to solve a variety of problems. Finding the angle for a given value of the sine is called the inverse sine or *arcsine* and is symbolized by $\sin^{-1} x$ or arcsin x. Check your calculator for either of these symbols (or use a table).

EXAMPLE 1   Find the angle whose sine is $\frac{4}{7}$.

Answer

$\sin x = \frac{4}{7}$

  $x = \sin^{-1} \frac{4}{7}$ 1. Find the inverse sine.

  $x = 34°51'$ 2. Give your answer in degrees and minutes.

To solve a triangle means to find all of the side lengths and all of the angle measures. In a right triangle, if you know two sides or one side and one acute angle, the remaining angles and sides may be found.

EXAMPLE 2   Solve △*ABC*.

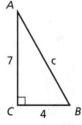

Answer

$a^2 + b^2 = c^2$ 1. To solve △*ABC*, you must find *AB* (length of $\overline{AB}$) using the Pythagorean theorem.

$7^2 + 4^2 = c^2$
$49 + 16 = c^2$
$65 = c^2$
$c = \sqrt{65}$ Give the exact value of *c*. Use the approximation $c \approx 8.1$ for further

Continued ▶

	computations or interpretation as a length in word problems.
$\tan A = \frac{4}{7}$ $\tan A \approx 0.571428571$	2. Set up a trig ratio for the measure of $\angle A$. Use the tangent ratio since both leg lengths are given. Convert the ratio to decimal form.
$A \approx 29.7448813°$	3. Find the angle measure by finding $\tan^{-1}$ (or arctan).
$A = 29°45'$	4. Convert from decimal parts of a degree to degrees and minutes.
$B = 90° - A = 90° - 29°45'$ $\qquad = 89°60' - 29°45'$ $\qquad = 60°15'$	5. Subtract to find $\angle B$ since $\angle A$ and $\angle B$ are complementary (sum of 90°).
$A = 29°45' \qquad a = 4$ $B = 60°15' \qquad b = 7$ $C = 90° \qquad c = \sqrt{65}$	6. Summarize the results.

To use trigonometry to solve problems, you will need to know two definitions.

Definitions

Angle of elevation   the angle formed by a horizontal line and the line of sight toward an object that is above the horizontal.

Angle of depression   the angle formed by a horizontal line and the line of sight toward an object that is below the horizontal.

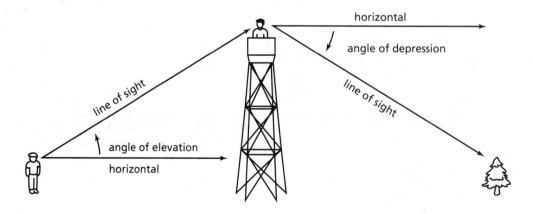

Study the next two examples to see how trigonometry is used to solve word problems.

EXAMPLE 3   An engineer sets up a transit (surveying instrument) in a
convenient spot and measures the distance to the base of a
building to be 75 feet. If the angle of elevation of the top of
the building measures 67°, find the height of the building.
Assume the transit is 5 feet high.

Answer $\tan 67° = \frac{x}{75}$

$x = 75 \tan 67°$

$x \approx 176.7$ feet

The building is
$176.7 + 5 \approx 181.7$ feet high.

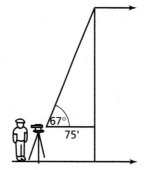

EXAMPLE 4   Jeff wants to know the approximate distance across a certain
part of the lake from A to B. He measures a distance along
the shore from A to C to be 33 paces (100 ft.). He estimates
$\angle C$ to be 80°. Find the distance across the lake from A to B.

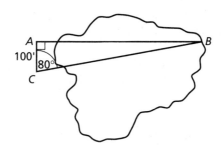

Answer $\tan 80° = \frac{AB}{100}$ Since $\overline{AB}$ is opposite $\angle C$ and $\overline{AC}$ is

$AB = 100 \tan 80°$ adjacent, use the tangent ratio.

$AB \approx 567$ feet

▶ A. Exercises

Find the measure of the angle to the nearest minute.
1. $\tan A = 0.3249$
2. $\sin B = 0.1045$
3. $\cos A = 0.5157$

4. $\sin A = 0.9511$
5. $\cos B = 0.8857$
6. $\tan B = 0.0378$
7. $\sin A = 0.8969$
8. $\tan A = 1.144$
9. $\cos B = 0.7346$
10. $\sin B = 0.2000$

Given right triangle ABC, solve each triangle. Round lengths of sides to the nearest tenth and angle measures to the nearest minute.

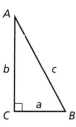

11. $A = 38°, b = 5$
12. $a = 12, c = 25$
13. $a = 3, b = 8$
14. $B = 12°, c = 8$
15. $b = 6, c = 9$

▶ B. Exercises

Solve each word problem, using trigonometry. Use your own judgment as to rounding.

16. What is the horizontal distance between the point where an airplane begins its descent and where it lands if the airplane descends at an angle of depression of 5° and is 7200 feet high when it begins its descent?

17. A 40-foot guy wire helps support a pole and is placed in the ground at an angle of 68° with the ground. How high does the wire reach on the pole?

18. Find the distance across the river from A to C as shown in the diagram.

19. A 20-foot ladder is placed against a house, and it reaches a height of 18 feet on the house. What is the measure of the angle that the ladder makes with the ground?

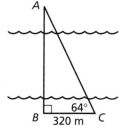

20. Andy knows that Camp Creek Bald and Big Knob are rivals for the highest point in his county. His map shows that they are 3.8 miles apart (about 20,000 feet) and that Camp Creek Bald has an elevation of 4844 feet. The topographic contours show that Big Knob is between 4840 and 4880 feet, but no elevation is given. Andy climbs the lookout tower on the bald and uses a clinometer to estimate that the angle of elevation to Big Knob is about a tenth of a degree. What is the height of Big Knob?

▶ C. Exercises

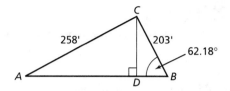

21. Find *AD* to locate the point *D* where a perpendicular from *C* to $\overline{AB}$ would intersect $\overline{AB}$.

22. Solve $\sin 53° = \frac{\sin 41°}{319 - x}$ for *x* but do not substitute decimals for the sines of the angles.

▶ Dominion Modeling

23. Would an exponential model work for the tidal data? Explain.
24. Would a quadratic model work for the tidal data? Explain.

▦ Cumulative Review

Find the distance between

25. -8 and -11 on the number line.
26. *a* and *b* on a number line.
27. $(2, 5)$ and $(-4, 6)$ in the plane.
28. (a, b) and (c, d) in the plane.
29. $(1, 2, 4)$ and $(-1, 3, -2)$ in space.

10.3 Special Triangles and Reciprocal Ratios

Many times you will work with 30°, 60°, and 45° angles and the trigonometric ratios associated with them. It is essential that you know these important ratios. The best way to learn them is to memorize the side lengths of the basic triangles associated with the angles.

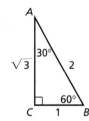 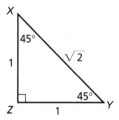

If you can recall these triangles, you can find the trigonometric ratios for 30°, 60°, and 45° angles without using a calculator or trigonometric table. Although a triangle may not have the same side lengths as the ones given, the side lengths are in the same ratio because the triangles are similar.

The basic 30–60–90 triangle has side lengths in the ratio 1:2:$\sqrt{3}$. The basic 45–45–90 triangle has side lengths in the ratio 1:1:$\sqrt{2}$. Before determining the various trig ratios from these lengths, verify that these side lengths are correct. Consider right $\triangle ABC$ with $m\angle A = 30°$ and $a = 1$.

Then $\sin 30° = \frac{1}{c}$ By Pythagorean theorem

$c \sin 30° = 1$ $a^2 + b^2 = c^2$

$c = \frac{1}{\sin 30°}$ $1^2 + b^2 = 2^2$

$c = 1 \div 0.5$ $1 + b^2 = 4$

$c = 2$ $b^2 = 3$

                     $b = \sqrt{3}$

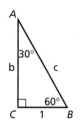

Next, consider right $\triangle XYZ$ with $m\angle X = 45°$ and $x = 1$. From geometry, if two angles of a triangle are congruent, the sides opposite them are congruent, therefore $y = 1$.

By the Pythagorean theorem,

$$z^2 = 1^2 + 1^2$$
$$z^2 = 2$$
$$z = \sqrt{2}$$

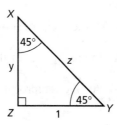

EXAMPLE 1   Solve $\triangle EFG$.

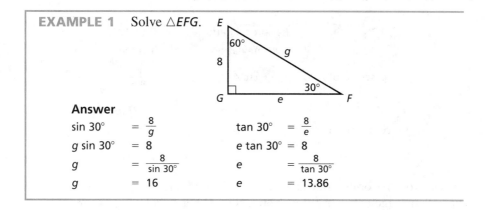

Answer

$\sin 30°$	$= \dfrac{8}{g}$		$\tan 30°$	$= \dfrac{8}{e}$
$g \sin 30°$	$= 8$		$e \tan 30°$	$= 8$
g	$= \dfrac{8}{\sin 30°}$		e	$= \dfrac{8}{\tan 30°}$
g	$= 16$		e	$= 13.86$

Using the **30–60** right triangle at the beginning of the lesson, we see that the side opposite the **30°** angle of $\triangle EFG$ is eight times that of the side opposite 30° angle in $\triangle ABC$. Since the triangles are similar, the side opposite the **60°** in $\triangle EFG$ must be eight times the side opposite the corresponding angle in $\triangle ABC$. A calculator check will show that $8\sqrt{3} \approx 13.86$, which agrees with the trig solution given.

EXAMPLE 2   Find the exact value of sin 60° and cos 45°.

Answer

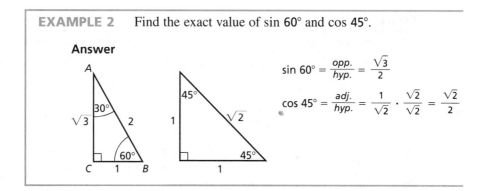

$$\sin 60° = \frac{opp.}{hyp.} = \frac{\sqrt{3}}{2}$$

$$\cos 45° = \frac{adj.}{hyp.} = \frac{1}{\sqrt{2}} \cdot \frac{\sqrt{2}}{\sqrt{2}} = \frac{\sqrt{2}}{2}$$

The sine, cosine, and tangent are the three basic trigonometric ratios, but there are three more related ratios called *reciprocal ratios*.

Definitions

Cosecant of A   the reciprocal of the sine of A.

Secant of A   the reciprocal of the cosine of A.

Cotangent of A   the reciprocal of the tangent of A.

The reciprocal ratios are summarized in the table.

Reciprocal Ratios		
Name	Abbreviation	Meaning
cosecant of A	csc A	$\frac{1}{\sin A}$
secant of A	sec A	$\frac{1}{\cos A}$
cotangent of A	cot A	$\frac{1}{\tan A}$

Given two sides or one side and an acute angle of a right triangle, you can find all six trigonometric ratios. Notice that with a calculator you can find a reciprocal ratio by using the $\frac{1}{x}$ button. To find csc A, find sin A and push $\frac{1}{x}$.

EXAMPLE 3   Find the six trigonometric ratios for $\angle A$ in $\triangle ABC$.

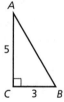

Answer

$$a^2 + b^2 = c^2$$
$$5^2 + 3^2 = c^2$$
$$25 + 9 = c^2$$
$$c = \sqrt{34}$$

1. Use the Pythagorean theorem to find the length of the hypotenuse.

$\sin A = \dfrac{3}{\sqrt{34}} = \dfrac{3\sqrt{34}}{34}$ $\csc A = \dfrac{\sqrt{34}}{3}$

$\cos A = \dfrac{5}{\sqrt{34}} = \dfrac{5\sqrt{34}}{34}$ $\sec A = \dfrac{\sqrt{34}}{5}$

$\tan A = \dfrac{3}{5}$ $\cot A = \dfrac{5}{3}$

2. Determine the six trigonometric ratios for $\angle A$.

► A. Exercises

Without using a calculator or trigonometric table, find the exact value of the following ratios. Leave your answers in fractional form.

1. $\cos 60°$

2. $\tan 45°$

3. $\sin 45°$

4. $\sin 30°$

5. $\tan 60°$

6. $\cos 30°$

7. $\tan 30°$

8. $\cot 60°$

9. $\sec 30°$

10. $\csc 45°$

► B. Exercises

Use a calculator to find the ratios or the angles.

11. $\sec 37°51'$
12. $\cot A = 1.71$
13. $\csc 83°12'$
14. $\sec A = 2.4$

Calculate the following.

15. $2 \sin 35° \cos 35°$
16. $\csc 40° \tan 40°$
17. $(\sin 19°)^2 + (\cos 19°)^2$
18. $\dfrac{\sin 42°}{\cos 42°}$

Solve each triangle. Give exact values.

19.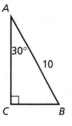

20.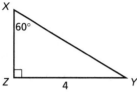

21.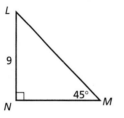

22.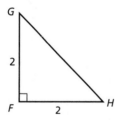

Give the six trigonometric ratios for each acute angle in each triangle.

23.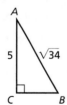

24.

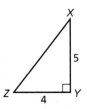

25.

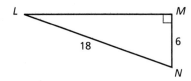

26.

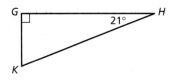

▶ C. Exercises

Using the triangle shown,

27. find the ratio $\frac{\sin A}{\cos A}$ and draw a conclusion.
28. find sin A and cos B. Express their relationship using an equation and generalize it using words.

▶ Dominion Modeling

29. Generate a sinusoidal model for the tidal data.
30. It is easy to find data for high and low tides in any given harbor. Our model does more than this, however. What else does the tidal model give, and why might this be useful?

▌Cumulative Review

Identify each type of number. Be specific.

31. $\frac{11}{3}$
32. $5 - 6i$
33. -4
34. $\sqrt{3}$
35. 0

10.4 Trigonometry in the Cartesian Plane

Trigonometry is not restricted to right triangles. In this section you will determine the trigonometric ratios for any angles in the Cartesian plane.

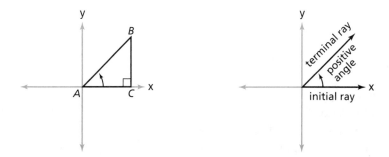

In the diagram $\angle A$ is in *standard position.* This means that the vertex of the angle is at the origin. One ray called the *initial ray* is on the positive *x*-axis. The other ray of the angle is the *terminal ray.* Angles measured in a counter-clockwise direction are considered positive angles, and those measured in a clockwise direction are *negative.* In addition, angle measures may exceed 360° if there is more than a complete rotation.

Given the measure of an angle and having drawn it in standard position, you can always form a right triangle by dropping a perpendicular from any point on the terminal ray to the *x*-axis. This right triangle is called a *reference triangle* and the positive acute angle that has its vertex at the origin is called the *reference angle.* Reference triangles are useful because the reference angle and the original angle have sines with the same absolute value. This is also true of the cosines and tangents of the two angles.

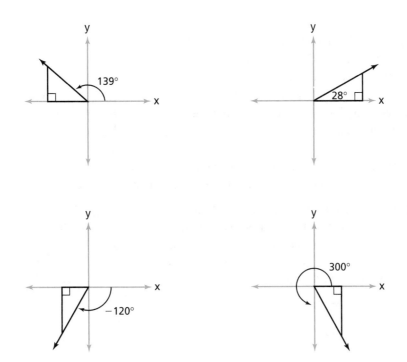

Draw a perpendicular from any point on the terminal ray to the *x*-axis to form the reference triangle. Using the letter *r* for the distance from the origin to the given point on the terminal ray, redefine the trigonometric ratios in terms of *x*, *y*, and *r*. Since *r* is a distance, it is always positive; whereas, *x* and *y* represent the coordinates of the point and can be positive or negative.

Since $AC = x$, $BC = y$, and the terminal ray of the angle lies in the first quadrant, *x* and *y* will be positive.

$$\sin A = \frac{\text{opp.}}{\text{hyp.}} = \frac{y}{r} \qquad \csc A = \frac{1}{\sin A} = \frac{r}{y}$$

$$\cos A = \frac{\text{adj.}}{\text{hyp.}} = \frac{x}{r} \qquad \sec A = \frac{1}{\cos A} = \frac{r}{x}$$

$$\tan A = \frac{\text{opp.}}{\text{adj.}} = \frac{y}{x} \qquad \cot A = \frac{1}{\tan A} = \frac{x}{y}$$

If the terminal ray lies in the third quadrant, both *x* and *y* will be negative. This results in the sine and cosine being negative, since *r* is always positive. The tangent of the angle, however, is positive since it is the quotient of two negative values.

Since the trigonometric ratios are computed using x, y, and r, angles with the same terminal ray have the same ratios. For example $-340°$ has the same terminal side as $20°$. Therefore $\sin -340° = \sin 20°$. You can use reference triangles to determine trigonometric ratios for any angle.

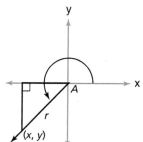

If the terminal ray is on an axis, you cannot make a reference triangle and must use the ratios that involve x, y, and r.

A very valuable tool in understanding trigonometric ratios is the unit circle (radius of 1 and centered at the origin). For any point on the unit circle, $r = 1$. This means the definitions for $\cos A$ and $\sin A$ reduce as follows:

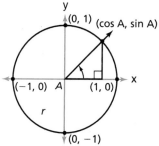

$\cos A = \dfrac{x}{r} = \dfrac{x}{1} = x$ and

$\sin A = \dfrac{y}{r} = \dfrac{y}{1} = y$.

Since $x = \cos A$ and $y = \sin A$, any point on the unit circle has coordinates $(\cos A, \sin A)$. Reference angles may be drawn within the unit circle, and the legs of the triangle become $\cos A$ and $\sin A$.

From this diagram we can see that when $A = 0°$, $x = 1$, $y = 0$, and $r = 1$. Thus, $\sin 0° = 0$ and $\cos 0° = 1$.

EXAMPLE 1 Find $\sec 230°$.

Answer

1. Draw a 230° angle in standard position and find the reference angle.

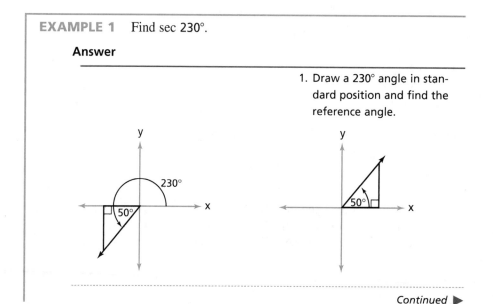

Continued ▶

$$\cos 230° = -\cos 50° \approx -0.6428$$

2. Use the 50° reference angle but recall that cos $A < 0$ in the third quadrant ($x < 0$ and r is always positive).

$$\sec 230° = \frac{1}{\cos 230°} \approx \frac{1}{-0.6428} \approx -1.5557$$

3. The secant is the reciprocal of the cosine.

EXAMPLE 2 Find the sine, cosine, and tangent of a 180° angle.

Answer

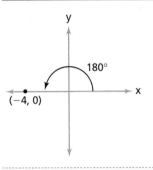

1. Draw the angle. The terminal ray is on the negative x-axis.

2. Choose any point on the terminal ray.

3. The value of x is -4, y is 0, and r is 4.

$$\sin 180° = \frac{y}{r} = \frac{0}{4} = 0$$

$$\cos 180° = \frac{x}{r} = \frac{-4}{4} = -1$$

$$\tan 180° = \frac{y}{x} = \frac{0}{-4} = 0$$

4. Use these values and the definitions to find the appropriate ratios.

Although this example works with any point on the terminal ray, it is easier to choose $(-1, 0)$ on the unit circle. This immediately gives you the values of sine and cosine since any point on the unit circle has coordinates ($\cos \theta$, $\sin \theta$). In addition, $\tan \theta = \frac{\sin \theta}{\cos \theta}$.

▶ **A. Exercises**

For each angle measure, draw the reference triangle and give the measure of the reference angle.

1. 52°
2. 345°
3. −140°
4. 110°
5. 210°
6. 170°

Find the sine, cosine, and tangent for ∠X if its terminal ray passes through the given point.

7. (−2, 1)
8. (−6, −4)
9. (1, 4)
10. (−8, 0)
11. (0, 6)
12. Determine the sign of all trigonometric ratios for an angle whose terminal ray lies in quadrant I; quadrant II; quadrant III; and quadrant IV.

Find the sine, cosine, and tangent for the given angle measures.
Do not use a calculator or trigonometric table.

13. 90°
14. 270°

▶ B. Exercises

Find the ratios by using reference angles.

15. sin 200°
16. cos −12°
17. csc 112°10′
18. tan 340°

Find each ratio using special triangles as reference triangles.

19. cos 135°
20. sin 300°
21. tan −45°
22. csc 210°
23. cot −120°

▶ C. Exercises

Find the exact and decimal ratios for an angle A in standard position, whose terminal ray passes through $\left(-1, \sqrt{5}\right)$.

24. cos A
25. csc A

▶ Dominion Modeling

26. Kayakers find it less dangerous to pass through the Reversing Falls during "slack tide," the time when the Bay of Fundy and the St. John River are in equilibrium. When is the first slack tide on this date? (Hint: look for the middle of the sine wave.)

27. Your model for the projected tidal data was specifically for April 11, 2011. List several reasons why extrapolations might not provide the correct wave height on other days.

Cumulative Review

If $z = 3 - 2i$, find each of the following.

28. real part of z
29. imaginary part of z
30. conjugate of z
31. square of z
32. reciprocal of z
33. absolute value of z

Row-Reducing

In this section you will learn a skill called *row-reducing* that you will use in later chapters. There are three operations that can be used to row-reduce a matrix.

1. Multiply the entries of any row of a matrix by a nonzero factor.
2. Add a multiple of the entries in any row to another row of the matrix.
3. Interchange any two rows of a matrix.

If a row of a matrix represents an equation, row operation 1 is equivalent to the multiplication property of equality. Row operation 2 is similar to solving a system of equations by addition, although a variable need not be eliminated.

The main goal of using row operations, as the above three rules are often called, is to change a matrix to the identity matrix. Study the following progression of steps to see how this is done. r_1 represents "row 1." $-4r_1 + r_2$ means that each entry in row 1 is multiplied by -4 and added to the corresponding entry in row 2 (row 1 remains the same, row 2 changes). $r_1 \leftrightarrow r_2$ means that row 1 and row 2 are interchanged. Note that each new matrix that is obtained after a row operation is performed is a different matrix. The matrices are *row-equivalent*, but they are not equal.

$$\begin{bmatrix} 4 & 3 & -1 \\ 2 & 0 & 4 \\ 5 & 3 & 6 \end{bmatrix} \xrightarrow{r_1 \leftrightarrow r_2} \begin{bmatrix} 2 & 0 & 4 \\ 4 & 3 & -1 \\ 5 & 3 & 6 \end{bmatrix} \xrightarrow{\frac{1}{2}r_1} \begin{bmatrix} 1 & 0 & 2 \\ 4 & 3 & -1 \\ 5 & 3 & 6 \end{bmatrix} \xrightarrow{-4r_1 + r_2}$$

$$\begin{bmatrix} 1 & 0 & 2 \\ 0 & 3 & -9 \\ 5 & 3 & 6 \end{bmatrix} \xrightarrow{\frac{1}{3}r_2} \begin{bmatrix} 1 & 0 & 2 \\ 0 & 1 & -3 \\ 5 & 3 & 6 \end{bmatrix} \xrightarrow{-5r_1 + r_3} \begin{bmatrix} 1 & 0 & 2 \\ 0 & 1 & -3 \\ 0 & 3 & -4 \end{bmatrix} \xrightarrow{-3r_2 + r_3}$$

$$\begin{bmatrix} 1 & 0 & 2 \\ 0 & 1 & -3 \\ 0 & 0 & 5 \end{bmatrix} \xrightarrow{\frac{1}{5}r_3} \begin{bmatrix} 1 & 0 & 2 \\ 0 & 1 & -3 \\ 0 & 0 & 1 \end{bmatrix} \xrightarrow{-2r_3 + r_1} \begin{bmatrix} 1 & 0 & 0 \\ 0 & 1 & -3 \\ 0 & 0 & 1 \end{bmatrix} \xrightarrow{3r_3 + r_2}$$

$$\begin{bmatrix} 1 & 0 & 0 \\ 0 & 1 & 0 \\ 0 & 0 & 1 \end{bmatrix}$$

a b a
c d c
C^T $X = \dfrac{\det (A_i)}{\det (A)}$
$(m \times n)(n \times p)$ $[A \vdots I]$
Matrix Algebra 10

Row-Reducing a Matrix

1. Get a 1 in the upper left-hand corner of the matrix. Find the easiest way to get the 1 in this location, using any of the three row operations.
2. Next get a zero in every other position in the first column by using basic row operations.
3. Get a 1 in the second row, second column.
4. Apply step 2 to column two.
5. Continue for all columns.

▶ Exercises

Row-reduce each of the matrices shown. If it does not reduce to the identity, give the reduced matrix.

1. $\begin{bmatrix} 1 & 7 \\ 2 & 5 \end{bmatrix}$

2. $\begin{bmatrix} 3 & 1 & 4 \\ 8 & 3 & 4 \\ 1 & 5 & -1 \end{bmatrix}$

3. $\begin{bmatrix} 4 & 8 & 6 \\ 4 & 8 & 6 \\ 7 & 1 & 2 \end{bmatrix}$

4. Find the determinants of the matrices above.
5. What do you notice about the determinant of a matrix that does not row-reduce to the identity?

10.5 Radian Measure

The equation $x^2 + y^2 = 1$ describes the *unit circle* with center **(0, 0)** and radius 1 unit. It is used extensively in trigonometry to study angle measures and the ratios associated with them. The unit circle is helpful in the study of *trigonometric functions,* an extension of trigonometric ratios. In this study, you will need to know how to measure angles not only in degrees but also in units called *radians.*

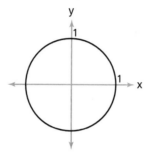

Definition

Radian the measure of an angle that intercepts the unit circle in an arc one unit in length and has its vertex at the center of the circle.

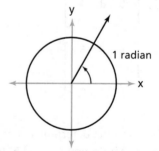

It is important that you learn to change degree measure of an angle to radian measure and radian measure to degree measure. Also important is the relationship between the two forms of measurement. Consider the unit circle.

$$C = 2\pi r$$

$$C = 2\pi(1)$$

$$C = 2\pi$$

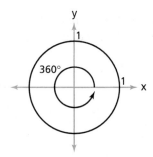

The radian measure of a unit circle is 2π, whereas the degree measure is $360°$. Therefore 2π radians $= 360°$. Since $\dfrac{2\pi}{360°}$ and $\dfrac{360°}{2\pi}$ are both equivalent to one, their reduced forms, $\dfrac{\pi}{180°}$ and $\dfrac{180°}{\pi}$, are useful for converting between degrees and radians as illustrated below.

To change from one unit to the other, do the appropriate multiplication as shown.

$$(m \text{ deg})\left(\frac{\pi \text{ rad}}{180 \text{ deg}}\right) = x \text{ rad} \qquad (m \text{ rad})\left(\frac{180 \text{ deg}}{\pi \text{ rad}}\right) = x \text{ deg}$$

If no unit of measure is given in a problem, the measure is considered to be in radians.

EXAMPLE 1 Convert the following radian measures to degree measures: $\dfrac{\pi}{2}, \dfrac{3\pi}{4}, \dfrac{\pi}{6}$

Answer Multiply each radian measure by the conversion factor $\dfrac{180°}{\pi}$ to cancel radians.

$\dfrac{\pi}{2}$ rad $\qquad\qquad$ $\dfrac{3\pi}{4}$ rad $\qquad\qquad$ $\dfrac{\pi}{6}$ rad

$\dfrac{\pi}{2}\left(\dfrac{180°}{\pi}\right)$ $\qquad$ $\dfrac{3\pi}{4}\left(\dfrac{180°}{\pi}\right)$ $\qquad$ $\dfrac{\pi}{6}\left(\dfrac{180°}{\pi}\right)$

$90°$ $\qquad\qquad\qquad$ $135°$ $\qquad\qquad\qquad$ $30°$

EXAMPLE 2 Change the following degree measures to radian measures: $38°, 45°, 290°$

Answer Multiply each degree measure by the conversion factor $\dfrac{\pi}{180°}$ to cancel degrees.

$38°$ $\qquad\qquad\qquad$ $45°$ $\qquad\qquad\qquad$ $290°$

$\overset{19}{\cancel{38}°}\left(\dfrac{\pi}{\underset{90}{\cancel{180°}}}\right)$ $\qquad$ $\overset{1}{\cancel{45}°}\left(\dfrac{\pi}{\underset{4}{\cancel{180°}}}\right)$ $\qquad$ $\overset{29}{\cancel{290}°}\left(\dfrac{\pi}{\underset{18}{\cancel{180°}}}\right)$

$\dfrac{19\pi}{90}$ rad $\qquad\qquad$ $\dfrac{\pi}{4}$ rad $\qquad\qquad$ $\dfrac{29\pi}{18}$ rad

EXAMPLE 3 Change 420° to radians and find the sine, cosine, and tangent of it.

Answer

420°

1. Convert to radians

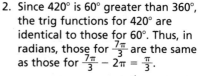

$\frac{7\pi}{3}$

$\sin 60° = \sin \frac{\pi}{3} = \frac{\sqrt{3}}{2}$

$\cos 60° = \cos \frac{\pi}{3} = \frac{1}{2}$

$\tan 60° = \tan \frac{\pi}{3} = \sqrt{3}$

Therefore, $\sin 420° = \frac{\sqrt{3}}{2}$, $\cos 420° = \frac{1}{2}$, and $\tan 420° = \sqrt{3}$.

2. Since 420° is 60° greater than 360°, the trig functions for 420° are identical to those for 60°. Thus, in radians, those for $\frac{7\pi}{3}$ are the same as those for $\frac{7\pi}{3} - 2\pi = \frac{\pi}{3}$.

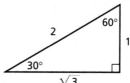

▶ A. Exercises

Draw the following angles in standard position.

1. 420°
2. $\frac{\pi}{3}$
3. $\frac{4\pi}{3}$

4. $-\frac{3\pi}{2}$
5. $\frac{5\pi}{4}$
6. $-\frac{2\pi}{3}$

Convert each radian measure to degree measure.

7. $\frac{\pi}{3}$

8. $\frac{3\pi}{2}$

9. $-\frac{5\pi}{4}$

10. 3π

11. $\frac{\pi}{5}$

12. $\frac{4\pi}{9}$

13. $\frac{9\pi}{5}$

14. $\frac{\pi}{6}$

Convert each degree measure to radian measure.

15. 15°

16. 280°

17. −320°

18. 175°

19. 212°

20. 180°

▶ B. Exercises

Find the exact values.

21. $\cos \frac{2\pi}{3}$

22. $\tan \frac{3\pi}{4}$

23. $\sin -\frac{\pi}{6}$

24. $\tan \frac{5\pi}{6}$

25. Convert 1.5927 radians to degrees and minutes and then to an angle whose radian measure is a decimal fraction of π.

26. Convert 8.41π radians to a first quadrant angle and then convert it to degrees and minutes.

Draw a −40° angle in standard position and then draw its reference angle. Answer the following questions.

27. Find the cosines of the angles drawn. Write an equation relating these cosines.

28. Find the sines of the angles drawn. Write an equation relating these sines.

▶ C. Exercises

29. Repeat exercise 27 for an angle in the third quadrant. Draw a general conclusion.

30. Repeat exercise 28 for an angle in the third quadrant. Draw a general conclusion.

▶ Dominion Modeling

31. On Tuesday, April 12, 2011, St. John is projected to have a high tide of 7.16 m at **5:44** and a low tide of 1.60 m at **12:10**. How well do these projections fit with your model? (Hint: Use the fact that these times are **24** hours later than the original data.)

32. Some claim that, in the region about St. John, at least thirty variables control the heights of tides. What could some of those variables be?

▪ Cumulative Review

Let $f(x) = 2x^2 - 8x + 3$.

33. Find $f(2)$.

34. Complete the square.

35. Find the maximum or minimum point.

36. Find the y-intercept.

37. Find the discriminant of the equation $f(x) = 0$.

38. Classify the solutions.

10.6 Trigonometric Functions

You saw the mathematical definition of a function in Chapter 3 and will review it again now. But first think of the word *function* from a more general standpoint. Each of us has a special function for which God has prepared us. Each of you has a job in the body of Christ that you are expected to perform. Whether the Lord has given you talent in art, music, English, history, or mathematics, He expects you to develop your talents and use them for His glory. Read I Corinthians 12:12-27. Verse 18 states that "God set the members every one of them in the body, as it hath pleased him." And verse 27 states, "Now ye are the body of Christ, and members in particular."

A function in mathematics performs a mathematical job. As you recall, it is a set of ordered pairs in which every first element is paired with one and only one second element. A function rule relates each first element to its corresponding second element. Rules for the trigonometric functions involve the trigonometric ratios that you have been studying.

Definitions

Sine function $f(x) = \sin x$, where x is an angle measure in radians.

Cosine function $f(x) = \cos x$, where x is an angle measure in radians.

Tangent function $f(x) = \tan x$, where x is an angle measure in radians.

To see the graphs of these functions, you can construct a table of ordered pairs and plot the points to form a curve.

EXAMPLE 1   Graph $f(x) = \sin x$ where $x \in \mathbb{R}$ including $0 \leq x \leq 2\pi$.

Answer

x	$\sin x$
0	0
$\frac{\pi}{6}$	0.5000
$\frac{\pi}{4}$	0.7071
$\frac{\pi}{3}$	0.8660
$\frac{\pi}{2}$	1
$\frac{2\pi}{3}$	0.8660
$\frac{3\pi}{4}$	0.7071
$\frac{5\pi}{6}$	0.5000
π	0

x	$\sin x$
$\frac{7\pi}{6}$	−0.5000
$\frac{5\pi}{4}$	−0.7071
$\frac{4\pi}{3}$	−0.8660
$\frac{3\pi}{2}$	−1
$\frac{5\pi}{3}$	−0.8660
$\frac{7\pi}{4}$	−0.7071
$\frac{11\pi}{6}$	−0.5000
2π	0

1. Construct a table of ordered pairs. Notice that angle measures are in radians.

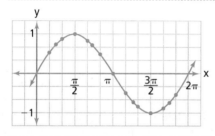

2. Plot these points on a graph and connect them with a smooth curve.

The arrows on the graph indicate that the curve continues in both directions. Example 2 shows that the pattern continues to follow this cycle for all real numbers.

EXAMPLE 2   Graph $f(x) = \sin x$ where $x \in \mathbb{R}$ including $-4\pi \leq x \leq 4\pi$.

Answer

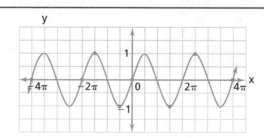

EXAMPLE 3   Graph $f(x) = \cos x$ where $x \in \mathbb{R}$ including $0 \le x \le 2\pi$.

Answer

1. Construct a table of ordered pairs.

x	$\cos x$
0	1
$\frac{\pi}{6}$	0.8660
$\frac{\pi}{4}$	0.7071
$\frac{\pi}{3}$	0.5000
$\frac{\pi}{2}$	0
$\frac{2\pi}{3}$	−0.5000
$\frac{3\pi}{4}$	−0.7071
$\frac{5\pi}{6}$	−0.8660
π	−1

x	$\cos x$
$\frac{7\pi}{6}$	−0.8660
$\frac{5\pi}{4}$	−0.7071
$\frac{4\pi}{3}$	−0.5000
$\frac{3\pi}{2}$	0
$\frac{5\pi}{3}$	0.5000
$\frac{7\pi}{4}$	0.7071
$\frac{11\pi}{6}$	0.8660
2π	1

2. Plot these points on a graph and connect them with a smooth curve.

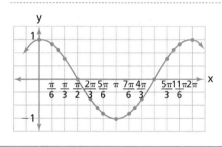

Notice that the graphs of $f(x) = \sin x$ and $f(x) = \cos x$ are identical except for a horizontal shift. In contrast, the tangent function is quite different.

EXAMPLE 4   Graph $f(x) = \tan x$ including values of x where the function is defined in the interval $0 \le x \le 2\pi$.

Answer

1. Construct a table of ordered pairs.

x	$\tan x$
0	0
$\frac{\pi}{6}$	0.5774
$\frac{\pi}{4}$	1
$\frac{\pi}{3}$	1.732
$\frac{\pi}{2}$	undefined
$\frac{2\pi}{3}$	−1.732
$\frac{5\pi}{6}$	−0.5774
π	0

x	$\tan x$
$\frac{7\pi}{6}$	0.5774
$\frac{5\pi}{4}$	1
$\frac{4\pi}{3}$	1.732
$\frac{3\pi}{2}$	undefined
$\frac{5\pi}{3}$	−1.732
$\frac{7\pi}{4}$	−1
$\frac{11\pi}{6}$	−0.5774
2π	0

Continued ▶

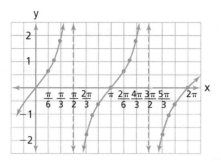

2. Graph the points. Place a dotted vertical line (asymptote) at the places where the function is undefined.

The dotted lines on the graph of the tangent function are asymptotes. The tangent graph gets closer and closer to the asymptotes, but it will never reach the dotted line. The idea of asymptotes should be easy for you after your work with rational functions. Use the vertical asymptotes as guidelines for graphing as you did with rational functions.

Notice how the graph starts its pattern over again to the right of each asymptote. Functions with graphs that continually repeat a pattern of *y*-values are called *periodic*. All of the trigonometric functions are periodic functions. In the tangent graph the pattern begins again after a break in the graph. Functions with breaks or jumps in the graph are *discontinuous*. The sine and cosine functions are continuous.

▶ A. Exercises

Sketch a graph for each relation. Use the vertical line test to decide if it is a function.

1. $y = \cos x$
2. $y = \sin x$
3. $y = \tan x$

Make a table and graph each function.

4. $y = 2 \cos x$
5. $y = \frac{1}{4} \sin x$
6. $y = 4 \sin \theta$
7. Are $f(x) = \sin x$ and $f(x) = \cos x$ continuous?
8. Is $f(x) = \tan x$ continuous?

Give the domain of each function.

9. $y = \sin x$
10. $y = \cos x$
11. $y = \tan x$

Give the range of each function.

12. $y = \sin x$

13. $y = \cos x$

14. $y = \tan x$

▶ B. Exercises

Make a table and sketch a graph for each of the following functions.

15. $f(x) = \frac{1}{2} \tan x$

16. $f(x) = 3 \tan x$

17. $f(x) = \cos 2x$

18. $f(x) = \sin 2x$

▶ C. Exercises

Let $f(x) = \cot x$.

19. Graph $f(x)$.

20. Is $f(x)$ periodic?

21. Is $f(x)$ continuous?

22. Give the domain and range.

▶ Dominion Modeling

23. According to the model, when does the first high tide occur and the first low tide of the day?

Cumulative Review

Consider the graph of each function below and decide if it is continuous. (Sketch the graph if necessary.)

24. $f(x) = |x|$

25. $y = [x]$

26. $g(x) = (x - 1)^2 + 3$

27. $y = 2^x$

28. $y = \frac{4}{x - 1}$

29. Are polynomial functions always continuous? (Remember that this includes constant, linear, quadratic, and higher degree polynomials.)

LEONHARD EULER

Leonhard Euler was one of the key figures in the history of mathematics. He also had strong biblical convictions. It is encouraging to study the example of a man of such brilliance who also had a saving knowledge of Jesus Christ and a good testimony to those around him.

Leonhard was born to Paul and Marguerite Brucker Euler on April 15, 1707, in Basel, Switzerland. The family soon moved to Riechens, a small village where his father, a Calvinist, was the pastor of the village church. Though Paul Euler, also an accomplished mathematician, introduced his young son to mathematics, he wanted Leonhard to follow in his footsteps as a preacher. Therefore, young Leonhard entered the University of Basel to study theology and Hebrew. Because he loved mathematics, he continued taking private math lessons each week from Johann (I) Bernoulli. At age seventeen, Leonhard had to give up temporarily his study of mathematics for theology. Finally Bernoulli convinced Leonhard's father that Leonhard was destined to be a great mathematician. Then, with his father's approval, Leonhard turned his full attention to mathematics. His early training in theology served him well, however, and he never renounced one tenet of orthodoxy. As an old man, Leonhard conducted family prayers for his whole household, usually ending devotions with a sermon.

In 1727 at the age of twenty, Euler became chairman of mathematics at the New St. Petersburg Academy, founded by Peter the Great. In 1735 he spent only three days solving a very difficult problem that other prominent mathematicians required several months to solve. The problem, though solved, caused eyestrain that resulted in an illness and the loss of his sight in his right eye.

Euler earned his livelihood as a professor of math. He worked in Russia most of his life, but in 1741 he moved to Berlin to head the Prussian Academy, where he served for almost twenty-five years. Unhappy in Berlin, he moved back to Russia in 1766. By the time he returned to Russia, a cataract in his left eye had rendered him completely blind.

Despite his blindness Euler continued working for over fifteen years. He had a remarkable memory and the ability to concentrate amid loud disturbances. Perhaps he developed this ability because he was accustomed to working with his thirteen children gathered around him. He wrote 886 books and papers, enough to fill 73 large volumes. Of these 530 were published before his death in Petrograd on September 7, 1783.

The most important of Euler's works, *Introduction to infinite analysis (Introduction analysin infinitorum)*, forms the cornerstone of this branch of mathematics. Euler's mathematical achievements include classical research in algebra, trigonometry, analytic geometry, and calculus. He extended methods of analysis and greatly improved mathematical notation by introducing the following notations: $f(x)$ for functions; a, b, and c for the sides of triangle ABC; and i for the imaginary number $\sqrt{-1}$.

Leonhard lived a long, fruitful Christian life and should be remembered as one of the great mathematicians in history. The perfect order and beauty of God's creation finds expression in Euler's formula which relates the five most important numbers in all of mathematics: $e^{i\pi} + 1 = 0$. That these numbers are related in this way glorifies the Creator for the grandeur of His design.

Euler's mathematical achievements include classical research in algebra, trigonometry, analytic geometry, and calculus.

10.7 Amplitude and Period

The sine and cosine functions are called sine and cosine waves or *sinusoidal waves*. The general equations for the sine and cosine functions follow.

$y = a \sin bx$ and $y = a \cos bx$ where $a, b, x \in \mathbb{R}$

You studied the most basic sine and cosine functions in the last section. Notice that both functions fit the general form above where *a* and *b* are both equal to 1. Review their graphs below.

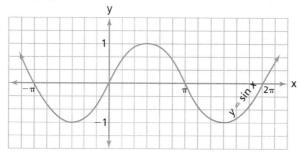

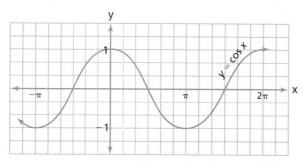

This transmitter broadcasts microwaves for television as far as the horizon. Microwave lengths range between 0.04 inch and 1 foot.

Notice that the maximum value of both the sine and cosine functions is 1, while the minimum value is −1, so the maximum distance the wave deviates from the x-axis in the functions shown is 1 unit. To put it another way, one-half the distance from its highest to lowest point is $\frac{1}{2}(2) = 1$, and this quantity is called the *amplitude* of the function.

In the last section you had some exercises in which the value of *a* was something other than 1. Notice how the graph of such a function differs from the basic wave.

The major difference between the graphs of $y = \sin x$ and $y = 3 \sin x$ is the amplitude of the function. In general, the amplitude of a sinusoidal wave is $|a|$.

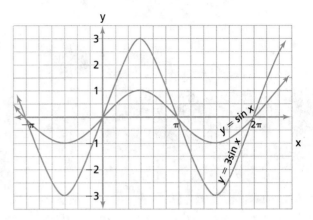

The other characteristic of a sinusoidal wave is the length of the wave's repeating cycle. For example, look at the graph of the basic cosine function defined by $y = \cos x$.

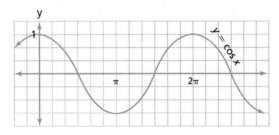

Starting at the point $(0, 1)$ and moving right, the curve decreases until it reaches the point $(\pi, -1)$, then increases until it reaches the point $(2\pi, 1)$. At this point the pattern starts again, and the wave repeats over and over again to infinity. Likewise, the pattern also repeats in the opposite direction to negative infinity. The important thing is the length of the cycle, called the *period* of the function. The period of the function $y = \cos x$ is 2π. Now compare the following functions.

$$y = \cos x \text{ and } y = \cos 2x$$

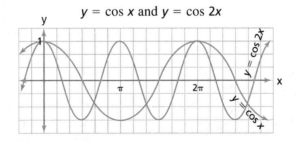

Do you see that the length of the wave's cycle for the second function is π units rather than 2π? The fact that $b = 2$ in the general equation illustrates that you can find the period of a sinusoidal function such as sine or cosine by evaluating $\frac{2\pi}{|b|}$.

Drivers on the four-month-old Tacoma Narrows Bridge at Tacoma, Washington, experienced wave crests and troughs before the 2800-foot center span began to twist.

Engineers had failed to foresee the results of harmonics for a wind blowing at 42 mph. The November 7, 1940, bridge collapse reminds us that structural engineering affects our lives daily.

By using these two facts and determining a few maximum and minimum values and *x*-intercepts for a sine or cosine function, you can quickly draw the graph of a function without constructing a large table.

EXAMPLE 1   Graph $y = 2 \sin \frac{1}{4}x$.

Answer

amplitude = $|a| = |2| = 2$

period = $\frac{2\pi}{|b|} = \frac{2\pi}{\left|\frac{1}{4}\right|} = \frac{2\pi}{\frac{1}{4}} = 8\pi$

1. Determine the amplitude and period of this sine function.

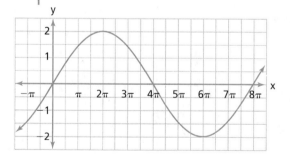

2. Compare to $y = \sin x$, which has *x*-intercepts at the ends and midpoint of each period. Graph the *x*-intercepts at ends of periods, $0 \pm 8\pi$, and at midpoints, $\pm 4\pi$.

3. Compare to $y = \sin x$, which has a maximum $\frac{1}{4}$ of the way through the period and a minimum $\frac{3}{4}$ of the way. The maximum is at $(2\pi, 2)$, and the minimum is at $(6\pi, -2)$.

4. Draw a smooth curve from zero to 8π. Draw additional periods if desired.

If the value of *a* is negative, the graph of the function is reflected across the *x*-axis. Study the example given here.

EXAMPLE 2   Graph $y = -3 \cos x$.

Answer

1. The amplitude is $|-3|$, or 3, and the period is $\frac{2\pi}{1}$, or 2π.

2. Since $a < 0$, the graph reflects across the *x*-axis.

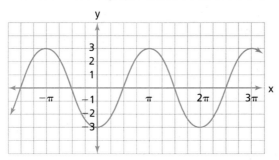

▶ A. Exercises

Graph and state the amplitude and period for each function.

1. $y = 4 \sin x$

2. $f(x) = \cos 4x$

3. $g(x) = \sin \frac{1}{3}x$

4. $h(x) = \frac{1}{2} \cos x$

5. $k(x) = -3 \sin x$

6. Give the period of $y = \tan x$.

7. Give the domain of all of the functions in exercises 1-5.

Find the range of the functions from the exercises above.

8. $f(x)$

9. $g(x)$

10. $h(x)$

11. $k(x)$

▶ B. Exercises

Graph and state the amplitude and period for each function.

12. $y = 2 \cos \frac{1}{2}x$

13. $y = -4 \cos \frac{1}{2}x$

14. $y = -2 \sin 6x$

15. $y = \sin 3x$

16. $y = \frac{1}{4} \cos 2x$

Find the range of each function.

17. $y = a \sin bx$ if $a > 0$

18. $y = a \cos bx$ if $a \neq 0$

▶ C. Exercises

19. Graph $y = 2 \cos \frac{1}{2}x + 1$

20. Graph $y = \cos \left(x - \frac{\pi}{4} \right)$

▶ Dominion Modeling

21. When, throughout the day, is the St. John tide expected to be 5 meters high?

▬ Cumulative Review

Find A.

22. $A^2 - 1 = 7$

23. $2^{A-1} = 16$

24. $2A - 1 = 5$

25. $\sqrt{A} - 1 = 6$

26. $\frac{2}{A - 1} = 8$

27. $\sin A = \frac{1}{2}$

28. $\tan A = 5$

Solve the triangles; consider the altitudes.

1. Solve △ABC, where no angle is a right angle.

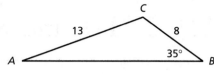

2. Solve △XYZ.

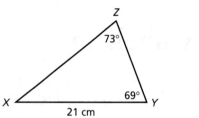

Algebra *and* Scripture

Symbolism

In Chapter 8 you studied the importance of contexts of numbers. Now discover some rules of context. Decide what the symbol "I" means in each sentence below.

1. When Mrs. Graves suggests it, I revise my essay.
2. If you revise point I of your outline, your essay will be stronger.
3. What topical clues helped you to correctly decide the meaning of the symbol in each sentence? What grammatical clues helped?

The above questions should suggest the following principle.

Rule 1: Grammar and context determine whether a word or numeral is meant.

Now decide what each symbol means without context. Explain.

4. CLVII   5. CIVIL
6. In the sentence "The men rebelled against the civil authorities," do the numerical values of the word *civil* aid your understanding?
7. Which combination of digits is not correctly expressed as a natural number? Why? 537, 203, 160, 015, 700

Now you can draw another conclusion.

Rule 2: Spelling and numeral formation rules determine whether a word or numeral is meant.

In Greek and Hebrew every letter of the alphabet is also used as a numeral (much as the English letters C and V are also Roman numerals). This means that every word has a numerical total.

8. Would a reader of Greek or Hebrew confuse a word with a numeral? Why?

Gematria refers to the practice of adding up the numbers of the words to find hidden or symbolic meaning. This *mystical* use of numbers breaks the rules of context. It supposes that word and verse counts add meaning to the words based on what the numerical total supposedly symbolizes.

9. If the word "my" occurs 5 times in a paragraph, what can you say?

10. Is there meaning in the number of times (5) the word occurred?

Rule 3: Repetition demonstrates emphasis, but there is no hidden meaning in the number of repetitions.

GREATER AMPLITUDE.

The mystical use of numbers can be traced to an ancient mathematician who said "All things are fittingly ordered according to the nature of numbers; number is the eternal essence; God is number; number is God." Who was he?

In the ancient Bible documents, since all numbers were written out ("twenty-three" instead of 23), no letter ever represents a numeral in Scripture. Mystical uses of numbers are always wrong, but not all symbolism is mystical. Both passages below use symbolism. Which one uses the number seven symbolically? Explain.

11. Rev. 5:6.   **12.** Rev. 1:11-20.

Revelation 1:4 provides another example of the symbolic use of the number seven.

Absolute Values

JOHN TO THE SEVEN churches which are in Asia: Grace be unto you, and peace, from him which is, and which was, and which is to come; and from the seven Spirits which are before his throne. ❧

REVELATION 1:4

Chapter Review

Find the sine, cosine, and tangent for both acute angles in each triangle.

1.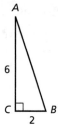

2.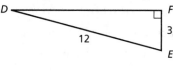

Solve the following right triangles. (Round side lengths to the nearest tenth and angle measures to the nearest minute.)

3.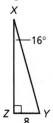

4.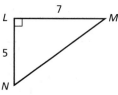

Solve.

5. Candy wants to know how high a 15-inch piece of wood will reach on a night stand she is building if the angle it forms with the horizontal piece of wood is 47°.

Without using a calculator or trigonometric table, find the following.

6. cos 30°

7. tan 60°

8. sin 45°

Solve each triangle. Give exact values.

9.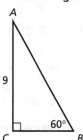

10.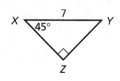

Give the six trigonometric ratios for each acute angle of each triangle in decimals.

11.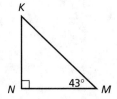

12.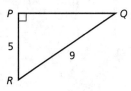

Find the sine, cosine, and tangent for the angle θ that is in standard position and whose terminal ray passes through the given point.

13. (5, −4)

14. (−2, 8)

Convert to radian measure.

15. 36°

16. 335°

Convert to degree measure.

17. $\frac{\pi}{8}$

18. $\frac{-2\pi}{3}$

Find angle A to the nearest minute.

19. tan A = 0.4639

20. cos A = 0.3475

Find the value by using reference triangles. Give exact values where possible.

21. sin −56°

22. cos 150°

23. tan 540°

24. sec 290°

Graph.

25. $y = \sin \theta$

26. $y = \tan \theta$

27. $y = \cos \theta$

28. $y = 3 \sin \theta$

29. $y = \cos \frac{1}{2}\theta$

30. $y = 2 \sin 4\theta$

31. Evaluate the model for the tide data.

32. What is the mathematical significance of Revelation 1:4.

11 Identities

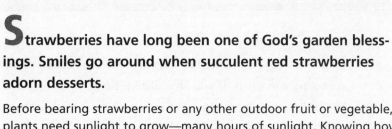

Strawberries have long been one of God's garden blessings. Smiles go around when succulent red strawberries adorn desserts.

Before bearing strawberries or any other outdoor fruit or vegetable, plants need sunlight to grow—many hours of sunlight. Knowing how many hours of sunlight occur throughout the year helps us know which varieties to plant and when they will thrive. Some of the juiciest strawberries can flower with less than ten hours of sunlight daily. Others need over twelve hours daily, and still others can flower anytime during the strawberry season.

Here are projections for the city of Quebec in A.D. 2012, giving hours of sunlight for scattered days of the year. The cyclic nature of trig functions (described by period identities) makes them useful in analyzing this kind of data.

Date	Day	Hours	Date	Day	Hours
Jan. 4, 2012	4	8.67	July 4, 2012	186	15.75
Jan. 18, 2012	18	9.05	July 18, 2012	200	15.38
Feb. 1, 2012	32	9.62	Aug. 1, 2012	214	14.85
Feb. 15, 2012	46	10.32	Aug. 15, 2012	228	14.20
Feb. 29, 2012	60	11.08	Aug. 29, 2012	242	13.47
Mar. 14, 2012	74	11.85	Sept. 12, 2012	256	12.72
Mar. 28, 2012	88	12.63	Sept. 26, 2012	270	11.95
Apr. 11, 2012	102	13.42	Oct. 10, 2012	284	11.17
Apr. 25, 2012	116	14.15	Oct. 24, 2012	298	10.42
May 9, 2012	130	14.82	Nov. 7, 2012	312	9.72
May 23, 2012	144	15.37	Nov. 21, 2012	326	9.13
June 6, 2012	158	15.73	Dec. 5, 2012	340	8.72
June 20, 2012	172	15.88	Dec. 19, 2012	354	8.53

After this chapter you should be able to

1. state and apply the Law of Sines.
2. state and apply the Law of Cosines.
3. give the meaning of *trigonometric identity*.
4. prove trigonometric identities.
5. state and apply the sum identities and double-angle identities.
6. solve trigonometric equations.

11.1 Law of Sines

In this section you will see how trigonometry can be used to solve triangles that are not right triangles. If you know the measures of two angles and one side of a triangle, you can use the Law of Sines, which will be developed in this section, to solve the triangle. You will also learn a new way to find the area of a triangle.

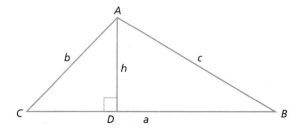

One way you can determine the area of △ABC is one-half the base times the altitude.

$$\text{Area } \triangle ABC = \tfrac{1}{2}ah$$

In △ADC, $\sin C = \frac{h}{b}$ and $h = b \sin C$.

Substituting for h in the area equation,

$$\text{Area } \triangle ABC = \tfrac{1}{2}ab \sin C.$$

Using this same procedure, you can show that

$$\text{Area } \triangle ABC = \tfrac{1}{2}ac \sin B \text{ and Area } \triangle ABC = \tfrac{1}{2}bc \sin A.$$

By the transitive property

$$\tfrac{1}{2}bc \sin A = \tfrac{1}{2}ac \sin B = \tfrac{1}{2}ab \sin C.$$

Dividing each expression by $\tfrac{1}{2}abc$, you obtain the Law of Sines.

$$\frac{\tfrac{1}{2}bc \sin A}{\tfrac{1}{2}abc} = \frac{\tfrac{1}{2}ac \sin B}{\tfrac{1}{2}abc} = \frac{\tfrac{1}{2}ab \sin C}{\tfrac{1}{2}abc}$$

$$\frac{\sin A}{a} = \frac{\sin B}{b} = \frac{\sin C}{c}$$

Law of Sines

For any $\triangle ABC$, $\dfrac{\sin A}{a} = \dfrac{\sin B}{b} = \dfrac{\sin C}{c}$.

EXAMPLE 1 Solve $\triangle ABC$. Round answers to the nearest tenth.

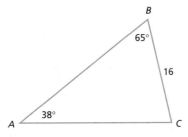

Answer

$A = 38°$	$a = 16$
$B = 65°$	$b =$
$C =$	$c =$

1. Determine which values are given and which values you need to find. (Abbreviate this situation SAA since the side is not between the two angles).

- -

$C = 180° - (38° + 65°)$
$C = 180° - 103°$
$C = 77°$

2. Find the measure of $\angle C$.

- -

$\dfrac{\sin A}{a} = \dfrac{\sin B}{b}$

$\dfrac{\sin 38°}{16} = \dfrac{\sin 65°}{b}$

$b \sin 38° = 16 \sin 65°$

$b = \dfrac{16 \sin 65°}{\sin 38°}$

$b \approx 23.6$

$\dfrac{\sin A}{a} = \dfrac{\sin C}{c}$

$\dfrac{\sin 38°}{16} = \dfrac{\sin 77°}{c}$

$c \sin 38° = 16 \sin 77°$

$c = \dfrac{16 \sin 77°}{\sin 38°}$

$c \approx 25.3$

3. Use the information that is given and the Law of Sines to find b and c.

The solution to $\triangle ABC$ is

$A = 38°$	$a = 16$
$B = 65°$	$b \approx 23.6$
$C = 77°$	$c \approx 25.3$

In Example 1, a side and two angles were known (SAA), but the sine law also applies in other cases. If two angles and the side between them are known (ASA), first find the third angle (since the sum of the angles of any triangle is 180°) and then follow Example 1. The following case where only one angle is known is a bit different.

EXAMPLE 2 Solve △*XYZ*.

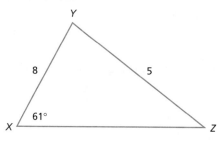

Answer

$X = 61°$	$x = 5$	1. Determine what you know and which values you need. (Do you see why this case is SSA?)
$Y =$	$y =$	
$Z =$	$z = 8$	

$$\frac{\sin X}{x} = \frac{\sin Z}{z}$$

2. Use the Law of Sines to find the angle measures.

$$\frac{\sin 61°}{5} = \frac{\sin Z}{8}$$

$$5 \sin Z = 8 \sin 61°$$

$$\sin Z = \frac{8 \sin 61°}{5}$$

$$\sin Z \approx 1.3994$$

3. You should recognize that a value greater than one for sin *Z* is impossible, but if you do not, your calculator will. The maximum value for the sine ratio is one.

Impossible
Therefore no solution
exists.

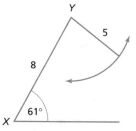

In Example 2, the side opposite the angle is too short to reach the third side. Despite this, knowing two sides and an angle opposite one of these sides (SSA) is not always impossible. Sometimes there is one solution, and at other times there may even be two solutions (when the side opposite the angle is shorter than the adjacent side). Because SSA does not always uniquely determine a triangle, it is called the *ambiguous case.* The Law of Sines will help you solve each situation, but remember to be very careful.

In Example 3 you will see a case that has two triangles as solutions. Study the diagrams and steps in solving it.

EXAMPLE 3   Solve △PRQ.

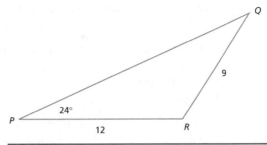

Answer

$P = 24°$	$p = 9$	1. What values are you looking
$Q =$	$q = 12$	for? This is also the SSA case.
$R =$	$r =$	

$$\frac{\sin P}{p} = \frac{\sin Q}{q}$$

2. Use the Laws of Sines to find the unknowns.

$$\frac{\sin 24°}{9} = \frac{\sin Q}{12}$$

$$9 \sin Q = 12 \sin 24°$$

$$\sin Q = \frac{12 \sin 24°}{9}$$

$$\sin Q \approx 0.5423$$

$Q \approx 32°50'$ or $147°10'$

3. Since sin Q is positive, $\angle Q$ can be in the first or second quadrant. Use a calculator to find the value in the first quadrant; the angle in the second quadrant is supplementary to it.

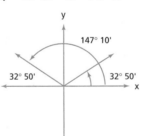

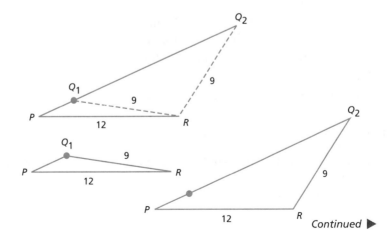

Continued ▶

The diagram illustrates the two possible measures of $\angle Q$.

Use the fact that the sum of the angles of a triangle is 180° and $P = 24°$ to find the two possible measures for $\angle R$.

If $Q = 32°50'$, then
$R = 123°10'$.
If $Q = 147°10'$, then
$R = 8°50'$.

4. Find the value of R in both cases.

5. Determine the two side lengths, r by using the Law of Sines.

Case 1

$\frac{\sin P}{p} = \frac{\sin R}{r}$

$\frac{\sin 24°}{9} = \frac{\sin 123°10'}{r}$

$r \sin 24° = 9 \sin 123°10'$

$r = \frac{9 \sin 123°10'}{\sin 24°}$

$r \approx 18.5$

Case 2

$\frac{\sin P}{p} = \frac{\sin R}{r}$

$\frac{\sin 24°}{9} = \frac{\sin 8°50'}{r}$

$r \sin 24° = 9 \sin 8°50'$

$r = \frac{9 \sin 8°50'}{\sin 24°}$

$r \approx 3.4$

6. Summarize the two solutions to this triangle.

Case 1

$P = 24°$	$p = 9$
$Q = 32°50'$	$q = 12$
$R = 123°10'$	$r = 18.5$

Case 2

$P = 24°$	$p = 9$
$Q = 147°10'$	$q = 12$
$R = 8°50'$	$r = 3.4$

▶ A. Exercises

For each set of values below, classify the data (SSS, SSA, SAA, SAS, ASA, AAA) and find the length or measure indicated.

1. If $A = 35°$, $B = 17°$, and $b = 5$, find a.
2. If $A = 35°$, $C = 17°$, and $b = 5$, find B.
3. If $A = 85°$, $a = 6$, and $b = 5$, find C.
4. If $B = 107°$, $C = 43°$, and $a = 9$, find A.
5. If $B = 82°$, $C = 57°$, and $a = 6$, find c.
6. If $A = 96°$, $a = 5$, and $c = 6$, find b.

▶ B. Exercises

Identify the number of triangles in each case below and find the measure(s) of angle B.

7. $C = 84°$, $b = 3$, $c = 6$.
8. $A = 4°$, $C = 73°$, $b = 2$.

9. $A = 38°, C = 65°, a = 7.$
10. $C = 46°, a = 5, c = 4.$
11. $A = 59°, a = 3, b = 5.$
12. $A = 23°, a = 2, b = 3.$

Solve $\triangle ABC$ in each problem. Identify any exercise that is SSA and give all solutions.

13. $A = 46°, B = 54°, a = 6$
14. $B = 16°, C = 83°, c = 18$
15. $A = 39°, C = 62°, a = 4$
16. $B = 45°, a = 6, b = 8$
17. $C = 38°, a = 12, c = 6$
18. $B = 92°, C = 12°, b = 4$
19. $A = 67°, a = 8, b = 6$
20. $A = 25°, a = 4, b = 5$

▶ **C. Exercises**

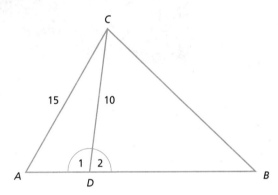

21. Find the ratio of the sin ∠2 to the sin ∠A. Are the measures of the angles in that same ratio? Why or why not?
22. Find the perimeter of trapezoid $ABCD$ if $\overline{AB}$ is perpendicular to the parallel sides $\overline{BC}$ and $\overline{AD}$ with $m\angle BAC = 25°$, $AB = 26$, and $CD = 31$.

▶ **Dominion Modeling**

23. Would a linear, exponential, or quadratic model be appropriate for the sunlight data?
24. Would a cubic model be appropriate?

25. Simplify $3(y^3 - 5y^2 + 3y - 4) - (2y^3 + 7 - 3y + y^2)$.
26. Factor $y^3 - 8y^2 + 12y$.

Solve.

27. $7x - 3 = 4(x + 2)$
28. $|3x - 2| = 7$
29. $5 - 3x < 9$

A rope just reaches from the top to the bottom of a well. The rope can be wrapped around the cylindrically shaped windlass fifteen times and the drum has a 4-inch radius. How deep is the well?

At what time after 11:00 will the minute hand and the hour hand form a straight angle on the face of a clock?

11.2 Law of Cosines

If you know two sides and an included angle or three sides of the triangle, you will not be able to solve the triangle by using the Law of Sines. But there is a method of solving these triangles called the Law of Cosines. We can develop this law by applying the Pythagorean theorem and some basic trigonometric concepts.

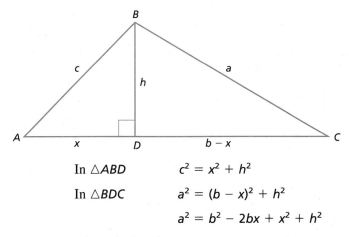

In $\triangle ABD$ $c^2 = x^2 + h^2$

In $\triangle BDC$ $a^2 = (b - x)^2 + h^2$

                        $a^2 = b^2 - 2bx + x^2 + h^2$

$\therefore$ by substitution,

                        $a^2 = b^2 - 2bx + c^2$

But in $\triangle ABD$, $\cos A = \frac{x}{c}$ and $x = c \cos A$

      Finally, $a^2 = b^2 + c^2 - 2bc \cos A$

By erecting a perpendicular from A to the opposite side and then from C to the opposite side, two other forms of the same law can be written for triangles.

Law of Cosines
For any $\triangle ABC$, the following equations are true:

$a^2 = b^2 + c^2 - 2bc \cos A$

$b^2 = a^2 + c^2 - 2ac \cos B$

$c^2 = a^2 + b^2 - 2ab \cos C$

EXAMPLE 1   Solve $\triangle XYZ$.

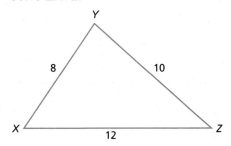

Continued ▶

Answer

$x^2 = y^2 + z^2 - 2yz \cos X$ $10^2 = 12^2 + 8^2 - 2(12)(8) \cos X$ $100 = 144 + 64 - 192 \cos X$ $100 = 208 - 192 \cos X$ $-108 = -192 \cos X$	1. Three sides are given (SSS), so use the Law of Cosines to find the angle measures.
$0.5625 \approx \cos X$ $X \approx 55°46'$	2. Find the measure of X by finding the angle having a cosine of 0.5625.
$z^2 = x^2 + y^2 - 2xy \cos Z$ $8^2 = 10^2 + 12^2 - 2(10)(12) \cos Z$ $64 = 100 + 144 - 240 \cos Z$ $64 = 244 - 240 \cos Z$ $-180 = -240 \cos Z$ $0.7500 \approx \cos Z$ $Z \approx 41°25'$	3. Use the Law of Cosines to find another angle measure.
$Y = 180° - (55°46' + 41°25')$ $Y = 180° - 97°11'$ $Y = 82°49'$	4. After you find two angles, you can easily determine the third angle by subtracting the sum of the known angles from 180°.

If you work a problem like this and the cosine of an angle is negative, it must be an angle in the second quadrant. Therefore the angle measure must be greater than 90°. Keep this in mind while working these problems.

EXAMPLE 2 Solve $\triangle ABC$ if $b = 4$, $c = 9$, $A = 27°$.

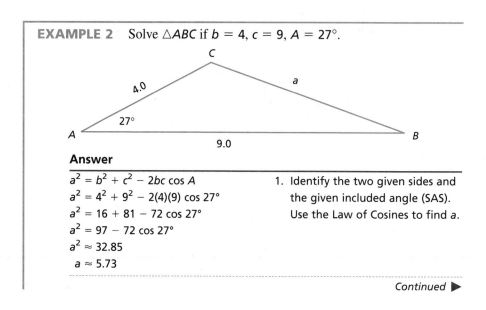

Answer

$a^2 = b^2 + c^2 - 2bc \cos A$ $a^2 = 4^2 + 9^2 - 2(4)(9) \cos 27°$ $a^2 = 16 + 81 - 72 \cos 27°$ $a^2 = 97 - 72 \cos 27°$ $a^2 \approx 32.85$ $a \approx 5.73$	1. Identify the two given sides and the given included angle (SAS). Use the Law of Cosines to find a.

Continued ▶

Method 1 using the Law of Sines.

$$\frac{5.73}{\sin 27°} = \frac{4}{\sin B}$$

$$\sin B = \frac{4 \sin 27°}{5.73}$$

$$\sin B \approx 0.3169$$
$$B \approx 18°29'$$

Method 2 using the Law of Cosines.

$$b^2 = a^2 + c^2 - 2ac \cos B$$
$$4^2 = (5.73)^2 + 9^2 - 2(5.73)(9) \cos B$$
$$16 = 32.83 + 81 - 103.14 \cos B$$
$$16 = 113.83 - 103.14 \cos B$$
$$-97.83 = -103.14 \cos B$$
$$\cos B \approx 0.9485$$
$$B \approx 18°28'$$

$$180° - (27° + 18°29') = C$$
$$180° - 45°29' = C$$
$$C = 134°31'$$

2. You now have two ways to find $\angle B$. Both methods are shown. Notice a 1' rounding difference in the value found for $\angle B$.

3. Determine C by subtracting the sum of A and B from 180°. The value of B is from Method 1.

► A. Exercises

Classify the given information for each triangle (SSS, SAS, SSA, ASA, SAA, AAA). Next identify which law (Law of Sines or Law of Cosines) would be used to solve the triangle.

1. $A = 12°, b = 5, c = 3$
2. $a = 54, B = 73°, C = 49°$
3. $a = 22, b = 29, c = 47$
4. $A = 9°, B = 12°, b = 8$
5. $A = 43°, a = 7, b = 9$
6. $a = 20, b = 11, C = 57°$

Find the indicated value using the Law of Cosines.

7. If $a = 4, b = 5$, and $c = 7$, find A.
8. If $a = 3, b = 9$, and $C = 10°$, find c.
9. If $a = 6, b = 13$, and $c = 8$, find B.
10. If $a = 4, B = 41°$, and $c = 5$, find A.
11. If $a = 7, b = 12$, and $c = 5$, find C.
12. If $a = 5, B = 127°$, and $c = 6$, find b.

Solve △ABC, using the given information.

13. $a = 4, b = 6, c = 9$
14. $a = 2, b = 7, c = 8$
15. $B = 82°, a = 3, c = 7$
16. $a = 7, b = 9, c = 11$
17. $A = 62°, B = 34°, b = 6$
18. $A = 52°, b = 3, c = 8$

▶ C. Exercises

19. Given △ABC with $C = 48°$, $a = 12$, and $b = 8$.
    a. Solve for c, rounding your answer first to the nearest tenth and then to the nearest hundredth.
    b. Use the Law of Sines with your first answer for c to find A.
    c. Use the Law of Sines with your second answer for c to find A.
    d. Use the Law of Cosines to find $\angle A$ using your first answer for c.
    e. Use the Law of Cosines to find $\angle A$ using your second answer for c.
    f. Find $\angle B$ using the two measures found in part *a*.
    g. Is $\angle A$ acute or obtuse? Why?
20. Given △ABC with $A = 60°$, $a = 9$, and $b = 7$, use the Law of Cosines to find c. Why is the Law of Sines easier?

▶ Dominion Modeling

21. Would a quartic model be helpful for the sunlight data? (*Hint:* A quartic function is a fourth-degree polynomial.)

Cumulative Review

Solve △ABC.

22. $A = 90°, b = 4, c = 7$
23. $A = 73°, B = 90°, a = 6$
24. $A = 39°, B = 51°, c = 5$
25. $a = 45, b = 51, c = 24$
26. Why can these be done without the Law of Sines or the Law of Cosines?

11.3 Problem Solving Using Trigonometry

Proverbs 2:2 says to "apply thine heart to understanding." Understanding is extremely important to God in all areas of your life. You should strive to understand everything that you study, whether biblical or academic, so you can apply your knowledge to all facets of your education and life. In particular, you need to understand the material you are studying in this class so that you can apply it to more advanced math classes, projects, or work situations you will face.

To estimate the height of Ribbon Falls in Arizona, Steve paced off 54 feet from the base and measured an inclination of 70 degrees. Use Steve's data to estimate the height.

To apply the Law of Sines or the Law of Cosines, first diagram the problem, label the appropriate parts of the triangles, and determine which law you should use. Then solve the problem and decide if the answer is reasonable.

EXAMPLE 1 Two jets take off from the same airport at the same time, and one travels at an average speed of **510** knots (nautical miles per hour) while the other travels **420** knots. The angle between their paths is **56°**. How far apart are the two jets after a half-hour?

Answer

---

1. ***Read.*** Diagram the problem.

Continued ▶

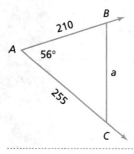

2. **Plan.** Label known values. After a half-hour the faster jet is 255 nautical miles from the airport and the other jet is 210 nautical miles from the airport. The distance between the two jets is *a*.

$a^2 = b^2 + c^2 - 2bc \cos A$
$a^2 = 255^2 + 210^2 - 2(255)(210) \cos 56$
$a^2 = 65{,}025 + 44{,}100 - 107{,}100 \cos 56$
$a^2 = 109{,}125 - 59{,}890$
$a^2 = 49{,}235$
$a \approx 222$

3. **Solve.** Use the Law of Cosines since you know two sides and an included angle (SAS).

The two jets are 222 nautical miles apart.

4. **Check.** Interpret in the context.

EXAMPLE 2   Two streets meet at a 72° angle in such a way as to form a triangular lot. One of the angles at the back of the lot measures 37°, and the road frontage opposite the 37° angle is 80 feet. What is the perimeter of the lot?

Answer

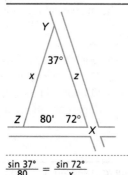

1. **Read.** What are you trying to find? Find the other two sides of the triangle to determine the perimeter of the lot.

2. **Plan.** Draw a picture for the problem.

$\dfrac{\sin 37°}{80} = \dfrac{\sin 72°}{x}$

$x = \dfrac{80 \sin 72°}{\sin 37°}$

$x \approx 126.4$

$\angle Z = 180 - (37 + 72) = 71°$

$\dfrac{\sin 37°}{80} = \dfrac{\sin 71°}{z}$

$z = \dfrac{80 \sin 71°}{\sin 37°}$

$z \approx 125.7$

3. **Solve.** Use the Law of Sines to find the other two sides.

Continued ▶

$P = x + y + z$
$P \approx 126.4 + 80 + 125.7$
$P \approx 332.1$ ft.

4. **Check.** The context requires the perimeter. Find it by adding the lengths of the three sides together.

EXAMPLE 3 A surveyor needs the distance between points *B* and *C*, so he makes an offset to point *A* and records the distances and angles given from point *A*. How far is *B* from *C*?

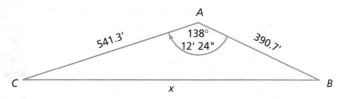

Answers $a^2 = b^2 + c^2 - 2bc \cos A$

$x^2 = (541.3)^2 + (390.7)^2 - 2(541.3)(390.7) \cos (138°12'24'')$

$x^2 = 761,000.3216$

$x \approx 872.4$ feet

▶ A. Exercises

1. What must be known to use the Law of Sines?
2. Why can ASA always be solved using the Law of Sines?
3. What must be known to use the Law of Cosines?
4. Which two cases require the Law of Sines? Why?
5. What case cannot be solved by either method? Why?
6. Which case can be solved by either method? Which is easier?
7. If the Law of Cosines is applied to a right triangle, what is the result?
8. If the Law of Sines is applied to a right triangle, what happens?
9. What methods should be used to solve right triangles?
10. In solving right triangles, why should the Law of Sines and Law of Cosines never be used?

▶ B. Exercises

11. Two sides of a triangular plot of land have side lengths 125 feet and 210 feet. The angle between these two sides measures 73°. What does the third side of the triangle measure?
12. How far apart are the legs of a 12-foot stepladder if the angle between the legs is 19°?

13. Two planes leave an airport at the same time and fly in paths that form an angle of 23°. One plane travels 168 mph, and the other flies 212 mph. How far apart are they after 2 hours?

14. A person observes a hot air balloon from the west with an angle of elevation of 62°, while a person from the east observes the balloon with an angle of elevation of 41°. If the two people are 350 feet apart, what is the air distance from the observer to the west to the hot air balloon? How high is the balloon?

15. There are two ranger stations in the forest, and they are 15 miles apart. A ranger can see the reservoir from each of the stations. If the angle between the line of sight to the reservoir and the line of sight to the other ranger station is 28° at one station and 65° at the other, how far is each ranger station from the reservoir?

16. An antenna is on top of a high building. A man observes the antenna from a point 412 feet away from the building. If the angle of elevation from the man to the top of the antenna is 63° and the angle of elevation of the base of the antenna is 59°, how tall is the antenna?

This view of the Diamond, a sheer face of Longs Peak in Colorado, is about a half-mile away and roughly level with the base. How high is the Diamond if the inclination to the top is about 21 degrees?

17. An airplane sights an airport runway at an angle of depression of 47°. After the plane flies 4 miles closer, the angle of depression from the plane to the runway is 62°. What is the air distance from the plane to the end of the runway at the second sighting?

18. The Milwaukee Road chugs due north from Chicago at 42 mph. The Rock Island line leaves Chicago an hour later traveling due west at 35 mph. How far apart are the trains after the first one travels three hours?

▶ C. Exercises

19. From the top of a building that is 32 meters high, a man looks down at a tree and finds that the angle of depression of the top of the tree is 34° and the angle of depression of the base of the tree is 59°. How tall is the tree?

20. Astronomers in Halifax and Victoria, 4000 miles apart, simultaneously measure the inclination of the sun at $89°59'55\frac{1}{2}''$. Give the approximate distance to the sun.

▶ Dominion Modeling

21. What characteristics of the sunlight data indicate that a sinusoidal model is appropriate?

22. Find a sinusoidal model for the sunlight data for day *d* and hours of sunlight *h*.

▮ Cumulative Review

Graph each relation. Identify the domain and range and decide whether the relation is a function.

23. $\{(3, 2), (-2, -6), (1, -5), (-2, 4)\}$
24. $y = \frac{4}{3}x - 1$
25. $f(x) = |x|$
26. $x = 2$
27. $y < -3x + 2$

11.4 Basic Identities

God is unchanging. Hebrews 13:8 states clearly that Jesus Christ is "the same yesterday, and to day, and for ever." Because God does not change, His Word also does not change; its promises hold true for all the ages—past, present, and future. The immutability of God and His Word is a comfort to the Christian but a threat of judgment to the unsaved. Are you comforted by the thought of our unchanging God?

An equation that is true for all values in the domain of the variable is an identity. An identity is an unchanging truth no matter what value the variable represents. For example, the statement

$$\cot \theta = \frac{1}{\tan \theta} \text{ (where } \tan \theta \neq 0)$$

is true for any value in the domain of the function. Use the trigonometric table to convince yourself that this statement is always true.

There are eight basic identities that you will use to prove other identities. In the last chapter three reciprocal ratios were defined. Since these definitions make up three of the eight basic identities, they are also called *reciprocal identities.*

$$\csc \theta = \frac{1}{\sin \theta}$$

$$\sec \theta = \frac{1}{\cos \theta}$$

$$\cot \theta = \frac{1}{\tan \theta}$$

Two more basic trigonometric identities are given here. These are the *quotient identities.* To derive these identities, you can again go back to the definitions of the three basic trigonometric ratios (see Section 10.1).

$$\tan \theta = \frac{\sin \theta}{\cos \theta}$$

$$\cot \theta = \frac{\cos \theta}{\sin \theta}$$

We now prove $\tan \theta = \frac{\sin \theta}{\cos \theta}$ by beginning with the statement $\frac{\sin \theta}{\cos \theta} = \frac{\sin \theta}{\cos \theta}$.

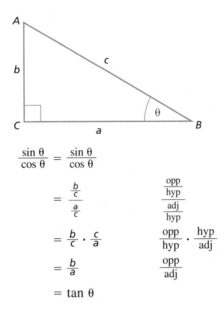

$$\frac{\sin \theta}{\cos \theta} = \frac{\sin \theta}{\cos \theta}$$

$$= \frac{\frac{b}{c}}{\frac{a}{c}} \qquad\qquad \frac{\frac{\text{opp}}{\text{hyp}}}{\frac{\text{adj}}{\text{hyp}}}$$

$$= \frac{b}{c} \cdot \frac{c}{a} \qquad\qquad \frac{\text{opp}}{\text{hyp}} \cdot \frac{\text{hyp}}{\text{adj}}$$

$$= \frac{b}{a} \qquad\qquad \frac{\text{opp}}{\text{adj}}$$

$$= \tan \theta$$

When proving a trigonometric identity, you must work with one side of the equation, making substitutions and simplifying it until you obtain the other side of the equation. You may not apply properties of equality to the original identity, because you do not know whether the original identity is true. Trying to prove a statement by starting with the unproven statement and applying properties to it results in circular reasoning.

The last three basic identities are developed with the use of the Pythagorean theorem and are called the *Pythagorean identities*. Before stating them, we will review some thoughts about the trigonometric ratios that we have examined. Consider right △*ABC*.

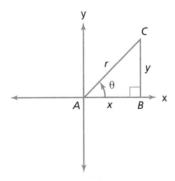

The trigonometric ratios can be stated as

$$\sin \theta = \frac{y}{r} \qquad\qquad \cos \theta = \frac{x}{r}$$

$$y = r \sin \theta \qquad\qquad x = r \cos \theta$$

Now consider the Pythagorean theorem and $\triangle ABC$.

$$y^2 + x^2 = r^2$$

$$(r \sin \theta)^2 + (r \cos \theta)^2 = r^2$$

$$r^2 \sin^2 \theta + r^2 \cos^2 \theta = r^2$$

$$\frac{r^2 \sin^2 \theta}{r^2} + \frac{r^2 \cos^2 \theta}{r^2} = \frac{r^2}{r^2}$$

$$\sin^2 \theta + \cos^2 \theta = 1$$

This is the basic Pythagorean identity. The other two Pythagorean identities can be developed from it. They are

$$1 + \cot^2 \theta = \csc^2 \theta$$

$$\tan^2 \theta + 1 = \sec^2 \theta$$

You can use these eight basic trigonometric identities to prove other identities.

Reciprocal Identities	$\csc A = \frac{1}{\sin A}$, $\sec A = \frac{1}{\cos A}$, $\cot A = \frac{1}{\tan A}$
Quotient Identities	$\tan \theta = \frac{\sin \theta}{\cos \theta}$, $\cot \theta = \frac{\cos \theta}{\sin \theta}$
Pythagorean Identities	$\sin^2 \theta + \cos^2 \theta = 1$ $1 + \cot^2 \theta = \csc^2 \theta$ $\tan^2 \theta + 1 = \sec^2 \theta$

▶ A. Exercises

Using the triangle shown, verify that the following basic identities are true.

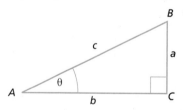

1. $\cot \theta = \frac{\cos \theta}{\sin \theta}$
2. $1 + \cot^2 \theta = \csc^2 \theta$
3. $\tan^2 \theta + 1 = \sec^2 \theta$

Write an expression equivalent to the given expression. Simplify as much as possible.

4. $\sin^2 \theta - 1$
5. $\sec^2 \theta - 1$
6. $1 - \csc^2 \theta$

7. $\cot \theta \tan \theta$
8. $\tan \theta \cos \theta$
9. $1 - \cos^2 \theta$

▶ B. Exercises

Show the steps to simplify the first expression to the second expression.

10. $\dfrac{\cos^2 \theta}{1 - \sin^2 \theta}$, 1

11. $\dfrac{\sec \theta}{\csc \theta}$, $\tan \theta$

12. $\dfrac{1 + \tan^2 \theta}{1 + \cot^2 \theta}$, $\tan^2 \theta$

13. $\sin \theta + \cos \theta \tan \theta$, $2 \sin \theta$

14. $\dfrac{\csc^2 \theta - \cot^2 \theta}{1 + \tan^2 \theta}$, $\cos^2 \theta$

▶ C. Exercises

15. Expand $(3 \cos^2 \theta + 2 \sec^2 \theta)^2$.
16. Factor $\cos^4 \theta - 1$.
17. Verify $\tan^2 \theta + 1 = \sec^2 \theta$ by dividing each term of $\sin^2 \theta + \cos^2 \theta = 1$ by $\cos^2 \theta$. When can you not perform this division? What is the value of $\tan \theta$ at these times?

▶ Dominion Modeling

18. On which day, according to the sunlight model, will there be the most hours of sunlight? What date is this?
19. When are the fewest hours of sunlight?

Cumulative Review

Solve.

20. $4x^2 - 6 = 5x$
21. $(x + 3)^2 = 7$
22. $x(x - 1) = 3x + 2$
23. $x^2 - 3x - 28 < 0$
24. The perimeter of a rectangular reflecting pool in a formal garden is going to be 288 feet. If the surface area of the water is to be 4895 ft.², give the dimensions.

BRITISH MATH

Cambridge and Oxford,
two of Europe's
oldest universities, have
been key centers for
mathematics.

The most significant British contribution to mathematics came through the genius of Isaac Newton. Newton was both a physicist and an accomplished mathematician who wrote about algebra, analysis by series, fluxions, and quadrature of curves. His theory of fluxions and quadrature of curves was actually calculus. The development of Newton's Law of Universal Gravitation, the expanding fields of mechanics, and the use of clock pendulums demanded a means of calculation that could deal with objects in motion. Newton recognized that an apple falling from a tree does not travel at the same speed all the time—distance, velocity, and acceleration are all functions of time. But to express these values at a given time required that changing magnitudes be dealt with by taking smaller differences between smaller and smaller intervals. Thus Newton developed the calculus of infinitesimals, which he called fluxions. (Today we use a simpler notation that was developed by the German Gottfried von Leibnitz.) This calculus applies to trigonometric functions and to other functions.

Another mathematician from the British Isles was Colin Maclaurin from Scotland. At the beginning of the nineteenth century, Colin—as an eleven-year-old boy—entered the University of Glasgow to study mathematics. Four years later he received his master's degree, and at the age of twenty-one he published his first important work

Oxford University, England, which dates from the 1100s (one of the five oldest European universities), produced several great mathematicians.

on geometry. Along with James Stirling and Brook Taylor, he made important contributions to the mathematics of infinite series, such as those known as power series. Examples of these follow.

$$e^x = 1 + x + \frac{x^2}{2!} + \frac{x^3}{3!} + \ldots \frac{x^n}{n!} + \ldots$$

$$\sin x = x - \frac{x^3}{3!} + \frac{x^5}{5!} - \frac{x^7}{7!} + \frac{x^9}{9!} - \ldots$$

$$\cos x = 1 - \frac{x^2}{2!} + \frac{x^4}{4!} - \frac{x^6}{6!} + \ldots$$

These series have become valuable calculating tools in the computer age. Using power series, many functions can be approximated to any desired accuracy.

Abraham DeMoivre, a French Huguenot, was educated in England after fleeing religious persecution in France in 1685. He is best known for DeMoivre's Theorem, a trigonometric identity involving complex numbers.

$$(\cos \theta + i \sin \theta)^n = \cos n\theta + i \sin n\theta$$

When John Napier began developing his logarithm tables, astronomer Henry Briggs championed their publication and acceptance, even assisting with computation. Making up the log tables was laborious, but once done, the effort it saved in subsequent calculations was tremendous. Imagine the multiplication task involved in finding a compound interest factor such as $(1.0025)^{15}$. Napier's original tables did not use base ten, but he and Briggs cooperated on a later work that gave the base ten logarithms of all numbers from 1 to 1000.

Cambridge and Oxford, two of Europe's oldest universities, have been key centers for mathematics. John Wallis first stated rules for negative exponents in 1656 at Oxford while Sir George Gabriel Stokes, who taught at Cambridge for over 50 years, made important contributions to the calculus of several variables. Arthur Cayley, who taught at Cambridge, and his friend James Joseph Sylvester, who taught at Oxford, also developed theories of matrices.

Hadrian's Wall in northern Britain has remained a landmark from ancient Roman times. Its history and location would have been familiar to the great British mathematicians.

Cambridge University in England (another of the five oldest universities in Europe) also produced some of the great mathematicians of history.

11.5 Strategies for Proving Identities

Using the eight basic trigonometric identities that you studied in the last section, you can prove other trigonometric identities. You must be certain to work on only one side of an identity. You *cannot* move things from one side of the equation to the other side, because then you would be assuming that the two sides are equal, which is what you are trying to prove. Start with a statement that the more complicated side is equal to itself (reflexive property) and simplify it.

EXAMPLE 1 Prove $\csc^2 x(1 - \cos^2 x) = 1$.

Answer

$\csc^2 x(1 - \cos^2 x) = \csc^2 x(1 - \cos^2 x)$ 1. Apply the reflexive property of equality to the left side.

$= \dfrac{1}{\sin^2 x}(1 - \cos^2 x)$ 2. Since $\csc x = \dfrac{1}{\sin x}$, $\csc^2 x = \dfrac{1}{\sin^2 x}$.

$= \dfrac{1}{\sin^2 x}(\sin^2 x)$ 3. Since $\cos^2 x + \sin^2 x = 1$, it follows that $1 - \cos^2 x = \sin^2 x$.

$= \dfrac{\sin^2 x}{\sin^2 x}$ 4. Simplify.

$= 1$

EXAMPLE 2 Prove $\cos x(\tan x - \cos x) = \sin^2 x + \sin x - 1$.

Answer

$\cos x(\tan x - \cos x) = \cos x(\tan x - \cos x)$ 1. Apply the reflexive property to the more complicated side.

$= \cos x \tan x - \cos^2 x$ 2. Use the distributive property.

$= \cos x \cdot \dfrac{\sin x}{\cos x} - (1 - \sin^2 x)$ 3. Substitute for $\tan x$ and for $\cos^2 x$ using basic identities.

Continued ▶

$$= \sin x - 1 + \sin^2 x$$
$$= \sin^2 x + \sin x - 1$$

4. Simplify and write the powers of sine in descending order.

Algebraic Strategies for Proving Identities

1. Identify the more complicated side of the identity and use it to state the reflexive property.
2. Simplify using algebra or previous identities. If you have difficulty, you may find that changing to basic ratios from the definitions will help. Some suggestions follow.
   a. Express every term using sines and cosines.
   b. Substitute $1 - \cos^2 x$ for $\sin^2 x$ or $\cos^2 x$ for $1 - \sin^2 x$.
   c. You may multiply using the distributive property or FOIL.
   d. You may factor monomial terms, the difference of squares, or trinomials.
   e. If $a = b$, then $a^2 = b^2$; for example, $\tan x = \frac{\sin x}{\cos x}$ implies $\tan^2 x = \frac{\sin^2 x}{\cos^2 x}$.
   f. If the identity contains more than one angle, for example, x and $2x$, use identities to replace one of them.
   g. You may replace 1 with an equivalent form such as $\frac{\cos^2 x}{\cos^2 x}$.
3. You are finished when you obtain the other side of the original equation.

If you have difficulty, you may want to work on both sides on scratch paper to see how the expressions relate, but be sure to write your final answer in the format shown. You cannot assume that the identity is true and work on both sides.

EXAMPLE 3 Prove $\csc x \cos^2 x + \sin x = \csc x$.

Answer

$\csc x \cos^2 x + \sin x = \csc x \cos^2 x + \sin x$

1. The left side is more complicated, so apply the reflexive property of equality to it.

$= \frac{1}{\sin x} \cdot \cos^2 x + \sin x$

$= \frac{\cos^2 x}{\sin x} + \sin x$

2. Use substitution to begin simplifying toward $\csc x$.

Continued ▶

$$= \frac{\cos^2 x}{\sin x} + \frac{\sin^2 x}{\sin x}$$

3. To perform the addition, a common denominator is required.

$$= \frac{\cos^2 x + \sin^2 x}{\sin x}$$

$$= \frac{1}{\sin x}$$

4. From the Pythagorean identity substitute 1 for $\cos^2 x + \sin^2 x$.

$$= \csc x$$

5. Use the reciprocal identity $\frac{1}{\sin x} = \csc x$.

▶ A. Exercises

Prove this identity in a two-column format by supplying the reason for each step.

$$\frac{\cos^2 x + \sin^2 x}{\sin x \cos x \tan x} = \csc^2 x$$

1. $\dfrac{\cos^2 x + \sin^2 x}{\sin x \cos x \tan x} = \dfrac{\cos^2 x + \sin^2 x}{\sin x \cos x \tan x}$

2. $ = \dfrac{1}{\sin x \cos x \tan x}$

3. $ = \dfrac{1}{\sin x \cos x \frac{\sin x}{\cos x}}$

4. $ = \dfrac{1}{\sin^2 x}$

5. $ = \csc^2 x$

6. The preceding identity is true because all the steps are equal. In particular the top left is equal to the bottom right. What property guarantees the equality of the first and last steps?

How would you begin the proof of each identity below? Give the first step only.

7. $\dfrac{\tan^2 \theta}{\sec \theta - 1} = 1 + \sec \theta$

8. $1 + \csc \theta \cos \theta \cot \theta = \csc^2 \theta$

▶ B. Exercises

Prove.

9. $\sin \theta = \csc \theta - \cos \theta \cot \theta$

10. $\sec \theta = \sin \theta \tan \theta + \sin \theta \cot \theta$

11. $\cos x - \sin x = \cos x \, (1 - \tan x)$

12. $\cot x \, (\tan x + \sec x) = 1 + \csc x$

13. $\tan x + \cot x = \dfrac{\sec^2 x}{\tan x}$

14. $3 \cos^2 \theta = 2 \cos^2 \theta - \sin^2 \theta + 1$

15. $\sec^2 x - 1 = \sec^2 x \sin^2 x$

16. $\cos x (\sec x + \tan x) - 1 = \sin x$

17. $(\csc x - \cot x)(\csc x + \cot x) = 1$

18. $1 + 2 \sin \theta \cos \theta = (\sin \theta + \cos \theta)^2$

19. $\sin^2 x (\sec^2 x + \csc^2 x) = \sec^2 x$

▶ C. Exercises

Prove.

20. $\dfrac{\sin^2 x + 2 \sin x + 1}{\cos^2 x} = \dfrac{1 + \sin x}{1 - \sin x}$

21. $1 - \tan^2 x = (1 - 2 \sin^2 x)(1 + \tan^2 x)$

22. $\dfrac{\cos^2 x - \sin^2 x}{\tan^2 x} = \cot^2 x \cos^2 x - \cos^2 x$

▶ Dominion Modeling

23. In the Quebec data, what is the amplitude of the sinusoidal model, and what does this mean physically? Give units for your answers.

▪ Cumulative Review

Graph each relation. Give the domain and range and decide whether it is a function.

24. $y = 2(x - 1)^2 + 3$

25. $f(x) = x^3 - 7x + 6$

26. $y \geq x^2 + 4x - 1$

27. Use the Remainder Theorem to identify at least one zero of $f(x) = x^4 + 2x^3 - 4x^2 - 5x - 6$.

28. Use the Factor Theorem to find a polynomial with integer coefficients and zeros at $\frac{2}{3}$ and -4.

11.6 Techniques for Proving Identities

The unit circle can be used to develop some additional identities. Study the unit circle shown.

The coordinates of *B* in usual terms are (x, y). Since the radius of this circle is 1 and $\cos \alpha = \frac{x}{1}$, $x = \cos \alpha$. Likewise $\sin \alpha = \frac{y}{1}$, so $y = \sin \alpha$. Therefore the coordinates of *B* are $(\cos \alpha, \sin \alpha)$.

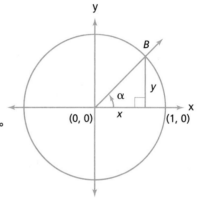

In the identities that you will study in this lesson, two angles are involved instead of one. Notice that $15° = (45° - 30°)$. Both 45° and 30° are commonly used angles, and you already know how to find the exact value of their sines and cosines. From this knowledge and the identities that you will learn in this lesson, you will be able to find exact sines and cosines for several other angles.

The unit circle below shows two angles α and β, both in standard position. Point *U* is on the terminal side of angle α and has coordinates $(\cos \alpha, \sin \alpha)$. Likewise, *V* is on the terminal side of angle β and has coordinates $(\cos \beta, \sin \beta)$.

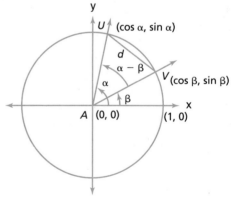

Using these new coordinates and the distance formula, the distance *d* between points *U* and *V* can be found.

$$d = \sqrt{(\cos \alpha - \cos \beta)^2 + (\sin \alpha - \sin \beta)^2}$$
$$d^2 = (\cos \alpha - \cos \beta)^2 + (\sin \alpha - \sin \beta)^2$$
$$d^2 = \cos^2 \alpha - 2 \cos \alpha \cos \beta + \cos^2 \beta + \sin^2 \alpha - 2 \sin \alpha \sin \beta + \sin^2 \beta$$
$$d^2 = \cos^2 \alpha + \sin^2 \alpha + \cos^2 \beta + \sin^2 \beta - 2 \cos \alpha \cos \beta - 2 \sin \alpha \sin \beta$$
$$d^2 = 1 + 1 - 2 \cos \alpha \cos \beta - 2 \sin \alpha \sin \beta$$
$$d^2 = 2 - 2 \cos \alpha \cos \beta - 2 \sin \alpha \sin \beta$$

Now we apply the law of cosines to the same figure to find *UV*. Recall that $AU = AV = 1$.

$$d^2 = (AU)^2 + (AV)^2 - 2(AU)(AV) \cos (\alpha - \beta)$$
$$d^2 = 1 + 1 - 2 \cos (\alpha - \beta)$$
$$d^2 = 2 - 2 \cos (\alpha - \beta)$$

By the transitive property, the two quantities for d^2 are equal.

$$2 - 2 \cos(\alpha - \beta) = 2 - 2 \cos \alpha \cos \beta - 2 \sin \alpha \sin \beta$$
$$-2 \cos(\alpha - \beta) = -2 \cos \alpha \cos \beta - 2 \sin \alpha \sin \beta$$
$$\cos(\alpha - \beta) = \cos \alpha \cos \beta + \sin \alpha \sin \beta$$

The identity for the cosine of a sum of two angles can be developed from the difference identity as follows by rewriting the sum as a difference. Simplification, however, requires you to recognize what happens to trig functions when angles are moved between quadrants. In Section 10.5 (exercises 25-28), you discovered that $\cos (-B) = \cos B$ and $\sin (-B) = -\sin B$.

$$\cos (\alpha + \beta) = \cos [\alpha - (-\beta)]$$
$$\cos (\alpha + \beta) = \cos \alpha \cos(-\beta) + \sin \alpha \sin (-\beta)$$
$$\cos (\alpha + \beta) = \cos \alpha \cos \beta - \sin \alpha \sin \beta$$

The sum and difference identities for the sine function can be developed from the cosine of a difference and from $\cos \left(\frac{\pi}{2} - \alpha\right) = \sin \alpha$. Recall that in a right triangle the sine of one acute angle equals the cosine of the other acute angle and the angles are complementary. (Their sum is $\frac{\pi}{2}$.) From this, we use $\cos \left[\frac{\pi}{2} - (\alpha - \beta)\right] = \sin (\alpha - \beta)$ to develop the sine of a difference. All four are summarized here.

Sum and Difference Identities

$$\cos (\alpha + \beta) = \cos \alpha \cos \beta - \sin \alpha \sin \beta$$
$$\cos (\alpha - \beta) = \cos \alpha \cos \beta + \sin \alpha \sin \beta$$
$$\sin (\alpha + \beta) = \sin \alpha \cos \beta + \cos \alpha \sin \beta$$
$$\sin (\alpha - \beta) = \sin \alpha \cos \beta - \cos \alpha \sin \beta$$

Learn to use these identities to find sines and cosines of angles.

EXAMPLE 1 Find cos 105° without using a table or calculator.

Answer $\cos 105° = \cos (60° + 45°)$

$$= \cos 60° \cos 45° - \sin 60° \sin 45°$$
$$= \frac{1}{2}\left(\frac{\sqrt{2}}{2}\right) - \frac{\sqrt{3}}{2}\left(\frac{\sqrt{2}}{2}\right)$$

$$= \frac{\sqrt{2}}{4} - \frac{\sqrt{6}}{4}$$

$$= \frac{\sqrt{2} - \sqrt{6}}{4}$$

Notice that cos 105° is negative since $\sqrt{2} < \sqrt{6}$. This is true since *x*, and therefore $\frac{x}{r}$, is negative in the second quadrant.

Since the sum and difference identities have been proved, they can be used to prove additional identities. For instance, the period identities describe the periods of the trigonometric functions, which you learned from their graphs in Chapter 10. The periods of sine and cosine are 360° or 2π radians. Adding 2π to an angle does not change its sine: $\sin(x + 2\pi) = \sin x$. You will prove this period identity in the exercises.

The double-angle identities can also be proved from the sum and difference identities. Study the proof of the double-angle identity for cosine.

$$\cos(\alpha + \beta) = \cos \alpha \cos \beta - \sin \alpha \sin \beta$$

Let $\alpha = \beta$, and substitute α for β in the identity.

$$\cos(\alpha + \alpha) = \cos \alpha \cos \alpha - \sin \alpha \sin \alpha$$
$$\cos 2\alpha = \cos^2\alpha - \sin^2\alpha$$

From the double-angle identity for cosine, two other forms that are often used follow. Their proofs are saved for the exercises.

$$\cos 2\alpha = 1 - 2 \sin^2 \alpha \quad \text{and} \quad \cos 2\alpha = 2 \cos^2 \alpha - 1$$

Likewise the double-angle identity for the sine function can be developed from the sum identity of the sine.

$$\sin (\alpha + \beta) = \sin \alpha \cos \beta + \cos \alpha \sin \beta$$

Let $\alpha = \beta$

$$\sin (\alpha + \alpha) = \sin \alpha \cos \alpha + \cos \alpha \sin \alpha$$
$$\sin 2\alpha = 2 \sin \alpha \cos \alpha$$

You can use these identities to find the sine or cosine of an angle that is twice the size of an angle with which you are familiar. Remember to use the properties and identities that you know.

EXAMPLE 2 Find sin 120° without using a table or calculator.

Continued ▶

Answer

$\sin 2\alpha = 2 \sin \alpha \cos \alpha$	1. Note that 120° is two times
$\sin 120° = \sin 2(60°) = 2 \sin 60° \cos 60°$	60°, which is an angle measure whose sine and cosine you already know.

$= 2\left(\dfrac{\sqrt{3}}{2}\right)\left(\dfrac{1}{2}\right)$	2. Use the double-angle formula for sine.
$\sin 120° = \dfrac{\sqrt{3}}{2}$	

The answer to Example 2 shows that this technique is consistent with the use of a reference angle to find this value. Besides using sum, difference, and double-angle identities, you may be able to prove an identity by factoring.

EXAMPLE 3 Prove $\cos^4 x + \cos^2 x \sin^2 x + \sin^2 x = 1$.

Answer

$$\cos^4 x + \cos^2 x \sin^2 x + \sin^2 x = \cos^4 x + \cos^2 x \sin^2 x + \sin^2 x$$

$$= \cos^2 x \left(\cos^2 x + \sin^2 x\right) + \sin^2 x$$

$$= \cos^2 x \,(1) + \sin^2 x$$

$$= \cos^2 x + \sin^2 x$$

$$= 1$$

Another useful technique is similar to that used in dividing complex numbers. Recall that a conjugate is used for this method.

EXAMPLE 4 Prove $\dfrac{\sin x}{1 - \cos x} = \dfrac{1 + \cos x}{\sin x}$

Answer

$\dfrac{\sin x}{1 - \cos x} = \dfrac{\sin x}{1 - \cos x}$	
$= \dfrac{\sin x}{1 - \cos x} \cdot \dfrac{1 + \cos x}{1 + \cos x}$	1. Use the "conjugate" to obtain the factored form of a difference of squares.
$= \dfrac{\sin x(1 + \cos x)}{1 - \cos^2 x}$	

$= \dfrac{\sin x(1 + \cos x)}{\sin^2 x}$	2. Simplify.
$= \dfrac{1 + \cos x}{\sin x}$	

▶ A. Exercises

If $\cos A = \frac{3}{5}$ and A is in the first quadrant, find the following.

1. $\sin A$
2. $\cos 2A$
3. $\sin 2A$

If $\sin B = 0.8192$ and B lies in the second quadrant, find the following by using $\sin^2 x + \cos^2 x = 1$.

4. $\cos B$
5. $\cos 2B$
6. $\sin 2B$

Without using a table or calculator, evaluate the following.

7. $\cos 75°$
8. $\sin 105°$
9. $\cos 195°$
10. $\sin 120°$

Use the diagram to find

11. $\sin (\alpha + \beta)$.
12. $\cos (\alpha + \beta)$.

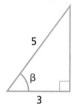

▶ B. Exercises

Prove the following identities.

13. $\cos 2\alpha = 1 - 2 \sin^2 \alpha$
14. $\cos 2\alpha = 2 \cos^2 \alpha - 1$
15. $\tan^2 \theta - \sin^2 \theta = \tan^2 \theta \sin^2 \theta$
16. $\dfrac{\cos^2 \beta}{1 + \sin \beta} = 1 - \sin \beta$
17. $\sin (x + 360°) = \sin x$
18. $\sin \theta \cos \theta - \sec \theta \sin \theta = -\sin^2 \theta \tan \theta$
19. $\sin 8x = 8 \cos 4x \cos 2x \cos x \sin x$
20. $\cos (90° - x) = \sin x$
21. $\cos (180° + x) = -\cos x$
22. $\cos 4x = \cos^4 x - 6 \cos^2 x \sin^2 x + \sin^4 x$
23. $\tan 2x = \dfrac{2 \tan x}{1 - \tan^2 x}$
24. $\cos^4 \theta + 2 \cos^2 \theta \sin^2 \theta + \sin^4 \theta = 1$
25. $\cos\left[\dfrac{\pi}{2} - (x - y)\right] = \sin (x - y)$

► C. Exercises

Prove the following identities.

26. $\dfrac{\tan x}{\sin x - \cos x} = \dfrac{\sin x(\tan x + 1)}{\cos 2x}$

27. $\dfrac{\sin(\alpha - \beta)}{\sin(\alpha + \beta)} = \dfrac{\tan \alpha - \tan \beta}{\tan \alpha + \tan \beta}$

28. Develop the formula for the tangent of the sum of angles in terms of the tangent of the separate angles α and β. $\left(Hint:\ \text{Use } \tan(\alpha + \beta) = \dfrac{\sin(\alpha + \beta)}{\cos(\alpha + \beta)}.\right)$

► Dominion Modeling

29. Reconsider the sunlight data for Quebec. What is the period of the sinusoidal model, and what does this mean physically? Give units for your answers.

■ Cumulative Review

Simplify.

30. $\left(2 - \sqrt{8}\right)\left(\sqrt{2} - 3\right)$

Solve.

31. $25^x = \dfrac{1}{125}$

32. $\sqrt{x + 12} = 3 + \sqrt{x}$

Graph.

33. $x - y < 2$
$x + 3y \geq 12$

34. $f(x) = \sqrt{x} - 1$

A^T

$r_1 - r_2$

$B = \begin{bmatrix} a & b & c \\ x & y & z \end{bmatrix}$

Z^T

$A = [x \ y \ z]$

$|A| = \det A = \begin{vmatrix} a & b \\ c & d \end{vmatrix}$

Square Matrices

The transpose of a matrix A^T is found by interchanging the rows and columns.

$$A = \begin{bmatrix} 2 & 7 & 3 \\ 1 & 5 & 6 \end{bmatrix} \qquad A^T = \begin{bmatrix} 2 & 1 \\ 7 & 5 \\ 3 & 6 \end{bmatrix}$$

Notice that the transpose operation reverses the dimensions of the original matrix. The dimensions of the transpose are the same as the original matrix if the original is a square matrix.

Three values are associated with square matrices—the determinant, the trace, and the characteristic values. The trace, tr(A), is the sum of the main diagonal elements. The characteristic values (or eigenvalues), λ, are the solutions of the determinant equation $|A - \lambda I| = 0$. (λ is a Greek letter called lambda.)

EXAMPLE For $A = \begin{bmatrix} 2 & 3 \\ 5 & 1 \end{bmatrix}$, find det($A$), tr($A$), and the eigenvalues.

Answer $\det(A) = \begin{vmatrix} 2 & 3 \\ 5 & 1 \end{vmatrix} = 2 - 15 = -13$

$$\text{tr}(A) = 2 + 1 = 3$$

$$|A - \lambda I| = \left| \begin{bmatrix} 2 & 3 \\ 5 & 1 \end{bmatrix} - \lambda \begin{bmatrix} 1 & 0 \\ 0 & 1 \end{bmatrix} \right| = \begin{vmatrix} 2 - \lambda & 3 \\ 5 & 1 - \lambda \end{vmatrix}$$

$$= (2 - \lambda)(1 - \lambda) - 15 = \lambda^2 - 3\lambda - 13$$

Thus, $|A - \lambda I| = 0$ when $\lambda^2 - 3\lambda - 13 = 0$

or when $\lambda = \dfrac{3 \pm \sqrt{61}}{2}$.

Notice that $|A - \lambda I|$ is a function, $f(\lambda) = \lambda^2 - 3\lambda - 13$, called the characteristic polynomial of the matrix. Other determinants, such as $\begin{vmatrix} \cos \theta & \sin \theta \\ 1 & \sec \theta \end{vmatrix} = 1 - \sin \theta$, can result in other types of functions. A Jacobian, named for Carl Jacobi, is a special determinant that requires knowledge of calculus.

$$(m \times n)(n \times p) \qquad [A : I]$$

$$C^T \qquad X = \frac{\det(A_i)}{\det(A)}$$

Finding these various functions and values associated with square matrices is a useful tool in behavioral research, in advanced business applications, and in engineering.

▶ **Exercises**

$$A = \begin{bmatrix} 5 & 4 \\ 7 & 2 \end{bmatrix} \qquad B = \begin{bmatrix} \cos\theta & -\sin\theta \\ \sin\theta & \cos\theta \end{bmatrix} \qquad C = \begin{bmatrix} \cos\theta & \sin\theta \\ \sin\theta & \cos\theta \end{bmatrix}$$

$$D = \begin{bmatrix} 1 & 2 & 0 \\ -3 & 5 & 6 \\ 4 & -1 & 2 \end{bmatrix} \qquad E = \begin{bmatrix} 3 & 7 \\ 0 & 5 \end{bmatrix}$$

Find and simplify.

1. $|B|$

2. $|C|$

3. $\mathrm{tr}(D)$

Find characteristic polynomials and characteristic values of each matrix.

4. A

5. E

11.7 Trigonometric Equations

Many people today speak the language of a Christian but do not actually know Jesus Christ as their personal Savior. A person must not only believe in his heart that Jesus Christ died on the cross but also trust in the Lord as his Savior. Romans 10:9-10 says, "If thou shalt confess with thy mouth the Lord Jesus, and shalt believe in thine heart that God hath raised him from the dead, thou shalt be saved. For with the heart man believeth unto righteousness; and with the mouth confession is made unto salvation." Do you truly understand salvation: do you believe and trust in Jesus Christ with your heart, or is it knowledge that you have learned without true heart understanding?

In the last two chapters you studied trigonometry, and you now have head knowledge of this branch of mathematics. This has been only an introduction to the subject. To gain a true understanding, you will have to study it further in future years; but this is an adequate foundation on which to build.

The last section of this chapter introduces you to the idea of trigonometric equations. Whereas trigonometric identities are true for all angle measures, a trigonometric equation is true for only certain angle measures. Since trigonometric functions are periodic, if an equation containing them has a solution, it will have an infinite number of solutions. Equations having solutions will have at least one and usually two or more solutions in each period. You will use your knowledge of trigonometric identities to help you solve some of these trigonometric equations.

EXAMPLE 1 Solve $\cos x = \frac{1}{2}$, where $0 \le x < 2\pi$.

Answer

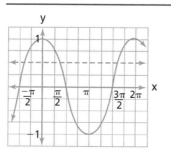

1. You must find all values of x between $0°$ and $360°$ that have a cosine of $\frac{1}{2}$.

2. Look at the graph of the cosine function. Where does $\cos x = \frac{1}{2}$?

3. Since $\cos \frac{\pi}{3} = \frac{1}{2}$ and $\cos \frac{5\pi}{3} = \frac{1}{2}$, $x = \frac{\pi}{3}$ and $\frac{5\pi}{3}$. Other values of x have a cosine of $\frac{1}{2}$, but these are the only two between 0 and 2π.

EXAMPLE 2   Solve $2 - 2\cos^2 \theta = 0$, where $0 \le \theta < 2\pi$.

Answer

$2 - 2\cos^2 \theta = 0$	1. Solve this equation for $\cos \theta$.
$-2\cos^2 \theta = -2$	
$\cos^2 \theta = 1$	
$\cos \theta = \pm 1$	2. What values of θ will make the cosine equal to ± 1?

$\cos \theta = 1$ when $\theta = 0$,
$\cos \theta = -1$ when $\theta = \pi$

Therefore the answers that satisfy $0 \le \theta < 2\pi$ are $\theta = 0, \pi$.

EXAMPLE 3   Solve $4 \sin x \cos x = \sqrt{3}$, where $0 \le x < 2\pi$.

Answer

$4 \sin x \cos x = \sqrt{3}$	1. Try to change the equation into a single function of x. Notice that this equation looks similar to one of the trigonometric identities that you studied in the last section.
$2(2 \sin x \cos x) = \sqrt{3}$	
$2(\sin 2x) = \sqrt{3}$	
$\sin 2x = \dfrac{\sqrt{3}}{2}$	
$2x \in \left\{ \dfrac{\pi}{3}, \dfrac{2\pi}{3}, \dfrac{7\pi}{3}, \dfrac{8\pi}{3} \right\}$	2. What angles make the sine function equal to $\dfrac{\sqrt{3}}{2}$? Since $0 \le x < 2\pi$, it follows that $0 \le 2x < 4\pi$. The quantity $2x$ is equal to values up to but not including 4π.
$x \in \left\{ \dfrac{\pi}{6}, \dfrac{\pi}{3}, \dfrac{7\pi}{6}, \dfrac{4\pi}{3} \right\}$	3. Solve by taking $\frac{1}{2}$ of each $2x$ angle measure.

You may have wondered why $\frac{7\pi}{3}$ and $\frac{8\pi}{3}$ were included in step 2 since they are greater than 2π. This requires planning ahead for step 3. Step 3 involves division by 2 and you will see that all four final answers are between 0 and 2π. Angles between 0 and 4π must be considered at step 2 to plan ahead for the division by 2. What range of angles should you consider to solve $\sin 5x = \frac{1}{2}$? Since x can be up to but not including 2π, $5x$ can be up to but not including 10π. There will be $2\left(\frac{10\pi}{2\pi}\right) = 10$ solutions.

▶ A. Exercises

Solve. Let $0 \leq x < 2\pi$.

1. $\sin x = -\frac{\sqrt{2}}{2}$

2. $\tan x - 1 = 0$

3. $\cos^2 x = \frac{1}{4}$

4. $\csc x = 2$

5. $4 \cos x = 2 \cos x + 2$

6. $2 \cos x - \sin 2x = 0$

7. $\sin^2 x + 1 = \cos^2 x$

8. $\tan^2 x = 1$

9. $\cos^2 x - 2 \sin x = 1$

10. $3 \sin^2 x = \cos^2 x$

Decide the range of values that must be considered to solve each trig equation below and state the number of solutions. Do not solve.

11. $\cos 2x = \frac{1}{3}$

12. $\sin 3x = -0.7$

13. $\cos 7x = \frac{5}{6}$

14. $\sec 5x = -3$

15. $\sin \frac{1}{2}x = 0.8480$

▶ B. Exercises

Solve. Let $0 \leq x < 2\pi$.

16. $\cos 2x = \frac{\sqrt{2}}{2}$

17. $\sin 4x = \frac{\sqrt{2}}{2}$

18. $4 \cos^2 x - 3 = 0$

19. $\cos x = 2 \sin^2 x - 1$

20. $2 \sin^2 2x - 1 = 0$

► C. Exercises

Solve. Let $0° \leq x < 360°$.

21. $\sin^2 x + 5 \sin x + 2 = 0$
22. $\cot^2 x - 4 = 2 \cot x$

► Dominion Modeling

23. What is Quebec's first day of the year 2012 with 15 hours of sunlight?
24. For how many days would Quebec have at least twelve hours of sunlight?

Cumulative Review

Use the following polynomial functions to identify the number of solutions to each equation. $P(x)$ has degree 2; $Q(x)$ has degree 1. Assume $A > 0$ and $B < 0$.

25. $\left| Q(x) \right| = A$
26. $P(x) = 0$ if the discriminant of $P(x)$ is also zero.
27. $\sqrt{P(x)} = B$
28. $P(x)\, Q(x) = 0$
29. $Q(x) = Q(x)$

Algebra and Scripture

Truth

Truth is an attribute of God. Name the member of the Trinity identified with truth in each passage.

1. John 14:17
2. John 14:6
3. Roman 3:4

Truth comes from God. According to each passage, where should we find truth on earth?

4. John 17:17
5. I Timothy 3:15
6. Ephesians 4:25

What do the following verses tell you about truth?

7. John 8:44
8. I John 2:21
9. Revelation 21:8

It should be clear to you that truth is important to God. Truth and error (lies) are contrary. A half-truth is still false. Math honors God because it presents the same view of truth that God does. Every statement is true or false, and we seek to distinguish true ones from false ones. The solution set distinguishes true equations from false ones. The solution set for $x^2 + 3x + 2 = 0$ is $\{-2, -1\}$. Every other value makes the sentence false, but these two values make it true.

10. How do you determine if a set is really a solution set?

What do these verses tell you about distinguishing truth and error?

11. John 8:31-32

12. Colossians 2:8

13. I John 4:1-6

14. Philippians 4:8

As you develop skills in evaluating the truth of an equation, and in proving identities you learn to test truth and to distinguish it from error.

15. What did the woman do that pleased Jesus (Mark 5:33)?

16. What should you seek wholeheartedly, sparing no expense (Prov. 23:23)?

You may be surprised that the Bible says this much about truth, but if you check "true" and "truth" in a concordance, you will see that the Bible says much more.

GREATER AMPLITUDE.
Find one other verse about truth that you think is important and explain why?

Memorize the classic verse on truth, John 14:6, to remind you that truths in math reflect their Creator.

Absolute Values

JESUS SAITH UNTO HIM, I am the way, the truth, and the life: no man cometh unto the Father, but by me.

JOHN 14:6

Chapter 11 Review

Find *x* in each diagram.

1.

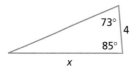

4.

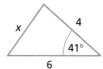

2.

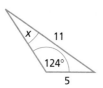

5.

3.

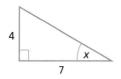

Solve △*ABC* in each problem. Express angles to the nearest minute and sides to the nearest tenth.

6. $A = 38°, B = 72°, b = 12$
7. $A = 78°, C = 46°, c = 3$
8. $a = 7, b = 5, c = 4$
9. $A = 56°, b = 8, c = 6$
10. $A = 52°, a = 3, b = 4$

Solve.

11. Mr. Davis wants to enclose a triangular field with a three-strand electric fence. From a recent survey of an adjacent field, he knows that the angle the field makes with the roadway is **112°** and that the footage along that side is **212** feet. If the frontage along the road is **156** feet, how much fencing does he need to enclose the field?

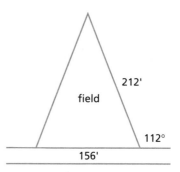

Prove.

12. $\cos^2 x + 2 \sin^2 x = 1 + \sin^2 x$
13. $\sec x \csc x = 2 \csc 2x$
14. $\cos^4 x - \sin^4 x = \cos 2x$
15. $2 \cos^2 x - 1 = 1 - 2 \sin^2 x$

Without using a table or calculator, evaluate the following.

16. $\sin 15°$ 17. $\cos 195°$

If $\sin A = \frac{4}{7}$ and A is in the first quadrant, find the following.

18. $\cos A$ 19. $\sin 2A$

Solve. Let $0 \le x < 2\pi$

20. $\sin^2 x = \sin x$
21. $\sin^2 x - \cos x - \cos^2 x = 1$
22. $\sqrt{3} \tan \theta = -1$
23. $\sec \alpha = 2$
24. $\cos 3x = \frac{-\sqrt{2}}{2}$

Supply reasons for the proof of the identity.

$$\sin^2 \theta + \cos^2 \theta = 1$$

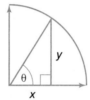

25. $x^2 + y^2 = 1^2$
26. $\cos^2 \theta + y^2 = 1$
27. $\cos^2 \theta + \sin^2 \theta = 1$
28. Evaluate the model for the sunlight data.
29. Give the mathematical significance of John 14:6.

12 Inverse Functions

$A = Pe^{rt}$

$(\cos t, \sin t)$

Following World War II, the United States was the undisputed economic power in the world. The Soviet Union posed military challenges, but not economic. When the Soviet Union fell in December 1991, the United States seemed to be the last superpower.

But as the Soviet Union unraveled, Western Europe united. In 1993 many European nations signed the Treaty on European Union to establish a common currency, the *euro*. Europe sought to join the exclusive club of economic powers.

One way to compare economic prosperity in the European Union (EU) and the USA is to compare compensation costs. The data below describe *compensation costs* (in U.S. dollars) for manufacturing workers, both in the European Union and in the United States. The overall costs of compensation (such as withholding taxes, employee education and other benefits, etc.) should parallel wages.

	EU	USA			EU	USA
1975	$5.03	$6.36		1994	$19.05	$16.87
1980	$9.83	$9.87		1995	$21.75	$17.19
1985	$7.85	$13.01		1996	$21.87	$17.70
1990	$17.09	$14.91		1997	$20.24	$18.24
1993	$18.14	$16.51				

After this chapter you should be able to

1. demonstrate an understanding of an inverse relation.
2. evaluate and graph inverse trigonometric functions.
3. convert between exponential and logarithmic notation.
4. state and apply the laws of logarithms.
5. distinguish common and natural logarithms.
6. apply logarithms to solve exponential equations.
7. use exponential equations and logarithms to solve problems.

12.1 Inverses

Before studying inverse relations and functions, you need to review the ideas of relation and function. In Chapter 2 you learned their definitions. Both a relation and a function are sets of ordered pairs.

This skyscraper reflects the Old City Hall in Toronto to form a graph of the building.

A relation is any set of ordered pairs. A function is a special relation in which the first element of each ordered pair corresponds to a unique second element. Therefore, of the relations below, only g is not a function (since both **8** and **4** correspond to **2**).

$$g = \{(1, 3), (2, 8), (-4, 7), (2, 4)\}$$

$$h = \{(a, b), (c, d), (l, m), (n, o)\}$$

$$k = \{(5, 7), (3, -8), (1, -4), (10, 2)\}$$

An *inverse relation* is a relation in which the first and second elements are switched. The inverse of relation g is $\{(3, 1), (8, 2), (7, -4), (4, 2)\}$. This inverse relation is a function. The notation used to indicate the inverse of g is g^{-1}. Do not confuse this with a negative exponent; it is simply the notation used to designate an inverse relation. This notation is used to indicate other inverses, such as 3^{-1}, which is $\frac{1}{3}$, since $\frac{1}{3}$ and **3** are multiplicative inverses. Likewise f^{-1} indicates the inverse of f with respect to composition.

In Chapter 3 you also learned about function notation. For example, $f(x) = 2x + 4$ is a rule for finding the range elements for a particular domain. Suppose $f(x) = 2x + 4$ and the domain $D = \{-3, 4, 8\}$, then $f(x) = \{(-3, -2), (4, 12), (8, 20)\}$. Switching the domain and range, $f^{-1}(x) = \{(-2, -3), (12, 4), (20, 8)\}$. Since f^{-1} was found by reversing the x-coordinates and y-coordinates of ordered pairs in f, the variables should be reversed in our original function. This will allow us to find the rule that will describe the inverse relation. Remember that the basic difference between a function and its inverse is that x and y are switched. See how this is applied to finding the inverse rule.

EXAMPLE 1   Find the rule that describes the inverse relation of
$f(x) = 2x + 4$.

Answer

$f(x)$	$= 2x + 4$	
y	$= 2x + 4$	1. Substitute y for $f(x)$.
x	$= 2y + 4$	2. Switch x and y, which gives the inverse, and solve for y.
$-2y$	$= -x + 4$	
y	$= \frac{1}{2}x - 2$	
$f^{-1}(x)$	$= \frac{1}{2}x - 2$	3. Use the inverse notation to describe the inverse relation since it is a function.

Now use the domain of f^{-1} which is $\{-2, 12, 20\}$ to verify that $f^{-1}(x) = \frac{1}{2}x - 2$ gives the range $\{-3, 4, 8\}$.

EXAMPLE 2   Find the rule that describes the inverse relation of
$g(x) = 3x^2 - 2$.

Answer

$g(x) = 3x^2 - 2$

$y = 3x^2 - 2$ 1. Substitute y for $g(x)$.

$x = 3y^2 - 2$ 2. Interchange x and y and solve for y.

$x + 2 = 3y^2$

$\frac{x + 2}{3} = y^2$

$y = \pm\sqrt{\frac{x + 2}{3}} \cdot \frac{\sqrt{3}}{\sqrt{3}} = \pm\frac{\sqrt{3x + 6}}{3}$

Notice that $g(x)$ is a function, but the inverse relation is not, since it would fail the vertical line test. If $x = 7$, $y = \pm\sqrt{3}$. Therefore $\left(7, \sqrt{3}\right)$ and $\left(7, -\sqrt{3}\right)$ are both in the relation.

▶ **A. Exercises**

1. Give an example of a relation that is not a function. Give the inverse of this relation.
2. Give an example of a function. Give the inverse of this function.
3. Give an example of a function whose inverse is not a function.

Given domain $D = \{-5, 3, 1, 7\}$, give the function in set form if the function has the following rule.

4. $f(x) = x - 4$
5. $g(x) = 2x + 6$
6. $h(x) = 3x - 8$
7. $l(x) = x^2 + 4$
8. Write the set of inverse ordered pairs for the functions in exercises 4-7.

▶ B. Exercises

Use the function rules in exercises 4-7 to find the following inverse rules.

9. $f^{-1}(x)$
10. $g^{-1}(x)$
11. $h^{-1}(x)$
12. $l^{-1}(x)$

In Section 3.6 you learned how to find the composition of functions. Review this material and then find the following using your answers to exercises 9 and 10.

13. $(f \circ f^{-1})(x)$
14. $(f^{-1} \circ f)(x)$
15. $(g \circ g^{-1})(x)$
16. $(g^{-1} \circ g)(x)$
17. From exercises 13-16, can you find a general rule about the composition of a function and its inverse?
18. Find $(f \circ g)(x)$ if $f(x) = x^2 - 3$ and $g(x) = x$.
19. What function is the identity function for composition?

▶ C. Exercises

20. Compare the inverse property for composition of functions (exercise 17) to the inverse property for multiplication of real numbers. What is the role of the identity?
21. Graph $y = 2x + 1$, find the function rule for its inverse and graph it on the same coordinate system. Graph $y = x$ on the same system. What conclusion can you draw?

▶ Dominion Modeling

22. Give a scatterplot for the wage data. Use the EU values for the horizontal axis (input) and the USA values for the vertical (output).

Simplify.

23. $\dfrac{10x^3y}{14xy^4}$

24. $\dfrac{x^4 - 4x^3}{2x^2y - 8xy}$

25. $\dfrac{x^2 - 4x + 3}{x^2 + 4x - 5}$

26. $\dfrac{6x^3 - x^2 - 12x}{3x^3 - 17x^2 - 28x}$

27. $\dfrac{x^3 + 8}{x^2 + 4x + 4}$

12.2 Inverse Trigonometric Functions

Remember that an inverse relation is found when the *x* and *y* values are interchanged. To find inverse trigonometric functions, interchange the *x* and the *y* values. Consider the sine function.

$y = \sin x$

x	y
0	0
$\frac{\pi}{6}$	0.5000
$\frac{\pi}{4}$	0.7071
$\frac{\pi}{3}$	0.8660
$\frac{\pi}{2}$	1
$\frac{2\pi}{3}$	0.8660
$\frac{3\pi}{4}$	0.7071
$\frac{5\pi}{6}$	0.5000
π	0

x	y
$\frac{7\pi}{6}$	-0.5000
$\frac{5\pi}{4}$	-0.7071
$\frac{4\pi}{3}$	-0.8660
$\frac{3\pi}{2}$	-1
$\frac{5\pi}{3}$	-0.8660
$\frac{7\pi}{4}$	-0.7071
$\frac{11\pi}{6}$	-0.5000
2π	0

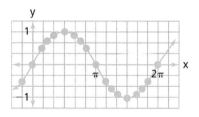

Now interchange the *x* and *y* coordinates and graph the new ordered pairs.

x	y
0	0
0.5000	$\frac{\pi}{6}$
0.7071	$\frac{\pi}{4}$
0.8660	$\frac{\pi}{3}$
1	$\frac{\pi}{2}$
0.8660	$\frac{2\pi}{3}$
0.7071	$\frac{3\pi}{4}$
0.5000	$\frac{5\pi}{6}$
0	π

x	y
−0.5000	$\frac{7\pi}{6}$
−0.7071	$\frac{5\pi}{4}$
−0.8660	$\frac{4\pi}{3}$
−1	$\frac{3\pi}{2}$
−0.8660	$\frac{5\pi}{3}$
−0.7071	$\frac{7\pi}{4}$
−0.5000	$\frac{11\pi}{6}$
0	2π

The graph of these ordered pairs is shown.

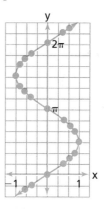

This is the inverse trigonometric relation for the sine function. Notice that it is not a function. The inverse relation is denoted by $y = \sin^{-1} x$, read *y* equals the inverse sine of *x*. Another notation for this inverse relation is $y = \arcsin x$. If you are asked to find $\sin^{-1} \frac{1}{2}$, you are looking for all angle measures whose sine is $\frac{1}{2}$. Therefore $\sin^{-1} \frac{1}{2} = \frac{\pi}{6}, \frac{5\pi}{6}, \frac{13\pi}{6}, \ldots$. There are an infinite number of answers (also negative angles), which means the graph shown is not a function. In order to have a function, we restrict the domain on $y = \sin x$. To do this, take the domain $\frac{-\pi}{2} \le x \le \frac{\pi}{2}$. For the inverse of $y = \sin x$ with this restricted domain, the range of $y = \sin^{-1} x$ is $-\frac{\pi}{2} \le y \le \frac{\pi}{2}$. Of all the solutions for the relation, only $\frac{\pi}{6}$ is in the range.

This value is called the *principal value* of the inverse sine. If the principal value is required as the solution, the notation has a capital letter for the first letter of the word. Calculators are programmed to give the principal value of trig functions when $\sin^{-1}$, $\cos^{-1}$, or $\tan^{-1}$ are used.

$$\text{Sin}^{-1} \frac{1}{2} = \frac{\pi}{6} \text{ or Arcsin } \frac{1}{2} = \frac{\pi}{6}$$

The following is a graph of the *inverse sine function*.

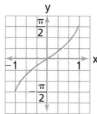

The cosine and the tangent functions also have inverses requiring restricted domains. These will be developed in the exercises. The graphs of the inverse cosine and inverse tangent functions are shown here.

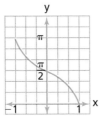 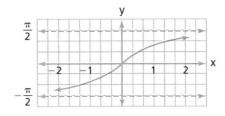

Notice that the values of $y = \text{Cos}^{-1}x$ are in the range $0 \leq y \leq \pi$, which is different from the range for the inverse sine function. The range for $y = \text{Tan}^{-1}x$ is $\frac{-\pi}{2} < y < \frac{\pi}{2}$ just as it was for the inverse sine function except for the end points. Study the graph of $y = \tan x$ to see why the equality is missing on this interval.

EXAMPLE 1   Find $\text{Tan}^{-1} 1$.

Answer $\text{Tan}^{-1} 1$ You are to find the principal value that makes the tangent function equal to 1.

Since $\tan \frac{\pi}{4} = 1$ and $\frac{-\pi}{2} < \frac{\pi}{4} < \frac{\pi}{2}$, $\text{Tan}^{-1}1 = \frac{\pi}{4}$

EXAMPLE 2   Find $\text{Cos}^{-1} 0.9272$. Give the answer in radians and degrees.

Answer   Find $\text{Cos}^{-1} 0.9272$

$\text{Cos}^{-1} 0.9272 = 22°$ Find the angle whose cosine is 0.9272. If using a calculator, be sure it is set for the correct type of angle measure.

or $\text{Cos}^{-1} 0.9272 = 0.3839$ rad

▶ A. Exercises

1. Make a table of ordered pairs and draw a graph of the cosine function.
2. Make a table of ordered pairs and draw a graph of the tangent function.
3. From the table in exercise 1 make a table of ordered pairs for the inverse cosine relation. Graph this inverse relation.
4. From the table in exercise 2 make a table of ordered pairs for the inverse tangent relation. Graph this inverse relation.

5. Use the principal values of the inverse cosine relation, $0 \le y \le \pi$, to make a table of ordered pairs for the function $y = \text{Cos}^{-1}x$.
6. Use the principal values of the inverse tangent relation, $-\frac{\pi}{2} < y < \frac{\pi}{2}$, to make a table of ordered pairs for the function $y = \text{Tan}^{-1}x$.

Give all values between 0 and 2π.

7. $\sin^{-1} \frac{\sqrt{2}}{2}$

8. $\tan^{-1} \sqrt{3}$

9. $\cos^{-1} -\frac{\sqrt{2}}{2}$

10. $\sin^{-1} \frac{-1}{2}$

▶ B. Exercises

Give exact angle measures by using reference angles in the principal range.

11. $\text{Sin}^{-1} \frac{\sqrt{2}}{2}$

12. $\text{Cos}^{-1} \frac{\sqrt{3}}{2}$

13. $\text{Sin}^{-1} -\frac{\sqrt{3}}{2}$

14. $\text{Tan}^{-1} \sqrt{3}$

15. $\text{Tan}^{-1} -1$

16. $\text{Cos}^{-1} \frac{1}{2}$

Use a calculator to find the angle in radians.
17. $\text{Tan}^{-1} 0.1944$
18. $\text{Cos}^{-1} 0.4226$
19. $\text{Sin}^{-1} 0.7660$
20. $\text{Cot}^{-1} -3.450$

▶ C. Exercises

21. Consider the relation $y = \sec^{-1} x$.
    a. Explain how you would find the values for which it is undefined and find them.
    b. Using your answer to a, explain why $y = \cos x$ is never undefined.
22. Find $\sin \text{Sec}^{-1} 1.5$.

▶ Dominion Modeling

23. Find and evaluate a linear model for the wage data.
24. According to a linear model, if EU compensation increased by an American dollar, how much would USA compensation increase?

▪ Cumulative Review

Simplify.

25. $4^{20} - 8^{12}$
26. $3^{12}(3^5)^3$
27. $\dfrac{9^5 \cdot 5^{11}}{3^{12} \cdot 25^4}$
28. Graph $y = 4^x$.
29. Solve $8^x = 32$.

12 Matrix Algebra

Matrix Inverses

Earlier you learned how to do inverses of 2×2 matrices. You may have wondered how to invert larger matrices, but at the time you did not know row-reduction, which is useful for this purpose.

To invert matrix $A = \begin{bmatrix} 1 & 2 & 6 \\ 0 & 1 & 3 \\ 3 & 4 & 2 \end{bmatrix}$, form the matrix with A and I side by side.

This is called an *augmented matrix* and you may use a segment between A and I as shown. $[A \,|\, I]$

$$\left[\begin{array}{ccc|ccc} 1 & 2 & 6 & 1 & 0 & 0 \\ 0 & 1 & 3 & 0 & 1 & 0 \\ 3 & 4 & 2 & 0 & 0 & 1 \end{array}\right]$$

By row reducing the left side to I, you will obtain A^{-1} on the right.

$$\left[\begin{array}{ccc|ccc} 1 & 2 & 6 & 1 & 0 & 0 \\ 0 & 1 & 3 & 0 & 1 & 0 \\ 3 & 4 & 2 & 0 & 0 & 1 \end{array}\right] \xrightarrow{-3r_1 + r_3} \left[\begin{array}{ccc|ccc} 1 & 2 & 6 & 1 & 0 & 0 \\ 0 & 1 & 3 & 0 & 1 & 0 \\ 0 & -2 & -16 & -3 & 0 & 1 \end{array}\right]$$

$$\xrightarrow{-2r_2 + r_1} \left[\begin{array}{ccc|ccc} 1 & 0 & 0 & 1 & -2 & 0 \\ 0 & 1 & 3 & 0 & 1 & 0 \\ 0 & -2 & -16 & -3 & 0 & 1 \end{array}\right]$$

$$\xrightarrow{2r_2 + r_3} \left[\begin{array}{ccc|ccc} 1 & 0 & 0 & 1 & -2 & 0 \\ 0 & 1 & 3 & 0 & 1 & 0 \\ 0 & 0 & -10 & -3 & 2 & 1 \end{array}\right]$$

$$\xrightarrow{-\frac{1}{10}r_3} \left[\begin{array}{ccc|ccc} 1 & 0 & 0 & 1 & -2 & 0 \\ 0 & 1 & 3 & 0 & 1 & 0 \\ 0 & 0 & 1 & \frac{3}{10} & \frac{-1}{5} & \frac{-1}{10} \end{array}\right]$$

$$\xrightarrow{-3r_3 + r_2} \left[\begin{array}{ccc|ccc} 1 & 0 & 0 & 1 & -2 & 0 \\ 0 & 1 & 0 & \frac{-9}{10} & \frac{8}{5} & \frac{3}{10} \\ 0 & 0 & 1 & \frac{3}{10} & \frac{-1}{5} & \frac{-1}{10} \end{array}\right]$$

$$A^{-1} = \begin{bmatrix} 1 & -2 & 0 \\ -\dfrac{9}{10} & \dfrac{8}{5} & \dfrac{3}{10} \\ \dfrac{3}{10} & \dfrac{-1}{5} & \dfrac{-1}{10} \end{bmatrix}$$

▶ Exercises

1. Multiply $A^{-1} \cdot A$ above, to verify that A^{-1} is the inverse of A.

2. Use A^{-1} from the example to solve $\begin{bmatrix} 1 & 2 & 6 \\ 0 & 1 & 3 \\ 3 & 4 & 2 \end{bmatrix} \begin{bmatrix} x \\ y \\ z \end{bmatrix} = \begin{bmatrix} 20 \\ 5 \\ 10 \end{bmatrix}$.

3. Give the augmented matrix for $\begin{bmatrix} 3 & 2 \\ 1 & 5 \end{bmatrix}$.

Use row reduction to find each inverse.

4. $\begin{bmatrix} 2 & 5 \\ 4 & 9 \end{bmatrix}$

5. $\begin{bmatrix} 1 & 4 & 3 \\ 0 & 2 & 1 \\ 0 & 0 & 4 \end{bmatrix}$

12.3 Logarithm Functions

Let us again consider the exponential function $y = a^x$. Review the table of ordered pairs shown here for the particular exponential function $y = 2^x$.

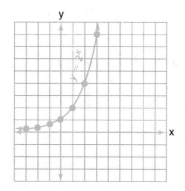

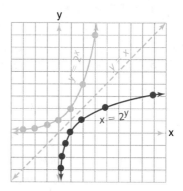

$y = 2^x$

x	y
0	1
1	2
2	4
3	8
−1	$\frac{1}{2}$
−2	$\frac{1}{4}$
−3	$\frac{1}{8}$

Consider the inverse relation of this exponential function. The ordered pairs are $\left\{(1, 0), (2, 1), (4, 2), (8, 3), \left(\frac{1}{2}, -1\right), \left(\frac{1}{4}, -2\right), \left(\frac{1}{8}, -3\right)\right\}$. To find the rule or equation for the inverse relation, recall that the procedure is to interchange x and y and solve for y.

$$y = 2^x$$

$$x = 2^y$$

As we showed in the graph, the two curves are reflections in the line $y = x$.

At this point there is no way to solve this equation for y. A definition is needed to express the inverse relation for an exponential function.

Definition

Logarithmic function   the function denoted by $y = \log_a x$, where $a \neq 1$, $a > 0$, and $x > 0$, is the inverse of the exponential function $y = a^x$.

The notation $y = \log_a x$ is read "y equals the logarithm of x in base a." There is a log form and an exponential form of the logarithmic function. You need to be able to convert quickly between logarithms and exponentials. Both forms are shown for the graph above.

Exponential Form	*Logarithmic form*
$x = 2^y$	$y = \log_2 x$

You can see from the exponential form that y is the exponent. In the other form, y is the logarithm. This indicates that a **logarithm is an exponent**. Look at the parts of the logarithmic function notation carefully.

$$x = a^y \qquad\qquad y = \log_a x$$

x is the number.

a is the base.

y is the exponent.

EXAMPLE 1   Change $2^4 = 16$ to log form.

Answer   If $2^4 = 16$, then $\log_2 16 = 4$.

EXAMPLE 2   Change $\log_5 125 = 3$ to exponential form.

Answer   If $\log_5 125 = 3$, then $5^3 = 125$.

EXAMPLE 3 Find $\log_3 \frac{1}{81}$.

Answer

$\log_3 \frac{1}{81}$

$y = \log_3 \frac{1}{81}$	1. Let y equal the expression.
$3^y = \frac{1}{81}$	2. Change the log to exponential form.
$3^y = \frac{1}{3^4}$	3. Express 81 as a power of 3.
$3^y = 3^{-4}$	
$y = -4$	4. Since the bases are equal, the exponents are equal to each other.

Therefore $\log_3 \frac{1}{81} = -4$.

▶ A. Exercises

Change the following statements to log form.

1. $5^2 = 25$
2. $4^3 = 64$
3. $7^4 = 2401$
4. $2^6 = 64$
5. $3^{-2} = \frac{1}{9}$
6. $6^3 = 216$
7. $2^{-5} = \frac{1}{32}$
8. $8^4 = 4096$
9. $4^{-2} = \frac{1}{16}$
10. $3^{-5} = \frac{1}{243}$

Change the following statements to exponential form.

11. $\log_{0.1} 0.001 = 3$
12. $\log_3 81 = 4$
13. $\log_4 \frac{1}{64} = -3$
14. $\log_{10} 1000 = 3$
15. $\log_9 6561 = 4$
16. $\log_3 \frac{1}{729} = -6$
17. $\log_{10} \frac{1}{10,000} = -4$
18. $\log_5 625 = 4$
19. $\log_{\frac{1}{4}} \frac{1}{64} = 3$
20. $\log_{\frac{1}{3}} 81 = -4$

▶ B. Exercises

Evaluate.

21. $\log_{10} 100{,}000$

22. $\log_8 4096$

23. $\log_3 \frac{1}{27}$

24. $\log_{10} 0.01$

25. $\log_2 256$

26. $\log_7 343$

27. $\log_3 \frac{1}{243}$

28. $\log_9 81$

▶ C. Exercises

29. Why is $\log_7 7^u = u$?
30. Why is $3^{\log_3 x} = x$?

▶ Dominion Modeling

31. A quadratic function fits the wage data quite well. How well does it fit? Why would some reject a quadratic model?
32. Sketch the graph of a function that *always* increases while the rate of increase slows down. What kind of function does this?

▮ Cumulative Review

Simplify.

33. $\dfrac{4x^3 y}{x - 1} \cdot \dfrac{x - 1}{2xy}$

34. $\dfrac{x^3 y^5 z}{6xy^3 z^4} \div \dfrac{10x^2 y^4 z^2}{9x^4 yz}$

35. $\dfrac{x^2 - y^2}{3x + 3y - 9} \div \dfrac{3x^2 + 9xy - 12y^2}{x^2 + 2xy + y^2 - 9}$

36. $\dfrac{x^2 - 25}{2x^2 + 5x} \cdot \dfrac{2x^2 + 11x + 15}{x^2 - 2x - 15}$

12.4 Laws of Logarithms

A law is a rule established by authority. The supreme authority—God—establishes the law of the Bible. The law was established to be our schoolmaster according to Galatians 3:24; "Wherefore the law was our schoolmaster to bring us unto Christ, that we might be justified by faith." The law shows us our sinful condition in the eyes of God and our need of salvation through Jesus Christ.

Likewise there are laws that show the correct use of logarithms in mathematics. Three logarithm laws stem directly from the exponent laws. (Remember that a logarithm is an exponent.) The first law is the *product law of logarithms*. Recall that according to the exponent law for products, you find the product of terms with like bases by adding the exponents.

	logarithm laws	corresponding exponent laws
product law	$\log_b(xy) = \log_b x + \log_b y$	$b^x(b^y) = b^{x+y}$
quotient law	$\log_b\left(\dfrac{x}{y}\right) = \log_b x - \log_b y$	$\dfrac{b^x}{b^y} = b^{x-y}$
power law	$\log_b x^a = a \log_b x$	$(b^x)^a = b^{ax}$

According to the product law, $\log_2(16 \cdot 32) = \log_2 16 + \log_2 32$. The following will verify this. Consider the left side. Let $x = \log_2(16 \cdot 32)$.

$$x = \log_2(16 \cdot 32)$$
$$x = \log_2\left(2^4 \cdot 2^5\right)$$
$$x = \log_2 2^{4+5}$$

$2^x = 2^{4+5}$ 	Change to exponential form by the definition of logarithms.

$x = 4 + 5$ 	Since the expressions have equal bases, the exponents
$x = 9$ 	must be equal.

Consider the right side of the equation. Let $y = \log_2 16 + \log_2 32$.

$$y = \log_2 16 + \log_2 32$$

$$y = \log_2 2^4 + \log_2 2^5$$

$$y = 4 + 5 \qquad \text{If } z = \log_2 2^4, \text{ then } 2^z = 2^4 \text{ and } z = 4.$$

$$y = 9 \qquad (\log_a a^b = b)$$

$\therefore$ by the transitive property, $\log_2 (16 \cdot 32) = \log_2 16 + \log_2 32$.

These laws can be used to solve equations involving logarithms.

EXAMPLE 1 Solve $\log_2 5 + \log_2 x = \log_2 20$.

Answer

$\log_2 5 + \log_2 x = \log_2 20$	
$\log_2 5x = \log_2 20$	1. Use the product law to combine the terms on the left into a single log.
$5x = 20$	2. When the logs of two quantities are equal, the quantities are equal.
$x = 4$	

Do you know why $5x$ can be set equal to 20? To solve for an unknown we must undo the operation being performed on the variable. The inverse of a logarithm of base 2 is the exponential function with a base of 2. Remember that if $x = y$, then $2^x = 2^y$. Therefore $2^{\log_2 5x} = 2^{\log_2 20}$. The exponential "undoes" the logarithm, and we are left with $5x = 20$.

EXAMPLE 2 Use $\log_3 4 = 1.262$ and $\log_3 5 = 1.465$ to find $\log_3 20$.

Answer

$\log_3 20 = \log_3 (4 \cdot 5)$	1. Express 20 in terms of given values.
$= \log_3 4 + \log_3 5$	2. Use the product law.
$= 1.262 + 1.465$	3. Substitute the given values.
$= 2.727$	

▶ A. Exercises

Use the laws of logarithms to express the following in equivalent terms.

1. $\log_5 ab$
2. $\log_3 b^4$
3. $\log_7 a^2 c$
4. $\log_2 \dfrac{a}{b}$
5. $\log_4 \dfrac{a^2}{c^3}$
6. $\log_b 3.17a^2$
7. $\log_6 \sqrt{a}$
8. $\log_5 \sqrt{a^2 b}$
9. $\log_{10} (5.7 \times 10^3)$
10. $\log_a \sqrt[3]{b^2}$

There are two other exponent properties that correspond to logarithm laws. Write each exponent property below as a law of logarithms.

11. $a^0 = 1$
12. $a^1 = a$

▶ B. Exercises

Use $\log_{10} 2 = 0.3010$ and $\log_{10} 5 = 0.6990$ to determine the logarithms of the following numbers. You may need the laws in exercises 11 and 12 for some of them.

13. $\log_{10} 10$
14. $\log_{10} 8$
15. $\log_{10} 25$
16. $\log_{10} 20$
17. $\log_{10} 50$
18. $\log_3 1$
19. $\log_{10} \dfrac{1}{2}$
20. $\log_{10} \sqrt{2}$

Solve.

21. $\log_4 x = \log_4 5$
22. $\log_8 2 + \log_8 x = \log_8 7$
23. $\log_5 x - \log_5 3 = \log_5 8$
24. $2 \log_2 x = \log_2 9$
25. $\log_3 x = 5(\log_3 4 + \log_3 2)$

► C. Exercises

26. For what range of values of x will we have $\log_{10} x < 0$?

27. Give the domain and range of $y = \log_{10} x$.

► Dominion Modeling

28. Find a logarithmic model for the wage data. (*Hint:* Let the European Union be the independent variable.)

29. What does a logarithmic model suggest that a linear model cannot?

■ Cumulative Review

Simplify.

30. $i^{43} - i^{22}$

31. $(2 - 3i)^3$

32. $(1 + 5i)^{-1}$

Solve.

33. $x^2 + 2 = 2x$

34. Find the sum by graphing the corresponding vectors. $(1 - 2i) + (3 + i)$

A devious blacksmith tells a man he will shoe his horse if he is paid 1¢ for the first nail, 2¢ for the second, 4¢ for the third, 8¢ for the fourth, etc. If the blacksmith must use twenty-eight nails, how much would it cost to shoe the horse, and what is the easiest way to find the answer?

JOHN NAPIER

John Napier was born at Merchiston Castle near Edinburgh, Scotland, in 1550. He was born into a young household, his father being only sixteen years of age. At the age of thirteen, he finished his home education and went to the University of St. Andrews. After spending time in Europe, Napier came back to Scotland, married in 1572, and settled down on an estate owned by his father. He performed agricultural experiments and invented a hydraulic screw designed to remove water from flooded coal pits. After seven years of marriage, his wife died. A few years later, however, he remarried.

Napier was a follower of John Knox and took his religion seriously. He was ardently anti-Catholic and in 1593 published *A Plaine Discovery of the Whole Revelation of Saint John,* which was an attack on the Church of Rome. It declared that the pope was Antichrist. Although radical, it was a popular seller and underwent twenty-one editions.

Napier is known for his imagination. One time he announced that his rooster could detect which servant or servants had been stealing from him. He sent his servants into a dark room, telling them to pat the rooster on the back. The superstitious thief, thinking to outwit Napier, did not pat the bird. Unknown to the servants, the bird's back had been coated with lampblack, and after seeing all the servants except one return with black hands, Napier knew he had found the culprit.

Napier put his imagination to work by designing war instruments. One weapon was a mirror that set ships on fire, and another was a metal chariot with small holes through which shots could be fired.

In the field of mathematics, Napier invented a device to aid in rapid multiplication. With this method an individual needed only to be skilled in addition. This device, known as "Napier's bones" or "Napier's rods," was made up of ten adjustable rods that were composed of wood, metal, bones, or cardboard. This invention was the forerunner of the slide rule. Each rod started with a number from 0 to 9, and beneath the number the multiples of the number were listed. Rod 5 listed the multiples 5, 10, 15, 20, and so on. When working with the problem 2635 × 357, a person would assemble rods 2, 6, 3 and 5 and would then examine rods 3, 5, and 7. Starting from the right side and the ones digit (7 in this example), he would add diagonally, getting 18445. He would then consider rows 5 and 3. Finally, he would arrange the products in the traditional manner and find their sum to obtain the answer.

Napier is best known for his discovery of logarithms, which decreased the computation necessary for many areas of mathematics. This discovery has saved multitudes of hours for mathematicians throughout the years. In 1614, after twenty years of work, Napier published a small book entitled *Mirifici Logarithmorum Canonis Descriptio*. Ninety pages of the book are filled with math tables. After the book's publication, Napier and Henry Briggs decided it would be best to have the tables of logarithms in base 10, which is the base of our number system. Today the new name of these tables is "Briggsian" logarithms. Napier died on April 4, 1617.

Napier is best known for his discovery of logarithms, which decreased the computation necessary for many areas of mathematics.

12.5 Natural and Common Logarithms

The word *natural* means "not acquired but inherited." The Bible speaks of the natural man. The natural man is man as he is when he comes into this world. He inherits a sinful nature and remains in that state until he is born again into the family of God through faith in the shed blood of Jesus Christ. The man who has not trusted Jesus Christ as Savior is a natural man forever. "But the natural man receiveth not the things of the Spirit of God: for they are foolishness unto him: neither can he know them, because they are spiritually discerned" (I Cor. 2:14).

A natural logarithm is a special logarithm whose base is the number e. The number e is an irrational number that is used frequently in the sciences and in business. You will learn the definition of this number in a more advanced math class. For now its approximate value is sufficient.

$$e \approx 2.7182818$$

The notation *ln* for a natural logarithm is used rather than $\log_e$. The log form and exponential form are illustrated by

$$\ln 8.57 \approx 2.1483 \text{ if and only if } e^{2.1483} \approx 8.57$$

In addition to natural logs, the other frequently used logarithm is base 10, because it is the base of our number system. When the subscript is not shown, as in the case of log 175, a base of 10 is understood.

Mathematicians have developed tables for both common logs and natural logs (see pp. 610-611).

EXAMPLE 1   Find ln 4.38 and log 4.38 and change to exponential form.

Answer $\ln 4.38 \approx 1.4770$ $\log 4.38 \approx 0.6415$

$\quad\quad\quad\quad e^{1.4770} \approx 4.38$ $10^{0.6415} \approx 4.38$

> **EXAMPLE 2**   Find $\ln e^3$.
>
> **Answer** $\ln e^3$
>
> $\log_e e^3$ Remember that $\ln$ means $\log_e$
>
>   3   Since the base of the log and exponential
>   functions are equal, they are inverses.

Earlier you learned how to solve exponential equations such as $2^x = 32$. Remember that to solve this equation, factor the base numbers into a product of primes, and since the two base numbers are equivalent, set the exponents equal to each other.

$$2^x = 32$$

$$2^x = 2^5$$

$$x = 5$$

Equations such as this are easy to solve, but what do you do if the bases, when factored, are not equivalent? For example, how do you solve the following equation?

$$3^x = 32$$

You can solve it by finding the logarithm of both sides and using the laws of logarithms to find the value of x. Compare the three methods below.

$3^x = 32$	$3^x = 32$	$3^x = 32$
$\log_3 32 = x$	$\log 3^x = \log 32$	$\ln 3^x = \ln 32$
	$x \log 3 = \log 32$	$x \ln 3 = \ln 32$
	$x = \dfrac{\log 32}{\log 3}$	$x = \dfrac{\ln 32}{\ln 3}$
	$x \approx \dfrac{1.5051}{0.4771}$	$x \approx \dfrac{3.4657}{1.0986}$
	$x \approx 3.1547$	$x \approx 3.1547$

The first method is the fastest if you do not need a decimal approximation. Since calculators can evaluate only common or natural logs, the first method is rarely practical. Notice that both of the other methods give the same answer and $3^{3.1547} \approx 32$.

Calculators have rendered the use of logarithms for computation obsolete, but logarithms are still essential for solving equations.

EXAMPLE 3 Solve $4^{x+5} = 12$.

Answer

$$4^{x+5} = 12$$

$$\log 4^{x+5} = \log 12 \qquad \text{1. Find the log of both sides of the equation.}$$

$$(x+5)\log 4 = \log 12 \qquad \text{2. Use the power property of logs and solve.}$$

$$x + 5 = \frac{\log 12}{\log 4}$$

$$x = \frac{\log 12}{\log 4} - 5$$

$$x \approx -3.208$$

To solve an equation containing log x, it is best to write the equation in exponential form and use a calculator. Powers of 10 can be found by entering the power and pressing the 10^x button.

EXAMPLE 4 Solve $\log x = 5.37$.

Answer

$$\log x = 5.37$$

$$10^{5.37} = x \qquad \text{1. Write in exponential form.}$$

$$x \approx 234{,}423 \qquad \text{2. Evaluate the power of ten.}$$

When natural logs are used the e^x button is required rather than the 10^x button.

EXAMPLE 5 Solve $\ln x = 2.4715$.

Answer

$$\ln x = 2.4715$$

$$e^{2.4715} = x \qquad \text{1. Write in exponential form.}$$

$$x \approx 11.84 \qquad \text{2. Evaluate the power of e.}$$

Although scientific calculators contain a $\sqrt[x]{y}$ button, logarithms enable a calculator that has only a square root button to extract higher roots. The example below shows how your calculator uses logarithms to find roots. It will also enable you to find roots that are too big for your calculator.

EXAMPLE 6   Compute $\sqrt[3]{2.48}$ using logs.

Answer

$y = \sqrt[3]{2.48}$	1. Name the radical y and change the radical form to exponential form.
$y = (2.48)^{\frac{1}{3}}$	
$\log y = \frac{1}{3} \log 2.48$	2. Use logs and their laws to evaluate.
$\log y \approx 0.1315$	
$10^{0.1315} \approx y$	
$y \approx 1.35$	

Of course you could also do Example 6 with natural logs.

▶ A. Exercises

1. Find log 1 and ln 1.
2. Find log 10 and ln 10.
3. Find log 0.5 and ln 0.5.
4. Find log 1,000,000 and ln 1,000,000.

Without a calculator, find

5. $\ln e^7$.
6. $\ln e$.
7. $\ln \sqrt[3]{e^2}$.

Write as a single logarithm.

8. $4 \ln 3$
9. $\ln 20 - 2 \ln 3 + 5 \ln 2$
10. $2 \ln e + \ln e^2 + \ln e^4$

Solve. Express answers in natural logs first and then as approximate decimals.

11. $2^x = 5$
12. $6^x = 7$
13. $3^{2x} = 2$
14. $4^{x+1} = 9$
15. $6^{2x-1} = 3$
16. $0.7^x = 0.43$
17. $7^{-4x} = 16$
18. $5^{x-7} = 20$

▶ B. Exercises

Solve.
19. $2^{x-6} = 5^{x+3}$
20. $8^{3x+4} = 3^x$
21. $18^{3x} = 2^{4x-5}$
22. $2^{6x+3} = 264$

Solve, leaving answers in scientific notation.
23. $\log x = 35.0170$
24. $\ln x = 25$
25. Use logs to find $\sqrt[7]{4.82 \times 10^{358}}$.
26. Find log log 200.

▶ C. Exercises

27. Solve $5^{\sin 2x} = 3.307$
28. Find $\log \cos \frac{\pi}{5}$.

▶ Dominion Modeling

29. By the logarithmic model, what European Union compensation corresponds to a \$20 compensation in the USA?
30. For the wage data, could an exponential model be used instead of a logarithmic one?

Cumulative Review

Solve.

31. $\frac{x}{21} - \frac{5}{12} = \frac{x}{28}$

32. $\frac{x-3}{4x} = \frac{x+2}{10x}$

33. $\frac{3x}{x^2-9} = \frac{5x}{x^2+6x+9} + \frac{2}{x+3}$

34. If the area of a square is numerically the same as the length of its diagonal, find the length of a side and the perimeter.

35. Ben and Teresa can fertilize the garden in 50 minutes working together. If Teresa requires 70 minutes by herself, how long does Ben take?

12.6 Problem Solving

There are many applications of logarithmic and exponential equations in business, biology, and economics. This section will present sample applications from these areas.

Recall the formula for simple interest, $I = Prt$. In this formula I represents the interest gained; P, the principal invested; r, the annual interest rate in decimal form; and t, the amount of time the money is invested in years. Given the same interest rate, it is more beneficial to you as an investor if your investment continuously compounds interest. The formula for interest compounded continuously is the exponential equation

$$A = Pe^{rt}$$

In this equation P represents the amount of money invested, r represents the annual interest rate in decimal form, t represents the time in years, and A represents the value of the investment after t years.

EXAMPLE 1   Bob made an investment of **$26,000** in an account that pays an annual rate of **10.45%** compounded continuously. What is the value of the account after **3** years of continually compounded interest? How long will it take the investment to grow to **$50,000**?

Answer

$A = Pe^{rt}$	1. Select the appropriate formula.
$A = 26{,}000\ e^{(0.1045)(3)}$	2. Substitute the known values into the formula.
$A = \$35{,}573.34$	3. Use a calculator.

In three years the account grows to $35,573.34. Now use the formula to find how long before the investment grows to 50,000.

$A = Pe^{rt}$	1. Substitute known values into the formula.
$50{,}000 = 26{,}000\ e^{0.1045t}$	
$\dfrac{50{,}000}{26{,}000} = e^{0.1045t}$	
$\ln \dfrac{50}{26} = \ln e^{0.1045t}$	2. Take the natural log of each side to undo the exponential with base e.
$\ln \dfrac{50}{26} = 0.1045\ t$	

Continued ▶

$$\frac{\ln \frac{50}{26}}{0.1045} = t$$ 3. Solve for t.

- -

$t \approx 6.26$ years   4. Use a calculator to approximate.

In the preceding example, natural logs have an advantage over common logs because $\ln e = 1$.

Radioactive substances decay according to the exponential equation $A = C \cdot 2^{\frac{-t}{T}}$.

In this equation, A represents the amount of the decaying substance remaining after t days or years, C represents the initial amount of the substance, and T represents the half-life of the substance.

EXAMPLE 2   Carbon-14 has a half-life of 5730 years. Suppose that a piece of gopher wood from the ark is found containing 19 grams of carbon-14. If the ark is about 4000 years old, how much carbon-14 was there originally?

Answer

$A = C \cdot 2^{\frac{-t}{T}}$ 1. Determine that you must use the decay equation to find x, the original amount of carbon-14.

- -

$19 = C \cdot 2^{\frac{-4000}{5730}}$ 2. Substitute the given values for the variables into the equation.

$C = \dfrac{19}{2^{\frac{-4000}{5730}}}$

$C \approx 30.8$ gram

4000 years ago, there was 30.8 grams of carbon-14 present.

Another area in which an exponential function exists is in the study of population growth. An exponential equation can describe the growth of a bacteria culture in a biological laboratory or the growth of population in a city. The equation that describes this growth is similar to the equation for radioactive decay except that the exponent is positive.

$$A = Ce^{0.2t}$$

Rodent reproduction illustrates exponential growth and makes them popular as lab animals.

In this equation, *A* represents the number of individuals in the growing population after *t* days or years, and *C* is the population at the beginning of the study.

EXAMPLE 3   Bogen City's population is growing steadily. If its population was **9800** at the beginning of a study and is presently **12,000**, how many years ago was the study begun?

Answer

$A = Ce^{0.2t}$

1. **Read.** Identify the appropriate exponential equation for this population growth problem.

- -

$12,000 = 9800\ e^{0.2t}$

2. **Plan.** Substitute the known values into the equation.

- -

$\dfrac{12,000}{9800} = e^{0.2t}$

$\ln \dfrac{120}{98} = \ln e^{0.2t}$

$\ln 120 - \ln 98 = 0.2t \ln e$

$\dfrac{\ln 120 - \ln 98}{0.2} = t$

$t \approx 1.01$

3. **Solve.** Find the natural log of both sides.

- -

The study began 1.01 years ago, or slightly over 1 year ago.

4. **Check.** Interpret the value in context.

▶ **A. Exercises**

State the formulas from this section that apply to each application.
1. Continuously compounded interest
2. Half-life
3. Populations
4. Which of the above formulas describe exponential growth?
5. Which of the formulas describe exponential decay?

▶ B. Exercises

6. Evelyn wants to make a 30-month investment of $12,000 into a certificate of deposit that compounds continuously at an annual interest rate of 9.8%. What will be the value of the certificate at maturity?

7. Brent invested $8000 in an account that compounded interest continuously, and the annual interest rate was 10.25%. When he withdrew the money from the account, he received $11,500. How long had it been invested?

8. An investment of $550,000 grew to $827,000 after 4 years of drawing interest compounded continuously. What annual rate did the bank pay?

9. How much of 75 grams of carbon-14 will remain after 2000 years?

10. A sample of 20 grams of magnesium-28 has a half-life of 21 hours. How long will it take before only 5 grams are left?

11. Candy wants to determine the half-life of bromine-80. After one hour 10 grams of it have diminished to 0.942 grams. What is its half-life?

12. Dallastown has a population of 15,300 and is growing at an exponential rate. What will be the population of the city in 5 years if it continues to grow at the same rate?

13. Millsville is growing at an exponential rate. Several years ago the population was 3450, and now the population is 13,800. How many years ago was the population 3450?

14. If there are 150 bacteria in a certain culture at the beginning of an experiment and the culture is checked in 2 days, how many bacteria will there be in the culture?

▶ C. Exercises

15. The earthquake equation that defines magnitude on the Richter scale is $y = \log \frac{x}{x_0}$. Find the magnitude of an earthquake that has a measure of $x = 10,000,000x_0$.

16. Explain what you think x_0 and x represent in problem 15.

▶ Dominion Modeling

17. On the logarithmic model, how much did the USA wages increase as the EU wages increased from $4 to $5? From $15 to $16?

Find each trigonometric ratio, giving exact values where possible.

18. $\sin 53°$

19. $\sec 30°$

20. $\cos 99°10'$

21. $\tan x$

22. $\csc -45°$

Algebra *and* Scripture

Interest and Taxes

You know that simple interest is computed as a percentage of the principal, and in this chapter you expanded your skills to certain compound interest problems requiring exponential functions.

Savings, loans, taxes, and transactions involve percentages or exponentials. Study the biblical principles governing such transactions.

1. If you want to help someone, would you most likely give him what he needs, loan it to him, or loan it while charging interest?

2. Read the following passages and explain what the Jews were forbidden to do to help the poor.

   Exodus 22:25
   Leviticus 25:36-37
   Deuteronomy 23:19

3. What exception to this law was permitted according to Deuteronomy 23:20?

4. What promise does God give in Psalm 15:5 for obedience in this area?

5. By comparing Proverbs 13:22 and 28:8 you can find God's curse for disobedience in this area.

6. Read the verses below. Explain why they are not breaking the commands above. (Research "interest" in a Bible dictionary if you need help).

   Matthew 25:27   Luke 19:23

Jeremiah had a good financial testimony.

7. What did he claim in Jeremiah 15:10?

*Y*our use of finances reveals whether your heart is full of generosity or greed. These attitudes can influence your relationship with the Lord and also your testimony to others. Likewise, your payment of taxes influences these relationships.

Read Matthew 17:24-27.

8. Who collects tribute?
9. Who is exempt from paying tribute?
10. Why did the Lord pay tribute?

Read Luke 20:25.

11. What did Jesus command concerning taxes?

Read Romans 13:7.

12. What is the difference between custom and tribute?
13. Must we pay both tribute and custom?

Read Ezra 4:13, 20; 7:24.

14. What does toll mean in these verses?
15. Which disciple collected custom?

GREATER AMPLITUDE.
Find a reference to support your answer to question 15.

Absolute Values

*A*ND HE SAID UNTO THEM, Render therefore unto Caesar the things which be Caesar's, and unto God the things which be God's.

LUKE 20:25

Chapter 12 Review

For each function, give the inverse and tell whether it is a function.
1. $f = \{(1, 7), (2, 8), (-3, 9)\}$
2. If $f(x) = 3x - 7$, find $f^{-1}(x)$
3. If $g(x) = 2x^2 - 8$, find $g^{-1}(x)$

Change each expression to log form.
4. $3^4 = 81$
5. $7^{-2} = \frac{1}{49}$

Change each expression to exponential form.
6. $\log_2 \frac{1}{16} = -4$
7. $\ln 7.8 = 2.0541$

Give each answer in radians.

8. $\text{Cos}^{-1} \frac{\sqrt{3}}{2}$

9. $\text{Sin}^{-1} \frac{\sqrt{3}}{2}$

10. $\text{Tan}^{-1} -1$

Use the laws of logarithms to express the following in equivalent terms.
11. $\log_4 ab^2$

12. $\log \sqrt{\frac{x^2}{y}}$

13. $\log \sqrt{x^2yz^3}$

Evaluate.
14. $\log_4 32$
15. $\log_5 \frac{1}{25}$

Evaluate.
16. $\log 3.87$
17. $\log 2240$
18. $\log 0.000953$

Find x if
19. $\log x = 4.8028$.
20. $\ln x = -2.1572$.

Evaluate.
21. $\ln 5.77$
22. $\ln 28.9$

Solve.

23. $3^{x+9} = 32$

24. $2^{4x} = 18$

25. $2 \log_5 x = \log_5 25$

Solve, expressing answers in logs and then evaluating.

26. $10^{x-2} = 1.64$

27. $2e^x = 7$

Solve.

28. $\log x + \log 4 = 3$

Compute using logs.

29. $\sqrt[5]{79}$

30. Faith Baptist Church wants to invest $15,000 in an 18-month account that pays 9.6% interest compounded continuously. How much money will the church receive upon maturity of the account?

31. Jan discovers that a certain bacterium in her lab is growing at an exponential rate. If there are 50 bacteria in a culture at the beginning of a study, how many hours will it be before there are 800 bacteria in the culture?

32. When graphing the wage data, three points (from 1975, 1980, and 1985) lie quite far from the rest of the data. If you think of the data as weights on a seesaw, are these three points just as influential as the rest of the data points? Explain what consequence this has for modeling.

33. Give the mathematical significance of Luke 20:25.

13 Probability and Statistics

$$A = Pe^{rt}$$

$y = \dfrac{a}{b}$

Nick, age 16, was shocked at his first auto insurance bill. Young, unmarried men pay the most. Why?

Probability and statistics answer such questions. The National Highway Traffic Safety Administration (NHTSA) found that teen drivers are three times as likely as adult drivers to die in an accident. Further, male teens are 30% more likely than females to be a driver in a fatality. In 1998, the NHTSA published the data below.

	Males			Females		
Age	Licensed Drivers (1000s)	Drivers in all Crashes (1000s)	Drivers in All Fatal Crashes	Licensed Drivers (1000s)	Drivers in all Crashes (1000s)	Drivers in All Fatal Crashes
0-16	816	244	1106	764	178	557
17	1198	233	1013	1115	175	414
18	1342	243	1271	1212	164	469
19	1454	229	1214	1333	145	412
20-24	7866	951	6148	7394	618	1747
25-29	9356	899	5073	8946	595	1558
30-34	10,121	875	4834	9871	571	1561
35-39	10,521	901	4414	10,439	566	1503
40-44	9776	692	3563	9752	455	1180
45-49	8754	667	2935	8710	390	957
50-54	6840	390	2164	6763	247	752
55-59	5341	290	1655	5258	165	522
60-64	4565	218	1398	4486	133	498
65-69	4234	191	1154	4231	121	491
70-74	3604	167	1055	3749	104	550
75-79	2563	118	894	2716	77	485
80-84	1400	61	684	1516	45	314
85+	767	34	435	767	20	176
Total	90,519	7403	41,010	89,021	4771	14,146

After this chapter you should be able to

1. count outcomes using combinations and permutations.
2. use the binomial theorem to expand binomials.
3. compute probabilities of simple, compound mutually exclusive, and independent events.
4. compute the mean, range, and standard deviation.
5. apply the standard normal distribution to interpret test scores.

13.1 Counting Problems

Eight out of ten doctors recommend Super Bran cereal as a supplement to your diet. One-half of all high school graduates attend college. Have you heard comments like these? They are concerned with the field of mathematical study called *probability theory*. This field helps you evaluate such comments and is also useful for quality control in manufacturing and the study of genetics.

God has established all things, and in His eyes all things are certain. Proverbs 16:33 says, "The lot is cast into the lap; but the whole disposing thereof is of the Lord." Man does not possess God's omniscience, and many things appear to man to happen by chance. God has allowed this to be so. Probability theory is the study of such events that appear to happen by chance.

Unfortunately, probability theory began as an investigation of questions posed by gamblers. God gave man the ability to calculate for his honor, and men perverted the use of probability toward these evil ends. In fact, probability shows that it does not pay to gamble. This addictive behavior has snared many, and Christians must be careful not to come under the power of anything except the Holy Spirit. I Corinthians 6:12 says, "All things are lawful for me, but I will not be brought under the power of any."

Before you can study probability, you must learn to count the number of ways a particular event can occur. While listing the possibilities and counting them may seem simple, it is virtually impossible when there are hundreds or thousands of possibilities. This chapter presents counting methods that are quick and accurate.

If John has two pair of shoes—one black and one brown—and has three different colors of socks—black, brown, and navy—how many different ways can he choose a pair of shoes and a pair of socks to wear? You can find the answer by listing all possible choices of a pair of shoes followed by all possible choices of a pair of socks.

Shoes	Socks
B	B
B	R
B	N
R	B
R	R
R	N

B – black
R – brown
N – navy

Another method of listing all of the possible ways is by drawing a *tree diagram.*

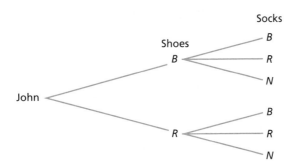

From this tree diagram you can list the six different ways of choosing a pair of shoes and a pair of socks: *BB, BR, BN, RB, RR, RN.* Notice that two choices of shoes and three choices of socks result in six ways to choose a shoe color followed by a sock color. This suggests the Fundamental Principle of Counting.

Fundamental Principle of Counting

If a particular process can be done in two steps where there are *m* different ways to do the first step *M* and *n* ways to do the second step *N*, then there are *m · n* ways to do the two-step process. (Lowercase letters represent the number of ways of doing the event represented by the corresponding capital letter.)

In the previous example, there were *m* = 2 ways to choose a pair of shoes and *n* = 3 ways to choose a pair of socks. Therefore there were *m · n* = 2 · 3 = 6 ways to choose a pair of shoes and then a pair of socks.

EXAMPLE How many different four-letter patterns can be formed from the letters *a*, *b*, *c*, and *d* if no letter is used more than once? Show these by a tree diagram, by listing, and by the Fundamental Principle of Counting.

Answer

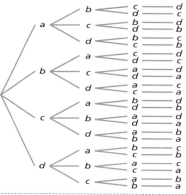

1. Draw a tree diagram with 24 leaves.

abcd, abdc, acbd, acdb, adbc, adcb,
bacd, badc, bcad, bcda, bdac, bdca,
cabd, cadb, cbad, cbda, cdab, cdba,
dabc, dacb, dbac, dbca, dcab, dcba

2. List the 24 orders.

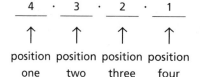

position position position position
  one   two   three   four

3. The number of patterns can be found by the Fundamental Principle of Counting. There are four choices for position one, leaving three choices for position two. There are two choices for position three and one choice for position four.

$4 \cdot 3 \cdot 2 \cdot 1 = 24$

4. Multiply to find the number of ways four letters can be arranged.

▶ A. Exercises

If process *A* and process *B* can be done in the numbers of ways shown, give the number of ways of doing *A* followed by *B*.

1. 9, 20
2. 300, 500
3. 6, 74
4. 89, 0

If each process can be done in the given number of ways, find the total number of ways to do all of them consecutively.

5. *A* in 7 ways, *B* in 5 ways, and *C* in 2 ways

6. *X* in 4 ways, *Y* in 2 ways, and *Z* in 11 ways

7. *M* in 25 ways, *N* in 1 way, and *O* in 14 ways

8. *P* in 8 ways, *Q* in 10 ways, *R* in 5 ways, and *S* in 9 ways

9. *F* in 11 ways, *G* in 17 ways, *H* in 8 ways, *K* in 21 ways, and *L* in 19 ways

10. *T* in 2 ways, *U* in 6 ways, *V* in 11 ways, and *W* in 4 ways

Show a tree diagram, make a list, and use the Fundamental Principle of Counting to find the number of possibilities in each exercise.

11. You have 4 coins: a penny, a nickel, a dime, and a quarter. What are the different ways the coins could land if each coin is flipped once? How many possibilities are there? (*Hint*: One possibility is that the penny lands heads, the nickel lands tails, the dime lands tails, and the quarter lands heads. This could be represented as HTTH.)

12. There are 3 balls in a box, and each is a different color. All three are drawn, one ball at a time, and lined up in the order of the draw. If the balls are blue, white, and green, find the different possible orders, and show by the Fundamental Principle of Counting how many orders there are.

▶ B. Exercises

13. Three-letter "words" are to be formed from the set of {a, k, l, m}. How many different ones are there if the letters can be used more than once? if each letter can be used only once?

14. One die is rolled twice, and the number is recorded each time. What are the possible pairs of numbers, and how many possibilities are there?

15. How many different license plates can be formed that are made up of 3 letters followed by 2 digits, where the letters and digits can be used more than once?

16. How many different license plates can be formed that are made up of 3 numbers followed by 3 letters, where the letters and numbers can be used only once (Assume the first number can be zero)?

17. How many seven-digit phone numbers can be formed if the digits can be used more than once? How many are there if the first digit cannot be 0 or a 1?

18. A café has available 5 meats, 6 vegetables, and 4 desserts. How many different dinners could be ordered if changing any one item is considered a different dinner?

19. There are 3 students running for president of the senior class, 5 running for vice-president, 3 for secretary, and 2 for treasurer. How many different slates of officers are possible?

▶ C. Exercises

20. How many different ways can a test be answered if there are 20 true-false questions and 15 multiple-choice questions that each have 5 possible answers?

21. How many different 5-character stock numbers can be formed if the first digit cannot be zero, the second digit must be odd, the third digit is alphabetic, and the last two digits correspond to a group of 20 different two-digit product codes.

▶ Dominion Modeling

22. Combine the NHTSA data to get a new table for all drivers, both male and female. List columns for driver ages, the number of licensed drivers, the number of drivers in all crashes, and the number of drivers in all fatal crashes. (This table will be needed for a future problem.)

■ Cumulative Review

Give two-decimal approximations.

23. ln 53
24. $\sqrt{22}$
25. [4.37]
26. sin 62°50′
27. The number of radians in 20 degrees.

13.2 Permutations and Combinations

In the last section you used the Fundamental Principle of Counting to find the number of ways particular events could occur. Did you notice that there are two major ways of considering the occurrence of an event? One way is to be concerned about the *order* in which the processes involved occur. The other way is to think of a set of occurrences or objects collectively without concern for their order.

Definitions

Permutation   An arrangement of objects in which the order is important.

Combination   A collection of elements in which order is not important.

The key words used in identifying permutations and combinations are arrangement and collection. An arrangement suggests order, while a collection does not. The arrangement *abcd* was different from *bcad* in the example in the last section because the order of the letters differed. To determine the number of different ways that the four letters can be arranged, you used the Fundamental Principle of Counting to find the product $4 \cdot 3 \cdot 2 \cdot 1 = 24$ different arrangements. *Factorial notation* abbreviates this by using an exclamation point.

$$4! = 4 \cdot 3 \cdot 2 \cdot 1$$

The symbol 4! is read "4 factorial." The general definition of $n!$ is given here.

Definition

n factorial, $n!$ the product of n and every natural number less than n.

$$n! = n(n - 1)(n - 2)(n - 3) \cdot \ldots \cdot 1$$

Note this specially defined case: $0! = 1$.

To arrange three objects from a set of five, the Fundamental Principle of Counting shows that you can arrange them $5 \cdot 4 \cdot 3 = 60$ different ways. By multiplying by 1 in the form of $\frac{2 \cdot 1}{2 \cdot 1}$, you can write this calculation using factorials: $\frac{5 \cdot 4 \cdot 3 \cdot 2 \cdot 1}{2 \cdot 1} = \frac{5!}{2!}$. The symbol for the number of permutations of 5 objects taken 3 at a time is $_5P_3$. Therefore $_5P_3 = \frac{5!}{2!} = \frac{5 \cdot 4 \cdot 3 \cdot 2 \cdot 1}{2 \cdot 1} = 60$.

In general, the permutation of n things taken r at a time is $_nP_r = \frac{n!}{(n-r)!}$.

EXAMPLE 1 Evaluate $_8P_5$, the permutation of eight objects taken five at a time.

Answer

$_nP_r = \frac{n!}{(n-r)!}$ 1. Use the permutation formula.

$_8P_5 = \frac{8!}{(8-5)!}$ 2. Evaluate.

$= \frac{8!}{3!}$

$= \frac{8 \cdot 7 \cdot 6 \cdot 5 \cdot 4 \cdot 3 \cdot 2 \cdot 1}{3 \cdot 2 \cdot 1}$

$= 6720$

There are 6720 ways to arrange eight objects five at a time.

Using the same notation, the number of permutations of all 8 objects would be $_8P_8 = 8! = 40{,}320$ (since $0! = 1$). In general, the formula for the number of permutations of n objects taken n at a time follows.

$$_nP_n = n!$$

There are always fewer combinations than permutations because the order does not matter with combinations. If there are ten boys on a basketball team, you might be interested in the number of possible combinations of five-man teams. In this example the order of the players is not important. The notation for combinations is $_nC_r$, read "the combination of n objects taken r at a time." Each collection of r objects can be listed in $r!$ arrangements. Thus $_nP_r$ is $r!$ times larger than $_nC_r$. Then

$$_nC_r = \frac{_nP_r}{r!}$$

$$= \frac{\frac{n!}{(n-r)!}}{r!}$$

$$= \frac{n!}{r!(n-r)!} \qquad \text{Invert and multiply to simplify the fraction.}$$

EXAMPLE 2 Find the number of different five-man basketball teams that can be formed from a 10-man squad.

Answer

$$_nC_r = \frac{n!}{r!(n-r)!}$$ 1. Use the combination formula.

$$_{10}C_5 = \frac{10!}{5!(10-5)!}$$ 2. Evaluate.

$$= \frac{10!}{5!5!}$$

$$= \frac{10 \cdot 9 \cdot 8 \cdot 7 \cdot 6 \cdot 5 \cdot 4 \cdot 3 \cdot 2 \cdot 1}{5 \cdot 4 \cdot 3 \cdot 2 \cdot 1 \cdot 5 \cdot 4 \cdot 3 \cdot 2 \cdot 1}$$

$$= 2 \cdot 9 \cdot 2 \cdot 7$$

$$= 252$$

Determining whether you should use a permutation or a combination for a particular problem is the first step in solving a counting problem. Remember that if the order is essential, you must use permutations. If the order is not essential, use combinations.

▶ A. Exercises

Evaluate.

1. $_7P_4$
2. $_3P_2$
3. $_5P_2$
4. $_8P_3$
5. $_4P_3$
6. $_8P_8$
7. $_{25}P_{18}$
8. $_5C_2$
9. $_{10}C_3$
10. $_8C_3$
11. $_6C_5$
12. $_8C_4$

▶ B. Exercises

Use combinations and permutations to find the following.

13. Mrs. Marshall has 9 different history books. How many ways can they be arranged on a shelf?
14. If a committee of 5 people is to be appointed from a group of 12, how many different committees can be formed?
15. How many different volleyball teams can be formed from a group of 14 girls if there are 6 girls on a team?
16. How many ways can the letters in the word *mother* be arranged?
17. If there are 15 students in a class, how many different arrangements of students can occupy the 6 chairs in the front row?
18. How many different groups of 5 teens can be chosen for a Bible quiz squad from a total of 9 team members?

19. How many ways can **4** boats be docked in a dock prepared for **8** boats? (*Hint:* The objects being used are not the boats but the **8** dock positions.)

20. How many combinations of 3 letters can be formed from the set $\{a, b, c, d, e, f\}$?

▶ C. Exercises

21. When choosing a **9**-man baseball team from a **15**-player roster, write (a) a question requiring combinations and (b) one requiring permutations.

22. How many 3-letter organizational names can be formed using the Greek alphabet (a) if no repetition is allowed and (b) if repetition is allowed.

▶ Dominion Modeling

23. Derive a new column for all drivers that will indicate the Fatal Crash Rate. Give your result per **100,000** drivers. (*Hint:* The "Fatal Crash Rate" comes from "Drivers in Fatal Crashes" and "Licensed Drivers." This table will be needed for future problems.)

■ Cumulative Review

Simplify.

24. $(x + 3)(x - 2) + x(x - 1) + 5$

25. $\dfrac{5}{x} - \dfrac{4}{x - 1}$

26. $\dfrac{\sin x}{\sec x} + \sin 2x$

27. $\left(\sqrt{x} - 1\right)^{-1}$

28. $\dfrac{x^3 - 4x}{x^3 + 7x^2 + 10x}$

This staff of seven lab technicians must include two chemists and four biologists. If there are eight biologists and five chemists to choose from, how many different lab staffs can be formed? If one particular biologist must be on the staff, how many different lab staffs can be formed?

13.3 Counting Formulas

Another type of counting problem is the *circular permutation*. Examine figures *a* and *b*. Are the arrangements of the people at the tables different (*B* still has *A* on his left and *C* on his right)? Compare figures *a* and *c*. Are the arrangements different at these table settings?

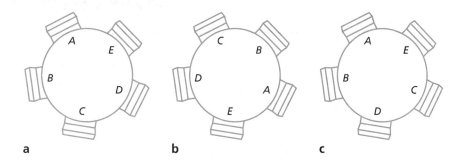

a   b   c

EXAMPLE 1   How many different ways can five people be arranged around a circular table?

Answer   Circular permutations are different from other permutations. Since each arrangement can begin at any of the 5 seats, the number of permutations found by the previous formula is 5 times too large. The answer for this circular permutation is not $_5P_5$ but $\frac{_5P_5}{5}$. Therefore, there are $\frac{_5P_5}{5} = \frac{5!}{5} = 4! = 24$ arrangements of the five people around the table.

In general for a *circular permutation*, the number of permutations is

$$\frac{_nP_n}{n} = \frac{n!}{n} = \frac{n(n-1)!}{n} = (n-1)!$$

EXAMPLE 2   Mrs. Larson has a lazy Susan in her kitchen. On it she has mustard, ketchup, mayonnaise, onions, salt, cheese, pickles, and salad dressing arranged as shown. Determine the total number of possible arrangements of these items.

Answer

$(n - 1)! = (8 - 1)!$ This is a circular
        $= 7!$ permutation, so use the
        $= 5040$ appropriate formula.

There are 5040 possible arrangements of the 8 items on the lazy Susan.

Permutations are basic, but when the number includes repeated arrangements, you must divide out the repeats. To count combinations you divided the permutations by the $r!$ permutations of each set. To count circular permutations you divided the number of permutations by the n repeated permutations of each cycle. Now you will see another situation where you must divide.

How would you find the number of arrangements of the letters of the word *capitol*? You would evaluate $_7P_7 = 7! = 5040$. Suppose you were asked to find the number of different arrangements of the letters in the word *Tennessee*. You might be tempted to write $_9P_9$ as your answer, but this is incorrect. The difficulty with this type of counting problem is that the four *e*s in the word are indistinguishable from each other, as are the two *n*s and the two *s*s. If all the multiple letters were unique, for example, $Te_1n_1n_2e_2s_1s_2e_3e_4$, there would be $_9P_9$ ways to arrange the letters. Since there are objects in the set that you cannot tell apart, there are not as many possible arrangements. To find the number of arrangements in this case, evaluate $\frac{n!}{p!q!r!}$, where n is the number of objects to be arranged and p of these objects are alike, q objects are alike, r objects are alike, and so on. (*Note: p + q + r + . . . = n.*) In the arrangement of the letters of the word *Tennessee, p = 4, q = 2,* and *r = 2.* To find the number of different arrangements of these letters, divide the permutations of the 9 letters by the number of indistinguishable arrangements. The 1! for the *T* need not be included in the denominator since it will not affect the result.

$$\frac{9!}{4!2!2!}$$

$$\frac{9 \cdot 8 \cdot 7 \cdot 6 \cdot 5 \cdot 4!}{4! \cdot 2 \cdot 2}$$

$$\frac{15,120}{4}$$

$$3780$$

There are **3780** arrangements of these letters instead of the previously expected $_9P_9 = 362,880$.

EXAMPLE 3 Mr. Wong keeps twelve books on the mantle for family devotions. The books consist of three identical Bibles, a concordance, a Bible dictionary, two copies of a favorite devotional book, a Bible atlas, and four copies of the family's favorite hymnal. Find the number of arrangements possible on the shelf.

Answer

$\dfrac{12!}{3!2!4!}$

1. There are three sets that are indistinguishable containing three, two, and four books respectively. Use the formula given in this section to find the number of arrangements.

$\dfrac{12 \cdot 11 \cdot 10 \cdot 9 \cdot 8 \cdot 7 \cdot 6 \cdot 5 \cdot 4!}{4! \cdot 6 \cdot 2}$ 2. Evaluate.

1,663,200

There are 1,663,200 ways to arrange these books on the shelf.

Two final counting formulas are important. How do you count the number of ways event *M* or event *N* can occur?

A choir has **22** sopranos, **24** altos, **25** tenors, and **17** basses. How large is the choir? Since no person sings more than one part, the parts do not overlap. They are mutually exclusive and you can add 22 + 24 + 25 + 17 to obtain an **88** member choir. If there is also a 55-piece orchestra that contains **12** of the choir members, how many will participate in a combined program? This time addition will count the 12 members twice (the sets are not mutually exclusive) so that number must be subtracted from the total: 88 + 55 − 12 = **131** people.

Definition

Mutually exclusive sets   Sets whose intersection is empty.

Counting Formulas

Event *M* occurs in *m* ways; Event *N* occurs in *n* ways.

M and then *N* occur $m \cdot n$ ways (Fundamental Principle of Counting).

M or *N* occurs $m + n$ ways if *M* and *N* are mutually exclusive.

M or *N* occurs $m + n - p$ ways if $M \cap N$ occurs *p* ways.

Permutations occur $_nP_r = \dfrac{n!}{(n-r)!}$ ways.

Combinations occur $_nC_r = \dfrac{_nP_r}{r!} = \dfrac{n!}{r!(n-r)!}$ ways.

Circular permutations occur $\dfrac{_nP_n}{n} = (n-1)!$ ways.

Permutations with indistinguishable objects occur $\dfrac{n!}{p!q!r!}$ ways if there are groups of *p*, *q*, and *r* identical objects.

▶ A. Exercises

Find the number of ways the letters in the following words can be arranged.

1. *Mississippi*
2. *Illuminate*
3. *Fission*
4. *Decigram*
5. *Sentence*

6. Mary has 15 balloons to use as decorations for Jennie's birthday party. Five are blue, 3 white, 2 pink, and 5 yellow. How many different arrangements of the balloons can she make?

7. There are 18 books on Mrs. Jones' shelf. She has 7 copies of her geometry text and 3 copies of her Algebra 2 text. How many different ways can she arrange her books on the shelf?

8. Sally is making a bead necklace. The necklace will require 8 different colors of beads strung one color after another. Assume the pattern chosen repeats itself and the number of beads used is a multiple of eight. How many different necklaces can be made?

9. How many ways can a family of 7 be seated around a table?

10. There is a circular tray that has 5 slots in it for various types of food. In how many different arrangements can 5 different foods be placed on the tray?

11. At the motor speedway, 12 cars are entered in a race. As they race around the track in single file, how many different arrangements of the cars are possible?

12. How many ways are there to position 6 boys in volleyball rotation?

13. A 20-player baseball roster shares 4 men with a 10-man basketball team. How many athletes are there?

▶ B. Exercises

14. There are 20 driving routes from Ottawa, Canada to Wichita and 11 routes from Wichita to Oaxaca. How many ways can you go from Wichita to either Ottawa or Oaxaca? From Ottawa to Oaxaca via Wichita?

15. How many ways can you arrange the letters of either *Hawaii* or *Alaska*?

16. From the letters of *Idaho* find the number of 3 or 4 letter "words" that can be made.

17. Find the number of circular permutations of 5 or 6 objects.

18. Nine stock cars will race on Friday evening, and each race involves four or five cars. How many arrangements of cars on the oval track are possible in any particular race?

19. Joan has 8 condiment containers but her rotating condiment dispenser can accommodate only 5 of them. How many arrangements of five of the containers can she make on the dispenser?

▶ C. Exercises

20. From a youth group of 9 boys and 11 girls, how many social committees of four people contain 1 or 2 boys?

The following problem is a cumulative counting example using three principles of counting. Name each one and calculate the answer.

21. From a group of 9 people, how many ways are there to seat 6 of them in a circle?

▶ Dominion Modeling

22. According to the NHTSA data, teens are what percent of all drivers? What percent of all auto fatalities involves teen drivers?

23. From the NHTSA data use a plot to compare the "Fatal Crash Rate" for different ages.

Cumulative Review

Solve.

24. $x - 5 = 10$

25. $|x - 5| = 10$

26. $(x - 5)(x + 2) = 0$

27. $x^2 - 5x = 0$

28. $\sqrt{x - 5} = 4$

13.4 The Binomial Theorem

A binomial is a polynomial that contains two terms. You should be efficient at multiplying two binomials together using the FOIL method. In fact, many of you can do this process mentally. When you raise a particular binomial to a power, you are expanding the binomial. Look at the expansions given here.

$$(x + y)^0 = 1$$
$$(x + y)^1 = x + y$$
$$(x + y)^2 = x^2 + 2xy + y^2$$
$$(x + y)^3 = x^3 + 3x^2y + 3xy^2 + y^3$$
$$(x + y)^4 = x^4 + 4x^3y + 6x^2y^2 + 4xy^3 + y^4$$
$$(x + y)^5 = x^5 + 5x^4y + 10x^3y^2 + 10x^2y^3 + 5xy^4 + y^5$$

These expansions continue and can be written for any positive integral power. With your knowledge of combinations and the awareness of a few basic patterns, you can expand any binomial to any such power. First look at some of the basic patterns by examining $(x + y)^n$.

1. The exponents on x begin with n and decrease by 1 in each successive term of the expansion until they reach 0.
2. The exponents on y begin with 0 and increase by 1 in each successive term of the expansion until they reach n.
3. If the sign between x and y is positive, then all the signs in the expansion are positive.
4. If the sign between x and y is negative, then the first term of the expansion is positive and successive terms alternate signs.

With these observations, you can identify the variables and their powers in the binomial expansion. But what about the coefficients of the terms? This is where your knowledge of combinations will help.

Theorem
Binomial theorem.
$$(x + y)^n = {}_nC_0x^n + {}_nC_1x^{n-1}y^1 + {}_nC_2x^{n-2}y^2 + {}_nC_3x^{n-3}y^3 + \ldots + {}_nC_ny^n$$

Study the example given here to see how the binomial theorem works.

EXAMPLE 1 Expand $(x + 3y)^4$.

Answer

$$(x + 3y)^4 = {}_4C_0x^4 + {}_4C_1x^3(3y)^1 + {}_4C_2x^2(3y)^2 + {}_4C_3x(3y)^3 + {}_4C_4(3y)^4$$

$$= 1x^4 + 4x^3(3y) + 6x^2(9y^2) + 4x(27y^3) + 1(81y^4)$$

$$= x^4 + 12x^3y + 54x^2y^2 + 108xy^3 + 81y^4$$

Notice that the exponents on x and $3y$ in any term always add up to the original exponent, 4.

EXAMPLE 2 Expand $(a - 2b)^5$.

Answer

$$(a - 2b)^5$$

$${}_5C_0a^5 - {}_5C_1a^4(2b) + {}_5C_2a^3(2b)^2 - {}_5C_3a^2(2b)^3 + {}_5C_4a(2b)^4 - {}_5C_5(2b)^5$$

$$1a^5 - 5a^4(2b) + 10a^3(4b^2) - 10a^2(8b^3) + 5a(16b^4) - 1(32b^5)$$

$$a^5 - 10a^4b + 40a^3b^2 - 80a^2b^3 + 80ab^4 - 32b^5$$

EXAMPLE 3 Find the term containing the 10th power of y in the expansion of $(x - y^2)^{12}$.

Answer

$(y^2)^5 = y^{10}$	1. y^{10} will result from raising y^2 to the fifth power.
The exponent on x is $12 - 5 = 7$.	2. The exponent on x is found by subtracting the power of y^2 from the original exponent of the expansion.
The coefficient is $-({}_{12}C_5) = -792$. The term is $-792x^7y^{10}$.	3. Coefficient is found by combinations where the second subscript matches the power of y^2. It is negative when the second subscript is odd.

▶ A. Exercises

Expand each binomial.
1. $(a + b)^3$
2. $(x - y)^4$
3. $(x - 4y)^6$
4. $(2a + b)^4$
5. $(3a + 2b)^4$
6. $(x - 5y)^5$
7. $(2a + 5)^4$
8. $(3x - 2)^5$
9. $(6a + 9)^3$
10. $(2a^2 + 7b)^4$

▶ B. Exercises

Find the term of each given expansion that contains the indicated power and simplify.
11. $(x + 3)^9$, x^5
12. $(x - y)^8$, y^7
13. $(x^4 + y^3)^3$, x^8
14. $(x^2 + y^5)^6$, y^{15}
15. $(x - y)^{14}$, x^5

Find
16. the third term of $(x + y)^{12}$.
17. the fifth term of $(x - 2y)^8$.
18. the last term of $(2x - y)^{11}$.
19. the 10th term of $(3x^2 + y^4)^{17}$.

▶ C. Exercises

20. Find the middle term of $(x - y)^{10}$.
21. Given that $15{,}360x^{21}y^{12}$ and $13{,}440x^{18}y^{16}$ are consecutive terms of a binomial expansion, write the factorization of the entire polynomial.

▶ Dominion Modeling

22. In the plot of the Fatal Crash Rate, what important features do you see?
23. Give reasons why these features are in the data.

Match each equation to the shape of its graph without sketching it.

24. $3x - 5y = 11$		**A.**	discontinuous
25. $y = \lvert x + 1 \rvert$		**B.**	exponential decay curve
26. $y = 5x^2 - 3x + 1$		**C.**	linear
27. $f(x) = 2^{-x}$		**D.**	parabolic
28. $x = 5$		**E.**	sinusoidal
29. $y = 2 \sin 3x$		**F.**	vertical line
30. $y = \dfrac{x}{x^2 - 1}$		**G.**	"V" shaped

13.5 Probability

Suppose you have an urn that contains four marbles, one each of white, black, red, and yellow. If you choose a marble without looking in the urn, you are choosing a marble at random. This activity is called an *experiment* in probability theory.

Monte Carlo, founded in 1856 in Monaco, is now the largest gambling center worldwide. A study of gambling prompted the theory of probability.

In probability, a set of descriptions of all possible outcomes in an experiment is called the *sample space* of the experiment. In the experiment described here, the sample space S would be the set of colors. $S = \{$white, black, red, yellow$\}$. This describes the set of possibilities on a draw of a marble from the urn.

EXAMPLE 1   An experiment consists of rolling a die. What is the sample space or set of possible outcomes of this experiment.

Answer $S = \{1, 2, 3, 4, 5, 6\}$.

EXAMPLE 2   Choose at random a two-person committee from the following people: Jack, Sue, Valerie, Bill, and Kim. Find the sample space for the experiment. How many elements are in this sample space?

Answer $S = \{(J, S), (J, V), (J, B), (J, K), (S, V), (S, B), (S, K), (V, B), (V, K), (B, K)\}$

There are ten elements in the sample space. These committees are actually combinations, so the number could be obtained by finding $_5C_2$.

A subset of a sample space is an *event*. In Example 1, an event could be "roll an even number," or "roll a number greater than 4." The events would be $E_1 = \{2, 4, 6\}$ and $E_2 = \{5, 6\}$ respectively. If the die is rolled and the outcome is 4, then E_1 has occurred. Outcomes are *equally likely* if they have the same chance of occurring. An example of an experiment that does not have equally likely outcomes is one in which an urn contains seven green balls and three blue balls. If the sample space is {green, blue}, you are more likely to choose a green ball than a blue ball; so the outcomes are not equally likely.

Probabilities are numbers that are assigned to events. The probability of an event E is denoted by $P(E)$ and is a measure of the likelihood of the occurrence of E when an experiment is performed.

For the remainder of this section, we will consider experiments in which the outcomes are equally likely. In these situations the probability of an event can be calculated according to the following definition.

Definition

Probability of an event, $P(E)$ The ratio of the number of favorable outcomes to the number of possible outcomes in which every outcome is equally likely.

In the marble example, each of the four marbles is equally likely to be chosen from the urn. Therefore the number of possible outcomes is four. If a favorable outcome is {red}, the number of favorable outcomes is one. From the definition of probability you can now find the likelihood of choosing a red marble on the draw.

$$P(E) = \frac{\text{number of favorable outcomes}}{\text{number of possible outcomes}}$$

$$= \frac{1}{4}$$

Be aware that this probability figure does not mean that you will choose a red marble exactly once out of every four tries, but it does give you the approximate proportion of times that you would get a red marble in repeated trials. For example, if you drew 400 times, you would expect a red marble about 100 times.

If E_1 is the event "choosing a marble that is not red," then $P(E_1) = \frac{3}{4}$.

A Venn diagram can often illustrate laws and facts about probability. The sample space S corresponds to the universal set. An event E is a subset of S.

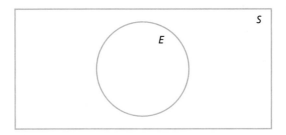

Basic Probability Laws

1. The probability of an event that is certain to happen is 1; $P(S) = 1$.
2. The probability of an impossible event is 0; $P(\varnothing) = 0$.
3. If $P(E)$ is the probability of any event E, then $0 \le P(E) \le 1$.
4. If the *complement* of an event, denoted E', is the set of all outcomes in a sample space that are not in E, then $P(E') = 1 - P(E)$.
5. If A and B are two events such that $A \cap B = \varnothing$, then they are called *mutually exclusive* and $P(A \cup B) = P(A) + P(B)$.

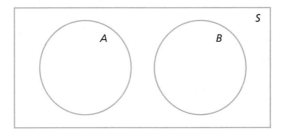

Consider an experiment that consists of a single roll of a die. The sample space is $S = \{1, 2, 3, 4, 5, 6\}$. If E is the event of rolling a number greater than or equal to 2, then $E = \{2, 3, 4, 5, 6\}$. The probability of this event can be found in two ways.

One way is to think of E as a union: $E = \{2\} \cup \{3\} \cup \{4\} \cup \{5\} \cup \{6\}$. Using this information and the fact that the probability of the union of mutually exclusive sets is the sum of the probabilities of the individual sets, you can find $P(E)$.

$$P(E) = P(2) + P(3) + P(4) + P(5) + P(6)$$

$$P(E) = \frac{1}{6} + \frac{1}{6} + \frac{1}{6} + \frac{1}{6} + \frac{1}{6}$$

$$P(E) = \frac{5}{6}$$

Another way to find $P(E)$ is to use E'. $E' = \{1\}$. From the fourth probability law,

$$P(E) = 1 - P(E')$$

$$P(E) = 1 - P(1)$$

$$P(E) = 1 - \frac{1}{6}$$

$$P(E) = \frac{5}{6}$$

EXAMPLE 3 A social committee of four is to be chosen from a group of five boys and four girls. If they are randomly selected, what is the probability of choosing an all-boy committee?

Answer The sample space for this experiment is all the possible four-person committees that can be formed from the group of nine students. The number of elements in this sample space is $_9C_4$. The outcomes are equally likely.

Let E = a committee of all boys   1. Define the event.

$P(E) = \dfrac{\text{number of favorable outcomes}}{\text{number of possible outcomes}}$ 2. To find the probability of this event, you must know the number of ways a committee of all boys can be chosen. This number is $_5C_4$.

$\quad = \dfrac{_5C_4}{_9C_4}$

$\quad = \dfrac{\frac{5!}{4!1!}}{\frac{9!}{4!5!}}$

$\quad = \dfrac{5!}{4!} \cdot \dfrac{4!5!}{9 \cdot 8 \cdot 7 \cdot 6 \cdot 5!}$

$\quad = \dfrac{120}{3024}$

$\quad = \dfrac{5}{126}$

The probability of choosing an all-boy committee is $\dfrac{5}{126} \approx .04$.

▶ A. Exercises

An experiment is conducted that consists of placing the numbers 1-15 in a hat and drawing one out. Find the probabilities of the following events.

1. $E_1 = \{9\}$
2. $E_2 = \{15\}$
3. $E_3 = \{3 \text{ or } 4\}$
4. $E_4 = \{17\}$
5. $E_5 = \{x > 10\}$
6. $E_6 = \{3 < x < 7\}$
7. $E_7 = \{0 < x < 16\}$
8. $E_8 = \{10 \leq x \leq 15\}$

A bag contains 3 red balls, 5 yellow balls, and 2 blue balls. One ball is drawn at random. Find the following probabilities.

9. Probability of choosing a yellow ball from the bag
10. Probability of choosing a yellow ball from the bag on the second draw after choosing a yellow ball from the bag on the first draw and then replacing it
11. Probability of choosing a yellow or a red ball on the first choice
12. Probability of not choosing a red ball

▶ B. Exercises

If a bag contains 3 red balls, 5 yellow balls, and 2 blue balls, find the following probabilities without replacement.

13. Probability that all yellow balls are selected in 4 draws
14. Probability that at least one blue ball is selected in 3 draws

There are 20 girls trying out for the varsity volleyball team. Twelve of the girls are juniors and 8 are seniors. There are 6 girls on a team. Assume all girls are equally likely to make the team. Answer the following questions.

15. What is the probability of an all-senior volleyball team?
16. What is the probability of an all-junior volleyball team?
17. What is the probability of having 2 juniors and 4 seniors on the team?
18. What is the probability of a team consisting of 3 juniors and 3 seniors?

▶ C. Exercises

There are 20 girls trying out for the varsity volleyball team. Twelve of the girls are juniors and 8 are seniors. There are 6 girls on a team. Answer the following questions.

19. Find the probability of having 1 or 2 seniors and the rest juniors.
20. Find the probability of having at least 1 senior and the rest juniors.
21. Explain the underlying assumption that shows that the exercises concerning the volleyball team are not realistic.

▶ Dominion Modeling

22. According to the NHTSA data, if a 17 year old has an accident, what is the approximate likelihood that at least one fatality will result? Why won't the data give a precise figure for 16 year olds?
23. Evaluate the following claim: "There are far more fatal accidents for all drivers in the 20-24 age bracket (7895 fatal accidents) than in all of the teenage years combined (6456 fatal accidents). Therefore teenage drivers are safer drivers than those in their early twenties."

Cumulative Review

If $f(x) = 3 \cos 5x$,

24. give the period of the graph.
25. give the amplitude of the graph.

On which side of the line or curve should the shading go?

26. $x - y < 4$
27. $x^2 - 2x + 5 \geq y$
28. $y < \log x$

a b a

c d c

C^T $X = \dfrac{\det(A_i)}{\det(A)}$

$(m \times n)(n \times p)$

$[A : I]$

Matrix Algebra 13

Advantages of Matrices

You have seen that matrices can summarize information. This applies even to probability. A probability matrix is a matrix in which each element is a probability and each column of probabilities adds up to one. The matrix below summarizes the percentage of gold mined in each region by year. If you were to obtain a piece of gold mined in 1995, the probability would be 0.26 that it was mined in Africa.

	1989	1992	1995	1998
Africa	0.32	0.31	0.26	0.22
North America	0.22	0.23	0.22	0.22
Australia	0.10	0.11	0.11	0.13
Other	0.36	0.35	0.41	0.43

Matrices are also useful for solving equations. You have seen that Cramer's Rule offers a simple formula, and in Chapter 14 you will see how to use row reduction to solve systems. However, you can also use matrix inverses to solve systems. This is especially advantageous in solving several systems having the same coefficient matrix.

Each system can be represented as a matrix equation and you already know how to solve matrix equations by multiplying both sides on the left by the inverse.

$$3x + 5y = 7 \qquad 3x + 5y = 5$$

$$x - y = 5 \qquad x - y = 1$$

The matrix $A = \begin{bmatrix} 3 & 5 \\ 1 & -1 \end{bmatrix}$ is the coefficient matrix for both systems.

The matrix equation for each is shown in the form $AX = B$ where $B = \begin{bmatrix} 7 \\ 5 \end{bmatrix}$ for the first system.

$$\begin{bmatrix} 3 & 5 \\ 1 & -1 \end{bmatrix}\begin{bmatrix} x \\ y \end{bmatrix} = \begin{bmatrix} 7 \\ 5 \end{bmatrix} \qquad\qquad \begin{bmatrix} 3 & 5 \\ 1 & -1 \end{bmatrix}\begin{bmatrix} x \\ y \end{bmatrix} = \begin{bmatrix} 5 \\ 1 \end{bmatrix}$$

Since $A^{-1} = -\dfrac{1}{8}\begin{bmatrix} -1 & -5 \\ -1 & 3 \end{bmatrix}$, the solutions to both are found using $A^{-1}B$.

$$\begin{bmatrix} x \\ y \end{bmatrix} = -\dfrac{1}{8}\begin{bmatrix} -1 & -5 \\ -1 & 3 \end{bmatrix}\begin{bmatrix} 7 \\ 5 \end{bmatrix} = \begin{bmatrix} 4 \\ -1 \end{bmatrix} \qquad\qquad \begin{bmatrix} x \\ y \end{bmatrix} = -\dfrac{1}{8}\begin{bmatrix} -1 & -5 \\ -1 & 3 \end{bmatrix}\begin{bmatrix} 5 \\ 1 \end{bmatrix} = \begin{bmatrix} \frac{5}{4} \\ \frac{1}{4} \end{bmatrix}$$

▶ Exercises

Which could be probability matrices?

1. $\begin{bmatrix} 0.5 & 0.3 & 0.9 \\ 0.4 & 0.4 & 0 \\ 0.1 & 0.3 & 0.1 \end{bmatrix}$ 2. $\begin{bmatrix} 0.2 & 1 & 0.3 \\ 0.2 & 0 & 0.3 \\ 0.6 & 0 & 0.3 \end{bmatrix}$

3. Give the matrix equation for the following system.

$x + 2y = 5$
$3x - 4y = 7$

Solve each system. Take advantage of the coefficient matrix by using inverses. See Chapter 12.

4. $2x + 5y = 5$
   $4x + 9y = 6$

5. $2x + 5y = 3$
   $4x + 9y = 4$

13.6 Algebra of Probability

Remember that when two events have nothing in common they are called *mutually exclusive events*. Since events are sets, two events, E_1 and E_2, are mutually exclusive if and only if $E_1 \cap E_2 = \varnothing$.

The eternal destinies of believers in Jesus Christ and of nonbelievers are mutually exclusive—they have nothing in common. Luke 16:19-31, the account of Lazarus and the rich man, clearly shows that heaven and hell have nothing in common. In verse 26 Abraham says, "between us and you there is a great gulf fixed: so that they which would pass from hence to you cannot; neither can they pass to us, that would come from thence." Be sure that your eternal destiny is heaven through Jesus Christ's shed blood.

The probability formulas are similar to the counting formulas. For the union of two events E_1 and E_2 where $E = E_1 \cup E_2$, use

$$P(E) = P(E_1) + P(E_2) \text{ if } E_1 \cap E_2 = \varnothing \text{ (mutually exclusive)}$$

$$P(E) = P(E_1) + P(E_2) - P(E_1 \cap E_2) \text{ otherwise}$$

Do you remember why you need to subtract?

mutually exclusive

not mutually exclusive

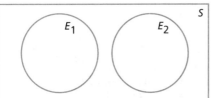
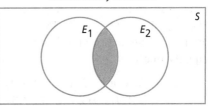

If you used the formula $P(E) = P(E_1) + P(E_2)$ to find the probability of E, in the right diagram, you would be including the $P(E_1 \cap E_2)$ twice, therefore you must subtract it once to obtain the correct probability.

EXAMPLE 1   In a certain algebra class, five of the eight girls have blue eyes and six of the ten boys have blue eyes. If one student is chosen randomly, what is the probability of selecting a blue-eyed student or a girl?

Answer

E_1 = blue-eyed student	1. Label the events.
E_2 = a girl	

$E_1 \cup E_2$ = set of students who are girls or have blue eyes   2. Determine whether E_1 and E_2 are mutually exclusive. *Note:* The blue-eyed girls are counted in both E_1 and E_2; $E_1 \cap E_2 \neq \varnothing$.

$P(E_1 \cup E_2) = P(E_1) + P(E_2) - P(E_1 \cap E_2)$ 3. Use the appropriate formula.

$P(E_1 \cup E_2) = \frac{11}{18} + \frac{8}{18} - \frac{5}{18}$

$P(E_1 \cup E_2) = \frac{7}{9}$

The likelihood of choosing a blue-eyed student or a girl is $\frac{7}{9}$.

Another way to solve this problem is to make a diagram. The information given in the problem is summarized below.

From this table you can see that fourteen of the eighteen students fit into the event E. Therefore $P(E) = \frac{14}{18} = \frac{7}{9}$.

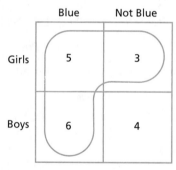

Consider an experiment that consists of tossing a coin and rolling a die. The sample space is $S = \{H1, H2, H3, H4, H5, H6, T1, T2, T3, T4, T5, T6\}$. There are twelve outcomes, and they are equally likely.

E_1 = the event of getting heads
$E_1 = \{H1, H2, H3, H4, H5, H6\}$
$P(E_1) = \frac{1}{2}$
$E_1 \cap E_2 = \{H3\}$

E_2 = the event of getting a 3
$E_2 = \{H3, T3\}$
$P(E_2) = \frac{1}{6}$
$P(E_1 \cap E_2) = \frac{1}{12}$

Note that $P(E_1 \cap E_2) = P(E_1) \cdot P(E_2)$. Events that satisfy this equation are said to be *independent*. The occurrence of one event does not affect the occurrence of the other. Mutually exclusive events and independent events are not the same thing. Mutually exclusive events are dependent, since the occurrence of one prohibits the occurrence of the other.

EXAMPLE 2 There are six white balls, three red balls, and one purple ball in a bag. An experiment consists of drawing a ball at random, replacing the ball, and drawing a second ball from the bag. What is the probability of getting a white ball followed by a red ball?

Answer

Let W = white $\quad$ R = red	1. Since the ball is replaced, the first draw does not affect the outcome of the second draw.
$P(W \text{ and } R) = P(W) \cdot P(R)$ $\quad = \frac{3}{5} \cdot \frac{3}{10}$ $\quad = \frac{9}{50}$	2. Multiply since the draws are independent events.

The likelihood of getting a white followed by a red is $\frac{9}{50} = 0.18$.

Reconsider Example 2 without replacement. In this case the events are dependent. The second event probability *depends* on what happened on the first draw. $P(B \mid A)$ will represent the probability of event B given that event A occurred previously.

EXAMPLE 3 The bag contains six white balls, three red balls, and one purple ball. If the second ball is drawn without replacement, what is the probability of drawing a white and then a red ball? Both red?

Answer

W = white $\qquad$ R = red $P(W) = \frac{6}{10} = \frac{3}{5}$ $P(R) = \frac{3}{10}$	1. First draws are calculated as before.
$P(R \mid W) = \frac{3}{9} = \frac{1}{3}$	2. If white was chosen, 3 red balls remain among the 9.
$P(R \mid R) = \frac{2}{9}$	3. If red was chosen first, only 2 red balls remain of the 9.

White then red
$P(W \cap R \mid W) = P(W) \cdot P(R \mid W)$
$\qquad\qquad = \frac{3}{5} \cdot \frac{1}{3}$
$\qquad\qquad = \frac{1}{5}$

Red then red
$P(R \cap R \mid R) = P(R) \cdot P(R \mid R)$
$\qquad\qquad = \frac{3}{10} \cdot \frac{2}{9}$
$\qquad\qquad = \frac{1}{15}$

Laws of Probability

1. Range of Probability $0 \leq P(E) \leq 1$
2. Complement $P(E') = 1 - P(E)$
3. Union $P(A \cup B) = P(A) + P(B) - P(A \cap B)$
   [If A and B are mutually exclusive, then $P(A \cup B) = P(A) + P(B)$]
4. Intersection $P(A \cap B) = P(A) \cdot P(B|A)$
   [If A and B are independent, then $P(A \cap B) = P(A) \cdot P(B)$]

▶ A. Exercises

There are 7 red marbles, 4 blue marbles, and 3 orange marbles in a bag. An experiment consists of drawing one marble at random from the bag. Find the following probabilities, using the "union" law for mutually exclusive events.

1. P(red)
2. P(red or orange)
3. P(white)

4. P(blue or red)
5. P(orange or white)

In a certain algebra class there are 8 girls and 9 boys. Three of the girls and 2 of the boys are left-handed. If a student is chosen at random, find the probability of each of the following, using the "union" law for events that are not mutually exclusive.

6. P(right-handed student)
7. P(left-handed student or girl)
8. P(student)

9. P(left-handed student or boy)
10. P(boy or right-handed student)

▶ B. Exercises

There are 8 yellow balls, 3 white balls, 4 green balls, and 2 blue balls in a box. An experiment consists of drawing a ball from the box at random and then replacing it. Then a second ball is drawn from the box. Find the following probabilities and answer the questions.

Find the following probabilities if
  E_Y = choosing a yellow ball
  E_W = choosing a white ball
  E_G = choosing a green ball
  E_B = choosing a blue ball

11. $P(E_Y$ followed by $E_G)$
12. $P(E_G$ followed by $E_Y)$
13. $P(E_G$ and $E_Y)$
14. $P(E_W$ and $E_B)$

15. P(2 white balls)
16. P(exactly one white ball)
17. P(no white balls)
18. P(at least one white ball)

19. What is the sum of the answers to exercises 15-17 and why?

There are 12 red tokens and 8 blue tokens in a bag. An experiment consists of choosing a token from the bag, replacing it, and choosing a second token. Find the following probabilities.

20. P(both draws red)
21. P(red followed by blue)
22. P(both draws blue)

There are 12 caramel and 8 cherry chocolates in a box. The two kinds are indistinguishable until eaten. If you choose 2 chocolates from the box without replacing them (because you eat the ones you choose), what are the following probabilities?

23. P(both caramel)
24. P(both cherry)
25. P(caramel followed by cherry)
26. P(cherry followed by caramel)

► C. Exercises

Write the following probabilities using combinations and evaluate. Refer to information given in the B Exercises.

27. P(cherry and caramel)
28. $P(E_W$ and $E_B)$

► Dominion Modeling

29. Someone has claimed that "accident rates fall dramatically by age 18." From the NHTSA data, argue for how much cheaper auto insurance should be for a 25 year old compared to a 17 year old. (*Hint:* Compare the number of drivers in all crashes.)

Cumulative Review

Classify the pairs of lines by matching. You need not graph.

30. $y = 3x + 1$
    $y = 2x - 5$

31. $5x - y = 3$
    $y = 5x - 2$

32. $y = \frac{1}{4}x - 2$
    $y = -4x$

33. $3x - 7y = 2$
    $2x + 5y = 7$

34. $12x + 3y = 6$
    $y = -4x + 2$

35. $8x - 2y = 3$
    $x + 4y = 1$

A. Identical
B. Parallel
C. Perpendicular
D. None of the above

ALGEBRA

AROUND THE WORLD

FRENCH MATH

France has a long and glorious heritage as a center for mathematics. The Frenchman René Descartes founded analytic geometry, which relates geometry to algebraic equations. Two Frenchmen also founded probability.

Blaise Pascal and Pierre de Fermat set down the elementary beginnings of probability while helping a gambler friend of Pascal's. The Chevalier de Mere, Antoine Gombaud, had come to seek mathematical help in gambling from his friend Pascal, who had developed the form of binomial coefficients known as Pascal's Triangle.

The title page of this 1527 math text shows Pascal's Triangle, proof that it was known at least 100 years before the birth of Pascal.

```
                1
              1   1
            1   2   1
          1   3   3   1
        1   4   6   4   1
      1   5  10  10   5   1
    1   6  15  20  15   6   1
```

Pascal corresponded with Fermat, and they determined the probabilities involved in gambling. However, the chevalier ignored the laws of probability and gambled anyway.

Probability later blossomed under French mathematicians such as DeMoivre, Laplace, and Poisson. Abraham DeMoivre produced a work called the *Doctrine of Chances* that dealt with annuities, life expectancies, and the idea of the normal distribution. Nearly a century later Pierre Simon Laplace produced a seven-hundred-page masterpiece on probability that applied calculus to the field. Siméon Denis Poisson, a student of Laplace, developed a probability distribution that is used to model traffic flow and radioactive decay.

In the 1700s, Joseph-Louis Lagrange worked in Paris. He strengthened the foundations of calculus and contributed to differential equations. In 1832, Evariste Galois died in Paris in a sword duel at age 20. Although he was young, his writings have kept mathematicians busy until the present. Henri Lebesque made Paris an important center for calculus research in the 1900s.

Paris has been a center for mathematics for centuries. Key schools of mathematics include the Sorbonne, the Ecole Normale (Normal School), the Ecole Polytechnique (Polytechnic School), and the College of France. The French Academy of Sciences also encouraged mathematical research and played a role similar to Britain's Royal Society of London. In fact, mathematics in Paris dates back to the University of Paris, Europe's second oldest university, founded in the 1100s.

The Ecole Polytechnique has been especially influential. Poisson taught here, and its first director, Gaspard Monge, applied math to problems of engineering and military weapons. Other teachers there included Camille Jordan, who proved Jordan's Curve Theorem in geometry; Jean Baptiste Joseph Fourier, whose Fourier series have many applications in engineering; Charles Hermite, an algebraist; and Augustine Louis Cauchy, whose many writings contributed much to make calculus a more rigorous discipline.

> *Paris has been a center for mathematics for centuries.*

Why would the Pont du Gard near Nimes, France, have been more familiar than the Eiffel Tower to these great French mathematicians?

The University of Paris is one of the five oldest universities in Europe and dates from the 12th century.

13.7 Descriptive Statistics

Statistics describe sets of data and help summarize information. You have studied some of these before; review the definitions below. Some symbols may be new: x is used to represent an individual score or value, $\bar{x}$ is the mean of a set of data, n is the number of scores in the set, and Σ (capital Greek letter sigma for summation) means add the numbers in a set of data.

Definitions

Mean The arithmetic average obtained from a set of data scores or values by dividing the total by the number of scores: $\bar{x} = \frac{\Sigma x}{n}$

Median The middle score or the average of the two middle scores if there is an even number of scores.

Mode The most frequent score if there is one.

Midrange The average of the highest and lowest score.

Range The difference between the highest and lowest score.

EXAMPLE 1 Find the mean, median, mode, midrange, and range of the student scores on a ten-point quiz.

6, 7, 9, 5, 10, 9, 9, 6, 8, 9

Answer

10, 9, 9, 9, 9, 8, 7, 6, 6, 5	1. Arrange the scores from highest to lowest.
$\Sigma x = 10 + 9 + 9 + 9 + 9 + 8 + 7 + 6 + 6 + 5 = 78$	2. Add the scores.

Continued ▶

$$\text{Mean } \bar{x} = \frac{\Sigma x}{n} = \frac{78}{10} = 7.8$$
$$\text{Median} = \frac{8+9}{2} = 8.5$$
$$\text{Mode} = 9$$
$$\text{Midrange} = \frac{10+5}{2} = 7.5$$
$$\text{Range} = 10 - 5 = 5$$

3. Use the definitions to calculate each measurement.

The mean is what is usually referred to as the average. The median is average in the sense that half of the students did better and half did worse than that number. The mode is the "average" in the sense of typical or most common. The midrange is "average" in being the midpoint of the range. These four values are called measures of central tendency.

The range is not a measure of central tendency. Instead, it measures variability (or dispersion). Such measures describe how spread out the data is. The range is the simplest such measurement. Suppose everyone had scored 5 except one person who scored 10. In that case the range would remain 5 even though only one score varies from all the others. This suggests the need for measures of variability based on all the data instead of just two values.

Deviations measure how far a score is from the mean. The person who scored a 10 deviates 10 − 7.8 or 2.2 points from the mean. The person who scored 7 deviates 7 − 7.8 or −0.8 from the mean. The negative sign tells you that the score is below the mean. If you add up all the deviations, the positive and negatives balance and the total is always zero. To get a useful measurement you must obtain a positive number. This can be done in either of two ways: taking absolute values or squaring before finding the sum.

Definitions

Mean deviation The mean of the absolute values of the deviations. $\frac{\Sigma |x - \bar{x}|}{n}$

Variance The mean of the squares of the deviations. $s^2 = \frac{\Sigma (x - \bar{x})^2}{n - 1}$

Standard deviation The square root of the variance. $s = \sqrt{s^2}$

Notice that the variance is divided by $n - 1$ instead of n. This change in divisor makes it a modified average. The modification turns out to make the calculation more useful for describing samples.

EXAMPLE 2 Calculate these measures of variability using the data from Example 1.

Answer

	$\bar{x}$	$(x - \bar{x})$	$\|x - \bar{x}\|$	$(x - \bar{x})^2$	
Score	Mean	Deviation	Absolute Deviation	Square of Deviation	
10	7.8	2.2	2.2	4.84	1. Make a chart
9	7.8	1.2	1.2	1.44	of your
9	7.8	1.2	1.2	1.44	calculations.
9	7.8	1.2	1.2	1.44	
9	7.8	1.2	1.2	1.44	
8	7.8	0.2	0.2	0.04	
7	7.8	−0.8	0.8	0.64	
6	7.8	−1.8	1.8	3.24	
6	7.8	−1.8	1.8	3.24	
5	7.8	−2.8	2.8	7.84	
78	7.8	0	14.4	25.6	2. Total each column.

You have already found the mean $\frac{\Sigma x}{n}$ in the first two columns and shown that $\Sigma(x - \bar{x}) = 0$ in the third column. Find the other measures using the last two columns.

$$\text{Range} = 10 - 5 = 5$$

$$\text{Mean deviation} = \frac{\Sigma |x - \bar{x}|}{n} = \frac{14.4}{10} = 1.44$$

$$\text{Variance, } s^2 = \frac{\Sigma(x - \bar{x})^2}{n - 1} = \frac{25.6}{10 - 1} = \frac{25.6}{9} = 2.84$$

$$\text{Standard deviation, } s = \sqrt{s^2} = \sqrt{2.84} = 1.69$$

▶ A. Exercises

The following data represents the number of homes built annually by a building contractor for the last seven years. Find each of the following.

15, 22, 16, 24, 8, 17, 12

1. mean
2. median
3. mode
4. range

5. sum of squares of deviations
6. variance
7. standard deviation

▶ B. Exercises

Use the data shown representing scores on a 100-point test. Find each measurement.

$$97 \quad 69 \quad 93 \quad 88 \quad 92 \quad 77$$
$$32 \quad 77 \quad 87 \quad 74 \quad 85 \quad 65$$

8. mean
9. median
10. mode
11. midrange

12. range
13. sum of squared deviations
14. variance
15. standard deviation

Answer the following questions about a set of scores.
16. If the variance is 70, what is the standard deviation?
17. If the standard deviation is 15, what is the variance?
18. If $\Sigma(x - \bar{x})^2 = 672$ and there were 40 scores, find s.
19. If $\Sigma x = 150$ and $\bar{x} = 7.5$, how many scores were there?

What can you conclude about a 100-point test if
20. the median is 96 and the range is 2?
21. the midrange is 70 and the range is 30?
22. the mean is 85 and the range is 4?

▶ C. Exercises

23. What can you conclude about a test with a median of 70 and a mean of 87?
24. Reconsider the set of data at the start of the B exercises. Contrast the sum of deviations and the mean deviation.
25. Explain why the variance is least like the other three measures of variability.

▶ Dominion Modeling

26. Based on the NHTSA data, which are safer, men or women drivers?

▣ Cumulative Review

Give the number of solutions to each equation and classify them as complex or real and if real as rational or irrational.
27. $x^2 + x - 5 = 0$
28. $3x^2 + x + 4 = 0$
29. $9x^2 + 12x + 4 = 0$
30. $x^2 - 7 = 8x$
31. $x(x + 1) = -2x^2 + 4$

13.8 Standard Normal Distribution

Tom scored 570 on his SAT test. The test results were "normally distributed." The national testing service calculated the mean for the test as 495 with a standard deviation of 102. To interpret his score, a *z-score* is calculated where $z = \frac{x - \bar{x}}{s}$. For Tom's test, $z = \frac{570 - 495}{102} \approx 0.74$

Since $570 - 495$ is his deviation from the mean, dividing by the standard deviation converts this number into units of standard deviation. Tom's score is 0.74 standard deviations above the mean.

To further interpret his test, we must learn about the *standard normal distribution,* which is a special exponential function:

$$f(x) = \frac{1}{\sqrt{2\pi}} e^{-\frac{1}{2}x^2}$$

The graph of this function is shown below. You can see why the standard normal distribution is often called "the bell-shaped curve."

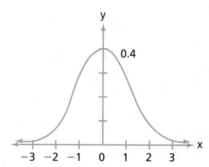

Since the graph is symmetric, the y-axis ($x = 0$) divides it in half. Therefore 0 is the median value. Notice the most frequent value (mode) is also zero since it is the highest spot on the graph. Zero is also the mean. You can use tables to find the percentage of scores between 0 and other x values.

EXAMPLE 1 Find the percent of scores between 0 and 1 on the normal curve and then between 0 and −2.4.

Continued ▶

Answer

$P(0 \le x \le 1) = 0.3413$ or 34.1%	1. Look up 1.00 on the table (p. 618).
$P(-2.4 \le x \le 0) = 0.4918$ or 49.2%	2. Since the graph is symmetric look up 2.40.

Returning to Tom's *z*-score of **0.74**, we look in the table to find $P(0 \le x \le 0.74)$ = **0.2704 ≈ 27%**. Since **50%** of the students who took the test have *z*-scores below the mean **50% + 27% = 77%** percent finished below Tom. This means that Tom scored in the 77th percentile, or that only **23%** of the students scored better than he scored.

EXAMPLE 2   What percent of scores occur (a) between −2.03 and 1.37? (b) between −3 and 3?

Answer

(a)
$$P(0 \le x \le 1.37) = 0.4147$$
$$P(-2.03 \le x \le 0) = 0.4788$$
$$P(-2.03 \le x \le 1.37) = 0.4147 + 0.4788$$
$$= 0.8935 \text{ or } 89.4\%$$

1. Use the table for percents between zero and each given value. Since the graph is symmetric look up 2.03. Combine the probabilities.

(b)
$$P(0 \le x \le 3) = 0.4987$$
$$P(-3 \le x \le 3) = 2(0.4987)$$
$$= 0.9974 \text{ or } 99.7\%$$

2. The graph is symmetric so look up the value for 3 and double it.

In Example 2a you added the shaded percents since the values had opposite signs. This is shown in the left diagram below. In Example 3 you must subtract as shown in the right diagram below. Drawing such a diagram will help you know whether to add or subtract.

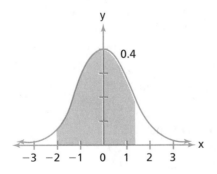 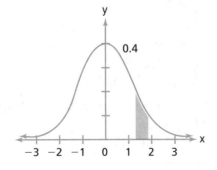

EXAMPLE 3   Find $P(1.4 \leq x \leq 1.9)$.

Answer

$P(0 \leq x \leq 1.4) = 0.4192$ $P(0 \leq x \leq 1.9) = 0.4713$	1. Find probabilities from the table.
$P(1.4 \leq x \leq 1.9) = 0.4713 - 0.4192$ $= 0.0521$ or 5.2%	2. Since values of x less than 1.4 should not be included (see graph), subtract the probabilities to eliminate them.

You can also use the table in reverse as shown in Example 4.

EXAMPLE 4   Find the value of a for which 30% of the scores occur between 0 and a.

Answer

$P(0 \leq x \leq a) = 0.3$	1. Express 30% as a decimal.
$a = 0.84$	2. Find the entry in the chart closest to 0.3. Read the answer in the margin.

30% of the scores fall between the mean and 0.84 standard deviations above it.

▶ A. Exercises

In the standard normal distribution, what percent of the scores occur between zero and

1. 2?
2. 0.5?
3. −1.2?

4. −2.7?
5. 1.74?
6. −0.89?

What percent of the scores occur between

7. −2 and 2?
8. −1.5 and 1.5?

9. −0.38 and 0.38?
10. −2.57 and 2.57?

What percent of scores occur between

11. −0.3 and 1.8?
12. −2.1 and 1.34?
13. 1.46 and 2.46?

14. 0.77 and 2.15?
15. −1.3 and −1.29?
16. −3 and −2.51?

▶ B. Exercises

Find the value of a such that $P(0 \le x \le a)$ is the given percent.

17. 17%
18. 40%

Find the value of a such that $P(-a \le x \le a)$ is the given percent.

19. 31%
20. 95%

▶ C. Exercises

21. Find the percent of scores such that $P(x \le -0.5 \text{ or } x \ge 0.5)$.
22. Find the value of a such that $P(x \le -a \text{ or } x \ge a) = 25\%$.

▶ Dominion Modeling

23. In the NHTSA data, consider female drivers from age **17** to **84**. Are the numbers of licensed female drivers normally distributed? (*Hint:* Data is normally distributed if a plot of the data looks like the normal distribution, even if it is not centered at $x = 0$.)

▮ Cumulative Review

Simplify. Be sure to follow the order of operations.

24. $\sqrt{5} - \sqrt{3} \cdot \sqrt{6} + \sqrt{45} \div 3$
25. $(i - 2)(3 + i) - 2i^6 \div i$
26. $i^{33} \div (i + 4)^2$
27. $\left(\sqrt{2}\right)^5 \div \left(3 - \sqrt{2}\right)$
28. $\sqrt{3}\left(5\sqrt{3} - \sqrt{6}i\right) + (i^2 - 9)$

Algebra *and* Scripture

Probability

Do you ever say that something is a "coincidence" or that "it just so happened?" Do you ever change your plans because you think it will "probably" rain? When playing a board game that uses a spinner, do you figure out your "chances" of getting the number you need to win? How often do you use words like "maybe" or "perhaps" to express unlikely "possibilities?" All of these are expressions of probability.

1. According to Proverbs 16:33, is there such a thing as probability or chance? Why?

2. What attribute of God shows this?

GREATER AMPLITUDE.
   Give a verse that shows that God has this attribute.

In light of this, you may be a bit concerned that you use those kinds of expressions. Indeed, if you are speaking to someone who might not understand your trust in God's ultimate control, it would be better to glorify God in your wording.

3. How did James suggest rephrasing future plans in James 4:13-15?

On the other hand, the Bible does *not* condemn the language of chance altogether. There is a certain place for it.

What is described using words about chance in each verse?

4. Deuteronomy 22:6
5. Ecclesiastics 9:11
6. Luke 10:31

There is no chance with God according to Proverbs, but the verses above recognize that many things seem like chance from the human perspective. Just as Jesus used the language of chance in the parable, a Christian can also use it and study it. The Christian must keep his studies in context, though, and not forget that the human perspective is not the whole picture.

7. Explain how words like "sunset" and "sunrise" also illustrate the human perspective.
8. Can you find examples of these or similar phrases in the Bible?

As you study probability, keep in mind God's perspective; be sure to balance your use of such phrases with ones that give God the glory for His providential control; and finally, avoid the world's view of chance. Consider some worldly uses briefly.

9. Gamblers, propagandists, and evolutionists all misuse probability and statistics. What sin is committed in their misuse?
10. Deuteronomy 18:10-12 names some occult groups who try to use God's created order to know and control the future. Sometimes they succeed with demonic assistance. What does God call such people?

> ### Absolute Values
>
> THE LOT IS CAST into the lap; but the whole disposing thereof is of the Lord.
>
> PROVERBS 16:33

Chapter 13 Review

Show a tree diagram, make a list, and use the Fundamental Principle of Counting to find the number of possibilities in this exercise.

1. A coin is flipped, and then a die is rolled. How many outcomes are possible, and what are they?

Evaluate.

2. $_7P_5$

3. $_3C_2$

4. $_8C_3$

5. $_4P_2$

6. How many different committees of 7 people can be chosen from a group of 10?

7. How many different arrangements of 8 different books are possible on a shelf?

8. How many ways can 5 bicycles be parked in a bicycle rack that has 12 slots?

9. How many different ways can the letters of the word *mouse* be arranged?

10. How many different ways can the letters of the word *algebra* be arranged?

11. How many ways can 6 children be arranged around a table?

12. Expand $(x + 4y)^3$.

13. Expand $(a - 6)^4$.

A bag has 5 orange, 3 purple, and 6 blue tokens in it. Find the probability of choosing the following token(s).

14. P(orange)

15. P(blue)

16. P(purple or orange)

Assuming replacement, find the following probabilities.

17. P(purple followed by orange)

18. P(orange followed by orange)

There are 7 girls and 6 boys in a class. Three of the girls and 2 of the boys have brown eyes. If a student is chosen at random, find the following probabilities.

19. P(brown-eyed girl)

20. P(brown-eyed boy)

21. P(brown-eyed student or a girl)

22. P(brown-eyed student or a boy)

The following are times for running the quarter mile in one gym class at a large school.

55.9	49.8	49.9
60.3	53.7	58.2
56.8	60.5	61.5
61.4	60.7	59.4
59.2	61.0	59.3

Find the following under the assumption that the times are normally distributed.

23. mean
24. median
25. range
26. variance
27. standard deviation
28. z-score for 53.7
29. The percent of students in the school that a time of 53.7 would beat if the school has a mean time of 56.9 with a standard deviation of 3.60.
30. Find $P(-1.1 \le z \le 0.72)$
31. Evaluate probabilities. Take the quotients of Drivers in Fatal Crashes and Licensed Drivers. Does this give the probability of being a driver in a fatal crash?
32. What is the mathematical significance of Proverbs 16:33?

14 Analytic Geometry

On December 12, 2012, Planet Earth will have an unusual visitor. Asteroid Toutatis will come within 4.63% of our distance from the sun—a "Potentially Hazardous Asteroid."

Orbits of minor planets (such as asteroids and comets) vary in shape, and astronomers model them with *conic sections* to determine which are hazardous. A few planetary orbits are nearly circular, but most are elliptical.

Here is the data for three extraterrestrial rocks. In the tables, q stands for *perihelion*, or the closest distance to the sun; and e is for *eccentricity*, a measure of the shape of the orbit. The perihelia are in *AU* or *Astronomical Units* (the distance from the earth to the sun).

	q	e	Shape	Perihelion date
Asteroid Toutatis	0.918	0.634	Ellipse	2012 Dec 12.28
Comet Machholz (1994r)	1.845571	1.0	Parabola	1994 Oct 2.5858
Comet Larsen (C/1998 M3)	5.767912	1.002391	Hyperbola	1998 July 16.9763

You will also need similar data for the major planets.

Major Planet	Perihelion, q	Eccentricity, e	Major Planet	Perihelion, q	Eccentricity, e
Mercury	0.307	0.2056	Saturn	9.086	0.0516
Venus	0.718	0.0068	Uranus	18.269	0.0443
Earth	0.983	0.0167	Neptune	29.893	0.0073
Mars	1.381	0.0934	Pluto	29.552	0.2481
Jupiter	4.951	0.0485			

After this chapter you should be able to

1. use *conical surfaces* to define the four conic sections.
2. define each conic section as a locus of points.
3. state the equations of the four conics in standard position.
4. graph and translate each type of conic section.
5. find related points and lines: vertices, centers, foci, directrices, axes, and asymptotes.
6. find the equation of conics from given information.
7. solve quadratic systems graphically and algebraically.

14.1 Conic Sections

In this chapter you will see the relation between several figures and the equations that describe them. These figures are frequently seen in design and architecture and are called *conic sections* because they are formed from the intersection of a plane and a conical surface.

Conical surface   The union of all lines through a given point that is not in a given plane and any point of a simple curve in the plane.

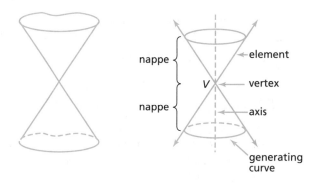

The curve in the given plane is called the *generating curve,* and the point not in the plane is the *vertex.* The lines that go through the given point *V* are called *elements* of the conical surface. The upper and lower sections of the conical surface are called *nappes* of the surface and the vertex is contained in both nappes.

If the generating curve is a circle, the conical surface is called a *circular cone.* Each circular cone has an *axis,* the line determined by the vertex and the center of the circle. This chapter focuses on right circular cones, which not only have a circle as a generating curve, but also have an axis perpendicular to the plane of the circle.

Figures obtained from the intersection of a plane and a cone are called conic sections or just conics. The shape of the figures depends on how a plane intersects a right circular cone.

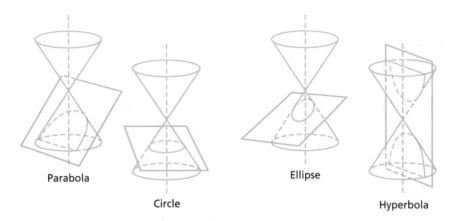

Parabola

Circle

Ellipse

Hyperbola

Analytic geometry is the branch of geometry that uses algebra and the Cartesian plane. Analytic geometry is a useful tool in proving geometric relationships. Study the following sample proofs so that you can understand the proofs related to conics later in this chapter.

Theorem
If two distinct nonvertical lines have the same slope, then the lines are parallel.

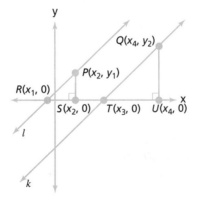

To prove this theorem, draw two lines on a Cartesian graph, and label their intersections with the x-axis R and T. Locate arbitrary points P and Q, one on each line. Drop perpendiculars from P and Q to the x-axis, meeting it in points S and U, respectively. Supply arbitrary coordinates for the points R, S, T, and U from left to right as shown. Since P and S have the same x-coordinate, the point P has coordinates (x_2, y_1). Likewise, Q has coordinates (x_4, y_2).

From this drawing and some analytic geometry, you should be able to prove the theorem.

Assume: $m_l = m_k$

Prove: $l \parallel k$

Proof.

STATEMENTS	REASONS
1. $m_l = m_k$, $x_2 > x_1$, $x_4 > x_3$	1. Assumed. Note that naming coordinates "left to right" justifies these inequalities.
2. $m_l = \dfrac{y_1 - 0}{x_2 - x_1} = \dfrac{y_1}{x_2 - x_1}$; $\quad m_k = \dfrac{y_2 - 0}{x_4 - x_3} = \dfrac{y_2}{x_4 - x_3}$	2. Definition of slope $\left(m = \dfrac{y_2 - y_1}{x_2 - x_1} \right)$
3. $\dfrac{y_1}{x_2 - x_1} = \dfrac{y_2}{x_4 - x_3}$	3. Substitution property
4. $PS = \left| y_1 - 0 \right| = \left| y_1 \right| = y_1$ $RS = \left| x_2 - x_1 \right| = x_2 - x_1$ $QU = \left| y_2 - 0 \right| = \left| y_2 \right| = y_2$ $TU = \left| x_4 - x_3 \right| = x_4 - x_3$	4. Definition of distance between points; also see step 1 assumptions.
5. $\dfrac{PS}{RS} = \dfrac{QU}{TU}$	5. Substitution property
6. $\dfrac{PS}{QU} = \dfrac{RS}{TU}$	6. Multiplication property of equality $\left(\text{by } \dfrac{RS}{QU} \right)$
7. $\angle PSR \cong \angle QUT$	7. Perpendicular lines form right angles, and all right angles are congruent.
8. $\triangle PSR \sim \triangle QUT$	8. SAS Similarity Theorem
9. $\angle PRS \cong \angle QTU$	9. Definition of similar triangles
10. $l \parallel k$	10. If two lines are cut by a transversal (x-axis) such that their corresponding angles are congruent, then the lines are parallel.
11. $\therefore$ If two distinct nonvertical lines have the same slope, then the lines are parallel.	11. Law of Deduction

You can see that this proof required both algebra and geometry. Steps 2, 3, 4, and 6 were primarily algebraic while the rest of the proof was geometric. Since all truth is related in Christ (Col. 2:3), your knowledge of all fields of learning affects your skills in other areas. Consider another proof involving analytic geometry.

Theorem

The diagonals of a rectangle are congruent.

Locate the rectangle on a Cartesian plane in an appropriate position. Place one vertex at the origin and label the other points with arbitrary ordered pairs.

Given: Quadrilateral $WXYZ$ is a rectangle.

Prove: $\overline{WY} \cong \overline{XZ}$

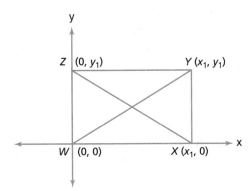

Proof:

STATEMENTS	REASONS
1. Quadrilateral $WXYZ$ is a rectangle.	1. Given
2. $WY = \sqrt{(x_1 - 0)^2 + (y_1 - 0)^2}$ $= \sqrt{x_1^2 + y_1^2}$ $XZ = \sqrt{(x_1 - 0)^2 + (0 - y_1)^2}$ $= \sqrt{x_1^2 + (-y_1)^2}$ $= \sqrt{x_1^2 + y_1^2}$	2. Distance formula $d = \sqrt{(x_2 - x_1)^2 + (y_2 - y_1)^2}$ and its application to XZ and WY
3. $WY = XZ$	3. Transitive property of equality
4. $\overline{WY} \cong \overline{XZ}$	4. Definition of congruence

▶ A. Exercises

Draw the following figures and then explain the answers.

1. The intersection of a right circular conical surface and a plane that is parallel to an element of the surface
2. The intersection of a right circular conical surface and a plane that is perpendicular to the axis of the cone

3. The intersection of a right circular conical surface and a plane that is parallel to the axis of the cone

4. The intersection of a right circular conical surface and a plane that is not parallel to an element or perpendicular to the axis and that intersects only one nappe of the surface

5. The intersection of a right circular conical surface and a plane that contains the axis of the cone

6. The intersection of a right circular conical surface and a plane containing exactly one element of the surface

7. The intersection of a right circular conical surface and a plane that is perpendicular to the axis of the cone and that intersects both nappes

8. The intersection of a right circular conical surface and a plane that intersects both nappes but not at the vertex

9. Which conic sections are subsets of only one nappe?

▶ B. Exercises

10. Use the diagram to prove the theorem: If two distinct nonvertical lines are perpendicular, then their slopes are negative reciprocals.

Assume: $l \perp k$

Prove: $m_l \cdot m_k = -1$

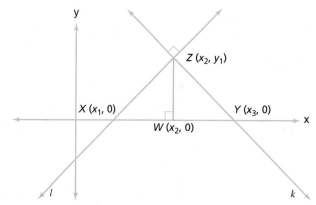

Supply the reason for each step in the proof of the given theorem.

Theorem
The altitude to the hypotenuse of an isosceles right triangle is a median.

Given: △*ABC* is an isosceles right triangle with $\overline{BD} \perp \overline{AC}$ at *D*.

Prove: $\overline{BD}$ is a median of △*ABC*.

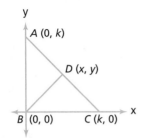

Proof:

STATEMENTS	REASONS
11. △*ABC* is an isosceles right triangle with $BD \perp AC$ at *D*.	**11.**
12. $m_{AC} = \dfrac{0 - k}{k - 0} = \dfrac{-k}{k} = -1$	**12.**
13. $m_{BD} = 1$	**13.**
14. Equation of $\overleftrightarrow{BD}$ is $y = x$ Equation of $\overleftrightarrow{AC}$ is $y = -x + k$	**14.**
15. $2y = k$	**15.**
16. $y = \dfrac{k}{2}$	**16.**
17. $x = \dfrac{k}{2}$ so $D\left(\dfrac{k}{2}, \dfrac{k}{2}\right)$	**17.**
18. *D* is the midpoint of $\overline{AC}$.	**18.**
19. $\overline{BD}$ is a median of △*ABC*.	**19.**

Prove the theorems.

20. The diagonals of an isosceles trapezoid are congruent.

21. If the diagonals of a parallelogram are congruent, then the parallelogram is a rectangle.

22. If the diagonals of a rhombus are congruent, then the rhombus is a square.

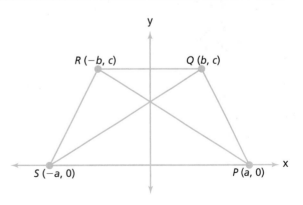

23. The diagonals of a rhombus are perpendicular to each other. (*Hint:* Find *a* in terms of *b* and *c*.)

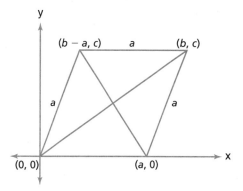

▶ C. Exercises

Prove the following theorems.

24. The diagonals of a parallelogram bisect each other.

25. The midpoint of the hypotenuse of a right triangle is equidistant from each vertex.

▶ Dominion Modeling

26. For the astronomy data, how many miles will Toutatis be from the earth at its closest? Is the moon closer? (*Hint:* The sun is about **92.96** million miles from the earth.)

Cumulative Review

Calculate each and explain what it represents.

27. $7!$

28. $_{18}C_3$

29. $_6P_2$

30. $\dfrac{_5P_5}{5}$

31. $\dfrac{16!}{9!5!2!}$

14.2 Circles

The first conic that you will study is the circle. The geometric definition that you discovered in the previous section follows.

Circles occur in architecture, especially inside domed cathedrals, such as the Basilica of St. Josaphat in Milwaukee, Wisconsin.

Definition

Circle The intersection of one nappe of a right circular conical surface and a plane that is perpendicular to the axis of the conical surface (not at the vertex).

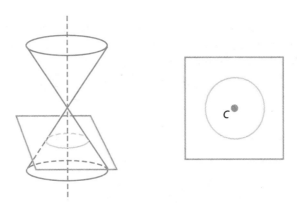

The second diagram shows a circle as a cross section of the conical surface. Like other conic sections, a circle can also be defined as a locus of points, that is, as a set of points that satisfy a given condition. You should be familiar with both definitions.

Definition

Circle The locus of points in a plane a fixed distance from a fixed point in the plane.

The fixed point is the *center* of the circle, and the fixed distance is the *radius* of the circle.

Each conic section also has an algebraic equation, which can be derived from the locus of points that defines it. Deriving the equations will require analytic geometry. You should keep a summary of the standard equations of the conics, and be able to use them to graph. To derive the equation of a circle, let the center C have coordinates (h, k). Label an arbitrary point P of the locus with coordinates (x, y).

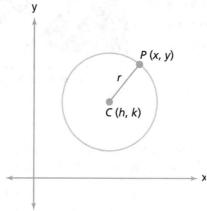

According to the definition, a circle is a set of points that are equidistant from C. Therefore the distance from P to C is r. You can now apply the distance formula to develop the equation of a circle.

$$d = \sqrt{(x_1 - x_2)^2 + (y_1 - y_2)^2}$$
$$r = \sqrt{(x - h)^2 + (y - k)^2}$$

Square both sides to eliminate the square root from the equation.

$$r^2 = (x - h)^2 + (y - k)^2$$
$$(x - h)^2 + (y - k)^2 = r^2$$

This is the general form of the equation for a circle with center (h, k) and a radius of r.

EXAMPLE 1   Write the equation of the circle having center (3, 7) and a radius of 6.

Answer $(x - h)^2 + (y - k)^2 = r^2$ 1. Write the general equation.

$(x - 3)^2 + (y - 7)^2 = 6^2$ 2. Since the center is (3, 7), $h = 3$
$(x - 3)^2 + (y - 7)^2 = 36$ and $k = 7$. The radius $r = 6$.
                                                            Substitute these values in the
                                                            general equation.

EXAMPLE 2   Give the center and radius of $(x + 5)^2 + (y - 1)^2 = 7$.

Answer $(x + 5)^2 + (y - 1)^2 = 7$

$[x - (-5)]^2 + (y - 1)^2 = (\sqrt{7})^2$ Write the equation in general form to deter-

$h = -5, k = 1, r = \sqrt{7}$ mine the values of h, k, and r.

The center is $(-5, 1)$, and the radius is $\sqrt{7}$.

EXAMPLE 3   Graph $(x - 2)^2 + (y + 4)^2 = 9$.

Answer $(x - 2)^2 + (y + 4)^2 = 9$ 1. Determine the center and radius.
$(x - 2)^2 + [y - (-4)]^2 = 3^2$
Center $(2, -4)$; $r = 3$

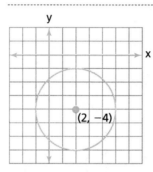

2. Graph the circle using this information.

Sometimes you will have to change an equation to the general form. To do this, complete the square as you learned in Chapter 4.

EXAMPLE 4   Graph $x^2 + 6x + y^2 - 4y = 8$.

Answer

$x^2 + 6x + y^2 - 4y = 8$

$(x^2 + 6x) + (y^2 - 4y) = 8$ 1. Group the x terms and the y terms together.

$(x^2 + 6x + 9) + (y^2 - 4y + 4) = 8 + 9 + 4$ 2. Complete the square inside both sets of parentheses, adding the same amounts to the right side of the equation.

Continued ▶

$(x + 3)^2 + (y - 2)^2 = 21$ 3. Factor the polynomials in both sets of parentheses.

Center $(-3, 2)$; $r = \sqrt{21} \approx 4.6$ 4. Identify the center and radius from the standard form.

5. Graph.

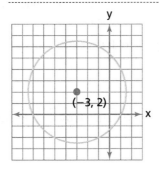

▶ A. Exercises

State the center and radius length of each circle described below.

1. $(x - 7)^2 + (y - 3)^2 = 49$
2. $(x - 1)^2 + (y - 2)^2 = 9$
3. $(x + 6)^2 + (y - 4)^2 = 36$
4. $(x + 9)^2 + (y + 5)^2 = 7$
5. $(x - 2)^2 + y^2 = 3$

6. $(x - 8)^2 + (y - 12)^2 = 25$
7. $x^2 + y^2 = 2$
8. $(x + 7)^2 + (y - 4)^2 = 19$
9. $(x - 8)^2 + (y + 14)^2 = 9$
10. $(x + 6)^2 + (y - 2)^2 = 18$

Graph.

11. $x^2 + y^2 = 16$
12. $(x - 3)^2 + (y - 2)^2 = 9$
13. $(x + 4)^2 + y^2 = 8$

14. $x^2 + (y - 5)^2 = 12$
15. $(x - 1)^2 + (y + 3)^2 = 36$

▶ B. Exercises

Write each equation in standard form.

16. $x^2 + 8x + y^2 + 6y = 18$
17. $x^2 + 12x + y^2 - 2y = 10$
18. $x^2 - 6x + y^2 + 10y = 23$
19. $x^2 - 8x + y^2 - 6y = 1$
20. $x^2 + 2x + y^2 - 9y = 7$

▶ C. Exercises

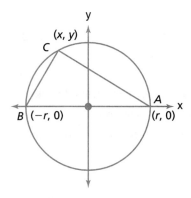

21. Prove: An angle inscribed in a semicircle is a right angle.

22. Write $\frac{1}{3}x^2 - 5x + \frac{1}{3}y^2 + \frac{2}{9}y = 7$ in general form and identify the center and radius.

▶ Dominion Modeling

23. From comets and asteroids at the beginning of the chapter, which orbit is closest to a circle? Why?

24. Of the major planets, which orbit is most circular? Why?

Cumulative Review

25. If $b^2 - 4ac = 11$,
    a. what can you say about the roots of $ax^2 + bx + c = 0$?
    b. what can you say about the x-intercepts of the function
       $f(x) = ax^2 + bx + c$?

    Assume $f(x) = \frac{P(x)}{Q(x)}$, $Q(x) \neq 0$, where $P(1) = -3$ and $Q(4) = 0$

26. What can you say about $P(x)$ according to the remainder theorem?

27. What point do we know is on $P(x)$? If we assume the point is the vertex and the curve opens downward, how many zeros does it have?

28. What point do we know on $Q(x)$, and what is the y-intercept of $Q^{-1}(x)$?

29. On the graph of $f(x) = \frac{P(x)}{Q(x)}$, what do the zeros of $P(x)$ and $Q(x)$ represent?

14.3 Parabolas

The next conic section that you will study is the *parabola*. The ancient Greek mathematician Apollonius introduced this term, which comes from a verb meaning "to throw along." It is an appropriate term because a ball thrown into the air traces out this type of curve.

It is no accident that the word *parabola* is similar to the word *parable*. The Greeks applied the same root word to a comparison. Figuratively speaking, a comparison throws one story alongside another to make a point. Jesus often used parables to teach spiritual truths. For example, he compared those who hear the Word of God to types of soil ranging from hard or stony to good (Mark 4:1-20). Which kind of soil represents you? Would Jesus say that the Word takes root and grows in your life?

You worked with parabolas when you studied quadratic functions. This section provides a general study of these curves. To begin the study, define parabola using geometric sections of a conical surface and also as a locus of points in the plane.

Definitions

Parabola   the intersection of a right circular conical surface and a plane that is parallel to an element of the conical surface.

Parabola   the locus of points in a plane that are equidistant from a fixed point and a fixed line.

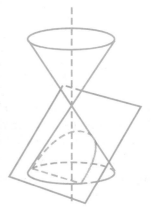

In the second definition, the fixed point F is called the *focus* and the fixed line $\overleftrightarrow{D_1 D_2}$ is called the *directrix*. The distance from the focus to a point of the parabola is equal to the distance from the directrix to the same point of the parabola: $L_1D_1 = L_1F$ and $L_2D_2 = L_2F$. Notice that the distance from the point to the directrix is the perpendicular distance.

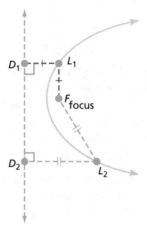

In the figure below, the midpoint (*V*) between the focus and the directrix is called the *vertex*. The vertex is the maximum point in a parabola that opens downward or the minimum point in one that opens upward. Since the vertex is at the origin and the focus is at $(0, p)$, p is the distance from the vertex to the focus and from the vertex to the directrix. Since p represents the distance from vertex to focus, it is called the *focal distance* of the parabola.

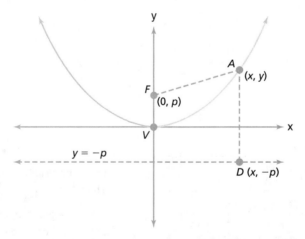

You can see that the locus of points looks like a parabola, but to be sure that it is precisely a parabola, you must derive the equation. The second definition guarantees that $AF = AD$, and the distance formula applies as follows.

$$AF = AD$$
$$\sqrt{(x - 0)^2 + (y - p)^2} = \sqrt{(x - x)^2 + (y + p)^2}$$
$$x^2 + (y - p)^2 = (y + p)^2$$

$$x^2 + y^2 - 2py + p^2 = y^2 + 2py + p^2$$

$$x^2 - 2py = 2py$$

$$x^2 = 4py$$

$$y = \frac{1}{4p}x^2$$

In Chapter 5 you studied parabolas as graphs of quadratic functions. The simplest form of these functions was $y = ax^2$, where a indicated the direction the parabola opens and its width. You should see by comparison that the formula derived is a quadratic function with $a = \frac{1}{4p}$. More precisely, to accommodate negative values of a (since p is a distance), $|a| = \frac{1}{4p}$ or $4p|a| = 1$. This provides a formula for the focal distance, $p = \frac{1}{4|a|}$.

The general form of a quadratic equation as you learned earlier is $y = a(x - h)^2 + k$, where (h, k) is the vertex of the parabola. We can establish the equation of a parabola from its graph by locating the vertex (h, k) and counting p units.

EXAMPLE 1   Find the equation of the graph shown.

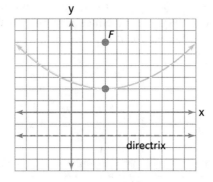

Answer

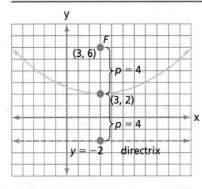

1. From the graph we see $p = 4$.
   Then $|a| = \frac{1}{4p} = \frac{1}{4(4)} = \frac{1}{16}$.

   Since the graph opens up, a is positive; therefore $a = \frac{1}{16}$.

2. Since the vertex is at $(3, 2)$, $h = 3$ and $k = 2$.

   Substituting into the formula $y = a(x - h)^2 + k$, we get $y = \frac{1}{16}(x - 3)^2 + 2$.

Since the curve opens up with vertex (3, 2) and $p = 4$, the focus is 4 units above the vertex at (3, 6). Since the directrix has to be 4 units below the vertex and horizontal, it passes through the point (3, −2) and has equation $y = -2$.

You should also develop skills at writing the equation of a parabola, given particular information. The general form of a parabola that opens up or down is

$$y = a(x - h)^2 + k$$

where (h, k) is the vertex and $|a| = \frac{1}{4p}$. The determination as to whether a is positive or negative is made by the direction the curve opens.

By the same methods used to derive the equation of a parabola opening up or down, the equation of a parabola opening left or right can be derived and is

$$x = a(y - k)^2 + h$$

where (h, k) is still the vertex. If $a > 0$, the curve opens right, and if $a < 0$, the curve opens left.

EXAMPLE 2 Write the equation of the parabola with focus (−1, 3) and directrix $x = 5$.

Answer

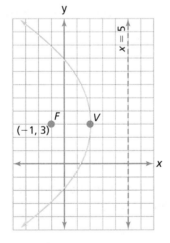

$a = -\frac{1}{12}$

$x = a(y - k)^2 + h$
$x = -\frac{1}{12}(y - 3)^2 + 2$

1. Locate the focus and the directrix.

2. The vertex is the midpoint between the focus and the directrix, and the parabola opens around the focus. Therefore the vertex, found by the midpoint formula, is $\left(\frac{-1 + 5}{2}, \frac{3 + 3}{2}\right)$ = (2, 3).

   From the graph we see $p = 3$. Therefore $|a| = \frac{1}{4p} = \frac{1}{12}$ Since the curve opens left, $a < 0$.

3. Write the equation using $(h, k) =$ (2, 3) and $a = -\frac{1}{12}$.

▶ A. Exercises

Graph each equation. Give the equation of the directrix and the coordinates of the focus for each.

1. $y = \frac{1}{3}(x - 1)^2 + 4$
2. $y = \frac{1}{8}(x + 1)^2 - 3$
3. $y = -3x^2 + 4$
4. $y = \frac{-1}{12}(x + 5)^2 + 4$
5. $y = 2(x - 1)^2$
6. $x = y^2$
7. $x = -\frac{1}{5}(y + 4)^2 - 2$
8. $y = -4x^2$

▶ B. Exercises

Graph each equation. Give the equation of the directrix and the coordinates of the focus for each.

9. $y = x^2 + 6x + 7$
10. $x = -\frac{1}{2}y^2 + 2y - 3$

Write the equation of the parabola that has the given characteristics.

11. vertex (3, 7) and focus (1, 7)
12. vertex (1, −2) and focus (1, 4)
13. vertex (−2, 1) and directrix $y = 6$
14. focus (2, 7) and directrix $x = 4$
15. focus (−6, 4) and directrix $y = -2$
16. focus (3, −2) and directrix $x = -1$

▶ C. Exercises

Write the equation of the parabola that has the given characteristics.

17. focus at the origin, opens up, passes through (4, 3)
18. focus at (−2, 1), opens down, passes through (4, 1)

▶ Dominion Modeling

19. In the astronomy data, Comet Machholz had a parabolic orbit. Find an equation for the orbit of Comet Machholz. (Hint: Assume that the parabola opens up, has a vertex at the origin, and is symmetric to the y-axis.)

20. Comet Machholz flew near the sun in 1994. If its orbit stayed the same, when should we expect it to fly by the sun again? Explain.

Cumulative Review

Simplify. Leave answers in factored form.

21. $\dfrac{x+1}{3x} - \dfrac{x-5}{3x}$

22. $\dfrac{3}{2x^2 + 5x - 3} + \dfrac{7}{6x^2 + 5x - 4}$

Graph.

23. $y = \dfrac{3}{2x + 5}$

24. $f(x) = \dfrac{4}{x^2 + 3x}$

25. $g(x) = \dfrac{x-2}{x^2 - 3x - 10}$

14.4 Ellipses

Do you recall how to form an ellipse from a conical surface?

The rings of Saturn are familiar examples of ellipses.

Definition

Ellipse   The intersection of a right circular conical surface and a plane that intersects only one nappe, is not parallel to any element, and is not perpendicular to the axis.

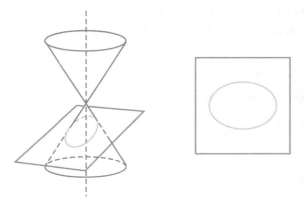

Now consider an ellipse as a locus of points.

Definition

Ellipse   the locus of points in the plane such that the sum of each point's distance from two fixed points is constant.

The two fixed points in this definition are called *foci* (plural form of *focus*). The equation can be developed algebraically from the locus of points that define it, but that development will be postponed until the next math course.

While the general shapes of ellipses are similar, the two primary ways for the ellipse to be elongated are horizontally or vertically. The *major axis* (or longer axis) of an ellipse always contains the foci (F_1 and F_2). The *minor axis* is the shorter axis. The *center* of the ellipse is the point where the major and minor axes intersect, and the *vertices* of an ellipse are the four points at which the major and minor axes intersect the ellipse.

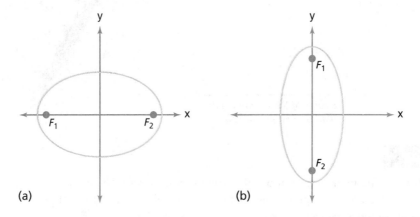

(a)   (b)

In diagram *a* the ellipse is elongated horizontally and the major axis lies on the *x*-axis, while in *b* the ellipse is elongated vertically and the major axis lies on the *y*-axis.

Certain letters represent specific lengths that are needed to write the equation of an ellipse. These letters and their meanings are given here.

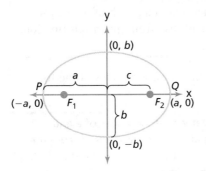

a—represents the distance from the center of the ellipse to an intercept on the major axis (vertex of the ellipse); often called the length of the *semi-major axis.*

b—represents the distance from the center of the ellipse to an intercept on the minor axis; often called the length of the *semi-minor axis.*

c—represents the distance from the center of the ellipse to the focus. In every ellipse, $c < a$.

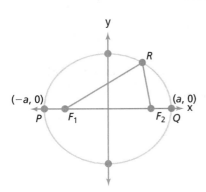

Let *P* be the point $(-a, 0)$, *Q* the point $(a, 0)$, and *R* any point on the ellipse. By definition of an ellipse, $F_1R + F_2R$ is a constant sum no matter where *R* is located. To determine the constant, consider point *Q* on the major axis. We know that $F_1Q + F_2Q = F_1R + F_2R$, but since $F_2Q = F_1P$, the constant sum is the length of the major axis which is $2a$.

There is also a special relationship between *a*, *b*, and *c*.

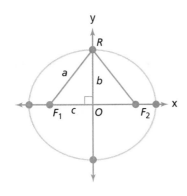

To find the relationship, let *R* be a vertex of the ellipse on its minor axis. Since the axes are perpendicular, $\triangle ROF_1$ and $\triangle ROF_2$ are congruent right triangles (SAS). Thus, the hypotenuses of the triangles are congruent, and $F_1R = F_2R$. Since *R* is on the ellipse, the sum of distances to the foci must be $2a$, and each hypotenuse is of length *a*.

Therefore by the Pythagorean theorem, $a^2 = b^2 + c^2$.

The equation for an ellipse with horizontal major axis and center at the origin is $\frac{x^2}{a^2} + \frac{y^2}{b^2} = 1$.

If the major axis is vertical, the equation is $\frac{x^2}{b^2} + \frac{y^2}{a^2} = 1$.

In an ellipse $a > b$ because a represents the length of the semi-major axis. The square of the length of the semi-major axis appears under the variable designating the axis on which it lies. You can sketch a graph of an ellipse from its equation or write the equation of an ellipse from given information.

EXAMPLE 1 Graph $\frac{x^2}{16} + \frac{y^2}{9} = 1$ and find the coordinates of the foci.

Answer

$a^2 = 16$	$b^2 = 9$	1. Determine the values of a and b. The major axis is the x-axis because the larger value, 16, is under the x^2. Graph the ellipse from this information.
$a = 4$	$b = 3$	

$a^2 = b^2 + c^2$
$16 = 9 + c^2$
$c^2 = 7$
$c = \sqrt{7} \approx 2.6$

2. Use $a^2 = b^2 + c^2$ to find c.

$(2.6, 0); (-2.6, 0)$

3. Find the coordinates of the foci.

4. Graph.

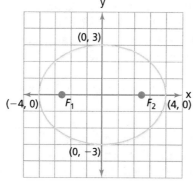

EXAMPLE 2 Write the equation of the ellipse with center (0, 0), foci (0, 5) and (0, −5), and vertices (2, 0) and (−2, 0).

Answer

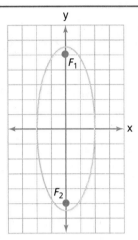

1. Sketching the graph may be helpful.

2. Determine the given information. You know $c = 5$ from the coordinates of the foci. Since the graph is elongated vertically, the vertices imply that $b = 2$.

$$a^2 = b^2 + c^2$$
$$a^2 = 2^2 + 5^2$$
$$a^2 = 29$$
$$a = \sqrt{29}$$

3. To determine the value of a, use the relationship $a^2 = b^2 + c^2$.

$$\frac{x^2}{2^2} + \frac{y^2}{(\sqrt{29})^2} = 1$$
$$\frac{x^2}{4} + \frac{y^2}{29} = 1$$

4. Since the ellipse is vertical ($\sqrt{29} > 2$), use the equation $\frac{x^2}{b^2} + \frac{y^2}{a^2} = 1$.

EXAMPLE 3 Graph $4x^2 + y^2 = 36$. Identify the foci.

Answer

$$4x^2 + y^2 = 36$$

$$\frac{4x^2}{36} + \frac{y^2}{36} = \frac{36}{36}$$

$$\frac{x^2}{9} + \frac{y^2}{36} = 1$$

1. Change the equation to the general form by dividing through both sides by 36.

$a^2 = 36$	$b^2 = 9$
$a = 6$	$b = 3$

2. The ellipse is vertical since the larger denominator is under the y^2. (Remember that the larger number, 36, represents a^2.)

Continued ▶

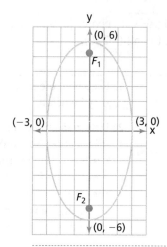

y

(0, 6)

F_1

(−3, 0)

(3, 0)
x

F_2

(0, −6)

3. Graph the ellipse. Plot the vertices using a and b: $(\pm 3, 0)$, $(0, \pm 6)$.

$a^2 = b^2 + c^2$

$36 = 9 + c^2$

$c^2 = 27$

$c = 3\sqrt{3} \approx 5.2$

Foci are $(0, 5.2)$ and $(0, -5.2)$

4. Find c and determine the coordinates of the foci. Remember that they are on the major axis.

Ellipses can be translated in the plane so that the center is any point (h, k). This means that major and minor axes are no longer on the x and y axes, but are parallel to them. The foci would be measured from (h, k) parallel to the appropriate axis, using the distance c. The more general form of the equation of an ellipse is $\frac{(x-h)^2}{a^2} + \frac{(y-k)^2}{b^2} = 1$ or $\frac{(x-h)^2}{b^2} + \frac{(y-k)^2}{a^2} = 1$.

▶ A. Exercises

Graph.

1. $\frac{x^2}{4} + \frac{y^2}{9} = 1$

2. $\frac{x^2}{16} + \frac{y^2}{25} = 1$

3. $\frac{x^2}{49} + \frac{y^2}{16} = 1$

4. $\frac{x^2}{9} + \frac{y^2}{64} = 1$

5. $x^2 + \frac{y^2}{4} = 1$

6. What are the three pieces of information you need in order to write the equation of an ellipse?

7. Write the equation of the ellipse where the x-intercepts are $(4, 0)$ and $(-4, 0)$, and the y-intercepts are $(0, 3)$ and $(0, -3)$

▶ B. Exercises

Find the foci.

8. $\frac{x^2}{49} + \frac{y^2}{9} = 1$

9. $\frac{x^2}{3} + \frac{y^2}{15} = 1$

10. $16x^2 + 2y^2 = 32$

11. $x^2 + 2y^2 = 8$

Write the equation of the ellipse from the given information.

12. Two vertices are (6, 0) and (−6, 0); the foci are (4, 0) and (−4, 0).
13. Two vertices are (0, 2) and (0, −2); the foci are (5, 0) and (−5, 0).
14. Two vertices are (8, 0) and (−8, 0); the foci are (0, 7) and (0, −7).
15. The foci are (0, 4) and (0, −4); the length of the major axis is 10.

Graph and locate the foci (round to the nearest tenth).

16. $2x^2 + 3y^2 = 6$
17. $\frac{(x - 1)^2}{7} + (y - 4)^2 = 1$
18. $\frac{(x - 2)^2}{4} + \frac{(y + 1)^2}{16} = 1$

19. What happens to the shape of the ellipse if $a = b$?

▶ C. Exercises

20. Find the coordinates of the foci: $\frac{(x - 2)^2}{16} + \frac{(y + 1)^2}{7} = 1$.
21. Find the equation of the ellipse with vertices (3, −1), (0, 5), (6, 5), and (3, 11).

▶ Dominion Modeling

22. For the astronomy data, q is the perihelion, or the closest distance to the sun. Given that for eccentricity, $e = \frac{c}{a}$, find an expression for q. (Hint: Sketch an ellipse and label a, b, c, and q. Substitute for c in your formula.)
23. Toutatis had an elliptical orbit. Find an equation for the orbit of Toutatis. (Hint: Use your formula for q. Assume that the ellipse's center is at the origin and that it is elongated horizontally.)
24. Pluto is usually considered farther from the sun than Neptune, yet Pluto's perihelion is the smaller of the two. How could this be? (Hint: The sun is a focus for each planetary orbit.)

▪ Cumulative Review

Let $f(x) = \frac{mx + d}{ax^2 + bx + c}$.

25. How would you find the vertical asymptotes?
26. What is the y-intercept?
27. Find the horizontal asymptote.
28. Find the x-intercept(s).
29. What is the difference between the notations $[f(x)]^{-1}$ and $f^{-1}(x)$?
30. Give $[f(x)]^{-1}$.

14.5 Hyperbolas

The final conic section is the hyperbola. The shadow of a lampshade on a wall is an example of a hyperbola. Practically everything in mathematics comes from a study of the universe God created. Mathematics is not just a discipline thought up in man's mind; it arises from the study of the orderliness and principles of God's universe. Psalm 19:1 states, "The heavens declare the glory of God; and the firmament sheweth his handywork."

The geometric definition of a hyperbola shows the relationship between a right circular conical surface and an intersecting plane.

Definition

Hyperbola   The intersection of a right circular conical surface and a plane that intersects both nappes but not the vertex.

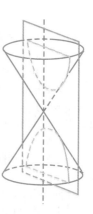

The definition states that the plane intersects both nappes of the surface. The plane does not have to be parallel to the axis of the cone.

The locus of points that defines a hyperbola is similar to the locus that defines an ellipse. Notice the difference between the two definitions.

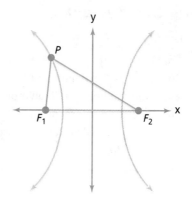

Definition

Hyperbola   The locus of points in a plane such that the difference of the distances from two fixed points to a point of the locus is constant.

The two fixed points in the definition are called the *foci* of the hyperbola. Thus, in the previous figure, $F_2P - F_1P$ is constant regardless of where P is located on the hyperbola. The two points V_1 and V_2 in the figure below are called *vertices* and the line passing through the vertices is the *transverse axis*.

Each hyperbola has two *asymptotes* associated with it that determine its shape. The next graph shows the asymptotes as dotted lines along with the hyperbola. The hyperbola gets closer and closer to the asymptotes but never intersects them.

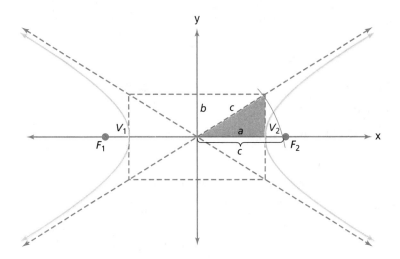

Notice the dotted rectangle drawn in the graph. The asymptotes contain the diagonals of the rectangle. Drawing the rectangle enables you to draw the asymptotes, which in turn provide a guide for your sketch of the hyperbola. As in the case of the ellipse, a represents the distance from the center to a vertex of the hyperbola, and the distance from the center to the foci is c.

Since the hyperbola does not intersect the other axis, it is called the *conjugate axis*, and b is the distance from the center to the rectangle on that axis. Thus, the length of the rectangle is $2a$, and the width is $2b$. Since $c > a$, which is opposite that of the ellipse, the equations relating a, b, and c are slightly different. For a hyperbola, b is related to a and c by the equation $a^2 + b^2 = c^2$. Unlike the ellipse, a need not be greater than b; rather, a is always measured along the transverse axis. If you can determine the values of a and b, you can write both the equation of the hyperbola and the equations of the asymptotes.

Figures of hyperbolas that open left and right and their equations are shown here. Also the equations for their corresponding asymptotes are given. Since the asymptotes are lines, their equations agree with $y = mx + b$ where $b = 0$ (provided the center is at the origin). Their slopes are $m = \pm\frac{b}{a}$ or $m = \pm\frac{a}{b}$ depending on whether the hyperbola crosses the x-axis or y-axis, respectively. Notice also that the first term in the equation indicates the axis intersected by the curve.

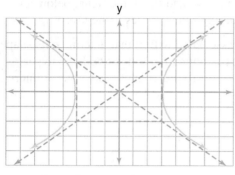

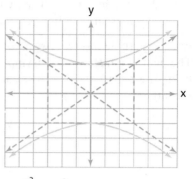

$$\frac{x^2}{a^2} - \frac{y^2}{b^2} = 1$$

$$y = \frac{b}{a}x \text{ and } y = -\frac{b}{a}x$$

$$\frac{y^2}{a^2} - \frac{x^2}{b^2} = 1$$

$$y = \frac{a}{b}x \text{ and } y = -\frac{a}{b}x$$

Use this information to graph a hyperbola and write its equation.

EXAMPLE 1   Graph $\frac{x^2}{9} - \frac{y^2}{4} = 1$ and find the foci.

Answer

$a^2 = 9$ $b^2 = 4$

1. Determine the values of a and b. Since the hyperbola opens horizontally (x is in first term), the general form is $\frac{x^2}{a^2} - \frac{y^2}{b^2} = 1$.

$a = 3$ $b = 2$

$y = \frac{2}{3}x$ and $y = -\frac{2}{3}x$ are the asymptotes.

2. Determine the asymptotes. Since the hyperbola opens horizontally, use the equations $y = \frac{b}{a}x$ and $y = \frac{-b}{a}x$.

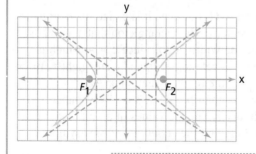

3. Graph the asymptotes and find the ordered pairs for the vertices. The vertices are $(a, 0)$ and $(-a, 0)$, which in this case are $(3, 0)$ and $(-3, 0)$.

$a^2 + b^2 = c^2$
$9 + 4 = c^2$
$c = \sqrt{13} \approx 3.6$

4. Calculate c and determine the coordinates of the foci.

$(3.6, 0)$ and $(-3.6, 0)$ are the foci.

EXAMPLE 2 Write the equation of the hyperbola with vertices (0, 5) and (0, −5) and foci (0, 8) and (0, −8).

Answer

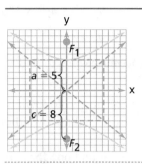

1. Sketch a graph of this hyperbola to get its general shape.

$$a^2 + b^2 = c^2$$
$$5^2 + b^2 = 8^2$$
$$25 + b^2 = 64$$
$$b^2 = 39$$
$$b = \sqrt{39}$$

2. From the graph identify that $a = 5$ and $c = 8$. Determine the values of a and b, the two essential values for writing the equation.

$$\frac{y^2}{5^2} - \frac{x^2}{(\sqrt{39})^2} = 1$$

$$\frac{y^2}{25} - \frac{x^2}{39} = 1$$

3. The general formula for a hyperbola that opens up and down is $\frac{y^2}{a^2} - \frac{x^2}{b^2} = 1$. Use this formula and the known values of a and b to write the equation.

As in the case of circles and ellipses, the center of a hyperbola can be translated to any point (h, k) in the plane. The hyperbola whose equation is $\frac{(x - 3)^2}{5} - \frac{(y + 2)^2}{49} = 1$ would have its center at $(3, -2)$. The asymptotes would intersect at $(3, -2)$, and the location of the foci would be measured from $(3, -2)$ rather than from the origin. This also means that at least one asymptote will have an equation of the form $y = mx + b$, where $b \neq 0$.

▶ A. Exercises

Graph. Be sure to include the asymptotes as dotted lines.

1. $\frac{x^2}{9} - \frac{y^2}{16} = 1$

2. $\frac{y^2}{25} - \frac{x^2}{4} = 1$

3. $\frac{y^2}{49} - \frac{x^2}{7} = 1$

4. $\frac{x^2}{16} - \frac{y^2}{25} = 1$

Write the equation of the hyperbola from the information given.

5. Foci are (0, 6) and (0, −6), and vertices are (0, 3) and (0, −3).

6. Foci are (5, 0) and (−5, 0), and vertices are (1, 0) and (−1, 0).

▶ B. Exercises

Graph. Be sure to include the asymptotes as dotted lines.

7. $\dfrac{(x + 2)^2}{36} - y^2 = 1$

8. $\dfrac{(y - 1)^2}{49} - \dfrac{(x - 3)^2}{4} = 1$

9. $x^2 - 4y^2 = 100$

10. $2y^2 - x^2 > 4$

11. What are the essential values you must know to find the equation of a hyperbola?

Write the equation of the hyperbola, given the following information.

12. Asymptotes are $y = \frac{3}{4}x$ and $y = \frac{-3}{4}x$, and the hyperbola opens left and right.

13. Asymptotes are $y = \frac{5}{4}x$ and $y = \frac{-5}{4}x$, and one focus is $(\sqrt{41}, 0)$.

14. One asymptote is $y = \frac{-2}{3}x$, and a vertex is $(0, 2)$.

15. Vertices are $(4, 1)$ and $(-4, 1)$, and the foci are $(6, 1)$ and $(-6, 1)$.

16. Is the hyperbola in exercise 13 a function? Why or why not? Is the hyperbola in exercise 14 a function? Why or why not?

Find the coordinates of the foci.

17. $\dfrac{x^2}{9} - \dfrac{y^2}{16} = 1$

18. $3y^2 - 4x^2 = 24$

▶ C. Exercises

Prove the following using analytic geometry.

19. If in a hyperbola $a = b$, then the asymptotes are perpendicular.

20. If a hyperbola has perpendicular asymptotes, then $a = b$.

21. Write a single statement from #19-20.

▶ Dominion Modeling

22. For the astronomy data, consider q as the perihelion. With $e = \frac{c}{a}$, find an expression for q. (Hint: Draw a hyperbola, and label a, b, c, and q. Substitute for c in your formula.)

23. Find an equation for the orbit of Comet Larsen. (Hint: Assume that the hyperbola centers at the origin and is oriented horizontally.)

24. Comet Larsen flew near the sun in 1998. If its orbit stayed the same, when should we expect it to fly by the sun again? Explain.

Cumulative Review

Graph.

25. $y = e^x$
26. $y = \text{Cos}^{-1} x$
27. $y = \dfrac{x}{x^2 - 1}$
28. $y = \sqrt{x - 1}$
29. $y = \tan x$

What is wrong with the following proof?

Theorem: $0 = 1$

Proof:

$0 = 0 + 0 + 0 + 0 + \ldots$

$\quad = [1 + (-1)] + [1 + (-1)] + [1 + (-1)] + [1 + (-1)] + \ldots$

$\quad = 1 + (-1) + 1 + (-1) + 1 + (-1) + 1 + (-1) + \ldots$

$\quad = 1 + (-1 + 1) + (-1 + 1) + (-1 + 1) + \ldots$

$\quad = 1 + 0 + 0 + 0 \ldots$

$0 = 1$

Solving Systems by Gaussian Elimination

The method of solving a system of equations shown in this section is called *Gaussian elimination*, named for Karl Friedrich Gauss, a German mathematician of the 1800s. The method uses row reduction.

EXAMPLE 1   Solve using matrices.

$$5x + 3y = 3$$
$$2x - 6y = 30$$

Answer

$$\begin{bmatrix} 5 & 3 & | & 3 \\ 2 & -6 & | & 30 \end{bmatrix} \xrightarrow{r_1 \leftrightarrow r_2} \begin{bmatrix} 2 & -6 & | & 30 \\ 5 & 3 & | & 3 \end{bmatrix} \xrightarrow{\frac{1}{2} r_1}$$

$$\begin{bmatrix} 1 & -3 & | & 15 \\ 5 & 3 & | & 3 \end{bmatrix} \xrightarrow{-5r_1 + r_2} \begin{bmatrix} 1 & -3 & | & 15 \\ 0 & 18 & | & -72 \end{bmatrix} \xrightarrow{\frac{1}{18} r_2}$$

$$\begin{bmatrix} 1 & -3 & | & 15 \\ 0 & 1 & | & -4 \end{bmatrix} \xrightarrow{3r_2 + r_1} \begin{bmatrix} 1 & 0 & | & 3 \\ 0 & 1 & | & -4 \end{bmatrix}$$

1. Augment the coefficient matrix with a column for the constants. Row-reduce this matrix.

$$x + 0y = 3$$
$$0x + y = -4$$

2. Rewrite the matrix as a system of equations.

Therefore, $x = 3$ and $y = -4$. The solution to the system is $(3, -4)$.

A system of any size can be solved by this method, so computer programmers learn this matrix technique to develop software that will solve large systems of equations.

▶ Exercises

Solve each system by Gaussian elimination.

1. $3x + 2y = 22$
   $5x - y = 2$

2. $7x + 2y = 7$
   $3x - 5y = 3$

3. $2x - 4y = -20$
   $3x + 6y = 6$

4. $4x - 8y = -22$
   $2x - 7y = -20$

5. $x + 3y - 2z = 22$
   $2x - y + z = -1$
   $5x + 4y - z = 37$

GREEK MATH

Classical Greek mathematics (600-300 B.C.) developed from geometry and from the Greek philosophy that mind and reason control all things. Greek scholars insisted on unity, completeness, and simplicity. They stressed the development of the mind, knowing that any necessary applications would be easy for a well-developed mind.

Eudoxus was the greatest mathematician of this period. More than anyone else, he is responsible for the formal deductive character of Greek mathematics. He approached the problem of measurement using only geometry since he was unwilling to accept the existence of irrational numbers. He also influenced the writings of Euclid. For example, in Book V of *Elements*, Euclid presented the theory of proportions developed by Eudoxus.

The Greeks always retained a love for geometry. Many mathematicians of the Alexandrian period (300 B.C.–A.D. 500) were great geometers. Apollonius of Perga wrote his eight-volume work *Conic Sections* near the start of this period. In these works, he coined the terms *parabola*, *ellipse*, and *hyperbola*.

Raphael depicted Plato and Aristotle walking together in his famous painting School of Athens.

Yet, because of the mixture of cultures and ideas from around the world at the great Library in Alexandria, mathematicians of the Alexandrian period also applied their ideas to engineering and astronomy. Archimedes invented a number of astonishing machines, including water pumps, pulleys, levers, gears, a steam-powered vehicle, and water-powered organs and fountains. Hipparchus of Nicaea made astronomical observations and developed the geometry of the sphere.

During the second century A.D., Menelaus extended the work of Hipparchus, and Ptolemy wrote his influential

Almagest. His work in trigonometry was especially valuable, but his astronomy promoted the erroneous geocentric theory that the planets and sun revolve around the earth. The Alexandrian astronomer Aristarchus (300 B.C.) had already proposed a heliocentric theory, but the Greeks accepted Ptolemy's incorrect theory instead and it remained dominant for a thousand years.

Even today astronomers accept false theories concerning the origin of the universe, but Scripture refutes them.

> For by him were all things created, that are in heaven, and that are in earth, visible and invisible, whether they be thrones, or dominions, or principalities, or powers: all things were created by him, and for him: And he is before all things, and by him all things consist (Col. 1:16-17).

Diophantus also lived during the Alexandrian period (about 250 A.D.). With Diophantus, the Greeks reached the apex of their developments in algebra. Diophantus recognized that algebra is an abstract science that can stand by itself apart from geometry. His six remaining works show the solutions of both equations and systems and introduce signs for negatives, reciprocals, and even unknowns. His treatment of algebra as a science in its own right and his introduction of variables earn for him recognition as the "Father of algebra."

The Greek culture began to decline after Diophantus, and Greek mathematics declined with it. The last few Greek mathematicians of note included Pappus, Proclus, and Hypatia.

Diophantus recognized that algebra is an abstract science that can stand by itself apart from geometry.

The astrolabe was an invention of the ancient Greeks and was used from the 15th to 18th centuries for determining latitude at sea.

The skyline at Alexandria, Egypt, overlooks the harbor as the famous lighthouse and the great Library once did.

14.6 Systems of Quadratic Relations

In Chapter 6 you studied systems of quadratic equations that involved parabolas and other conics. There you learned to solve these systems algebraically. In this section you will study both the graphical and algebraic solutions to systems of quadratic relations that involve various conic sections. Some will include one linear and one quadratic relation. Remember that the graphical solution to a system of equations is the intersection of the graphs that represent the equations.

EXAMPLE 1 Solve graphically.
$2x + y = 10$
$x^2 + y^2 = 25$

Answer

$2x + y = 10$ $x^2 + y^2 = 25$	1. Determine the types of figures described by the two equations. $2x + y = 10$ describes a line while $x^2 + y^2 = 25$ describes a circle.

$2x + y = 10$
$y = -2x + 10$
$m = -2, b = 10$
$x^2 + y^2 = 25$
center (0, 0); $r = 5$

2. Graph each figure on the same graph and find the points of intersection.

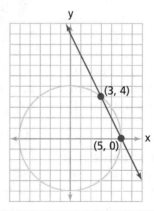

Solutions: (3, 4); (5, 0)

3. Find the solutions by locating the points of intersection.

You should be able to look at an equation and determine the shape of the graph. If you can do this quickly and accurately, it will help you understand and solve quadratic systems of equations.

The substitution or addition methods can be used to solve these systems algebraically. Sometimes one method will be easier, so you should try to determine which before actually solving the system.

EXAMPLE 2 Solve algebraically.
$$2x + y = 10$$
$$x^2 + y^2 = 25$$

Answer

$2x + y = 10$ $x^2 + y^2 = 25$	1. Look at the system. Would the substitution or addition method work better? Since you cannot align like terms for the addition method, use the substitution method.
$2x + y = 10$ $\quad y = -2x + 10$	2. Solve the linear equation for y and substitute it into the equation for the circle.
$x^2 + y^2 = 25$ $x^2 + (-2x + 10)^2 = 25$ $x^2 + 4x^2 - 40x + 100 = 25$ $5x^2 - 40x + 75 = 0$ $x^2 - 8x + 15 = 0$ $(x - 3)(x - 5) = 0$ $x = 3 \text{ or } x = 5$	3. Solve this quadratic equation.
$y = -2x + 10 \qquad y = -2x + 10$ $y = -2(3) + 10 \quad y = -2(5) + 10$ $y = 4 \qquad\qquad y = 0$ $(3, 4) \qquad\qquad (5, 0)$	4. Find the y values that correspond to these x values by substituting 3 and 5 into the linear equation.

The two solutions are (3, 4) and (5, 0) as were found graphically in Example 1.

Graphing a system will give an indication of the number of solutions as well as the approximate values of the solutions for that system. This fact can be valuable to you as you evaluate your work to see if it is reasonable.

▶ A. Exercises

1. There are five possible cases for a system containing a parabola and an ellipse, resulting in anywhere from zero to four answers. Sketch a picture showing each possible case.

2. How many cases are there for a system containing a circle and a hyperbola? Sketch each one.

3. A system consists of 2 parabolas. Find the maximum number of solutions if: (a) one opens up and one down, (b) both open up, and (c) one opens up and one opens right.

Solve graphically. You may need to approximate the values.

4. $5x + y = 9$
   $3x - 2y = 21$

5. $2x - y = 7$
   $x^2 + y^2 = 17$

6. $x^2 + y^2 = 4$
   $y = 2x^2 - 2$

7. $x^2 + y^2 = 36$
   $x^2 + 4y^2 = 36$

8. $y = x^2$
   $8x^2 - y^2 = 16$

9. $x^2 + y^2 = 25$
   $x - y = -1$

▶ B. Exercises

Solve algebraically and graphically.

10. $9x^2 + y^2 = 36$
    $x + y = 7$

11. $x^2 - y^2 = 21$
    $x + y = 7$

12. $x^2 + y^2 = 16$
    $9x^2 + y^2 = 48$

13. $x^2 - 4y^2 = 8$
    $x^2 + y^2 = 53$

14. $y = 3x^2$
    $x^2 + y^2 = 10$

15. $y = x^2$
    $y = -x^2 + 8$

16. $x^2 + 9y^2 = 81$
    $x^2 + y^2 = 16$

17. $16x^2 + y^2 = 16$
    $x^2 + (y - 2)^2 = 4$
18. $x^2 - y^2 = 1$
    $y - x = 2$

▶ C. Exercises

Use analytic geometry to justify.

19. The segment joining the midpoints of two sides of a triangle is parallel to the third side.
20. The length of the segment joining the midpoints of two sides of a triangle is one-half the length of the third side.

▶ Dominion Modeling

21. From the data you have seen so far, when would the path of Toutatis and Comet Machholz cross? To decide this question, one useful adjustment is to slide each orbit so the foci are the same. (The sun is at a focus for each planetary or cometary orbit.) Because Toutatis has a perihelion of 0.918 AU, a shifted equation is $\frac{(x + 1.590)^2}{2.508^2} + \frac{y^2}{1.939^2} = 1$. For Comet Machholz, we need the x-axis to be the "semi-major" axis; furthermore, since its perihelion is 1.846 AU, a shifted equation could be $x + 1.846 = 0.137y^2$. Graph these equations, and find where they would intersect. Finally, discuss what these intersection points mean.

▪ Cumulative Review

Sketch each system to determine the number of solutions.

22. $y = \frac{1}{x}$
    $y = \sin x$
23. $y = |x|$
    $y = x^2$
24. $x + 2y = 1$
    $y = 2^{-x}$
25. $y = x^3 - x$
    $y = \log x$
26. $y = \sqrt{x}$
    $y = \cos x$

Algebra *and* Scripture

Astronomy

Analytic geometry is used extensively in astronomy, but the basis of astronomy is in Scripture. In this lesson you will explore the relations between math, astronomy, and Scripture.

On which day of Creation were each of the following created?

1. outer space
2. the earth's atmosphere
3. the heavenly bodies (sun, moon, and stars)
4. Before God made the sun, He made two things that require the sun. Name one of the two things.

What does each verse below tell you about the creation of the heavenly bodies?

5. John 1:3   7. Genesis 1:14
6. Genesis 1:18, 31   8. Psalm 19:1

Now consider the orderliness of the heavenly bodies. The heavenly bodies follow paths around the sun that approximate conic sections, with the sun at one focus. We could consider a circle to have two foci, both at the center. As we separate the two foci, the figure becomes elliptical. As the distance increases, the curve elongates toward the shape of a parabola. A parabola can be thought of as having two foci that are an infinite distance apart.

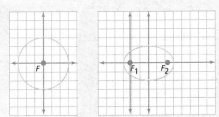 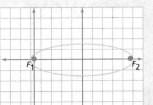 

One focus of each figure is at the origin, where the sun would be. For comparison, consider the center of a circle to be its focus so that $c = 0$ and a = radius. The formula for eccentricity, $e = \frac{c}{a}$, measures distortion from a circle. Use your knowledge of conic sections to match the following.

9. $e = 0$ **A.** parabola

10. $0 < e < 1$ **B.** ellipse

11. $e = 1$ **C.** hyperbola

12. $e > 1$ **D.** circle

13. The planets in our solar system have elliptical orbits. Which of these ellipses is closest to a circle?

     a. $0 < e < 0.1$ **b.** $0.1 \le e \le 0.8$ **c.** $0.8 < e < 1$

14. All but two planets have eccentricities in which range mentioned in exercise 13? Give the eccentricity of Jupiter.

GREATER AMPLITUDE.

Which range for eccentricities (exercise 13) describes most comets? most asteroids? the asteroid Juno?

Read Psalm 147:4.

15. What can you conclude from this verse about God? How does it relate space (geometry) to math (counting and algebra)?

> ## Absolute Values
>
> h̶E TELLETH THE NUMBER of the stars; he calleth them all by their names. ❧
>
> PSALM 147:4

Chapter Review

Find the distance between the two given points and then find the coordinates of the midpoint of the segment connecting them.

1. $(4, 5)$ and $(-3, 2)$
2. $(-6, 9)$ and $(-1, -8)$

Write the equation of the circle with the given center and radius.

3. center $(-6, 4)$ and radius 2
4. center $(0, 9)$ and radius 6

Write the equation of the figures described here.

5. parabola with vertex $(7, 3)$ and focus $(7, 8)$
6. parabola with focus $(2, 6)$ and directrix $x = -6$
7. ellipse with foci $(5, 0)$ and $(-5, 0)$ and y-intercepts $(0, 2)$ and $(0, -2)$
8. ellipse with x-intercepts $(3, 0)$ and $(-3, 0)$ and y-intercepts $(0, 8)$ and $(0, -8)$
9. hyperbola with asymptotes $y = \frac{4}{5}x$ and $y = \frac{-4}{5}x$ and foci $(-\sqrt{41}, 0)$ and $(\sqrt{41}, 0)$
10. hyperbola with vertices $(0, 4)$ and $(0, -4)$ and foci $(0, 6)$ and $(0, -6)$

Graph.

11. $(x - 4)^2 + (y - 8)^2 = 1$

12. $x^2 + y^2 = 25$

13. $y = \frac{-1}{12}(x - 2)^2 + 3$

14. $\frac{x^2}{16} + \frac{y^2}{9} = 1$

15. $x^2 - 9y^2 = 36$

16. $x = \frac{1}{4}(y + 3)^2 + 4$

17. $\frac{y^2}{36} - \frac{x^2}{16} = 1$

18. $\frac{(x - 1)^2}{49} + \frac{(y + 4)^2}{16} = 1$

19. $\frac{(x + 3)^2}{25} - \frac{(y - 2)^2}{9} = 1$

20. $(x - 2)^2 + \frac{y^2}{4} = 1$

Give the focus of each.

21. $y = \frac{1}{8}(x - 1)^2 + 3$

22. $\frac{x^2}{9} - \frac{y^2}{4} = 1$

23. $\frac{(x - 2)^2}{49} + \frac{(y - 3)^2}{81} = 1$

Solve each system.

24. $3x + y = 6$
    $x^2 + y^2 = 10$
25. $x^2 - y^2 = 5$
    $y = x^2 - 7$

26. Prove: The diagonals of a square are perpendicular.
27. Imagine a celestial rock coming from interstellar space. What kind of orbit would it have with the sun? Then, if the sun's gravity were strong enough, what shape would the rock's orbit take?
28. Give the mathematical significance of Psalm 147:4.

Symbols

$+$	addition, positive	$\lvert x \rvert$	absolute value of x	$\subset$	is a proper subset of
$-$	subtraction, negative	$=$	is equal to	$\varnothing$	empty set
$\times$	multiplication (times)	$\neq$	is not equal to	$\cup$	union
$\cdot$	multiplication	$\approx$	is approximately equal to	$\cap$	intersection
$\div$	division	$>$	is greater than	$\times$	cross product
$\frac{p}{q}$	division, fraction	$<$	is less than	$\vee$	or
$0.\overline{3}$	repeating decimal	$\geq$	is greater than or equal to	$\wedge$	and
$\mathbb{N}$	natural numbers	$\leq$	is less than or equal to	$/$	cancellation
$\mathbb{W}$	whole numbers	$\bar{x}$	average (mean) of x values	$\sqrt{}$	square root
$\mathbb{Z}$	integers	Σ	sum (summation notation)	$\sqrt[3]{}$	cube root
$\mathbb{Q}$	rational numbers	s	standard deviation	$\sqrt[n]{}$	nth root
$\mathbb{R}$	real numbers	$\{\ \ \}$	set braces	$!$	factorial
$^{\circ}$	degrees	$\{x \mid \ldots\}$	the set of x such that . . .	$_nP_r$	permutations
$\pm$	plus or minus	$\in$	is an element of	$_nC_r$	combinations
$\%$	percent	$\notin$	is not an element of	$f(x)$	function of x
π	pi	$\subseteq$	is a subset of		

Table of Natural Logarithms

	.0	.1	.2	.3	.4	.5	.6	.7	.8	.9
1	0.0000	0.0953	0.1823	0.2624	0.3365	0.4055	0.4700	0.5306	0.5878	0.6419
2	0.6931	0.7419	0.7885	0.8329	0.8755	0.9163	0.9555	0.9933	1.0296	1.0647
3	1.0986	1.1314	1.1632	1.1939	1.2238	1.2528	1.2809	1.3083	1.3350	1.3610
4	1.3863	1.4110	1.4351	1.4586	1.4816	1.5041	1.5261	1.5476	1.5686	1.5892
5	1.6094	1.6292	1.6487	1.6677	1.6864	1.7047	1.7228	1.7405	1.7579	1.7750
6	1.7918	1.8083	1.8245	1.8405	1.8563	1.8718	1.8871	1.9021	1.9169	1.9315
7	1.9459	1.9601	1.9741	1.9879	2.0015	2.0149	2.0281	2.0412	2.0541	2.0669
8	2.0794	2.0919	2.1041	2.1163	2.1282	2.1401	2.1518	2.1633	2.1748	2.1861
9	2.1972	2.2083	2.2192	2.2300	2.2407	2.2513	2.2618	2.2721	2.2824	2.2925
10	2.3026									

Table of Common Logarithms

	.0	.1	.2	.3	.4	.5	.6	.7	.8	.9
1	0.0000	0.0414	0.0792	0.1139	0.1461	0.1761	0.2041	0.2304	0.2553	0.2788
2	0.3010	0.3222	0.3424	0.3617	0.3802	0.3979	0.4150	0.4314	0.4472	0.4624
3	0.4771	0.4914	0.5051	0.5185	0.5315	0.5441	0.5563	0.5682	0.5798	0.5911
4	0.6021	0.6128	0.6232	0.6335	0.6435	0.6532	0.6628	0.6721	0.6812	0.6902
5	0.6990	0.7076	0.7160	0.7243	0.7324	0.7404	0.7482	0.7559	0.7634	0.7709
6	0.7782	0.7853	0.7924	0.7993	0.8062	0.8129	0.8195	0.8261	0.8325	0.8388
7	0.8451	0.8513	0.8573	0.8633	0.8692	0.8751	0.8808	0.8865	0.8921	0.8976
8	0.9031	0.9085	0.9138	0.9191	0.9243	0.9294	0.9345	0.9395	0.9445	0.9494
9	0.9542	0.9590	0.9638	0.9685	0.9731	0.9777	0.9823	0.9868	0.9912	0.9956
10	1.0000									

Table of Trigonometric Ratios

Degrees	Radians	sin	cos	tan	cot	sec	csc		
0°00'	0.0000	0.0000	1.0000	0.0000	—	1.000	—	1.5708	90°00'
10'	0.0029	0.0029	1.0000	0.0029	343.8	1.000	343.8	1.5679	50'
20'	0.0058	0.0058	1.0000	0.0058	171.9	1.000	171.9	1.5650	40'
30'	0.0087	0.0087	1.0000	0.0087	114.6	1.000	114.6	1.5621	30'
40'	0.0116	0.0116	0.9999	0.0116	85.94	1.000	85.95	1.5592	20'
50'	0.0145	0.0145	0.9999	0.0145	68.75	1.000	68.76	1.5563	10'
1°00'	0.0175	0.0175	0.9998	0.0175	57.29	1.000	57.30	1.5533	89°00'
10'	0.0204	0.0204	0.9998	0.0204	49.10	1.000	49.11	1.5504	50'
20'	0.0233	0.0233	0.9997	0.0233	42.96	1.000	42.98	1.5475	40'
30'	0.0262	0.0262	0.9997	0.0262	38.19	1.000	38.20	1.5446	30'
40'	0.0291	0.0291	0.9996	0.0291	34.37	1.000	34.38	1.5417	20'
50'	0.0320	0.0320	0.9995	0.0320	31.24	1.001	31.26	1.5388	10'
2°00'	0.0349	0.0349	0.9994	0.0349	28.64	1.001	28.65	1.5359	88°00'
10'	0.0378	0.0378	0.9993	0.0378	26.43	1.001	26.45	1.5330	50'
20'	0.0407	0.0407	0.9992	0.0407	24.54	1.001	24.56	1.5301	40'
30'	0.0436	0.0436	0.9990	0.0437	22.90	1.001	22.93	1.5272	30'
40'	0.0465	0.0465	0.9989	0.0466	21.47	1.001	21.49	1.5243	20'
50'	0.0495	0.0494	0.9988	0.0495	20.21	1.001	20.23	1.5213	10'
3°00'	0.0524	0.0523	0.9986	0.0524	19.08	1.001	19.11	1.5184	87°00'
10'	0.0553	0.0552	0.9985	0.0553	18.07	1.002	18.10	1.5155	50'
20'	0.0582	0.0581	0.9983	0.0582	17.17	1.002	17.20	1.5126	40'
30'	0.0611	0.0610	0.9981	0.0612	16.35	1.002	16.38	1.5097	30'
40'	0.0640	0.0640	0.9980	0.0641	15.60	1.002	15.64	1.5068	20'
50'	0.0669	0.0669	0.9978	0.0670	14.92	1.002	14.96	1.5039	10'
4°00'	0.0698	0.0698	0.9976	0.0699	14.30	1.002	14.34	1.5010	86°00'
10'	0.0727	0.0727	0.9974	0.0729	13.73	1.003	13.76	1.4981	50'
20'	0.0756	0.0756	0.9971	0.0758	13.20	1.003	13.23	1.4952	40'
30'	0.0785	0.0785	0.9969	0.0787	12.71	1.003	12.75	1.4923	30'
40'	0.0814	0.0814	0.9967	0.0816	12.25	1.003	12.29	1.4893	20'
50'	0.0844	0.0843	0.9964	0.0846	11.83	1.004	11.87	1.4864	10'
5°00'	0.0873	0.0872	0.9962	0.0875	11.43	1.004	11.47	1.4835	85°00'
10'	0.0902	0.0901	0.9959	0.0904	11.06	1.004	11.10	1.4806	50'
20'	0.0931	0.0929	0.9957	0.0934	10.71	1.004	10.76	1.4777	40'
30'	0.0960	0.0958	0.9954	0.0963	10.39	1.005	10.43	1.4748	30'
40'	0.0989	0.0987	0.9951	0.0992	10.08	1.005	10.13	1.4719	20'
50'	0.1018	0.1016	0.9948	0.1022	9.788	1.005	9.839	1.4690	10'
6°00'	0.1047	0.1045	0.9945	0.1051	9.514	1.006	9.567	1.4661	84°00'
10'	0.1076	0.1074	0.9942	0.1080	9.255	1.006	9.309	1.4632	50'
20'	0.1105	0.1103	0.9939	0.1110	9.010	1.006	9.065	1.4603	40'
30'	0.1134	0.1132	0.9936	0.1139	8.777	1.006	8.834	1.4573	30'
40'	0.1164	0.1161	0.9932	0.1169	8.556	1.007	8.614	1.4544	20'
50'	0.1193	0.1190	0.9929	0.1198	8.345	1.007	8.405	1.4515	10'
7°00'	0.1222	0.1219	0.9925	0.1228	8.144	1.008	8.206	1.4486	83°00'
10'	0.1251	0.1248	0.9922	0.1257	7.953	1.008	8.016	1.4457	50'
20'	0.1280	0.1276	0.9918	0.1287	7.770	1.008	7.834	1.4428	40'
30'	0.1309	0.1305	0.9914	0.1317	7.596	1.009	7.661	1.4399	30'
40'	0.1338	0.1334	0.9911	0.1346	7.429	1.009	7.496	1.4370	20'
50'	0.1367	0.1363	0.9907	0.1376	7.269	1.009	7.337	1.4341	10'
		cos	sin	cot	tan	csc	sec	Radians	Degrees

Degrees	Radians	sin	cos	tan	cot	sec	csc		
8°00′	0.1396	0.1392	0.9903	0.1405	7.115	1.010	7.185	1.4312	82°00′
10′	0.1425	0.1421	0.9899	0.1435	6.968	1.010	7.040	1.4283	50′
20′	0.1454	0.1449	0.9894	0.1465	6.827	1.011	6.900	1.4254	40′
30′	0.1484	0.1478	0.9890	0.1495	6.691	1.011	6.765	1.4224	30′
40′	0.1513	0.1507	0.9886	0.1524	6.561	1.012	6.636	1.4195	20′
50′	0.1542	0.1536	0.9881	0.1554	6.435	1.012	6.512	1.4166	10′
9°00′	0.1571	0.1564	0.9877	0.1584	6.314	1.012	6.392	1.4137	81°00′
10′	0.1600	0.1593	0.9872	0.1614	6.197	1.013	6.277	1.4108	50′
20′	0.1629	0.1622	0.9868	0.1644	6.084	1.013	6.166	1.4079	40′
30′	0.1658	0.1650	0.9863	0.1673	5.976	1.014	6.059	1.4050	30′
40′	0.1687	0.1679	0.9858	0.1703	5.871	1.014	5.955	1.4021	20′
50′	0.1716	0.1708	0.9853	0.1733	5.769	1.015	5.855	1.3992	10′
10°00′	0.1745	0.1736	0.9848	0.1763	5.671	1.015	5.759	1.3963	80°00′
10′	0.1774	0.1765	0.9843	0.1793	5.576	1.016	5.665	1.3934	50′
20′	0.1804	0.1794	0.9838	0.1823	5.485	1.016	5.575	1.3904	40′
30′	0.1833	0.1822	0.9833	0.1853	5.396	1.017	5.487	1.3875	30′
40′	0.1862	0.1851	0.9827	0.1883	5.309	1.018	5.403	1.3846	20′
50′	0.1891	0.1880	0.9822	0.1914	5.226	1.018	5.320	1.3817	10′
11°00′	0.1920	0.1908	0.9816	0.1944	5.145	1.019	5.241	1.3788	79°00′
10′	0.1949	0.1937	0.9811	0.1974	5.066	1.019	5.164	1.3759	50′
20′	0.1978	0.1965	0.9805	0.2004	4.989	1.020	5.089	1.3730	40′
30′	0.2007	0.1994	0.9799	0.2035	4.915	1.020	5.016	1.3701	30′
40′	0.2036	0.2022	0.9793	0.2065	4.843	1.021	4.945	1.3672	20′
50′	0.2065	0.2051	0.9787	0.2095	4.773	1.022	4.876	1.3643	10′
12°00′	0.2094	0.2079	0.9781	0.2126	4.705	1.022	4.810	1.3614	78°00′
10′	0.2123	0.2108	0.9775	0.2156	4.638	1.023	4.745	1.3584	50′
20′	0.2153	0.2136	0.9769	0.2186	4.574	1.024	4.682	1.3555	40′
30′	0.2182	0.2164	0.9763	0.2217	4.511	1.024	4.620	1.3526	30′
40′	0.2211	0.2193	0.9757	0.2247	4.449	1.025	4.560	1.3497	20′
50′	0.2240	0.2221	0.9750	0.2278	4.390	1.026	4.502	1.3468	10′
13°00′	0.2269	0.2250	0.9744	0.2309	4.331	1.026	4.445	1.3439	77°00′
10′	0.2298	0.2278	0.9737	0.2339	4.275	1.027	4.390	1.3410	50′
20′	0.2327	0.2306	0.9730	0.2370	4.219	1.028	4.336	1.3381	40′
30′	0.2356	0.2334	0.9724	0.2401	4.165	1.028	4.284	1.3352	30′
40′	0.2385	0.2363	0.9717	0.2432	4.113	1.029	4.232	1.3323	20′
50′	0.2414	0.2391	0.9710	0.2462	4.061	1.030	4.182	1.3294	10′
14°00′	0.2443	0.2419	0.9703	0.2493	4.011	1.031	4.134	1.3265	76°00′
10′	0.2473	0.2447	0.9696	0.2524	3.962	1.031	4.086	1.3235	50′
20′	0.2502	0.2476	0.9689	0.2555	3.914	1.032	4.039	1.3206	40′
30′	0.2531	0.2504	0.9681	0.2586	3.867	1.033	3.994	1.3177	30′
40′	0.2560	0.2532	0.9674	0.2617	3.821	1.034	3.950	1.3148	20′
50′	0.2589	0.2560	0.9667	0.2648	3.776	1.034	3.906	1.3119	10′
15°00′	0.2618	0.2588	0.9659	0.2679	3.732	1.035	3.864	1.3090	75°00′
10′	0.2647	0.2616	0.9652	0.2711	3.689	1.036	3.822	1.3061	50′
20′	0.2676	0.2644	0.9644	0.2742	3.647	1.037	3.782	1.3032	40′
30′	0.2705	0.2672	0.9636	0.2773	3.606	1.038	3.742	1.3003	30′
40′	0.2734	0.2700	0.9628	0.2805	3.566	1.039	3.703	1.2974	20′
50′	0.2763	0.2728	0.9621	0.2836	3.526	1.039	3.665	1.2945	10′
16°00′	0.2793	0.2756	0.9613	0.2867	3.487	1.040	3.628	1.2915	74°00′
10′	0.2822	0.2784	0.9605	0.2899	3.450	1.041	3.592	1.2886	50′
20′	0.2851	0.2812	0.9596	0.2931	3.412	1.042	3.556	1.2857	40′
30′	0.2880	0.2840	0.9588	0.2962	3.376	1.043	3.521	1.2828	30′
40′	0.2909	0.2868	0.9580	0.2994	3.340	1.044	3.487	1.2799	20′
50′	0.2938	0.2896	0.9572	0.3026	3.305	1.045	3.453	1.2770	10′
		cos	sin	cot	tan	csc	sec	Radians	Degrees

Degrees	Radians	sin	cos	tan	cot	sec	csc		
17°00′	0.2967	0.2924	0.9563	0.3057	3.271	1.046	3.420	1.2741	73°00′
10′	0.2996	0.2952	0.9555	0.3089	3.237	1.047	3.388	1.2712	50′
20′	0.3025	0.2979	0.9546	0.3121	3.204	1.048	3.356	1.2683	40′
30′	0.3054	0.3007	0.9537	0.3153	3.172	1.049	3.326	1.2654	30′
40′	0.3083	0.3035	0.9528	0.3185	3.140	1.049	3.295	1.2625	20′
50′	0.3113	0.3062	0.9520	0.3217	3.108	1.050	3.265	1.2595	10′
18°00′	0.3142	0.3090	0.9511	0.3249	3.078	1.051	3.236	1.2566	72°00′
10′	0.3171	0.3118	0.9502	0.3281	3.047	1.052	3.207	1.2537	50′
20′	0.3200	0.3145	0.9492	0.3314	3.018	1.053	3.179	1.2508	40′
30′	0.3229	0.3173	0.9483	0.3346	2.989	1.054	3.152	1.2479	30′
40′	0.3258	0.3201	0.9474	0.3378	2.960	1.056	3.124	1.2450	20′
50′	0.3287	0.3228	0.9465	0.3411	2.932	1.057	3.098	1.2421	10′
19°00′	0.3316	0.3256	0.9455	0.3443	2.904	1.058	3.072	1.2392	71°00′
10′	0.3345	0.3283	0.9446	0.3476	2.877	1.059	3.046	1.2363	50′
20′	0.3374	0.3311	0.9436	0.3508	2.850	1.060	3.021	1.2334	40′
30′	0.3403	0.3338	0.9426	0.3541	2.824	1.061	2.996	1.2305	30′
40′	0.3432	0.3365	0.9417	0.3574	2.798	1.062	2.971	1.2275	20′
50′	0.3462	0.3393	0.9407	0.3607	2.773	1.063	2.947	1.2246	10′
20°00′	0.3491	0.3420	0.9397	0.3640	2.747	1.064	2.924	1.2217	70°00′
10′	0.3520	0.3448	0.9387	0.3673	2.723	1.065	2.901	1.2188	50′
20′	0.3549	0.3475	0.9377	0.3706	2.699	1.066	2.878	1.2159	40′
30′	0.3578	0.3502	0.9367	0.3739	2.675	1.068	2.855	1.2130	30′
40′	0.3607	0.3529	0.9356	0.3772	2.651	1.069	2.833	1.2101	20′
50′	0.3636	0.3557	0.9346	0.3805	2.628	1.070	2.812	1.2072	10′
21°00′	0.3665	0.3584	0.9336	0.3839	2.605	1.071	2.790	1.2043	69°00′
10′	0.3694	0.3611	0.9325	0.3872	2.583	1.072	2.769	1.2014	50′
20′	0.3723	0.3638	0.9315	0.3906	2.560	1.074	2.749	1.1985	40′
30′	0.3752	0.3665	0.9304	0.3939	2.539	1.075	2.729	1.1956	30′
40′	0.3782	0.3692	0.9293	0.3973	2.517	1.076	2.709	1.1926	20′
50′	0.3811	0.3719	0.9283	0.4006	2.496	1.077	2.689	1.1897	10′
22°00′	0.3840	0.3746	0.9272	0.4040	2.475	1.079	2.669	1.1868	68°00′
10′	0.3869	0.3773	0.9261	0.4074	2.455	1.080	2.650	1.1839	50′
20′	0.3898	0.3800	0.9250	0.4108	2.434	1.081	2.632	1.1810	40′
30′	0.3927	0.3827	0.9239	0.4142	2.414	1.082	2.613	1.1781	30′
40′	0.3956	0.3854	0.9228	0.4176	2.394	1.084	2.595	1.1752	20′
50′	0.3985	0.3881	0.9216	0.4210	2.375	1.085	2.577	1.1723	10′
23°00′	0.4014	0.3907	0.9205	0.4245	2.356	1.086	2.559	1.1694	67°00′
10′	0.4043	0.3934	0.9194	0.4279	2.337	1.088	2.542	1.1665	50′
20′	0.4072	0.3961	0.9182	0.4314	2.318	1.089	2.525	1.1636	40′
30′	0.4102	0.3987	0.9171	0.4348	2.300	1.090	2.508	1.1606	30′
40′	0.4131	0.4014	0.9159	0.4383	2.282	1.092	2.491	1.1577	20′
50′	0.4160	0.4041	0.9147	0.4417	2.264	1.093	2.475	1.1548	10′
24°00′	0.4189	0.4067	0.9135	0.4452	2.246	1.095	2.459	1.1519	66°00′
10′	0.4218	0.4094	0.9124	0.4487	2.229	1.096	2.443	1.1490	50′
20′	0.4247	0.4120	0.9112	0.4522	2.211	1.097	2.427	1.1461	40′
30′	0.4276	0.4147	0.9100	0.4557	2.194	1.099	2.411	1.1432	30′
40′	0.4305	0.4173	0.9088	0.4592	2.177	1.100	2.396	1.1403	20′
50′	0.4334	0.4200	0.9075	0.4628	2.161	1.102	2.381	1.1374	10′
25°00′	0.4363	0.4226	0.9063	0.4663	2.145	1.103	2.366	1.1345	65°00′
10′	0.4392	0.4253	0.9051	0.4699	2.128	1.105	2.352	1.1316	50′
20′	0.4422	0.4279	0.9038	0.4734	2.112	1.106	2.337	1.1286	40′
30′	0.4451	0.4305	0.9026	0.4770	2.097	1.108	2.323	1.1257	30′
40′	0.4480	0.4331	0.9013	0.4806	2.081	1.109	2.309	1.1228	20′
50′	0.4509	0.4358	0.9001	0.4841	2.066	1.111	2.295	1.1199	10′
		cos	sin	cot	tan	csc	sec	Radians	Degrees

Degrees	Radians	sin	cos	tan	cot	sec	csc		
26°00'	0.4538	0.4384	0.8988	0.4877	2.050	1.113	2.281	1.1170	64°00'
10'	0.4567	0.4410	0.8975	0.4913	2.035	1.114	2.268	1.1141	50'
20'	0.4596	0.4436	0.8962	0.4950	2.020	1.116	2.254	1.1112	40'
30'	0.4625	0.4462	0.8949	0.4986	2.006	1.117	2.241	1.1083	30'
40'	0.4654	0.4488	0.8936	0.5022	1.991	1.119	2.228	1.1054	20'
50'	0.4683	0.4514	0.8923	0.5059	1.977	1.121	2.215	1.1025	10'
27°00'	0.4712	0.4540	0.8910	0.5095	1.963	1.122	2.203	1.0996	63°00'
10'	0.4741	0.4566	0.8897	0.5132	1.949	1.124	2.190	1.0966	50'
20'	0.4771	0.4592	0.8884	0.5169	1.935	1.126	2.178	1.0937	40'
30'	0.4800	0.4617	0.8870	0.5206	1.921	1.127	2.166	1.0908	30'
40'	0.4829	0.4643	0.8857	0.5243	1.907	1.129	2.154	1.0879	20'
50'	0.4858	0.4669	0.8843	0.5280	1.894	1.131	2.142	1.0850	10'
28°00'	0.4887	0.4695	0.8829	0.5317	1.881	1.133	2.130	1.0821	62°00'
10'	0.4916	0.4720	0.8816	0.5354	1.868	1.134	2.118	1.0792	50'
20'	0.4945	0.4746	0.8802	0.5392	1.855	1.136	2.107	1.0763	40'
30'	0.4974	0.4772	0.8788	0.5430	1.842	1.138	2.096	1.0734	30'
40'	0.5003	0.4797	0.8774	0.5467	1.829	1.140	2.085	1.0705	20'
50'	0.5032	0.4823	0.8760	0.5505	1.816	1.142	2.074	1.0676	10'
29°00'	0.5061	0.4848	0.8746	0.5543	1.804	1.143	2.063	1.0647	61°00'
10'	0.5091	0.4874	0.8732	0.5581	1.792	1.145	2.052	1.0617	50'
20'	0.5120	0.4899	0.8718	0.5619	1.780	1.147	2.041	1.0588	40'
30'	0.5149	0.4924	0.8704	0.5658	1.767	1.149	2.031	1.0559	30'
40'	0.5178	0.4950	0.8689	0.5696	1.756	1.151	2.020	1.0530	20'
50'	0.5207	0.4975	0.8675	0.5735	1.744	1.153	2.010	1.0501	10'
30°00'	0.5236	0.5000	0.8660	0.5774	1.732	1.155	2.000	1.0472	60°00'
10'	0.5265	0.5025	0.8646	0.5812	1.720	1.157	1.990	1.0443	50'
20'	0.5294	0.5050	0.8631	0.5851	1.709	1.159	1.980	1.0414	40'
30'	0.5323	0.5075	0.8616	0.5890	1.698	1.161	1.970	1.0385	30'
40'	0.5352	0.5100	0.8601	0.5930	1.686	1.163	1.961	1.0356	20'
50'	0.5381	0.5125	0.8587	0.5969	1.675	1.165	1.951	1.0327	10'
31°00'	0.5411	0.5150	0.8572	0.6009	1.664	1.167	1.942	1.0297	59°00'
10'	0.5440	0.5175	0.8557	0.6048	1.653	1.169	1.932	1.0268	50'
20'	0.5469	0.5200	0.8542	0.6088	1.643	1.171	1.923	1.0239	40'
30'	0.5498	0.5225	0.8526	0.6128	1.632	1.173	1.914	1.0210	30'
40'	0.5527	0.5250	0.8511	0.6168	1.621	1.175	1.905	1.0181	20'
50'	0.5556	0.5275	0.8496	0.6208	1.611	1.177	1.896	1.0152	10'
32°00'	0.5585	0.5299	0.8480	0.6249	1.600	1.179	1.887	1.0123	58°00'
10'	0.5614	0.5324	0.8465	0.6289	1.590	1.181	1.878	1.0094	50'
20'	0.5643	0.5348	0.8450	0.6330	1.580	1.184	1.870	1.0065	40'
30'	0.5672	0.5373	0.8434	0.6371	1.570	1.186	1.861	1.0036	30'
40'	0.5701	0.5398	0.8418	0.6412	1.560	1.188	1.853	1.0007	20'
50'	0.5730	0.5422	0.8403	0.6453	1.550	1.190	1.844	0.9977	10'
33°00'	0.5760	0.5446	0.8387	0.6494	1.540	1.192	1.836	0.9948	57°00'
10'	0.5789	0.5471	0.8371	0.6536	1.530	1.195	1.828	0.9919	50'
20'	0.5818	0.5495	0.8355	0.6577	1.520	1.197	1.820	0.9890	40'
30'	0.5847	0.5519	0.8339	0.6619	1.511	1.199	1.812	0.9861	30'
40'	0.5876	0.5544	0.8323	0.6661	1.501	1.202	1.804	0.9832	20'
50'	0.5905	0.5568	0.8307	0.6703	1.492	1.204	1.796	0.9803	10'
34°00'	0.5934	0.5592	0.8290	0.6745	1.483	1.206	1.788	0.9774	56°00'
10'	0.5963	0.5616	0.8274	0.6787	1.473	1.209	1.781	0.9745	50'
20'	0.5992	0.5640	0.8258	0.6830	1.464	1.211	1.773	0.9716	40'
30'	0.6021	0.5664	0.8241	0.6873	1.455	1.213	1.766	0.9687	30'
40'	0.6050	0.5688	0.8225	0.6916	1.446	1.216	1.758	0.9657	20'
50'	0.6080	0.5712	0.8208	0.6959	1.437	1.218	1.751	0.9628	10'
		cos	sin	cot	tan	csc	sec	Radians	Degrees

Degrees	Radians	sin	cos	tan	cot	sec	csc		
35°00′	0.6109	0.5736	0.8192	0.7002	1.428	1.221	1.743	0.9599	55°00′
10′	0.6138	0.5760	0.8175	0.7046	1.419	1.223	1.736	0.9570	50′
20′	0.6167	0.5783	0.8158	0.7089	1.411	1.226	1.729	0.9541	40′
30′	0.6196	0.5807	0.8141	0.7133	1.402	1.228	1.722	0.9512	30′
40′	0.6225	0.5831	0.8124	0.7177	1.393	1.231	1.715	0.9483	20′
50′	0.6254	0.5854	0.8107	0.7221	1.385	1.233	1.708	0.9454	10′
36°00′	0.6283	0.5878	0.8090	0.7265	1.376	1.236	1.701	0.9425	54°00′
10′	0.6312	0.5901	0.8073	0.7310	1.368	1.239	1.695	0.9396	50′
20′	0.6341	0.5925	0.8056	0.7355	1.360	1.241	1.688	0.9367	40′
30′	0.6370	0.5948	0.8039	0.7400	1.351	1.244	1.681	0.9338	30′
40′	0.6400	0.5972	0.8021	0.7445	1.343	1.247	1.675	0.9308	20′
50′	0.6429	0.5995	0.8004	0.7490	1.335	1.249	1.668	0.9279	10′
37°00′	0.6458	0.6018	0.7986	0.7536	1.327	1.252	1.662	0.9250	53°00′
10′	0.6487	0.6041	0.7969	0.7581	1.319	1.255	1.655	0.9221	50′
20′	0.6516	0.6065	0.7951	0.7627	1.311	1.258	1.649	0.9192	40′
30′	0.6545	0.6088	0.7934	0.7673	1.303	1.260	1.643	0.9163	30′
40′	0.6574	0.6111	0.7916	0.7720	1.295	1.263	1.636	0.9134	20′
50′	0.6603	0.6134	0.7898	0.7766	1.288	1.266	1.630	0.9105	10′
38°00′	0.6632	0.6157	0.7880	0.7813	1.280	1.269	1.624	0.9076	52°00′
10′	0.6661	0.6180	0.7862	0.7860	1.272	1.272	1.618	0.9047	50′
20′	0.6690	0.6202	0.7844	0.7907	1.265	1.275	1.612	0.9018	40′
30′	0.6720	0.6225	0.7826	0.7954	1.257	1.278	1.606	0.8988	30′
40′	0.6749	0.6248	0.7808	0.8002	1.250	1.281	1.601	0.8959	20′
50′	0.6778	0.6271	0.7790	0.8050	1.242	1.284	1.595	0.8930	10′
39°00′	0.6807	0.6293	0.7771	0.8098	1.235	1.287	1.589	0.8901	51°00′
10′	0.6836	0.6316	0.7753	0.8146	1.228	1.290	1.583	0.8872	50′
20′	0.6865	0.6338	0.7735	0.8195	1.220	1.293	1.578	0.8843	40′
30′	0.6894	0.6361	0.7716	0.8243	1.213	1.296	1.572	0.8814	30′
40′	0.6923	0.6383	0.7698	0.8292	1.206	1.299	1.567	0.8785	20′
50′	0.6952	0.6406	0.7679	0.8342	1.199	1.302	1.561	0.8756	10′
40°00′	0.6981	0.6428	0.7660	0.8391	1.192	1.305	1.556	0.8727	50°00′
10′	0.7010	0.6450	0.7642	0.8441	1.185	1.309	1.550	0.8698	50′
20′	0.7039	0.6472	0.7623	0.8491	1.178	1.312	1.545	0.8668	40′
30′	0.7069	0.6494	0.7604	0.8541	1.171	1.315	1.540	0.8639	30′
40′	0.7098	0.6517	0.7585	0.8591	1.164	1.318	1.535	0.8610	20′
50′	0.7127	0.6539	0.7566	0.8642	1.157	1.322	1.529	0.8581	10′
41°00′	0.7156	0.6561	0.7547	0.8693	1.150	1.325	1.524	0.8552	49°00′
10′	0.7185	0.6583	0.7528	0.8744	1.144	1.328	1.519	0.8523	50′
20′	0.7214	0.6604	0.7509	0.8796	1.137	1.332	1.514	0.8494	40′
30′	0.7243	0.6626	0.7490	0.8847	1.130	1.335	1.509	0.8465	30′
40′	0.7272	0.6648	0.7470	0.8899	1.124	1.339	1.504	0.8436	20′
50′	0.7301	0.6670	0.7451	0.8952	1.117	1.342	1.499	0.8407	10′
42°00′	0.7330	0.6691	0.7431	0.9004	1.111	1.346	1.494	0.8378	48°00′
10′	0.7359	0.6713	0.7412	0.9057	1.104	1.349	1.490	0.8348	50′
20′	0.7389	0.6734	0.7392	0.9110	1.098	1.353	1.485	0.8319	40′
30′	0.7418	0.6756	0.7373	0.9163	1.091	1.356	1.480	0.8290	30′
40′	0.7447	0.6777	0.7353	0.9217	1.085	1.360	1.476	0.8261	20′
50′	0.7476	0.6799	0.7333	0.9271	1.079	1.364	1.471	0.8232	10′
43°00′	0.7505	0.6820	0.7314	0.9325	1.072	1.367	1.466	0.8203	47°00′
10′	0.7534	0.6841	0.7294	0.9380	1.066	1.371	1.462	0.8174	50′
20′	0.7563	0.6862	0.7274	0.9435	1.060	1.375	1.457	0.8145	40′
30′	0.7592	0.6884	0.7254	0.9490	1.054	1.379	1.453	0.8116	30′
40′	0.7621	0.6905	0.7234	0.9545	1.048	1.382	1.448	0.8087	20′
50′	0.7650	0.6926	0.7214	0.9601	1.042	1.386	1.444	0.8058	10′
		cos	sin	cot	tan	csc	sec	Radians	Degrees

Degrees	Radians	sin	cos	tan	cot	sec	csc		
44°00′	0.7679	0.6947	0.7193	0.9657	1.036	1.390	1.440	0.8029	46°00′
10′	0.7709	0.6967	0.7173	0.9713	1.030	1.394	1.435	0.7999	50′
20′	0.7738	0.6988	0.7153	0.9770	1.024	1.398	1.431	0.7970	40′
30′	0.7767	0.7009	0.7133	0.9827	1.018	1.402	1.427	0.7941	30′
40′	0.7796	0.7030	0.7112	0.9884	1.012	1.406	1.423	0.7912	20′
50′	0.7825	0.7050	0.7092	0.9942	1.006	1.410	1.418	0.7883	10′
45°00′	0.7854	0.7071	0.7071	1.000	1.000	1.414	1.414	0.7854	45°00′
		cos	sin	cot	tan	csc	sec	Radians	Degrees

Normal Curve Table

AREAS UNDER THE STANDARD NORMAL CURVE

Percent of area under the curve between 0 and z.

	.00	.01	.02	.03	.04	.05	.06	.07	.08	.09
.0	.0000	.0040	.0080	.0120	.0160	.0199	.0239	.0279	.0319	.0359
.1	.0398	.0438	.0478	.0517	.0557	.0596	.0636	.0675	.0714	.0753
.2	.0793	.0832	.0871	.0910	.0948	.0987	.1026	.1064	.1103	.1141
.3	.1179	.1217	.1255	.1293	.1331	.1368	.1406	.1443	.1480	.1517
.4	.1554	.1591	.1628	.1664	.1700	.1736	.1772	.1808	.1844	.1879
.5	.1915	.1950	.1985	.2019	.2054	.2088	.2123	.2157	.2190	.2224
.6	.2257	.2291	.2324	.2357	.2389	.2422	.2454	.2486	.2517	.2549
.7	.2580	.2611	.2642	.2673	.2704	.2734	.2764	.2794	.2823	.2852
.8	.2881	.2910	.2939	.2967	.2995	.3023	.3051	.3078	.3106	.3133
.9	.3159	.3186	.3212	.3238	.3264	.3289	.3315	.3340	.3365	.3389
1.0	.3413	.3438	.3461	.3485	.3508	.3531	.3554	.3577	.3599	.3621
1.1	.3643	.3665	.3686	.3708	.3729	.3749	.3770	.3790	.3810	.3830
1.2	.3849	.3869	.3888	.3907	.3925	.3944	.3962	.3980	.3997	.4015
1.3	.4032	.4049	.4066	.4082	.4099	.4115	.4131	.4147	.4162	.4177
1.4	.4192	.4207	.4222	.4236	.4251	.4265	.4279	.4292	.4306	.4319
1.5	.4332	.4345	.4357	.4370	.4382	.4394	.4406	.4418	.4429	.4441
1.6	.4452	.4463	.4474	.4484	.4495	.4505	.4515	.4525	.4535	.4545
1.7	.4554	.4564	.4573	.4582	.4591	.4599	.4608	.4616	.4625	.4633
1.8	.4641	.4649	.4656	.4664	.4671	.4678	.4686	.4693	.4699	.4706
1.9	.4713	.4719	.4726	.4732	.4738	.4744	.4750	.4756	.4761	.4767
2.0	.4772	.4778	.4783	.4788	.4793	.4798	.4803	.4808	.4812	.4817
2.1	.4821	.4826	.4830	.4834	.4838	.4842	.4846	.4850	.4854	.4857
2.2	.4861	.4864	.4868	.4871	.4875	.4878	.4881	.4884	.4887	.4890
2.3	.4893	.4896	.4898	.4901	.4904	.4906	.4909	.4911	.4913	.4916
2.4	.4918	.4920	.4922	.4925	.4927	.4929	.4931	.4932	.4934	.4936
2.5	.4938	.4940	.4941	.4943	.4945	.4946	.4948	.4949	.4951	.4952
2.6	.4953	.4955	.4956	.4957	.4959	.4960	.4961	.4962	.4963	.4964
2.7	.4965	.4966	.4967	.4968	.4969	.4970	.4971	.4972	.4973	.4974
2.8	.4974	.4975	.4976	.4977	.4977	.4978	.4979	.4979	.4980	.4981
2.9	.4981	.4982	.4982	.4983	.4984	.4984	.4985	.4985	.4986	.4986
3.0	.4987	.4987	.4987	.4988	.4988	.4989	.4989	.4989	.4990	.4990
3.1	.4990	.4991	.4991	.4991	.4992	.4992	.4992	.4992	.4993	.4993
3.2	.4993	.4993	.4994	.4994	.4994	.4994	.4994	.4995	.4995	.4995
3.3	.4995	.4995	.4995	.4996	.4996	.4996	.4996	.4996	.4996	.4997
3.4	.4997	.4997	.4997	.4997	.4997	.4997	.4997	.4997	.4997	.4998
3.5	.4998									
4.0	.49997									
4.5	.499997									
5.0	.4999997									

Glossary

absolute value   The distance of a number from zero.

addition method   A method of solving a system of equations by adding the equations to eliminate one of the variables.

addition property of inequality   The principle that adding the same quantity c to both sides of an inequality does not change the truth value of the inequality; in symbols, if $a > b$, then $a + c > b + c$.

additive identity element   The number zero since it can be added to any number without changing the value.

additive inverse of a number   The number that gives a sum of 0 when added to a given number.

additive inverse property   The principle that $a + (-a) = 0$.

algebraic expression   A mathematical expression resulting from performing mathematical operations on any collection of variables and constants.

angle of depression   The angle between the horizontal and a line of sight to an object below the observer.

angle of elevation   The angle between the horizontal and a line of sight to an object above the observer.

associative property of addition   The principle that addends can be grouped in any order without affecting the sum; in symbols, $a + (b + c) = (a + b) + c$.

associative property of multiplication   The principle that factors can be grouped in any order without affecting the product; in symbols, $a(bc) = (ab)c$

asymptote   A line to which a curve approaches without touching.

axis of a right circular conical surface   The line through the vertex of the conical surface and the center of the circular base.

base   A quantity that is raised to a power.

binomial   A polynomial with exactly two terms.

Cartesian plane   The plane considered as the Cartesian product, $\mathbb{R} \times \mathbb{R}$.

circle   (1) The set of points in a plane that are a given distance from a given point. (2) The intersection of a right circular cone and a plane perpendicular to its axis.

closure property   The property of certain binary operations that always result in a value that is in the same set of numbers as the two numbers being combined.

coefficient   The constant factor accompanying the variables in a term.

column matrix   A matrix that has only one column.

combination   The number of sets determined by specified elements (order not important).

common denominator   The least common multiple (LCM) of the denominators.

common logarithm   A logarithm with base 10.

common monomial factor   A factor common to all the terms of a polynomial.

commutative property of addition   The principle that addends can be arranged in any order without affecting the sum; in symbols, $a + b = b + a$.

commutative property of multiplication   The principle that factors can be arranged in any order without affecting the product; in symbols, $ab = ba$.

completing the square   A method for obtaining a perfect square trinomial from another polynomial.

complex fraction   A fraction that contains a fraction in its numerator or denominator (or both).

complex numbers   The set $\mathbb{C}$ of numbers of the form $a + bi$ where a and b are real numbers and $i = \sqrt{-1}$.

complex rational expression   A rational expression that contains rational expressions in its numerator or denominator (or both).

composite function   A function obtained by using one function as the input for another. The composite of the functions f and g is given by $f \circ g(x) = f(g(x))$.

compound sentence   Two mathematical statements connected by *and* or *or*.

conic section   The intersection of a plane and a right circular conical surface.

conical surface   The union of all lines that connect a given point to a given curve in a given plane.

conjugate axis   The axis between halves of a hyperbola.

conjugates   Two binomials that are identical except that one is a sum and the other a difference.

conjunction   A compound mathematical sentence with the connecting word *and*.

consistent system   A system of equations with at least one solution.

constant   A symbol that represents a fixed number.

constant function   A function that has a horizontal line as its graph; in symbols, $y = k$ for some constant k.

constant of variation   The constant in the equation that expresses the relation among variables in direct, inverse, or joint variation.

cosecant   The trigonometric ratio that is the reciprocal of the sine.

cosine   The trigonometric ratio of the adjacent side over the hypotenuse in a right triangle; in symbols, $\frac{x}{r}$.

cotangent   The trigonometric ratio that is the reciprocal of the tangent.

Cramer's rule   A formula for solving systems of equations using determinants.

cube root   One of a number's three equal factors.

degree of a polynomial   The highest degree of the terms in a polynomial.

degree of a term   The sum of the exponents on the variables in a term.

dependent system   A consistent system of equations with an infinite number of solutions.

dependent variable   The variable representing the range (output) of a function.

determinant   A number calculated from the entries of a square matrix.

direct variation   A linear relation in which one variable is a multiple of the other and described by $y = kx$ where $k > 0$.

directrix   The fixed line in the definition of a parabola.

discriminant   The radicand in the quadratic formula.

disjunction   A compound mathematical sentence with the connecting word *or*.

distance formula   The formula $d = \sqrt{(x_1 - x_2)^2 + (y_1 - y_2)^2}$, which represents the distance between two points (x_1, y_1) and (x_2, y_2).

distributive property   The principle that the product of a quantity and a binomial is equal to the sum of the products of the quantity with each term in the binomial; in symbols, $a(b + c) = ab + ac$.

division property of inequality   The principle that when dividing both sides of an inequality by the same number, the inequality is reversed if and only if the divisor is negative.

division property of radicals   The principle that the nth root of a quotient is equal to the quotient of the nth roots; in symbols, $\sqrt[n]{\dfrac{x}{y}} = \dfrac{\sqrt[n]{x}}{\sqrt[n]{y}}$.

domain   The set of first elements from the ordered pairs describing a relation.

double-angle formulas   The two trigonometric identities: $\sin 2x = 2\sin x \cos x$ and $\cos 2x = \cos^2 x - \sin^2 x$.

element of a conical surface   Any of the lines that join the vertex to the plane curve in the definition of a conical surface.

elements   The members or objects in a set.

ellipse   (1) The locus of points in a plane whose distances to two fixed points in the plane have a constant sum. (2) The intersection of a right circular cone and a plane that intersects only one nappe and that is neither parallel to an element of the cone nor perpendicular to the axis.

entry   Any of the quantities in a matrix.

equivalent vectors   Vectors having the same length and the same direction.

event   A subset of the sample space in a probability experiment.

experiment   A trial in probability theory.

exponent   The superscript on a quantity that indicates the number of times that the base occurs as a factor.

exponential function   A function with variables in the exponent and a base that is a constant positive real number other than 1.

extraneous solution   A value that is obtained in the process of correctly solving an equation but does not check in the original equation.

factor   Any quantity that divides evenly into the given quantity.

factor theorem   The principle that $(x - a)$ is a factor of a polynomial $P(x)$ if and only if the remainder from dividing $P(x)$ by $(x - a)$ is zero.

factorial   The product of a number n and every natural number less than it; in symbols, $n! = n(n - 1)(n - 2) \ldots 3 \cdot 2 \cdot 1$.

focus   The fixed point(s) in the definitions of parabola, ellipse, and hyperbola.

FOIL   A method of multiplying binomials by finding the sum of products of the first, outer, inner, and last terms.

function   A relation in which each x-coordinate is paired with exactly one y-coordinate.

fundamental principle of counting   The principle that if there are m ways to do one thing and n ways to do a second thing, then there are $m \cdot n$ ways to do the first thing and then the second thing.

greatest integer function   The function for which each value of the range is the largest integer less than or equal to the given domain value; in symbols, $f(x) = [x]$.

hyperbola   (1) The locus of points in the plane such that their distances from two fixed points have a constant difference.   (2) The intersection of a right circular conical surface and a plane that intersects both nappes.

hypotenuse   The side of a right triangle that is opposite the right angle.

identity property of addition   The principle that adding zero to any number does not change the value; in symbols, $a + 0 = a = 0 + a$.

identity property of multiplication   The principle that multiplying quantities by 1 will not change them; in symbols, $1 \cdot a = a = a \cdot 1$.

imaginary number   A complex number involving the imaginary unit; in symbols, $a + bi$ with $b \neq 0$.

imaginary unit   The number i where $i^2 = -1$ or $i = \sqrt{-1}$.

inconsistent system   A system of equations that has no solution.

independent system   A consistent system of equations that has a finite number of solutions.

independent variable   The variable representing the domain (input) of the function.

index   The number in the hook of the radical sign that indicates the type of root.

integers   The set of whole numbers and their opposites; in symbols, $\mathbb{Z} = \{\ldots -4, -3, -2, -1, 0, 1, 2, 3, 4, \ldots\}$.

intersection   The set of elements common to two sets.

inverse relation   The relation formed by reversing the domain and range elements of a relation.

inverse variation   A relation described by $y = \dfrac{k}{x}$ where $k \neq 0$.

irrational numbers   Numbers that cannot be expressed as a ratio of integers.

joint variation   A variation involving more than one independent variable.

law of cosines   A formula used in solving triangles that relates the lengths of the three sides and the measure of one angle; in symbols, $a^2 = b^2 + c^2 - 2bc \cos A$.

law of sines   A formula used in solving triangles that relates the ratios of two sides to the measures of the angles opposite; in symbols, $\frac{\sin A}{a} = \frac{\sin B}{b}$.

least common multiple   (LCM) The smallest positive quantity that is a multiple of two given quantities.

like terms   Terms that have the same variable(s) with the same exponents.

line of symmetry   A line through the vertex of a parabola and across which the parabola displays symmetry.

linear equation   An equation of the first degree (its graph is a line).

linear function   A function that can be expressed as a rule in the form $f(x) = mx + b$.

linear programming   A method of solving problems that require finding a maximum or minimum value of an objective function subject to several conditions (constraints) in the form of inequalities that must be satisfied.

locus   A set of points that satisfy a given condition.

logarithm   The number obtained from the inverse of exponentiation (the exponent).

logarithmic function   The inverse of an exponential function.

major axis   The axis on which the foci of an ellipse are located.

matrix   A table of numerical values.

midpoint formula   The formula for finding the midpoint between two points (x_1, y_1) and (x_2, y_2) given by $\left(\frac{x_1 + x_2}{2}, \frac{y_1 + y_2}{2} \right)$.

minor axis   The shorter axis of an ellipse that is perpendicular to the major axis at the center.

monomial   A polynomial with exactly one term.

multiplication property of inequality   The principle that when multiplying both sides of an inequality by the same number, the inequality is reversed if and only if the factor is negative.

multiplicative identity element   The number 1 since any quantity can be multiplied by it without changing that quantity.

multiplicative inverse   The reciprocal of a nonzero real number; in symbols, $\frac{1}{a}$.

multiplicative inverse property   The principle that each product of a nonzero number and its multiplicative inverse is 1; in symbols, $a \cdot \frac{1}{a} = 1 = \frac{1}{a} \cdot a$ where $a \neq 0$.

mutually exclusive events   Two events in probability theory that have no intersection.

nappe   Either half of a conical surface including the vertex.

natural numbers   The counting numbers; in symbols, $\mathbb{N} = \{1, 2, 3, 4, \ldots\}$.

order of operations   The rule governing precedence of mathematical operations—grouping, exponents, multiplications, and additions.

ordered pair   A pair of coordinates in which the order is important.

origin   The point at which the axes cross in the Cartesian plane.

parabola   (1) The locus of points equidistant from a given point and a given line. (2) The intersection of a right circular cone and a plane parallel to an element of the cone. (3) The graph of a quadratic function.

perfect square trinomial   A trinomial that factors as the square of a binomial.

permutation   The number of arrangements of specified elements (order important).

point-slope form   A form of a linear equation involving the slope m and a given point (x_1, y_1): $y - y_1 = m(x - x_1)$.

polynomial   An algebraic expression with one or more terms, each of which is a product of a constant and variables with whole number exponents.

polynomial function   A function described by a rule that is a polynomial.

probability   The ratio of the number of successful outcomes to the number of possible outcomes.

product property of radicals   The principle that the root of a product is equal to the product of the roots; in symbols, $\sqrt[n]{xy} = \sqrt[n]{x} \sqrt[n]{y}$.

pure imaginary number   A complex number of the form bi where $b \neq 0$.

Pythagorean theorem   The principle that the sum of the squares of the lengths of the legs of a right triangle is equal to the square of the length of the hypotenuse.

quadratic equation   An equation that can be expressed in the general form $ax^2 + bx + c = 0$.

quadratic formula   The formula for the solutions of a quadratic equation in general form; in symbols, $x = \frac{-b \pm \sqrt{b^2 - 4ac}}{2a}$.

quadratic function   A polynomial function of degree 2.

radian   A unit of angle measure; one radian corresponds to an angle that intercepts an arc one unit long on a unit circle.

radical equation   An equation that contains a variable under a radical.

radical expression   Any algebraic expression involving a radical sign.

radical sign   The symbol $\sqrt[n]{\ }$, used to represent the inverse process for powers.

radicand   The quantity under the radical sign.

range   The set of second elements from the ordered pairs describing a relation.

rational equation   An equation containing a rational expression that contains a variable in the denominator.

rational expression   A ratio of two polynomials such that the denominator does not equal zero.

rationalizing the denominator   A process for changing the form of a radical expression so that no radicals appear in the denominator.

rational numbers   The set $\mathbb{Q}$ of numbers that can be expressed as a ratio of two integers.

real numbers   The set $\mathbb{R}$ of all numbers that can be represented on a number line, including both the rational and irrational numbers.

relation   Any set of ordered pairs.

remainder theorem   The principle that the remainder from dividing a polynomial $P(x)$ by a binomial of the form $(x - a)$ is equal to the value of $P(a)$.

row matrix   A matrix that has only one row.

row operations   Any of three basic operations on matrices: (1) interchanging two rows, (2) replacing a row with a multiple of it, and (3) replacing a row with the sum of that row and a multiple of another row.

row reduce   The process of obtaining an identity matrix by applying row operations.

sample space   The set of all possible outcomes of a probability experiment.

secant   A trigonometic ratio that is the reciprocal of the cosine.

sine   The trigonometric ratio of the opposite side over the hypotenuse in a right triangle; in symbols, $\frac{y}{r}$.

slope   The ratio of the change in y values between two points on a line to the corresponding change in x values.

slope-intercept form   The form of a linear equation that involves the slope and the y-intercept; in symbols, $y = mx + b$.

square matrix   A matrix that has the same number of rows as columns.

square root   One of a number's two equal factors.

substitution method   A method for solving a system of equations by substituting for one variable, solving for the other, and then finding the first variable from the known one.

system of equations   Two or more equations to be solved simultaneously.

tangent   The trigonometric ratio of the opposite side over the adjacent in a right triangle; in symbols, $\frac{y}{x}$.

term   A part of an algebraic expression separated from the rest of the expression by addition or subtraction signs.

theorem   A statement proved from definitions, postulates, and previously proved statements.

translation   A shifting or sliding of a graph to a new location in the plane without altering its shape.

transverse axis   The line that contains both vertices of a hyperbola.

trigonometric ratios   Any of the six ratios based on the sides of a right triangle: sine, cosine, tangent, cosecant, secant, and cotangent.

trinomial   A polynomial with exactly three terms.

union   The set consisting of all elements in either of two sets.

unit circle   A circle with a radius of one unit and with its center at the origin.

vector   A directed segment, having both length and direction.

vertex   The given point in the definitions of parabola and conical surface; the points where an ellipse or hyperbola crosses its axes of symmetry.

vertical line test   A method for checking whether the graph of a relation is a function by confirming that it does not cross any vertical lines more than once.

whole numbers   The set consisting of the natural numbers and zero; $\mathbb{W} = \{0, 1, 2, 3, \ldots\}$.

x-axis   The horizontal reference line in the Cartesian plane.

x-coordinate   The first element of an ordered pair; the abscissa.

x-intercept   The point at which the graph of a relation crosses the x-axis.

y-axis   The vertical reference line in the Cartesian plane.

y-coordinate   The second element of an ordered pair; the ordinate.

y-intercept   The point at which the graph of a relation crosses the y-axis.

zero product property   The principle that if the product of two quantities is zero, then at least one of the two factors is zero.

zero property of multiplication   The principle that whenever a number is multiplied by zero, the product will always be zero; in symbols, $a \cdot 0 = 0 = 0 \cdot a$.

zero of a function   The x-value of any x-intercept.

Selected Answers

Chapter 1—Operations

1.1

1.

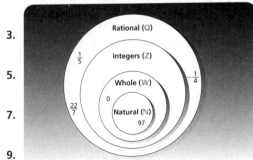

Real Numbers ($\mathbb{R}$)

Rational ($\mathbb{Q}$)

Integers ($\mathbb{Z}$)

$\frac{1}{5}$

Whole ($\mathbb{W}$)

$\frac{1}{4}$

0

$\frac{22}{7}$

Natural ($\mathbb{N}$)

97

3.

5.

7.

9.

11. $3 + 7 = 7 + 3$; Answers will vary.
13. $-5 + 0 = -5$; Answers will vary.
15. $2 + (-2) = 0$; Answers will vary.
17. $(-2)3 = 3(-2)$; Answers will vary.
19. No, $5 - 7 = -2$ and $-2 \notin \mathbb{W}$.
21. 17   23. 9   25. -41

1.2

1. monomial, degree 2
3. trinomial, degree 6
5. polynomial, degree 6
7. monomial, degree 0
9. trinomial, degree 4
11. $7x^2 - 6x - 6$ 13. $12c^2 + 9cd - 3d^2$
15. $2x^4y + 6x^2y^2 - 3xy^2 - 2xy^5$
17. $11c^2 - c + 8d^2$ 19. $6a + 7b - 10c$
27. Commutative property of addition [1.1]
29. Distributive property [1.1]

1.3

1. $15x^5$ 3. $4c^2d^3$ 5. x^8 7. 1   9. $32a^3b^4$
11. $6a^3 + 12a^2x - 27a^2$
13. $a^7cd^3 - 3a^3c^2d^4 + 7a^3cd^3$ 15. $a^2 + 2a - 24$
17. $b^2 + 5b - 14$ 19. $x^2 - 18x + 81$
21. $3a^2 - 3ab - 6b^2$ 23. 1   25. $x^2 + 2xy + y^2$
27. $5x^3 + 7x^2 - 4x - 6$
29. $4a^3 + 19a^2 - 38a + 10$
35. Zero property of exponents [1.3]
37. Commutative property of multiplication [1.1]
39. Product property of exponents [1.3]

1.4

1. $\frac{a^2c^3}{b^2}$ 3. $\frac{4y^2}{x}$ 5. $\frac{56x^4}{y}$ 7. $3c^3k^2 - c + 8c^7k^2$
9. $2a^3 - a^2 + 3a + 6$ 11. $8ab^2c$ 13. $a + 5$

15. $xy - 10y$ 17. $3a^2 - 7a + 8$ R. -16
19. $9x^3 + 36x^2 + 147x + 588$ R. 2340   21. $x + 7$
23. $6y - 2$ 25. $3a + 4$ R. -8 29. $21x^3y^3$ [1.3]
31. $2x^2 + x - 1$ [1.2]   33. $y^3 + 5y^2 + y - 10$ [1.3]

1.5

1. $3x(x - 5)$ 3. $8(3xy + 7ab)$ 5. $(x + 9)(x - 9)$
7. $(a + b)(a - b)$ 9. $(5x - 2y)(5x + 2y)$
11. $2x(x - 2)(x + 2)$ 13. $(y + 4)(y^2 - 4y + 16)$
15. $x(2y - 5)(4y^2 + 10y + 25)$ 17. $6(x - 7)(x + 7)$
19. $x^2(x - 4)(x^2 + 4x + 16)$
21. $6y^2(5y - 1)(5y + 1)$ 23. $8a^3(6a - 5)(6a + 5)$
29. FOIL [1.3] or distributive property
31. Commutative property of multiplication [1.1]
33. Identity property of addition [1.1]

1.6

1. $(x + 7)(x - 9)$ 3. $(3c + 2)(c - 5)$
5. $2ef^2g(5ef + 3g - 4f^3)$ 7. $(2x - 13)(x + 1)$
9. $(a - 1)(a - 18)$ 11. $(7x + 2)(5x - 6)$
13. $(b - 5c)^2$ 15. $4xy(3x - 1)(x + 9)$
17. $5a(2a - 11)(3a - 7)$ 19. $6y^2(7y - 2)(7y + 2)$
21. $(x^2 + 5)(x^2 - 3)$
23. $(x - 2)(x + 2)(x - 3)(x + 3)$ 29. $2x^2 - 10$ [1.2]
31. $2x - 1$ R. 8 [1.4]

1.7

1. $(x + 3)(x - y)$ 3. $(x^2 + y)(x - y)$
5. $(y + z)(x + 9)$ 7. $(x + 3)(x + 3 + y)$
9. $(a - 5 - y)(a - 5 + y)$
11. $(p + 5)(q + 2)(q^2 - 2q + 4)$
13. $(x^2 + 2)(x + 6)$ 15. $(a + 4b)(a - 2)(a + 2)$
17. $(x - 6)(x^2 - 9x + 21)$
19. $(x - 2y - 2)(x - 2y + 2)$
21. $x(a - b)(2a^2 + 3)$
27. F – first, O – outer, I – inner, L – last. [1.3]
29. The elements are powers of two. The set is closed under multiplication since $2^a \cdot 2^b = 2^{a+b} \in A$ for all nonnegative integers. It is not closed under addition since $2 + 4 = 6 \notin A$. [1.1]

Chapter 1 Review

1. Commutative property of addition
3. Identity property of multiplication
5. $5x$, answers will vary.   7. $7x^2 - 8x + 12$
9. $x^2 - 5x - 14$ 11. $144x^4y^2$ 13. $8xz^5 + 12z^6$
15. $a^5 + a^3b + a^2b + b^2$ 17. $5a^3 - 20a^2 - 60a$
19. xz^3 21. $x - 5$ 23. $3x^2 - 20x + 102$ R. -518
25. $(x - 6)(x + 6)$ 27. $(y + 5)^2$
29. $(5x - 3)(2x + 1)$ 31. $(x - 4)(x^2 + 4x + 16)$
33. $(x - 2)(x + 2)^2$

Chapter 2—Linear Equations

2.1

1. addition 3. symmetric 5. transitive
7. multiplication 9. multiplication 11. $x = 84$
13. $x = -2$ 15. $x = 9$ 17. $y = 2$ 19. $n = 12$
21. $x = 10$ 23. $x = -4$ 25. $x = 0.5$
27. $y = -12$ 29. $a = -1$ 31. $a = \frac{-7}{2}$ 33. $x = 7$
35. $m = \frac{-5}{28}$ 37. $a = 4$
45. Definition of subtraction or distributive property [1.1]
47. Associative property of addition [1.1]
49. Additive inverse property [1.1]

2.2

1.

3.
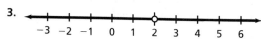

5. $x \geq -7$
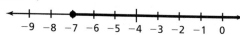

7. $x < 5$

9. $x \geq \frac{-4}{5}$ 11. $x \geq \frac{-1}{2}$ 13. $x > 4$ 15. $z > -3$
17. $x > \frac{11}{8}$ 19. $x > \frac{67}{11}$ 25. $\frac{3}{x^2}$ [1.4] 27. $\frac{x^{12}}{81}$ [1.4]
29. $x^5 y^3$ [1.4]

2.3

1. The number x is 7 units from zero on the number line.
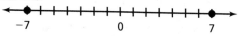

3. $|x| = 15$ 5. $y = \pm 4$ 7. $x = \frac{14}{5}, -2$
9. $x = 3, -9$ 11. $y = \frac{27}{14}, \frac{19}{14}$ 13. $x = \frac{5}{2}, \frac{-7}{2}$
15. $y = 16, \frac{2}{5}$ 17. $x = 6$ (0 is extraneous)
19. $|x - 6| = 2$ 23. $7(x - 2y + 1)$ [1.6]
25. $(x - 8)(x + 3)$ [1.6] 27. $(x^2 + 1)(x - 3)$ [1.7]

2.4

1. $m = -2, d = 20$ 3. $m = \frac{1}{2}, d = 11$
5. $m = \frac{7}{6}, d = 1$ 7. $x = 3, 13$ 9. no solutions
11. $|x - 6| = 5$ 13. $|x - 4| = 7$
15. $|x| = 5; x = 5$ or $x = -5$
17. $|x + 4| = 12; x = -16$ or $x = 8$

19. The distance from x to 7 is 4.
21. The distance from x to 0 is 3. 27. $x = 3$ [2.2]
29. Associative property of multiplication [1.1]

2.5

1. 315 miles 3. 3 5. 29 and -52 7. 19, 21, 23
9. going: 2 mph; returning: 3 mph
11. 8 peanut bars, 9 chocolate bars
13. 5.48 hours
15. 1st part: $1\frac{1}{2}$ hours, 2nd part: $\frac{3}{4}$ hour
23. $x - 3$ [1.3] 25. $x = \frac{-5}{2}$ [2.2]

2.6

1. $8.88 3. 40% salt 5. 1.52 gallons
7. $7550 at 8.5%; $7700 at 10%
9. 1 kilogram of 2% HCl solution, 2 kilograms of 11% HCl solution 11. 9 pounds of peanuts, 3 pounds of cashews 13. $87,000 at 15%; $65,000 at 21% 15. 6.5 ml of acetic acid
17. 110.25 bushels of corn and 69.75 bushels of oats 19. 23.8 kilograms of sugar, 1.2 kilograms of cinnamon 25. 17 [1.1]
27. $9x^2 + 30xy + 25y^2$ [1.3] 29. $4x^2 - 3x$ [1.2]

2.7

1. $x < -2$ or $x \geq 4$
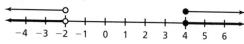

3. $x \geq 4$
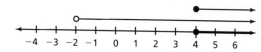

5. $-2 < x < 4$
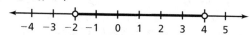

7. $\mathbb{R}$
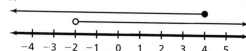

9. $\varnothing$ 11. $-4 \leq x \leq 4$ 13. $\frac{4}{5} \leq x < 6$
15. $x \leq -2$ or $x \geq 9$ 17. $z \geq 14$
21. $2x - 11$ R. 40 [1.4] 23. $\frac{2}{3x} - \frac{3}{y} + 5x$ [1.4]
25. $(5x + 7)(x - 2)$ [1.6]

2.8

1. $-9 < x < 9$ 3. $\frac{-11}{3} \leq x \leq 1$
5. $y < 0$ or $y > \frac{8}{3}$ 7. $x \leq \frac{-4}{11}$ or $x \geq 2$
9. $\frac{8}{5} < x < \frac{12}{5}$ 11. $-6.6 \leq x \leq 26.6$

13. $x < \frac{-14}{3}$ or $x > \frac{-10}{3}$ **15.** $\mathbb{R}$ **17.** $x \neq \frac{-1}{5}$

19. $\mathbb{R}$ **21.** $|x| > 3$

23. definition of absolute value **25.** conjunction

29. $x = 5$ or $x = -1$ [2.3] **31.** $x = 2$ [2.2]

33. $x \geq \frac{-3}{2}$ [2.7]

Chapter 2 Review

1. Transitive property of equality

3. Addition property of equality

5. Multiplication property of equality

7. $y = 2$ **9.** $z = -3$ **11.** $x = 2$ or $x = -8$

13. 12, 24, 18

15. $8000 at 10% and $11,000 at 8% **17.** $x \leq \frac{5}{3}$

19. $x \leq 2$ or $x > 5$ **21.** $\frac{-13}{3} < x < \frac{-1}{3}$ **23.** $\mathbb{R}$

25. $|x + 3| = 3$ **27.** $|x + 1| > 5$

Chapter 3—Linear Relations

3.1

1.

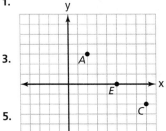

3.

5.

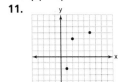

7. $(0, -4)$ **9.** $(-2, -2)$

11. **13.**

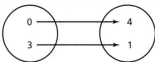

15. $\{(2, -1), (3, -1), (4, 7)\}$

17. $\{(1, 0), (2, 1), (3, 0), (4, 1), (5, 0)\}$

19.

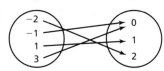

21.

23. $D = \{-3, 0, 2, 5\}$, $R = \{0, 4, 7\}$

25. $D = \{2, 3, 4\}$, $R = \{-1, 0, 1, 2\}$

33. $5 - \frac{8}{x}$ [1.4] **35.** $5x^2 - 8x$ [1.3]

3.2

1. function

3. not a function, not a set of ordered pairs

5. function

7. No. The domain value 1 has two range values (4 and 6).

9. Yes. Passes vertical line test.

11. $f(0) = 7$, $f(-3) = 4$, $f(8) = 15$

13. $h(2) = 6$, $h(6) = 8$, $h(-4) = 3$

15. $f(-2) = 12$, $f(5) = -23$, $f(0) = 2$

17. **19.**

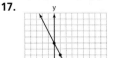
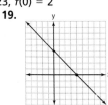

21. r **23.** $R = \{-5, 0, 5, 10\}$ **25.** $-15, 10x$

31. $(2x + 3)^2$ [1.6]

33. $3x(2x - 3)(4x^2 + 6x + 9)$ [1.5]

3.3

1. $f(x) = -8x + 5$, $m = -8$, $b = 5$

3. $\frac{3}{7}$ **5.** $\frac{23}{9}$ **7.** $\frac{16}{5}$ **9.** $\frac{-13}{22}$

11. $y = x$ **13.** $y = \frac{-1}{2}x + \frac{7}{4}$

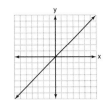

15. $y = -3x - 1$ **17.** $y = \frac{-5}{3}x - 5$

19. $y = \frac{8}{5}x - 2$ **21.** horizontal, 0

23. It is a horizontal line. The slope is zero. It is a function; $f(x) = r$, $y = 0x + r$, or $y = r$ (slope intercept form); $0x + 1y = r$ (standard form)

25. It is not a function; $x = 2$; no slope-intercept form exists. $1x + 0y = 2$ (standard form)

31. [3.2]   **33.** $f(-1) = -4$ or $f(1) = 2$ or $f(3) = 8$ [3.2]

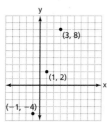

3.4

1. $2x - y = -7$ **3.** $4x - y = 2$ **5.** $3x - 6y = -4$

7. $y = 2x - 4$ **9.** $y = -3x + 1$ **11.** $y = \frac{1}{2}x + \frac{7}{2}$

13. $y = -9x + 15$ **15.** $x + 3y = 6$

17. $5x + y = -16$ **19.** $x - 4y = -18$

21. parallel, $m_1 = \frac{-5}{2}$, $m_2 = \frac{-5}{2}$, equal

23. Two parallel lines have equal slopes.

25. $y = -x + 9$ **27.** perpendicular, $m_1 = \frac{-1}{2}$ and $m_2 = 2$, negative reciprocals

29. $y = \frac{1}{3}x + 4$

35. [3.1]   **37.** $y = \frac{1}{2}x - 1$ [3.3]

39. d [2.2]

3.5

1. function   **3.** not a function   **5.** function

7. exponential   **9.** greatest integer

11. $f(3) = 64$, $f(-1) = \frac{1}{4}$ **13.** $f(-3) = -3$, $f\left(\frac{11}{4}\right) = 2$

15. $\left\{\left(\frac{1}{2}, 5\right), (-100, 5)\right\}$ **17.** $\left\{\left(-1, \frac{3}{2}\right), \left(3, \frac{8}{27}\right)\right\}$

19. $f(4) = 1$, $f(-2) = 8$

21. $D = \mathbb{R}$, $R = \{y \mid y \geq 0\}$

23. $D = \mathbb{R}$, $R = \{2\}$ **25.** $D = \mathbb{R}$, $R = \{y \mid y > 0\}$

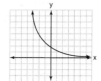

33. $\frac{-6}{5}$ [3.3]   **35.** $\frac{-11}{3}$ [3.3]   **37.** $\frac{-1}{3}$ [3.4]

3.6

1. $x^2 + 3x - 12$ **3.** $x^2 - \frac{x}{9}$ **5.** $9x$

7. $\frac{x(3x - 12)}{9}$ or $\frac{x(x - 4)}{3}$ **9.** $\frac{x^2}{9}$

11. $\{(-2, 12), (3, -6), (4, 7)\}$ **13.** $\frac{-2}{3}$, -8

15. $0, 3$ **17.** $6, 9$ **19.** $2, 2$ **21.** $10x - 14$, $10x - 1$

23. $|3x + 2|$, $3|x| + 2$

25. no, see Exercises 21–24   **29.** $y = \frac{-1}{3}x$ [3.4]

31. $y = -2x + 4$ [3.4]

3.7

1.   **3.**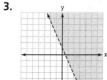

5.   **7.**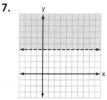

9.   **11.**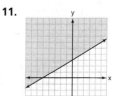

13.

15.

17.

19. both
21. relation only
23. both
27. $\frac{1}{32}$, $\sqrt{2}$, 8, 1 [3.5]
29. 3, $8\frac{1}{2}$, 11, 8 [3.2]
31. −5, 0, 3, 0 [3.5]

3.8

1. $2\sqrt{5}$, (1, 6)   **3.** 5, $\left(6, \frac{9}{2}\right)$ **5.** $\sqrt{202}$, $\left(\frac{-7}{2}, -\frac{3}{2}\right)$

7. $7\sqrt{5}$, $\left(1, \frac{1}{2}\right)$ **9.** $\sqrt{73}$, $\left(\frac{9}{2}, 8\right)$ **11.** 5   **13.** 9

15. $5\sqrt{2}$ **17.** $\frac{-3}{2}$ **19.** (4, 6, −1)

21.

29. [3.7]

31. $x = -4$ or $x = 6$ [2.3]

Chapter 3 Review

1. function   **3.** not a function   **5.** function
7. not a function   **9.** −14, −10, −4, 0
11. 8, 4, 13, 29   **13.** $D = \mathbb{R}$; $R = \{y \,|\, y \geq 0\}$
15. $4\sqrt{5}$, (0, 3), −2
17. perpendicular, the slopes are negative
reciprocals
19. $y = x - 2$ **21.** $y = \frac{4}{5}x - 5$

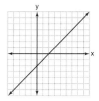

23. $y = 3x - 2$ **25.** $4x - 5$ **27.** $\frac{x^2 - 5x}{2}$ **29.** $\frac{x - 5}{2}$

31.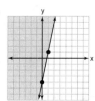

33.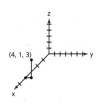

Chapter 4—Quadratic Equations

4.1

1. $x = -4, -2$ **3.** $x = \frac{-1}{2}, 5$ **5.** $x = -5, 9$

7. $x = -2, 1$ **9.** $x = 3, \frac{3}{4}$ **11.** $x = 0, \frac{-7}{2}$

13. $x = \frac{1}{8}, -3$ **15.** $x = \frac{-4}{3}, 8$ **17.** $x = \pm 7$

19. $x = -8, 1$ **21.** $x = 3, 9$ **23.** $x = \frac{-5}{2}, 6$

29. $x = -1, 7$ [2.3]   **31.** $x < 3$ [2.7]

33. $x = 0$ [4.1]

4.2

1. $x = -5, 9$ **3.** $x = -7, -1$ **5.** $x = 6, 2$

7. $x = -3, 4$ **9.** $x = 7, 12$ **11.** $x = \frac{-3 \pm \sqrt{30}}{3}$

13. $x = \frac{4 \pm \sqrt{14}}{2}$ **15.** $x = \frac{-2 \pm \sqrt{10}}{3}$

17. $x = \frac{-1}{3}, 5$ **19.** $x = \frac{1}{4}, -6$

25. $D = \{1, 2, 5, 6.7\}$, $R = \{-1, \frac{1}{2}, 3\}$ [3.1]
27. $D = \mathbb{R}$, $R = \{y \,|\, y \geq 0\}$ [3.5]
29. $D = \{-1, 0, 1\}$, $R = \{\frac{-1}{2}, 2, 3\}$ [3.1]
31. $D = \{x \,|\, x \geq 2\}$, $R = \{y \,|\, y \geq 0\}$ [3.2]

4.3

1. $x = -2, 1$ **3.** $x = \frac{7}{2}, -1$ **5.** $x = 9, -7$

7. $x = \frac{-7}{2}, 1$ **9.** $x = \frac{7}{4}, -1$ **11.** $x = \frac{-3 \pm \sqrt{41}}{4}$

13. $x = \frac{-3}{2}, 6$ **15.** $x = \frac{-11}{3}, \frac{5}{2}$

17. $x = -1, \frac{-3}{2}$ **19.** $x = -4 \pm \sqrt{17}$

21. Step 2   **27.** 1 [2.2]   **29.** 2 [4.2]

4.4

1. Quadratic formula   **3.** Factoring
5. 2, real, rational   **7.** 1, real, rational
9. 2, complex conjugates
11. 1, real, rational, $x = -3$

13. 2, real, irrational, $y = \frac{-5 \pm \sqrt{73}}{8}$

15. 2, real, rational, $t = -3$, or $t = 8$

17. 2, real, rational, $m = \frac{-1}{2}$, or $m = 6$

19. 2, real, rational, $a = \frac{2}{3}$, or $a = \frac{-5}{2}$

21. 2, real, irrational, $b = \dfrac{-4 \pm \sqrt{13}}{3}$

23. 1, real, rational, $c = \dfrac{-2}{7}$

25. 2, real, irrational, $z = \dfrac{-1 \pm \sqrt{21}}{5}$

29. $y = 6x - 7$ [3.4]   **31.** $y = \frac{1}{2}x + 4$ [3.4]

33. $y = -4x + 13$ [3.4]

4.5
  1. 18 and 19, −18 and −19
  3. −43 and −45; 43 and 45
  5. 27 and 45, −27 and −45   **7.** ±14   **9.** 3 feet
  11. 15 inches   **13.** $5\sqrt{15}$ ft.   **15.** $4\sqrt{2}$ in.
  21. $x = \pm\sqrt{2}$ [4.4]   **23.** $x \le 2$ [2.7]

4.6
  1. $-5 < x < 9$ **3.** $x \le -14$ or $x \ge -2$
  5. $x < -4$ or $x > 1$ **7.** $3 \le x \le 4$ **9.** $\frac{1}{2} < x < 5$
  11. $|x - 2| < 7$ **13.** $|x + 8| \ge 6$
  15. $\left|x + \frac{3}{2}\right| > \frac{5}{2}$ (or $|2x + 3| > 5$)
  17. $x \le -3$ or $x \ge 2$
  19. $\frac{-3}{4} \le x \le \frac{3}{4}$ **21.** $-8 \le x \le \frac{-2}{3}$ **23.** $x = -8$
  25. conjunction   **31.** $-x - 3$ [3.6]
  33.  [3.5]

Chapter 4 Review
  1. $x = 8, -4$ **3.** $x = -4, \frac{1}{3}$ **5.** $x = \frac{-3}{5}, \frac{1}{2}$
  7. $z = -3 \pm \sqrt{21}$ **9.** $x = -12, 9$
  11. $a = \dfrac{-4 \pm \sqrt{46}}{5}$
  13. 2, real, irrational, $x = \dfrac{5 \pm \sqrt{33}}{4}$
  15. 2, real, rational, $x = \frac{-7}{3}, 6$
  17. 26 and 28, or −26 and −28   **19.** 6, 8, 10
  21. $x < -3$ or $x > 9$ **23.** $|x - 3| > 6$
  25. $t = \dfrac{1 \pm \sqrt{13}}{6}$ **27.** $x = \pm\sqrt{3}$ **29.** $1 < x < 5$

Chapter 5—Polynomial Functions

5.1
  1. one, linear equation
  3. coordinate plane, linear function
  5. at most two, quadratic equation
  7. F   **9.** D   **11.** E
  13. max. (5, 4); $x = 5$; $D = \mathbb{R}$, $R = \{y\,|\,y \le 4\}$

15. min. (6, −3); $x = 6$; $D = \mathbb{R}$, $R = \{y\,|\,y \ge -3\}$
17.

x	y
−3	21
−2	12
−1	7
0	6
1	9
2	16
3	27

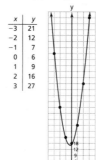

19.

x	y
−3	28
−2	14
−1	6
0	4
1	8
2	18

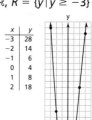

29. 7 [2.4]   **31.** 7 [3.8]   **33.** $3\sqrt{2}$ [3.8]

5.2
  1. $x = 0$, downward, maximum, (0, 0)
  3. $x = 0$, downward, maximum, (0, 0)
  5. $x = 0$, upward, minimum, (0, 0)
  7. −3   **9.** −5, 1, 4
  11. $y = 5x^2$, $y = \frac{-1}{8}x^2$
  13. $x = 0$, (0, 0), $\mathbb{R}$, $\{y\,|\,y \le 0\}$, maximum

  15. $x = 0$, (0, 0) $\mathbb{R}$, $\{y\,|\,y \le 0\}$, maximum

  17. They are negative reciprocals.

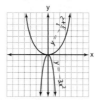

  19. maximum, 4, 1.   **25.** $2x^2 - 3$, $x^4 - 3x^2$, $x^4 - 3$, $x^4 - 6x^2 + 9$ [3.6]   **27.** $x^2 + x + 5$, $5x^2 + 5x$, 5, 30 [3.6]   **29.** $4x^2 + 3x - 7$, $3x^4 + 9x^3 - 11x^2 - 15x + 10$, $9x^4 - 21x^2 + 8$, $3x^4 + 18x^3 + 15x^2 - 36x + 7$ [3.6]

5.3

1. min. (0, 3); $x = 0$; up 3; upward
3. min. (6, 1); $x = 6$; right 6 and up 1; upward
5. max. (4, 7); $x = 4$; right 4 and up 7; downward
7. max. (0, −2); $x = 0$; down 2; downward
9. min. $\left(4, \frac{5}{4}\right)$; $x = 4$; right 4 and up $\frac{5}{4}$; upward

11. **13.**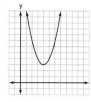

15. 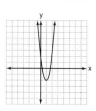 **17.**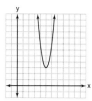

19. 3, −5
21. −5, 4
23.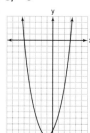
27. $x = 2$ [2.2]
29. $x = \pm\sqrt{2}$ [4.1]
31. $x = 5$ [4.1]

5.4

1. $f(x) = (x + 3)^2 - 4$ **3.** $y = -(x + 1)^2 + 2$
5. $y = \frac{1}{2}(x + 8)^2 - 2$ **7.** $f(x) = (x + 6)^2 - 18$
9. $y = (x - 5)^2 - 9$ **11.** $y = (x - 2)^2 + 4$
13. $f(x) = (x + 5)^2$ **15.** $y = -(x + 3)^2$
17. $y = -2(x + 1)^2 - 6$ **19.** $y = (x + 3)^2 - 10$

21. $g(x) = -2(x - 2)^2 + 1$ **23.** $y = (x + 1)^2 - 5$

 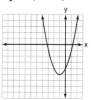

29. −2, −1; (0, 2) [5.3] **31.** $c > \frac{9}{4}$ [4.5]

5.5

1. $S(x) = x + \frac{120}{x}$ **3.** 4, −4 **5.** 21 and 21
7. 14′ × 14′
9. 4200 items for a maximum profit of $594,200
11. 154 feet in 3 seconds. **13.** 5 seconds, 400 feet
15. maximum income of $5000; selling price at $100
17. $950 approximately; $5.63 **21.** $4x^2 + 4x$ [1.2]
23. $8x^3 + 12x^2$ [1.3] **25.** $-\frac{1}{2}$, 3 [5.2] **27.** $\frac{1}{3}$ [5.2]

5.6

1. 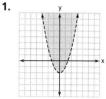 **3.**

5. 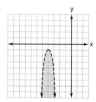 **7.**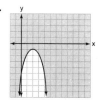

9. $D = \mathbb{R}$, $R = \mathbb{R}$ **11.** $D = \mathbb{R}$, $R = \{y \mid y < 4\}$
13. $y > 2(x + 3)^2 + 3$ **15.** $y < \frac{-1}{2}(x + 1)^2 + 2$

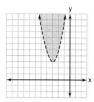

17. $D = \mathbb{R}$, $R = \{y \mid y > 3\}$, $x = -3$
19. $D = \mathbb{R}$, $R = \{y \mid y < 2\}$, $x = -1$
25. C [3.8] **27.** F [5.1] **29.** B [4.4]

5.7

1. 14 **3.** −66 **5.** 1364 **7.** −378 **9.** yes
11. no **13.** no **15.** yes **17.** $(x + 1)(x - 4)(x - 2)$
19. $(x - 3)(x - 2)(x - 1)$ **21.** $x = -2, 1, 5$

23. $x = -3, -1, 2$ **25.** 557   **29.** 9, $(0, -9)$ [5.2]
31. $-5, 9; (0, -45)$ [5.2]   **33.** $\frac{1}{3}, -2; (0, -2)$ [5.2]

5.8
1. $-5, -2, 0$ **3.** $1.2, -4.2$ **5.** $-1, 5, 1$
7. $-6, 2$
9.

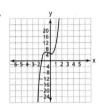

11.

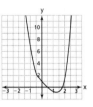

13.

15.

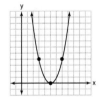

17.

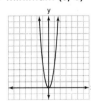

-1.3

25. F [4.1]
27. B [5.8]
29. A [2.8]

Chapter 5 Review
1. $(2, 9), (3, 4), (4, 1), (5, 0), (6, 1), (7, 4)$,
Answers may vary.

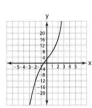

3. minimum $(0, 0)$

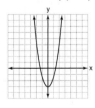

5. minimum $(0, -3)$

7. minimum $(2, 0)$

9. maximum $(1, -1)$

11. $63' \times 126'$; 7938 square feet
13.

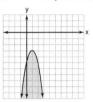

15. $0, -1, 2$
19.

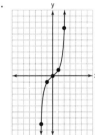

17. $(x - 2)(x + 1)(x - 5)$
21. $x = -3; (0, 22)$
23. $-4, -2, 1, 3$
25. $D = \mathbb{R}$,
$R = \{y \mid y \geq -3\}$

27.

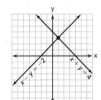

29.

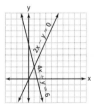

Chapter 6—Systems of Equations and Inequalities

6.1
1. $(1, 3)$

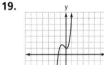

3. $(1, 2)$

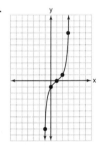

5. $(-3, -2)$

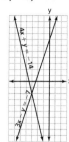

7. $(-3, 8)$

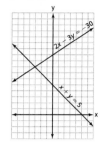

9. $(5, 2)$

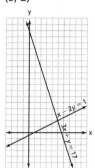

11. $(3, 1)$

13. $(9, 4)$

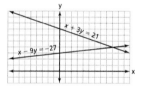

15. one

17. none; lines are parallel

19. infinitely many; same line

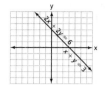

25. 17, 39 [5.1]

27. 7, 7 [3.5]

6.2

1. $(2, -8)$, consistent **3.** $(0, -9)$, consistent

5. $(1, 3)$, consistent **7.** $\left(\frac{-5}{2}, \frac{1}{2}\right)$, consistent

9. $\varnothing$, inconsistent **11.** $(2, \frac{1}{4})$, consistent

13. $(1, -5)$, consistent **15.** $(-4, 1)$, consistent

17. $\left(\frac{7}{10}, \frac{13}{17}\right)$, no

19. $\varnothing$, inconsistent

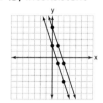

27. [3.1]

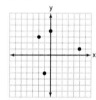

29. [3.5]

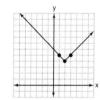

6.3

1. $(2, 8)$ **3.** $(-2, -6)$ **5.** $(4, 7)$ **7.** $(2, 1)$

9. $(7, 3)$ **11.** $\left(\frac{1}{4}, \frac{5}{6}\right)$ **13.** $(5, 9)$ **15.** $\left(\frac{1}{2}, -1\right)$

17. $(-4, 2)$ **19.** $\left(\frac{105}{29}, \frac{5}{29}\right)$

21. The addition method; it avoids computations with fractions

27. $x < -1$ [2.7] **29.** $x = 3, -11$ [2.3]

6.4

1. $2500 in each **3.** $3000 at 10%, $7000 at 5%.

5. 18 **7.** $2805 at 10%, $2705 at 12%

9. northbound: 2 hours; southbound: 6 hours

11. 62 **13.** Joe travels 51 mph, and Mary travels 43 mph. **15.** 48 **19.** $D = \mathbb{R}, R = \{y \mid y \geq -2\}$ [3.5]

21. $D = \mathbb{R}, R = \mathbb{Z}$ [3.5] **23.** $D = \mathbb{W}, R = \mathbb{N}$ [3.1]

6.5
1. (−4, 8), (1, 3)   **3.** (22, 5), (6, −3)
5. (4, 2), (2, 4)   **7.** ($\sqrt{7}$, 1), (−$\sqrt{7}$, 1), (−$\sqrt{7}$, −1), ($\sqrt{7}$, −1)   **9.** (0, 4), (4, 0)   **11.** (6, 2), (−5, −9)
13. (3, 0), (−3, 0)   **15.** $\left(\dfrac{-1 + \sqrt{73}}{6}, \dfrac{16 - \sqrt{73}}{3} \right)$,
$\left(\dfrac{-1 - \sqrt{73}}{6}, \dfrac{16 + \sqrt{73}}{3} \right)$ **17.** (2, 7)   **21.** $\dfrac{4}{3}$ [3.4]
23. $y = \dfrac{-3}{4}x + 3$ [3.4]
25. $y = 3x + 5$ (constant will vary) [3.4]

6.6
1.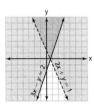
3.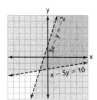
5.
7.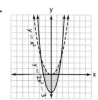
9.
11.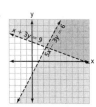
13.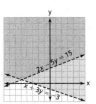
15.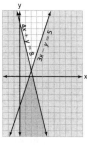
17.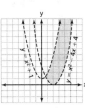
19.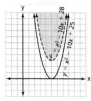

27. $\dfrac{4x^4}{y^8}$ [1.4]   **29.** $3x^3 + 10x^2 + 3x - 10$ [1.3]

6.7
1. 21 at (3, 5)   **3.** 30 at (6, 2)   **5.** 17 at (1, 4)
7. An infinite number; there is always a constraint on manufacturing time and a limit to the number that can be sold
9. 26 at (3, 4)   **11.** 58 at (2, 4)

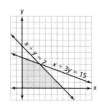

13. 15 at (3, 3)

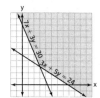

19. integer [1.1]
21. $x = -7, 1$ [4.2]

23. [5.6]

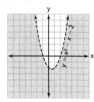

6.8
1. (−1, 4, 7)   **3.** (8, 2, −4)   **5.** (0, 0, 3)
7. (−3, −2, 1)   **9.** (2, 0, 7)   **11.** (4, 3, −2)
13. (8, 0.2, 1.5)   **15.** dependent system
21. $\sqrt{41}$ [3.9]   **23.** $\dfrac{5}{2}, \dfrac{-3}{8}$ [5.7]
25. $x^2 + 7x + 17$ R. 36 [1.4]

Chapter 6 Review
1. (3, 8)

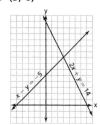

3. $(-1, 6)$, consistent   5. $\varnothing$, inconsistent
7. $\left(\frac{15}{2}, \frac{3}{2}\right)$, consistent
9. 11.5% on \$8400, 9% on \$9600
11.

13. $(-3, 4)$, $(4, -3)$
15. $(8, 3, -7)$
17. A
19. H
21. F
23. G

25. 4 hrs. in the plane; 6 hrs. in the car

Chapter 7—Radicals

7.1
1. $2^{\frac{3}{2}}$ 3. $2^{\frac{2}{3}}3^{\frac{1}{3}}a^{\frac{2}{3}}b^{\frac{1}{3}}$ 5. $13^{\frac{1}{2}}2^{\frac{1}{2}}c^{\frac{3}{2}}d$
7. $2^{\frac{5}{7}}x^{\frac{3}{7}}y^{\frac{2}{7}}z^{\frac{1}{7}}$ 9. $3x^{\frac{2}{3}}z^{\frac{5}{3}}$ 11. $\sqrt[3]{9x}$
13. $a^2\sqrt[5]{16b^2}$ or $\sqrt[5]{16a^{10}b^2}$ 15. $\sqrt[4]{3a^2b^3}$
17. 2   19. $\frac{1}{9}$ 21. $x\sqrt{3y}$ or $\sqrt{3x^2y}$
23. $7b\sqrt[3]{a^2}$ or $\sqrt[3]{343a^2b^3}$ 25. $2a^2$ 27. 14
29. 30   31. $81x^4$ 33. $16ab^5$ 39. $625x^{28}y^8z^4$ [1.3]
41. $12x^2y^3z - 20xy^4 + 16x^2y^4z$ [1.3]
43. $x^4 + 4x^3y + 6x^2y^2 + 4xy^3 + y^4$ [1.3]

7.2
1. 15   3. 36   5. $5x^3y^8$ 7. $4x^2\sqrt{2xy}$ 9. $12b^2\sqrt{ac}$
11. $6ac\sqrt[3]{6ab}$ 13. 6   15. $16x^6y^7\sqrt{3y}$
17. $|x^3yz|\sqrt[4]{z}$ 19. $2|x|$ 21. $|xz^3|$
23. $9|x|\sqrt{xy}$ 25. $-\sqrt[3]{4y^6}$ 31. $(-4, 5)$ [6.2]
33. $(7, 2)$, $(1, -4)$ [6.5]

7.3
1. $-2\sqrt{2}$ 3. $9\sqrt{5} - 2\sqrt{3}$ 5. $-6\sqrt{7}$ 7. $6x\sqrt{2y}$
9. $3y\sqrt{3xy}$ 11. $8^{10} - 7^{36}$ or $2^{30} - 7^{36}$
13. $7 \cdot 6x$ 15. $-5c^2d\sqrt{3c} + c\sqrt{57d}$
17. $-7a\sqrt{5a} + 5a^2\sqrt{3ab}$ 19. $-14ab^2 + 10\sqrt{13ab}$
21. $7 \cdot 2^{60}$
27. [3.3]

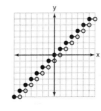

29. $\frac{5}{2}$ [3.4]   31. $y = 6x - 7$ [3.4]

7.4
1. $2\sqrt{14}$ 3. $24a^2$ 5. 2^{85} 7. $21 + 7\sqrt{2}$
9. $\sqrt{2} + 2$ 11. $x^2 - 5$ 13. $x^2 + 6x\sqrt{6} + 48$
15. $x^2\sqrt{11} + 4x\sqrt{22} + 6\sqrt{11}$
17. $x^2\sqrt{15} - 5x\sqrt{3} + 3x\sqrt{5} - 15$
19. $6a^2\sqrt{b} - 20a\sqrt{3ab}$
23. $x(x - 5)(x^2 + 5x + 25)$ [1.5]
25. $x^4(x^2 - 3)(x^2 + 3)$ [1.5]
27. $3(x - 2)(x + 8)$ [1.5]

7.5
1. $\frac{2\sqrt{5}}{5}$ 3. 4   5. $\frac{5\sqrt{6}}{2}$ 7. $\frac{5\sqrt[3]{9}}{3}$ 9. $\frac{\sqrt{2}}{2}$
11. $-5 + 5\sqrt{2}$ 13. $\frac{7^{11}}{5}$ 15. $\frac{\sqrt{6}}{3}$ 17. $\sqrt{6} - 2$
19. $3\sqrt{6} + 3\sqrt{3}$ 21. $\frac{\sqrt[4]{8}}{2}$ 23. $5 \cdot 2^{x+4}$
27. $x = \frac{5}{2}$ [2.2]   29. $x = \frac{3 \pm 3\sqrt{5}}{2}$ [4.2]

7.6
1. $\sqrt{3}(x - y)$ 3. $z\sqrt{5}(x - \sqrt{2})$ 5. $(x + \sqrt{5})^2$
7. $y = \frac{\sqrt{14}}{2}$ 9. $x = \frac{\sqrt{30}}{14}$
11. $(x - 3\sqrt{2})(x + 3\sqrt{2})$ 13. $5(x + 2\sqrt{5})^2$
15. $x = \frac{9\sqrt{5} - 5\sqrt{3}}{15}$ 17. $y = \frac{-2\sqrt{6} - 6}{3}$
19. $\frac{-3 + 3\sqrt{7}}{2}$ 21. $z = \frac{4\sqrt[3]{9} + 3\sqrt[3]{2}}{6}$
23. $x = 3\sqrt{2} + 3$ 25. $z = \frac{-4\sqrt{3} + 3\sqrt{2}}{60}$
31. [3.5]   33. [3.5]

7.7
1.   3.

5.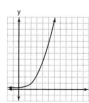

7. $D = \mathbb{R}$;
$R = \{y \mid y > 0\}$
9. $D = \mathbb{R}$;
$R = \{y \mid y > -3\}$

27. 12 and 13 or -13 and -12 [4.6]

Chapter 7 Review
1. $7^{\frac{1}{2}} x^{\frac{1}{2}} y^{\frac{5}{2}}$ **3.** $\sqrt[6]{256a}$ **5.** $b\sqrt[3]{3a^2}$ **7.** $2\sqrt[12]{2}$
9. $3a^2\sqrt{3ab}$ **11.** $6c^2 |ab| \sqrt{5ac}$ **13.** $18\sqrt{2}$
15. $7ab^2\sqrt[3]{5}$ **17.** $3ab^2\sqrt{2a}$ **19.** -2
21. $9x^2 + 6x\sqrt{7} + 7$ **23.** $-1 + \sqrt{5}$
25. $-6, \frac{-13}{2}, 25$

11.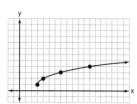

13.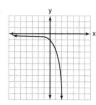

15. $D = \{x \mid x \geq h\}; R = \{y \mid y \geq k\}$
17. $0; \sqrt{x + 4}$
19.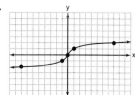

27. -2 [5.7]
29. ± 3 [5.7]
31. 5 [5.7]

7.8
1. $x = 4$ **3.** $x = \frac{3}{2}$ **5.** $x = \frac{5}{3}$ **7.** $x = 49$
9. $y = 115$ **11.** $x = \frac{-1}{3}$ **13.** $x = \frac{-1}{2}$ **15.** $x = 3$
17. $\varnothing$ **19.** $\varnothing$ **21.** $x = -6$ **23.** $x = \frac{2}{3}$ **25.** $x = -1$
27. $y = \frac{7}{4}$ **29.** $y = -1$ **35.** $(1, 4)$ [5.3]
37. $(0, 6)$ [5.1] **39.** none [5.7]

7.9
1. $x = 22$ **3.** $x = \frac{31}{2}$ **5.** $x = 9$ **7.** $x = 7$
9. $x = \frac{1}{3}$ **11.** $m = \frac{2k}{v^2}$ **13.** $E_2 = \pm\sqrt{E_1{}^2 - E_3{}^2}$
15. $c = \frac{\pm\sqrt{4d^2 + t^2u^2}}{}$ **17.** $P = \frac{N^2}{1 - r}$
19. $\left\{ x \mid x \geq \frac{-B}{A} \right\}$ **25.** 12 m
[2.5]

27.

29. $xy\sqrt{3}\,(x - 5)$
31. $y = 16 - 2\sqrt{7}$
33. $\varnothing$
35. $f = \frac{D^2 - d^2}{4D}$

Chapter 8—Complex Numbers
8.1
1. $\sqrt{2}i$ **3.** $4i$ **5.** $4\sqrt{3}i$ **7.** $5\sqrt{7}i$ **9.** 1 **11.** -1
13. -6 **15.** $-i$ **17.** $ab^2\sqrt{a}\,i$ **19.** $2a^2b\sqrt{6ab}\,i$
21. $x = \pm 2i$ **23.** $x = \pm 3\sqrt{14}i$ **25.** $x = \pm 5\sqrt{3}i$
31. $3\sqrt{7}$ [7.3] **33.** $11 \cdot 2^{19}$ [7.3]

8.2
1. $7 + 0i$ **3.** $0 - 3i$ **5.** $0 - 6i$ **7.** $5, 11$
9. $0, 10$ **11.** $2, 1$ **13.** $6 - 6i$ **15.** $4 - 8i$
17. $31 - 6i$ **19.** $7 - 7i$ **21.** $-4 - i$ **23.** $\frac{22}{5} - \frac{37}{30}i$
25. $4\sqrt{3} + 2\sqrt{6}i$ **29.** $x^2 + 5x - 24$ [1.3]
31. $12x^3 - 60x^2 + 75x$ [1.3] **33.** 1 [7.4]

8.3
1. $-6 - 15i$ **3.** $-12 + 2i$ **5.** $7 - i$ **7.** $4 - 8i$
9. $-1 + 30i$ **11.** $-34 - 31i$ **13.** $32 + 126i$
15. $6 + 2i$ **17.** $\frac{65}{6} + 10i$ **19.** $5.79 - 2.34i$
21. $-8\sqrt{3} - 13i$ **23.** $13 - 8\sqrt{3}i$
29. $x^2 + 4x - 3$ [4.7] **31.** $\frac{\sqrt{15}}{}$ [7.5]
33. $x + 5$ R. 3 [1.4]

8.4
1. $3 + 4i$ **3.** 7 **5.** $\frac{5}{4} + 2i$ **7.** $\frac{-5}{2}i$ **9.** 2 **11.** $3i$
13. $1 + 3i$ **15.** $\frac{3}{4} - \frac{3}{2}i$ **17.** $\frac{1}{2} + \frac{7}{2}i$ **19.** $\frac{11}{29} - \frac{42}{29}i$
21. $\frac{34}{53} - \frac{40}{53}i$ **23.** $\frac{2}{13} + \frac{3}{13}i$
27. $x = \frac{-3 \pm \sqrt{13}}{}$ [4.3] **29.** $x = \frac{-3 \pm \sqrt{113}}{4}$ [4.4]
31. $d = -16$; 2, complex [4.5]

8.5
1. $d = 13$, 2, irrational **3.** $d = -7$, 2, complex
5. $d = 64$, 2, rational **7.** $x = \frac{-2}{3} \pm \frac{2\sqrt{5}}{}i$

13. $z = -2 \pm \sqrt{10}$ **15.** $q = -\frac{2}{5} \pm \frac{\sqrt{11}}{5}i$

17. $x = \frac{1}{2} \pm \frac{\sqrt{11}}{2}i$ **19.** $w = \frac{3}{2} \pm \frac{\sqrt{11}}{2}i$

27. [5.3]   **29.** [5.3]

   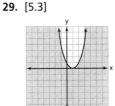

8.6

1.

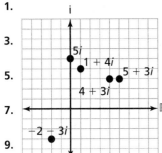

11. A: $4 + 5i$; B: $-1 + 2i$;
C: $-2 - 5i$; D: $5 + i$;
E: $-6i$; F: $-3 + 5i$;
G: $3 - 5i$; H: -6
13. $5\sqrt{2}$ **15.** $2\sqrt{13}$ **17.** $\sqrt{113}$ **19.** 12
23. $\sqrt{17}$ [3.9]   **25.** 2 [3.4]
27. $\sqrt{41}$, $(-\frac{1}{2}, -3)$, $-\frac{4}{5}$ [3.4 and 3.9]

8.7

1.

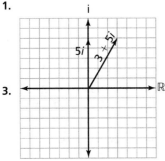

5. $2\sqrt{5}$, $m = -2$, pointing down to the right

7.

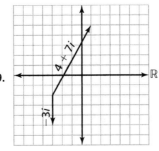

11. $-7 - 6i$
13. $2 - 3i$; $\sqrt{13}$ **15.** $-1 - 4i$; $\sqrt{17}$
17. $2 + 4i$; $2\sqrt{5}$ **19.** $(3 - 2i) + (-5 - i) = -2 - 3i$
21. $(-3 + i) + (5 + 2i) = 2 + 3i$
23. $7 + 2i$ **25.** $-4 - i$

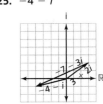   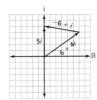

27. $5i$

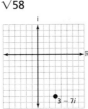

31. $y = -\frac{1}{3}x + 2$ [3.4]   **33.** $y = -\frac{3}{2}x + \frac{11}{2}$ [3.4]
35. $600 at 8%, $400 at 5%

Chapter 8 Review
1. $4\sqrt{2}i$ **3.** $4\sqrt{3}i$ **5.** $-4 + 8i$ **7.** $-3 + 10i$
9. $12 + 6i$ **11.** $10 - 5i$ **13.** $-29 + 29i$ **15.** $\frac{4}{5}i$
17. $-\frac{4}{17} + \frac{18}{17}i$
19. $\sqrt{58}$ **21.**

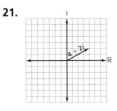

23. $2 + 3i$

25. $x = \dfrac{-3 \pm \sqrt{17}}{2}$

27. $x = \dfrac{-5}{2} \pm \dfrac{\sqrt{7}}{2}i$

29. $\sqrt{17}$, $m = \dfrac{-1}{4}$; down to the right

Chapter 9—Rational Expressions and Equations

9.1
1. $\dfrac{a}{3}$ **3.** $\dfrac{5x}{2}$ **5.** $\dfrac{2(5 + 7n)}{3mn}$ **7.** -1 **9.** $\dfrac{3a + b}{a - b}$
11. $\dfrac{2x - z}{x - z}$ **13.** $\dfrac{a + b}{2b}$ **15.** $\dfrac{a + b}{5a - 5b}$
17. $\dfrac{8x^2 - 8xy}{xy + 2y^2}$ **23.** $x = 5$ [2.1]
25. $y = (x + 4)^2 - 17$; minimum is $(-4, -17)$ [4.2]

9.2
1. $\dfrac{3xy^3}{10}$ **3.** $\dfrac{6b}{ac}$ **5.** 1 **7.** $\dfrac{a - 3}{2(a + 2)}$ **9.** $\dfrac{3}{x}$
11. $\dfrac{(a + 3)(a + 1)}{(a + 2)^2}$ **13.** $\dfrac{xz(x + z)}{3x + z}$ **15.** $\dfrac{(x + 4)^2(x + 1)}{x + 2}$
17. $\dfrac{a - 3}{a - 1}$ **23.** $x^2\sqrt{3x} - \sqrt{3x}$
25.

[5.2]

27. 6 ft. $\times$ 22 ft. [4.6]

9.3
1. 4 **3.** $\dfrac{5(x + 3)}{2x^2}$ **5.** $(x - 2)(x - 1)$ **7.** $\dfrac{c - d}{c + 2d}$
9. $\dfrac{(2d - 1)(4d + 3)}{(5d - 3)(4d - 5)}$ **11.** $\dfrac{x + 1}{(x - 8)(x + 3)}$ **13.** $\dfrac{xy}{x - 5}$
15. $2(x - 1)$ **17.** $\dfrac{(c + 2)(c - 1)}{c + 5}$ **19.** $\dfrac{5x^2}{3(x - 3)}$
25. $x = 2, 7$ [4.1] **27.** $2(2x - 3)(4x^2 + 6x + 9)$ [1.5]

9.4
1. $\dfrac{13}{5y}$ **3.** $\dfrac{x^2 + 2}{3}$ **5.** $\dfrac{5a^2 - 6a - 6b}{a(a + b)}$ **7.** $\dfrac{3}{m - 5}$
9. $\dfrac{c + 6}{c - 6}$ **11.** $\dfrac{-3r(r - 7)}{(r + 3)(r + 8)}$ **13.** $\dfrac{x + 8}{x + 4}$
15. $\dfrac{-3x(x + 13)}{(x - 4)(x + 3)(x - 2)}$ **17.** $\dfrac{a^2 + 2a + 10}{(a + 2)(a - 7)(a - 3)}$
19. $\dfrac{2(3n^2 + 16n - 9)}{(n + 3)(n + 1)(n + 7)}$ **21.** $\dfrac{x}{x - y}$ **23.** $\dfrac{2t - 3}{t + 5}$
29. $\dfrac{27}{61} + \dfrac{8}{61}i$ [8.4] **31.** $x = 22$ [7.8]
33. -4 (multiplicity 1), 1 (multiplicity 2) [5.7]

9.5
1. $-\dfrac{1}{4}$, undefined, $\dfrac{4}{9}$ **3.** $\dfrac{2}{5}, \dfrac{2}{3}$, undefined
5. $x = 0$ **7.** $x = -4$
9. y-intercept: $(0, 2)$, x-intercept: $(8, 0)$
11. y-intercept: $(0, 3)$, x-intercept: none
13.

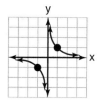

15.

17.

19. $\{x \,|\, x \neq 0\}$
21. $\{x \,|\, x \neq -1\}$

23.

25.

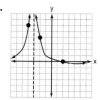

31. $\dfrac{x + 1}{x^2 - x + 1}$ [9.2]
33. [5.9]

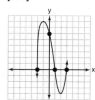

35. $z = 3x + 2y$; Profit is maximized (at \$8000) by making 2000 of each. [6.7]

9.6
1. $a = 3$ **3.** $a = 1$ **5.** $x = 12, -8$ **7.** $a = 7$
9. $a = 8, \dfrac{-25}{3}$ **11.** $x = -4$ **13.** $x = 0, 3$
15. $t = 0, -2$ **17.** $x = \dfrac{1}{2}$ **19.** $x = \dfrac{-13 \pm \sqrt{137}}{4}$
25. $x = \dfrac{-1 \pm \sqrt{141}}{10}$ [4.3] **27.** $6x - 7$ [3.6]

9.7
1. 48 **3.** 4 **5.** $\dfrac{1}{2}$ **7.** I varies jointly with p and r.
9. 864 revolutions per minute. **11.** 45.5 kg
13. $A = \dfrac{1}{2}ap$, $k = \dfrac{1}{2}$. **19.** $x = \dfrac{1}{48}$ [9.7]
21. $x(x - 3)(x + 2)(x^2 - 2x + 4)$ [1.7]

9.8

1. $\frac{1}{4}$ **3.** $\frac{2}{5}$ **5.** $\frac{7}{9}$ **7.** $\frac{7}{20}$ **9.** 12 hours

11. $5\frac{1}{3}$ days **13.** 4 hours **15.** $\frac{2}{7}$ hour ≈ 17 minutes

21. $\frac{6x^2\sqrt[3]{xy^2}}{y}$ [7.5] **23.** [9.6]

25. $k = 1$, $y = \frac{1}{8}$ [9.7]

Chapter 9 Review

1. $-3, \frac{1}{3}$ **3.** $(0, 2)$ **5.** $x = -2$ and $x = 2$

7. $\{x \mid x \neq 1\}$ **9.**

11. $\frac{5x}{9y^2}$ **13.** $\frac{5x}{x+3}$ **15.** $\frac{2x-3}{3x-5}$

17. $\frac{4x}{2x+5}$ **19.** $\frac{2}{x}$ **21.** $x = \frac{25}{7}$

23. $x = \frac{3}{5}$ **25.** $x = \pm 6$

27. $x = -37$ **29.** $\frac{1}{2}$

Chapter 10—Trigonometry

10.1

1. $\sin A = \frac{5\sqrt{29}}{29}$, $\cos A = \frac{2\sqrt{29}}{29}$, $\tan A = \frac{5}{2}$

$\sin B = \frac{2\sqrt{29}}{29}$, $\cos B = \frac{5\sqrt{29}}{29}$, $\tan B = \frac{2}{5}$

3. $\sin L = \frac{\sqrt{5}}{3}$, $\cos L = \frac{2}{3}$, $\tan L = \frac{\sqrt{5}}{2}$

$\sin M = \frac{2}{3}$, $\cos M = \frac{\sqrt{5}}{3}$, $\tan M = \frac{2\sqrt{5}}{5}$

5. $\sin F = 0.9455$, $\cos F = 0.3256$, $\tan F = 2.9042$
$\sin D = 0.3256$, $\cos D = 0.9455$, $\tan D = 0.3443$

7. 0.9781 **9.** 0.5398 **11.** 0.5243 **13.** 0.9689

15. 0.0582 **17.** 0.7071 or $\frac{\sqrt{2}}{2}$ **19.** 0.8387

21. 75°16′48″ **27.** 1.5 [3.2] **29.** −0.89 [5.1]

10.2

1. $A = 18°$ **3.** $A = 58°57′$ **5.** $B = 27°40′$
7. $A = 63°45′$ **9.** $B = 42°44′$
11. $B = 52°$, $C = 90°$, $a \approx 3.9$, $c \approx 6.3$
13. $A \approx 20°33′$, $B \approx 69°27′$, $C = 90°$, $c \approx 8.5$
15. $A \approx 48°11′$, $B \approx 41°49′$, $C = 90°$, $a \approx 6.7$
17. 37 feet **19.** 64° **25.** 3 [2.4]
27. $\sqrt{37}$ [3.9] **29.** $\sqrt{41}$ [3.9]

10.3

1. $\frac{1}{2}$ **3.** $\frac{\sqrt{2}}{2}$ **5.** $\sqrt{3}$ **7.** $\frac{\sqrt{3}}{3}$ **9.** $\frac{2\sqrt{3}}{3}$

11. 1.2664 **13.** 1.0071 **15.** 0.9397 **17.** 1

19. $B = 60°$, $a = 5$, $b = 5\sqrt{3}$
21. $L = 45°$, $l = 9$, $n = 9\sqrt{2}$
23. $\sin A = \frac{3\sqrt{34}}{34}$, $\cos A = \frac{5\sqrt{34}}{34}$, $\tan A = \frac{3}{5}$

$\csc A = \frac{\sqrt{34}}{3}$, $\sec A = \frac{\sqrt{34}}{5}$, $\cot A = \frac{5}{3}$

$\sin B = \frac{5\sqrt{34}}{34}$, $\cos B = \frac{3\sqrt{34}}{34}$, $\tan B = \frac{5}{3}$

$\csc B = \frac{\sqrt{34}}{5}$, $\sec B = \frac{\sqrt{34}}{3}$, $\cot B = \frac{3}{5}$

25. $\sin L = \frac{1}{3}$, $\cos L = \frac{2\sqrt{2}}{3}$, $\tan L = \frac{\sqrt{2}}{4}$

$\csc L = 3$, $\sec L = \frac{3\sqrt{2}}{4}$, $\cot L = 2\sqrt{2}$

$\sin N = \frac{2\sqrt{2}}{3}$, $\cos N = \frac{1}{3}$, $\tan N = 2\sqrt{2}$

$\csc N = \frac{3\sqrt{2}}{4}$, $\sec N = 3$, $\cot N = \frac{\sqrt{2}}{4}$

31. Rational [1.1] **33.** Integer [1.1]
35. Whole [1.1]

10.4

1. 52° **3.** 40°

5. 30°

7. $\sin X = \frac{\sqrt{5}}{5}$, $\cos X = \frac{-2\sqrt{5}}{5}$, $\tan X = \frac{-1}{2}$

9. $\sin X = \frac{4\sqrt{17}}{17}$, $\cos X = \frac{\sqrt{17}}{17}$, $\tan X = 4$

11. $\sin X = 1$, $\cos X = 0$, $\tan X$ is undefined
13. 1, 0, undefined **15.** −0.342 **17.** 1.0798

19. $-\frac{\sqrt{2}}{2}$ **21.** −1 **23.** $\frac{\sqrt{3}}{3}$ **29.** −2 [8.2]

31. $5 - 12i$ [8.3] **33.** $\sqrt{13}$ [8.7]

10.5

1.

3.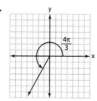

5.

7. 60°

9. −225°

11. 36° **13.** 324°

15. $\frac{\pi}{12}$ **17.** $-\frac{16\pi}{9}$

19. $\frac{53\pi}{45}$ **21.** $\frac{-1}{2}$

23. $\frac{-1}{2}$

25. 91.25° ≈ 91°15′ ≈ 0.507π radians

27. cos −40° = cos 40° = 0.766

33. −5 [5.1] **35.** (2, −5) is the minimum [5.4]

37. 40 [4.5]

10.6

1.

x	y
0	1
$\frac{\pi}{6}$	0.8660
$\frac{\pi}{4}$	0.7071
$\frac{\pi}{3}$	0.5000
$\frac{\pi}{2}$	0
$\frac{2\pi}{3}$	−0.5000
$\frac{3\pi}{4}$	−0.7071
$\frac{5\pi}{6}$	−0.8660
π	−1

x	y
$\frac{7\pi}{6}$	−0.8660
$\frac{5\pi}{4}$	−0.7071
$\frac{4\pi}{3}$	−0.5000
$\frac{3\pi}{2}$	0
$\frac{5\pi}{3}$	0.5000
$\frac{7\pi}{4}$	0.7071
$\frac{11\pi}{6}$	0.8660
2π	1

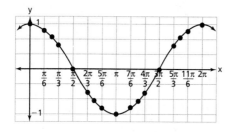

3.

x	y
0	0
$\frac{\pi}{6}$	0.5774
$\frac{\pi}{4}$	1
$\frac{\pi}{3}$	1.732
$\frac{\pi}{2}$	undefined
$\frac{2\pi}{3}$	−1.732
$\frac{5\pi}{6}$	−0.5774
π	0

x	y
$\frac{7\pi}{6}$	0.5774
$\frac{5\pi}{4}$	1
$\frac{4\pi}{3}$	1.732
$\frac{3\pi}{2}$	undefined
$\frac{5\pi}{3}$	−1.732
$\frac{7\pi}{4}$	−1
$\frac{11\pi}{6}$	−0.5774
2π	0

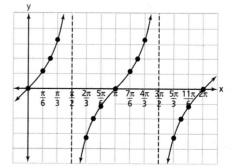

5.

x	y
0	0
$\frac{\pi}{6}$	0.125
$\frac{\pi}{4}$	0.1768
$\frac{\pi}{3}$	0.2165
$\frac{\pi}{2}$	0.2500
$\frac{2\pi}{3}$	0.2165
$\frac{3\pi}{4}$	0.1768
$\frac{5\pi}{6}$	0.125
π	0

x	y
$\frac{7\pi}{6}$	−0.125
$\frac{5\pi}{4}$	−0.1768
$\frac{4\pi}{3}$	−0.2165
$\frac{3\pi}{2}$	−0.2500
$\frac{5\pi}{3}$	−0.2165
$\frac{7\pi}{4}$	−0.1768
$\frac{11\pi}{6}$	−0.125
2π	0

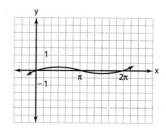

7. yes **9.** ℝ **11.** $\left\{x \mid x \neq \pm\frac{\pi}{2}, \pm\frac{3\pi}{2}, \pm\frac{5\pi}{2}, \ldots\right\}$

13. {y | −1 ≤ y ≤ 1}

15.

x	y
0	0
$\frac{\pi}{6}$	0.2887
$\frac{\pi}{4}$	0.5000
$\frac{\pi}{3}$	0.8660
$\frac{\pi}{2}$	undefined
$\frac{2\pi}{3}$	−0.8660
$\frac{5\pi}{6}$	−0.2887
π	0

x	y
$\frac{7\pi}{6}$	0.2887
$\frac{5\pi}{4}$	0.5000
$\frac{4\pi}{3}$	0.8660
$\frac{3\pi}{2}$	0
$\frac{5\pi}{3}$	−0.8660
$\frac{7\pi}{4}$	−0.5000
2π	0

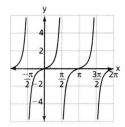

17.

x	y
0	1
$\frac{\pi}{6}$	0.5000
$\frac{\pi}{4}$	0
$\frac{\pi}{3}$	−0.5000
$\frac{\pi}{2}$	−1
$\frac{2\pi}{3}$	−0.5000
$\frac{3\pi}{4}$	0
$\frac{5\pi}{6}$	0.5000
π	1

x	y
$\frac{7\pi}{6}$	0.5000
$\frac{5\pi}{4}$	0
$\frac{4\pi}{3}$	−0.5000
$\frac{3\pi}{2}$	−1
$\frac{5\pi}{3}$	−0.5000
$\frac{7\pi}{4}$	0
$\frac{11\pi}{6}$	0.5000
2π	1

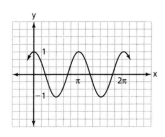

25. discontinuous [3.5] **27.** continuous [7.7]
29. yes [5.9]

10.7

1. $A = 4$, $P = 2\pi$

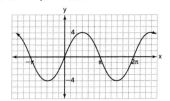

3. $A = 1$, $P = 6\pi$

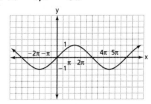

5. $A = 3$, $P = 2\pi$

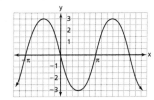

7. $\mathbb{R}$ is the domain for all of them.
9. $\{y \mid -1 \le y \le 1\}$ **11.** $\{y \mid -3 \le y \le 3\}$
13. $A = 4$, $P = 4\pi$

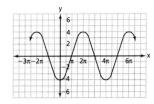

15. $A = 1$, $P = \frac{2\pi}{3}$

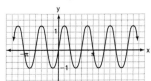

17. $\{y \mid -a \le y \le a\}$ **23.** $A = 5$ [7.8]
25. $A = 49$ [7.8]   **27.** $A = 30°$ or $\frac{\pi}{6}$ [10.2]

Chapter 10 Review

1. $\sin A = \dfrac{\sqrt{10}}{10}$, $\cos A = \dfrac{3\sqrt{10}}{10}$, $\tan A = \dfrac{1}{3}$

   $\sin B = \dfrac{3\sqrt{10}}{10}$, $\cos B = \dfrac{\sqrt{10}}{10}$, $\tan B = 3$

3. $Y = 74°$, $Z = 90°$, $y = 27.9$, $z = 29.0$
5. 11.0 inches   7. $\sqrt{3}$
9. $A = 30°$, $C = 90°$, $a = 3\sqrt{3}$, $c = 6\sqrt{3}$
11. $\sin K = 0.7314$, $\cos K = 0.6820$, $\tan K = 1.0724$
    $\csc K = 1.367$, $\sec K = 1.466$, $\cot K = 0.9325$
    $\sin M = 0.6820$, $\cos M = 0.7314$, $\tan M = 0.9325$
    $\csc M = 1.466$, $\sec M = 1.367$, $\cot M = 1.0724$
13. $\sin \theta = \dfrac{-4\sqrt{41}}{41}$, $\cos \theta = \dfrac{5\sqrt{41}}{41}$, $\tan \theta = -\dfrac{4}{5}$

15. $\dfrac{\pi}{5}$ 17. $22.5°$ 19. $24°53'$ 21. -0.8290
23. 0
25.

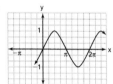

27.

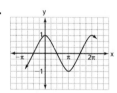

29.

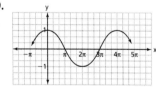

Chapter 11—Identities

11.1
1. $a = 9.8$; SAA   3. $C = 38°53'$; SSA
5. $c = 7.7$; ASA   7. 1; $B = 29°49'$ 9. 1; $B = 77°$
11. 0; impossible   13. $C = 80°$, $b = 6.7$, $c = 8.2$
15. $B = 79°$, $b = 6.2$, $c = 5.6$ 17. SSA, no solution
19. $B = 43°40'$, $C = 69°20'$, $c = 8.1$
25. $y^3 - 16y^2 + 12y - 19$ [1.3]
27. $x = \dfrac{11}{3}$ [2.2]   29. $x > \dfrac{-4}{3}$ [2.7]

11.2
1. SAS, Law of Cosines   3. SSS, Law of Cosines
5. SSA, Law of Sines   7. $A = 34°3'$
9. $B = 135°57'$ 11. $C = 0$, not a triangle
13. $A = 20°45'$, $B = 32°5'$, $C = 127°10'$

15. $A = 24°17'$, $C = 73°43'$, $b = 7.2$
17. $C = 84°$, $a = 9.5$, $c = 10.7$
23. $b = 6.3$, $c = 1.8$, $C = 17°$ [11.2]
25. $A = 61°56'$, $B = 90°$, $C = 28°4'$ [11.2]

11.3
1. Two angles and a side or an angle and its opposite side
3. At least 2 sides
5. AAA cannot be solved since infinitely many combinations of side lengths are possible.
7. Since $\cos 90 = 0$, the Law reduces to $a^2 + b^2 = c^2$, the Pythagorean theorem.
9. Use the Pythagorean theorem and the basic trigonometric ratio definitions.
11. 210.7 feet   13. 174.3 miles
15. 7.1 miles, 13.6 miles   17. 11.3 miles
23. $D = \{-2, 1, 3\}$;
    $R = \{-6, -5, 2, 4\}$;
    not a function [3.2]

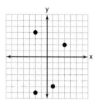

25. $D = \mathbb{R}$; $R = \{y \mid y \geq 0\}$;
    function [3.5]

27. $D = \mathbb{R}$; $R = \mathbb{R}$;
    not a function [3.7]

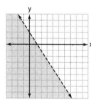

11.4
1. $\cot \theta = \dfrac{1}{\tan \theta} = \dfrac{1}{\frac{a}{b}} = \dfrac{b}{a} = \dfrac{\frac{b}{c}}{\frac{a}{c}} = \dfrac{\cos \theta}{\sin \theta}$

3. $\tan^2 \theta + 1 = \left(\dfrac{a}{b}\right)^2 + 1 = \dfrac{a^2}{b^2} + \dfrac{b^2}{b^2} + \dfrac{a^2 + b^2}{b^2} = \dfrac{c^2}{b^2} = \left(\dfrac{c}{b}\right)^2 = \sec^2 \theta$

5. $\tan^2 \theta$
7. 1
9. $\sin^2 \theta$

11.

$$\frac{\sec\theta}{\csc\theta} = \frac{\sec\theta}{\csc\theta}$$

$$= \frac{\frac{1}{\cos\theta}}{\frac{1}{\sin\theta}}$$

$$= \frac{1}{\cos\theta} \cdot \frac{\sin\theta}{1}$$

$$= \frac{\sin\theta}{\cos\theta}$$

$$= \tan\theta$$

13. $\sin\theta + \cos\theta\tan\theta = \sin\theta + \cos\theta\tan\theta$

$$= \sin\theta + \cos\theta\left(\frac{\sin\theta}{\cos\theta}\right)$$

$$= \sin\theta + \sin\theta$$

$$= 2\sin\theta$$

21. $x = -3 \pm \sqrt{7}$ [4.2]   **23.** $-4 < x < 7$ [4.7]

11.5

1. Reflexive property of equality

3. $\tan x = \frac{\sin x}{\cos x}$ (and Pythagorean Identity)

5. $\csc x = \frac{1}{\sin x}$ (and Pythagorean Identity)

7. $\frac{\tan^2\theta}{\sec\theta - 1} = \frac{\tan^2\theta}{\sec\theta - 1}$

9. $\csc\theta - \cos\theta\cot\theta = \csc\theta - \cos\theta\cot\theta$

$$= \frac{1}{\sin\theta} - \cos\theta\left(\frac{\cos\theta}{\sin\theta}\right)$$

$$= \frac{1 - \cos^2\theta}{\sin\theta}$$

$$= \frac{\sin^2\theta}{\sin\theta}$$

$$= \sin\theta$$

11. $\cos x(1 - \tan x) = \cos x(1 - \tan x)$

$$= \cos x - \cos x\tan x$$

$$= \cos x - \cos x\left(\frac{\sin x}{\cos x}\right)$$

$$= \cos x - \sin x$$

13. $\frac{\sec^2 x}{\tan x} = \frac{\sec^2 x}{\tan x}$

$$= \frac{\tan^2 x + 1}{\tan x}$$

$$= \frac{\tan^2 x}{\tan x} + \frac{1}{\tan x}$$

$$= \tan x + \cot x$$

15. $\sec^2 x\sin^2 x = \sec^2 x\sin^2 x$

$$= \frac{\sin^2 x}{\cos^2 x}$$

$$= \tan^2 x$$

$$= \sec^2 x - 1$$

17. $(\csc x - \cot x)(\csc x + \cot x)$

$$= (\csc x - \cot x)(\csc x + \cot x)$$

$$= \csc^2 x - \cot^2 x$$

$$= 1$$

19. $\sin^2 x(\sec^2 x + \csc^2 x) = \sin^2 x(\sec^2 x + \csc^2 x)$

$$= \sin^2 x\sec x + \sin^2 x\csc^2 x$$

$$= \frac{\sin^2 x}{\cos^2 x} + \frac{\sin^2 x}{\sin^2 x}$$

$$= \tan^2 x + 1$$

$$= \sec^2 x$$

25. $D = \mathbb{R}$; $R = \mathbb{R}$; function [5.9]

27. 2 or -3 [5.8]

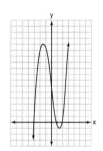

11.6

1. $\frac{4}{5}$ **3.** $\frac{24}{25}$ **5.** -0.3422 **7.** $\frac{\sqrt{6} - \sqrt{2}}{4}$

9. $\frac{-\sqrt{2} - \sqrt{6}}{4}$ **11.** $\frac{6 + 12\sqrt{5}}{35}$

13. $\cos 2a = \cos 2a$

$$= \cos^2 a - \sin^2 a$$

$$= 1 - \sin^2 a - \sin^2 a$$

$$= 1 - 2\sin^2 a$$

15. $\tan^2\theta - \sin^2\theta = \tan^2\theta - \sin^2\theta$

$$= \frac{\sin^2\theta}{\cos^2\theta} - \sin^2\theta\left(\frac{\cos^2\theta}{\cos^2\theta}\right)$$

$$= \frac{\sin^2\theta - \sin^2\theta\cos^2\theta}{\cos^2\theta}$$

$$= \frac{\sin^2\theta(1 - \cos^2\theta)}{\cos^2\theta}$$

$$= \frac{\sin^2\theta}{\cos^2\theta}(\sin^2\theta)$$

$$= \tan^2\theta\sin^2\theta$$

17. $\sin(x + 360°) = \sin(x + 360°)$

$$= \sin x\cos 360° + \cos x\sin 360°$$

$$= \sin x\cos 0° + \cos x\sin 0°$$

$$= \sin x(1) + \cos x(0)$$

$$= \sin x$$

19. $\sin 8x = \sin 8x$

$$= \sin[2(4x)]$$

$$= 2\cos 4x\sin 4x$$

$$= 2\cos 4x\sin[2(2x)]$$

$$= 2\cos 4x(2\sin 2x\cos 2x)$$

$$= 4\cos 4x\cos 2x\sin 2x$$

$$= 4\cos 4x\cos 2x(2\sin x\cos x)$$

$$= 8\cos 4x\cos 2x\cos x\sin x$$

21. $\cos(180 + x) = \cos(180 + x)$

$$= \cos 180\cos x - \sin 180\sin x$$

$$= (-1)\cos x - (0)\sin x$$

$$= -\cos x$$

23. $\dfrac{2 \tan x}{1 - \tan^2 x} = \dfrac{2 \tan x}{1 - \tan^2 x}$

$$= \dfrac{\dfrac{2 \sin x}{\cos x}}{\dfrac{\cos^2 x}{\cos^2 x} - \dfrac{\sin^2 x}{\cos^2 x}}$$

$$= \dfrac{\dfrac{2 \sin x}{\cos x}}{\dfrac{\cos^2 x - \sin^2 x}{\cos^2 x}}$$

$$= \dfrac{2 \sin x}{\cos x} \cdot \dfrac{\cos^2 x}{\cos^2 x - \sin^2 x}$$

$$= \dfrac{2 \sin x \cos x}{\cos^2 x - \sin^2 x}$$

$$= \dfrac{\sin 2x}{\cos 2x}$$

$$= \tan 2x$$

25. $\cos\left[\dfrac{\pi}{2} - (x - y)\right]$

$$= \cos\left[\dfrac{\pi}{2} - (x - y)\right]$$

$$= \cos\dfrac{\pi}{2} \cos(x - y) + \sin\dfrac{\pi}{2} \sin(x - y)$$

$$= (0)\cos(x - y) + (1)\sin(x - y)$$

$$= \sin(x - y)$$

31. $x = \dfrac{-3}{2}$ [7.8]

33. [6.6]

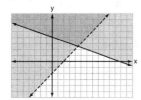

11.7

1. $x = \dfrac{5\pi}{4}, \dfrac{7\pi}{4}$ **3.** $x = \dfrac{\pi}{3}, \dfrac{2\pi}{3}, \dfrac{4\pi}{3}, \dfrac{5\pi}{3}$ **5.** $x = 0$

7. $x = 0, \pi$ **9.** $x = 0, \pi$

11. Consider $0 \leq 2x < 4\pi$; there are 4 solutions.

13. Consider $0 \leq 7x < 14\pi$; there are 14 solutions.

15. Consider $0 \leq \dfrac{1}{2}x < \pi$; there are 2 solutions.

17. $x = \dfrac{\pi}{16}, \dfrac{3\pi}{16}, \dfrac{9\pi}{16}, \dfrac{11\pi}{16}, \dfrac{17\pi}{16}, \dfrac{19\pi}{16}, \dfrac{25\pi}{16}, \dfrac{27\pi}{16}$

19. $x = \dfrac{\pi}{3}, \dfrac{5\pi}{3}, \pi$ **25.** 2 solutions [2.3]

27. no solutions [7.8]

29. infinitely many solutions [2.1]

Chapter 11 Review

1. 10.2 **3.** 29°45′ **5.** 37°18′ or 142°42′

7. $B = 56°$, $a = 4.1$, $b = 3.5$

9. $B = 77°2′$, $C = 46°58′$, $a = 6.8$ **11.** 1737 ft.

13. $\quad 2 \csc 2x = 2 \csc 2x$

$$= \dfrac{2}{\sin 2x}$$

$$= \dfrac{2}{2 \sin x \cos x}$$

$$= \dfrac{1}{\cos x \sin x}$$

$$= \sec x \csc x$$

15. $\quad 1 - 2 \sin^2 x = 1 - 2 \sin^2 x$

$$= 1 - 2(1 - \cos^2 x)$$

$$= 1 - 2 + 2 \cos^2 x$$

$$= 2 \cos^2 x - 1$$

17. $\dfrac{-\sqrt{2} - \sqrt{6}}{4}$ **19.** $\dfrac{8\sqrt{33}}{49}$

21. $x = \dfrac{\pi}{2}, \dfrac{3\pi}{2}, \dfrac{2\pi}{3}, \dfrac{4\pi}{3}$ **23.** $x = \dfrac{\pi}{3}, \dfrac{5\pi}{3}$

25. Pythagorean Theorem

27. Definition of sine, substitution;

$$\sin \theta = \dfrac{opp}{hyp} = \dfrac{y}{1} = y$$

Chapter 12—Inverse Functions

12.1

1. Answers will vary. {(1, 6), (1, −3), (2, 4), (7, 6)}; {(6, 1), (−3, 1), (4, 2), (6, 7)}

3. Answers will vary. {(1, 3), (2, 3), (5, 1)}

5. {(−5, −4), (3, 12), (1, 8), (7, 20)}

7. {(−5, 29), (3, 13), (1, 5), (7, 53)}

9. $f^{-1}(x) = x + 4$ **11.** $h^{-1}(x) = \dfrac{x + 8}{3}$ **13.** x

15. x **17.** $(f \circ f^{-1})(x) = (f^{-1} \circ f)(x) = x$

19. $f(x) = x$ **23.** $\dfrac{5x^2}{7y^3}$ [9.1]

25. $\dfrac{x - 3}{x + 5}$ [9.1] **27.** $\dfrac{x^2 - 2x + 4}{x + 2}$ [9.1]

12.2

1.

x	y		x	y
0	1		$\dfrac{7\pi}{6}$	−0.8660
$\dfrac{\pi}{6}$	0.8660		$\dfrac{5\pi}{4}$	−0.7071
$\dfrac{\pi}{4}$	0.7071		$\dfrac{4\pi}{3}$	−0.5000
$\dfrac{\pi}{3}$	0.5000		$\dfrac{3\pi}{2}$	0
$\dfrac{\pi}{2}$	0		$\dfrac{5\pi}{3}$	0.5000
$\dfrac{2\pi}{3}$	−0.5000		$\dfrac{7\pi}{4}$	0.7071
$\dfrac{3\pi}{4}$	−0.7071		$\dfrac{11\pi}{6}$	0.8660
$\dfrac{5\pi}{6}$	−0.8660		2π	1
π	−1			

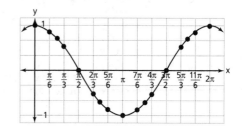

3.

x	y
1	0
0.8660	$\frac{\pi}{6}$
0.7071	$\frac{\pi}{4}$
0.5000	$\frac{\pi}{3}$
0	$\frac{\pi}{2}$
−0.5000	$\frac{2\pi}{3}$
−0.7071	$\frac{3\pi}{4}$
−0.8660	$\frac{5\pi}{6}$
−1	π

x	y
−0.8660	$\frac{7\pi}{6}$
−0.7071	$\frac{5\pi}{4}$
−0.5000	$\frac{4\pi}{3}$
0	$\frac{3\pi}{2}$
0.5000	$\frac{5\pi}{3}$
0.7071	$\frac{7\pi}{4}$
0.8660	$\frac{11\pi}{6}$
1	2π

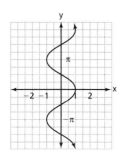

5.

x	y
1	0
.8660	$\frac{\pi}{6}$
.7071	$\frac{\pi}{4}$
.5000	$\frac{\pi}{3}$
0	$\frac{\pi}{2}$
−.5000	$\frac{2\pi}{3}$
−.7071	$\frac{3\pi}{4}$
−.8660	$\frac{5\pi}{6}$
−1	π

7. $\frac{\pi}{4}, \frac{3\pi}{4}$ **9.** $\frac{3\pi}{4}, \frac{5\pi}{4}$
11. $\frac{\pi}{4}$ **13.** $\frac{-\pi}{3}$ **15.** $\frac{-\pi}{4}$
17. 0.1920   **19.** 0.8726
25. $15 \cdot 2^{36}$ [7.3]
27. $\frac{125}{9}$ [7.5]
29. $x = \frac{5}{3}$ [7.8]

12.3
1. $\log_5 25 = 2$ **3.** $\log_7 2401 = 4$ **5.** $\log_3 \frac{1}{9} = -2$
7. $\log_2 \frac{1}{32} = -5$ **9.** $\log_4 \frac{1}{16} = -2$
11. $(0.1)^3 = 0.001$ **13.** $4^{-3} = \frac{1}{64}$ **15.** $9^4 = 6561$
17. $10^{-4} = \frac{1}{10,000}$ **19.** $\left(\frac{1}{4}\right)^3 = \frac{1}{64}$ **21.** 5   **23.** −3
25. 8   **27.** −5   **33.** $2x^2$ [9.2]
35. $\frac{(x+y)(x+y+3)}{9(x+4y)}$ [9.3]

12.4
1. $\log_5 a + \log_5 b$ **3.** $2\log_7 a + \log_7 c$
5. $2\log_4 a - 3\log_4 c$ **7.** $\frac{1}{2}\log_6 a$
9. $\log_{10} 5.7 + 3\log_{10} 10$ **11.** $\log_a 1 = 0$
13. 1   **15.** 1.398   **17.** 1.699   **19.** −0.3010
21. $x = 5$ **23.** $x = 24$ **25.** $x = 32,768$
31. $-46 - 9i$ [8.3]   **33.** $x = 1 \pm i$ [8.5]

12.5
1. $\log 1 = 0, \ln 1 = 0$
3. $\log 0.5 = -0.3010, \ln 0.5 = -0.6931$
5. 7   **7.** $\frac{2}{3}$ **9.** $\ln\left(\frac{640}{9}\right)$ **11.** $\frac{\ln 5}{\ln 2}; x \approx 2.32$
13. $\frac{\ln 2}{\ln 9}; x \approx 0.315$ **15.** $\frac{2\ln 3 + \ln 2}{2\ln 6}; x \approx 0.807$
17. $\frac{-\ln 2}{\ln 7}; x \approx -0.356$
19. $\frac{3\ln 5 + 6\ln 2}{\ln 2 - \ln 5}; x \approx -9.808$
21. $\frac{-5\ln 2}{6\ln 3 - \ln 2}; x \approx -0.588$ **23.** $x \approx 1.04 \times 10^{35}$
25. 1.74×10^{51} **31.** $x = 35$ [9.6]
33. $x = \frac{6 \pm 3\sqrt{6}}{2}$ [9.6]
35. 175 min. or 2 hr. 55 min. [9.8]

12.6
1. $A = Pe^{rt}$ **3.** $A = Ce^{0.2t}$ **5.** Half-life
7. $3\frac{1}{2}$ years.   **9.** 58.9 grams   **11.** 17.6 minutes
13. 6.93 years   **19.** $\frac{2\sqrt{3}}{3}$ [10.3]   **21.** $\frac{2\sqrt{10}}{3}$ [10.2]

Chapter 12 Review
1. $f^{-1} = \{(7, 1), (8, 2), (9, -3)\}$, function
3. $g^{-1}(x) = \frac{\pm\sqrt{2x + 16}}{2}$; not a function.
5. $\log_7 \frac{1}{49} = -2$ **7.** $e^{2.0541} = 7.8$ **9.** $\frac{\pi}{3}$
11. $\log_4 a + 2\log_4 b$
13. $\frac{1}{2}(2\log x + \log y + 3\log z)$ **15.** −2
17. 3.3502   **19.** $x = 63,504$ **21.** 1.7527
23. $x = -5.845$ **25.** $x = 5$
27. $x = \ln 3.5; 1.2528$ **29.** $x \approx 2.3962$
31. 13.86 hours

Chapter 13—Probability and Statistics

13.1
1. 180   3. 444   5. 70   7. 350   9. 596,904
11. 16

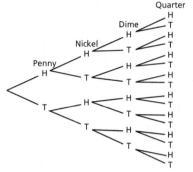

HHHH, HHHT, HHTH,HTHH. THHH
HHTT, HTHT, TTHH, THTH, THHT,
HTTH, HTTT, THTT, TTHT,TTTH,TTTT

13. 64; 24   15. 1,757,600
17. 10,000,000; 8,000,000   19. 90   23. 3.97 [12.7]
25. 4.00 [3.5]   27. 0.35 [10.5]

13.2
1. 840   3. 20   5. 24   7. 3.077621×10^{21}
9. 120   11. 6   13. 362,880   15. 3003
17. 3,603,600   19. 1680   25. $\frac{x-5}{x^2-x}$ [9.5]
27. $\frac{\sqrt{x}+1}{x-1}$ [7.5]

13.3
1. 34,650   3. 1260   5. 3360   7. 211,718,707,200
9. 720   11. 39,916,800   13. 26   15. 300   17. 144
19. 1344   25. $x = 15, -5$ [2.3]   27. $x = 0, 5$ [4.1]

13.4
1. $a^3 + 3a^2b + 3ab^2 + b^3$
3. $x^6 - 24x^5y + 240x^4y^2 - 1280x^3y^3 + 3840x^2y^4 - 6144xy^5 + 4096y^6$
5. $81a^4 + 216a^3b + 216a^2b^2 + 96ab^3 + 16b^4$
7. $16a^4 + 160a^3 + 600a^2 + 1000a + 625$
9. $216a^3 + 972a^2 + 1458a + 729$ 11. $10,206x^5$
13. $3x^8y^3$ 15. $-2002x^5y^9$ 17. $1120x^4y^4$
19. $159,497,910x^{16}y^{36}$ 25. G [3.5]   27. B [7.7]
29. E [10.7]

13.5
1. $\frac{1}{15}$ 3. $\frac{2}{15}$ 5. $\frac{1}{3}$ 7. 1   9. $\frac{1}{2}$ 11. $\frac{4}{5}$
13. $\frac{1}{42} \approx 0.0238$ 15. $\frac{7}{9690} \approx 0.0007$
17. $\frac{77}{646} \approx 0.1192$ 25. 3 [10.7]
27. below the curve [5.6]

13.6
1. $\frac{1}{2}$ 3. 0   5. $\frac{3}{14}$ 7. $\frac{10}{17}$ 9. $\frac{12}{17}$

11. $\frac{32}{289}$ 13. $\frac{64}{289}$ 15. $\frac{9}{289}$ 17. $\frac{196}{289}$
19. one, there are no other possible cases
21. $\frac{6}{25}$ 23. $\frac{33}{95}$ 25. $\frac{24}{95}$ 31. B [3.4]
33. D [3.4]   35. C [3.4]

13.7
1. 16.3   3. none   5. 181.43   7. 5.5   9. 81
11. 64.5   13. 3396   15. 17.57   17. 225   19. 20
21. Everyone scored between 55 and 85.
27. 2 real (irrational) solutions [4.5]
29. 1 real (rational) solution [4.5]
31. 2 real (rational) solutions [4.5]

13.8
1. 47.7%   3. 38.5%   5. 45.9%   7. 95.4%
9. 29.6%   11. 58.2%   13. 6.5%   15. 0.2%
17. 0.44   19. 0.4   25. $-7 - i$ [8.4]
27. $\frac{12\sqrt{2}+8}{7}$ [7.5]

Chapter 13 Review
1. 12

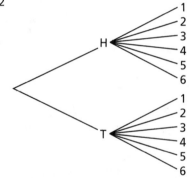

H1, H2, H3, H4, H5, H6,
T1, T2, T3, T4, T5, T6

3. 3   5. 12   7. 40,320   9. 120   11. 120
13. $a^4 - 24a^3 + 216a^2 - 864a + 1296$
15. $\frac{3}{7}$ 17. $\frac{15}{196}$ 19. $\frac{3}{13}$ 21. $\frac{9}{13}$ 23. 57.8
25. 11.7   27. 3.9   29. 81.3%

Chapter 14—Analytic Geometry

14.1
1. parabola

3. hyperbola

5. two intersecting lines

7. a point

9. circle, parabola, ellipse
11. Given   **13.** Exercise 10
15. Add. Prop. of Equality (Addition Method)
17. Substitution ($y = x$, step 14)
19. Definition of median
21. $d_{BD} = d_{AC}$

$d_{BD} = \sqrt{(a + b)^2 + (c)^2}$
$d_{AC} = \sqrt{(a - b)^2 + (c)^2}$
$\sqrt{(a + b)^2 + (c)^2} = \sqrt{(a - b)^2 + (c)^2}$
$(a + b)^2 + (c)^2 = (a - b)^2 + (c)^2$
$(a + b)^2 = (a - b)^2$
$a^2 + 2ab + b^2 = a^2 - 2ab + b^2$
$2ab = -2ab$
$4ab = 0$

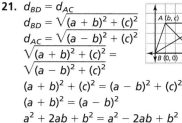

$a \neq 0$, so $b = 0$; therefore A is on the y-axis, and $\overline{AB} \perp \overline{BC}$. So $ABCD$ is a rectangle.

23.

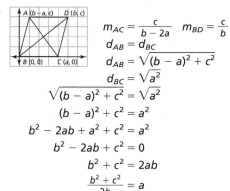

$m_{AC} = \dfrac{c}{b - 2a}$ $m_{BD} = \dfrac{c}{b}$

$d_{AB} = d_{BC}$

$d_{AB} = \sqrt{(b - a)^2 + c^2}$

$d_{BC} = \sqrt{a^2}$

$\sqrt{(b - a)^2 + c^2} = \sqrt{a^2}$

$(b - a)^2 + c^2 = a^2$

$b^2 - 2ab + a^2 + c^2 = a^2$

$b^2 - 2ab + c^2 = 0$

$b^2 + c^2 = 2ab$

$\dfrac{b^2 + c^2}{2b} = a$

Substitute this value into

$m_{AC} = \dfrac{c}{b - 2a} = \dfrac{c}{b - 2\left(\dfrac{b^2 + c^2}{2b}\right)}$

$= \dfrac{c}{\dfrac{b^2 - b^2 - c^2}{b}}$

$= \dfrac{c}{\dfrac{-c^2}{b}}$

$= \dfrac{cb}{-c^2}$

$= \dfrac{-b}{c}$ Since the slopes are negative reciprocals, $\overline{AC} \perp \overline{BD}$.

27. 5040, number of ways to arrange 7 objects in a row [13.2]
29. 30, number of ways to arrange 2 out of 6 objects [13.2]
31. 240,240, number of arrangements of 16 objects if 9 are identical, 5 others are identical and the last 2 are identical [13.3]

14.2 Circles
1. $(7, 3)$; $r = 7$ **3.** $(-6, 4)$; $r = 6$ **5.** $(2, 0)$; $r = \sqrt{3}$
7. $(0, 0)$; $r = \sqrt{2}$ **9.** $(8, -14)$; $r = 3$

11.

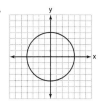

13.

15.

17. $(x + 6)^2 + (y - 1)^2 = 47$
19. $(x - 4)^2 + (y - 3)^2 = 26$
25. a. There are 2 real (irrational) roots; **b.** there are two x-intercepts with x-coordinates equal to the roots of the equation in part a. [4.4]
27. $(1, -3)$; no zeros [5.7]
29. The zeros of $P(x)$ are x-intercepts; the zeros of $Q(x)$ locate vertical asymptotes. [5.8]

14.3

1. $y = 3\frac{1}{4}$; focus $\left(1, 4\frac{3}{4}\right)$

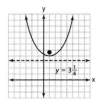

3. $y = 4\frac{1}{12}$; focus $\left(0, 3\frac{11}{12}\right)$

5. $y = -\frac{1}{8}$; focus $\left(1, \frac{1}{8}\right)$

7. $x = -\frac{3}{4}$; focus $\left(-3\frac{1}{4}, -4\right)$

9. $y = -2\frac{1}{4}$; focus $(-3, -1\frac{3}{4})$

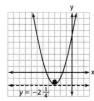

11. $x = \frac{-1}{8}(y - 7)^2 + 3$ **13.** $y = \frac{-1}{20}(x + 2)^2 + 1$

15. $y = \frac{1}{12}(x + 6)^2 + 1$ **21.** $\frac{2}{x}$ [9.4]

23. [9.6]

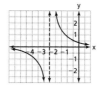

25. [9.6]

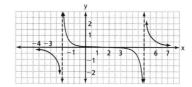

14.4

1.

3.

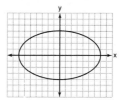

5.

7. $\frac{x^2}{16} + \frac{y^2}{9} = 1$

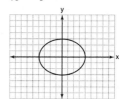

9. $(0, 2\sqrt{3})$; $(0, -2\sqrt{3})$
11. $(2, 0)$; $(-2, 0)$
13. $\frac{x^2}{29} + \frac{y^2}{4} = 1$ **15.** $\frac{x^2}{9} + \frac{y^2}{25} = 1$

17. $(-3.4, 4)$, $(-1.4, 4)$

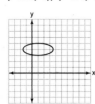

19. It is a circle.

25. Solve $ax^2 + bx + c = 0$. [9.5]

27. x-axis; $y = 0$ is an asymptote. [9.5]

29. $[f(x)]^{-1}$ designates the multiplicative inverse, while $f^{-1}(x)$ denotes the inverse relation of $f(x)$. [12.1]

29. [10.6]

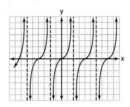

14.5

1.

3.

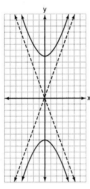

5. $\dfrac{y^2}{9} - \dfrac{x^2}{27} = 1$

7.

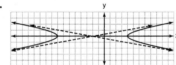

9.

11. any two of a, b, or c

13. $\dfrac{x^2}{16} - \dfrac{y^2}{25} = 1$

15. $\dfrac{x^2}{16} - \dfrac{(y-1)^2}{20} = 1$

17. $(5, 0)$ and $(-5, 0)$

25. [7.7]

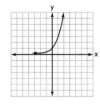

27. [9.7]

14.6

1.

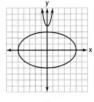

3. (a) 2; (b) 2; (c) 4

5. $(4, 1)$, $\left(\dfrac{8}{5}, \dfrac{-19}{5}\right)$

7. $(6, 0)$, $(-6, 0)$

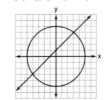

9. $(3, 4)$, $(-4, -3)$

11. $(5, 2)$

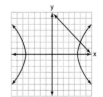

13. $(2\sqrt{11}, 3)$,
$(2\sqrt{11}, -3)$,
$(-2\sqrt{11}, 3)$,
$(-2\sqrt{11}, -3)$

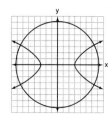

17.

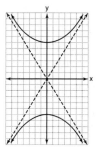

15. $(2, 4), (-2, 4)$

17. $(0, 4), \left(\dfrac{4\sqrt{14}}{15}, \dfrac{4}{15}\right)$,
$\left(\dfrac{-4\sqrt{14}}{15}, \dfrac{4}{15}\right)$

19.

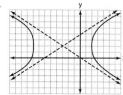

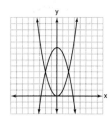
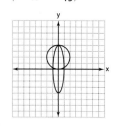

21. $(1, 5)$
23. $(2, 3 + 4\sqrt{2}); (2, 3 - 4\sqrt{2})$
25. $(3, 2); (-3, 2); (\sqrt{6}, -1); (-\sqrt{6}, -1)$

23. 3 solutions   **25.** 2 solutions

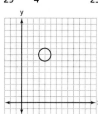
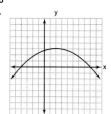

Chapter 14 Review

1. $\sqrt{58}; (\frac{1}{2}, \frac{7}{2})$

3. $(x + 6)^2 + (y - 4)^2 = 4$ **5.** $y = \dfrac{1}{20}(x - 7)^2 + 3$

7. $\dfrac{x^2}{29} + \dfrac{y^2}{4} = 1$ **9.** $\dfrac{x^2}{25} - \dfrac{y^2}{16} = 1$

11.   **13.**

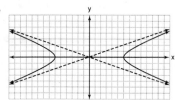

15.

Index

Notes

1. Henry Morris, *Education for the Real World* (San Diego: Master Books, 1977), 7.

2. J. Gresham Machen, "Christianity and Culture" in *Education, Christianity, and the State,* ed. John Robbins (Jefferson, MD: The Trinity Foundation, 1987), 50.

Acknowledgments

The cancer research data (Chapter 3) reprinted from "Cigarette Smoking and Cancers of the Urinary Tract: Geographic Variation in the United States," *Journal of the National Cancer Institute,* Volume 41, No. 5 (1968), 1205-1211, by Joseph F. Fraumeni. Reprinted with permission from Oxford University Press.

Galileo's data (Chapter 4) reprinted from "The Role of Music in Galileo's Experiments," *Scientific American,* Vol. 232, No. 6, 98-104, by Stillman Drake. Reprinted with permission from *Scientific American.*

Price index information (Chapter 7) obtained from the Bureau of Labor Statistics, U.S. Department of Labor. 1999. "Consumer Price Index, All Urban Consumers (CPI-U), U.S. city average." ftp://ftp.bls.gov/pub/special.requests/cpi/cpiai.txt. Accessed in September 1999.

The data on SAT Scores and education financing (Chapter 9) reprinted from "More Money for Massachusetts Schools: A Poor Investment," *On the Issue,* June 1992, No. 3, by Sanjiv Jaggia and Alison Kelly. Reprinted with permission from the Beacon Hill Institute at Suffolk University.

Tidal data (Chapter 10) obtained from WXTide32, version 2.5. Freeware published by Mike Hopper.

Compensation data (Chapter 12) obtained from the Bureau of Labor Statistics, U.S. Department of Labor. "Foreign Labor Statistics. Table 2: Hourly compensation costs in U.S. dollars for production workers in manufacturing, 29 countries or areas and selected economic groups, selected years, 1975-98." http://stats.bls.gov/news.release/ichcc.t02.htm. Accessed on May 26, 2000.

Auto accident data (Chapter 13) obtained from the National Highway Traffic Safety Administration. 1996. [This is the year of the data queried.] *Fatality Analysis Reporting System (FARS).* http://www-fars.nhtsa.dot.gov/www/main.html. Accessed in October 1999.

Toutatis and Comet Larsen data (Chapter 14) obtained from the Minor Planet Center at the Smithsonian Astrophysical Observatory. http://cfa-www.harvard.edu/iau/mpc.html. Accessed in October 1999.

Comet Machholz data (Chapter 14) obtained from John Walker. May 26, 2000. *Solar System Live.* http://www.fourmilab.ch/cgi-bin/uncgi/Solar. Accessed on May 26, 2000.

Cheerios, Golden Grahams, Total, and Wheaties are registered trademarks of General Mills, Inc.

All-Bran and Special K are registered trademarks of Kellogg Company.

100% Natural, Cap'n Crunch, Quaker Oat Life, and Quaker Toasted Oatmeal Squares are trademarks of the Quaker Oats Company.

Photograph Credits

The following agencies and individuals have furnished materials to meet the photographic needs of this textbook. We wish to express our gratitude to them for their important contribution.

Suzanne R. Altizer
CORBIS
Corel Corporation
Terry M. Davenport
Digital Stock
Bob Franklin
GE Power Systems
Göttingen University
Greater Milwaukee
    Convention &
    Visitors Bureau, Inc.
Philip Greenspun
Information Service,
    Rome
Institute for Advanced
    Study
Italian Tourist Agency
John Krause
Sam Laterza
Los Alamos National
    Laboratory
Master Builders, Inc.
Metropolitan Museum
    of Art
National Aeronautics and
    Space Administration
    (NASA)
National Cancer Institute
Oriental Institute of the
    University of Chicago
Tom Pantages
PhotoDisc, Inc.
Rene Descartes
    University, Paris
Eda Rogers
St. John Visitor &
    Convention Bureau
Ted Spiegel
Tacoma-Pierce County
    Visitor & Convention
    Bureau
Ron Tagliapietra
Graeme Teague
Tokyo Stock Exchange
U.S. Air Photo
University of Bologna
Unusual Films
www.arttoday.com
Washington State
    Historical Society,
    Tacoma

Nik Wheeler
World Bank

Cover
Corel Corporation
(dolphin, waterfall);
NASA (Saturn rings);
PhotoDisc, Inc.
(stopwatch, starfish,
x-ray of shell, curve sign,
freeway)

Title Page
PhotoDisc, Inc. ii
(both), iii (left); Corel
Corporation iii (middle);
NASA iii (right)

Introduction
Ron Tagliapietra viii
(top); Corel Corporation
viii (bottom); Tacoma-
Pierce County Visitor &
Convention Bureau ix

Chapter 1
PhotoDisc, Inc. x-1, 3,
28; Digital Stock 7, 9;
Corel Corporation 8

Chapter 2
Digital Stock 40-41;
PhotoDisc, Inc. 42; U.S.
Air Photo 58; Tokyo
Stock Exchange 64

Chapter 3
National Cancer Institute
84-85; Corel Corporation
86, 100, 105; PhotoDisc,
Inc. 92, 99 (bottom), 102;
Göttingen University,
Press and Information
Office 98, 99 (top);
Digital Stock 110; NASA
126 (both)

Chapter 4
Italian Tourist Agency
134-45; Nik Wheeler
148; © Fotolia XII/
Fotolia 149 (top);

PhotoDisc, Inc. 150,
160; © Immodinova C./
Wikimedia Commons/
GNU Free Documentation
License/Creative Commons
Attribution ShareAlike
3.0 149 (bottom);
Unusual Films, courtesy
of Bob Franklin 156

Chapter 5
World Bank 168-69;
Corel Corporation 176;
PhotoDisc, Inc. 178,
206; Ron Tagliapietra
186, 187

Chapter 6
Terry M. Davenport
216-17, 221; Digital
Stock 233; Information
Service, Rome 242;
University of Bologna
243 (top); photo cour-
tesy Philip Greenspun,
http://photo.net/philg/
243 (bottom), 255

Chapter 7
PhotoDisc, Inc. 264-65;
Göttingen University,
Press and Information
Office 274; Master
Builders, Inc. 292; Tom
Pantages 296 (both)

Chapter 8
Digital Stock 314-15;
Suzanne R. Altizer 316;
courtesy of GE Power
Systems 320; © Eda
Rogers 339

Chapter 9
PhotoDisc, Inc. 350-51;
Graeme Teague 368;
Institute for Advanced
Study 369 (top); Neg.
#CN86-3916 LANL
369 (bottom);
www.arttoday.com 384

Chapter 10
St. John Visitor &
Convention Bureau 392-
93; PhotoDisc, Inc. 430;
Washington State
Historical Society,
Tacoma 432 (both)

Chapter 11
Sam Laterza 440-41;
PhotoDisc, Inc. 448;
John Krause 453; Ron
Tagliapietra 456; Digital
Stock 462; Corel
Corporation 463 (both)

Chapter 12
PhotoDisc, Inc. 484-85,
503, 512 (both); Corel
Corporation 486

Chapter 13
PhotoDisc, Inc. 520-21,
530; Terry M. Davenport
532; Digital Stock 539;
photo from History of
Mathematics, by Carl B.
Boyer 552; Corel
Corporation 553 (top);
Rene Descartes
University, Paris 553
(bottom)

Chapter 14
NASA 566-67, 585;
Greater Milwaukee
Convention & Visitors
Bureau, Inc. 575; The
Bridgeman Art
Library/Getty Images
600; courtesy of the
Oriental Institute of the
University of Chicago
601 (top); PhotoDisc,
Inc. 601 (bottom)